NELSON

MATHEMATICS 9

Authors

David Zimmer
Chris Kirkpatrick
Ralph Montesanto

Kristina Farentino   Jane Youngberg

Nelson
Thomson Learning™

Australia • Canada • Denmark • Japan • Mexico • New Zealand • Phillipines
Puerto Rico • Singapore • South Africa • Spain • United Kingdom • United States

1120 Birchmount Road
Scarborough, Ontario M1K 5G4
www.nelson.com
www.thomson.com

ISBN 0-17-605999-7

Canadian Cataloguing in Publication Data

Main entry under title:

Mathematics 9

Includes index.
ISBN 0-17-605999-7

1. Mathematics. I. Zimmer, David.
II. Mathematics nine.

QA39.2.M335 1999   510   C99-931224-3

Director of Publishing
David Steele

Publisher, Mathematics
Cheryl Turner

Editor
Robert Templeton
First Folio Resource Group Inc.

Production Coordinator
Renate McCloy

Creative Director and Cover Design
Angela Cluer

Senior Composition Analyst/Design
Daryn DeWalt

Senior Designer
Suzanne Peden

Photo Researcher
Vicki Gould

Design
FIZZZ Design Inc.

The authors wish to thank David Hamilton,
Eileen Jung, Jonathan Lampert, all of First Folio
Resource Group; Angel Carter, Giampiero
De Ciantis, Edie Franks, Nelson Gonzalez,
Ann Goodes, Julie Greener, Sonia Rashid,
Don Rowsell, Matthew Sheehan, Steven Sloot,
Luke Tanur, Michael Waters, and
Kathleen Wilkie.

Creative Art/Technical Art
Bart Vallecoccia, Irma Ikonen, Pat Code,
Anthony De Ridder

Printed and bound in Canada
1 2 3 4 5 6 7 8 9 0 /ML/ 8 7 6 5 4 3 2 1 0 9

Reviewers

Contents

Chapter 7:

Measurement Relationships In Three-Dimensional Figures   399

Chapter 8:

The Geometry of Packaging   457

Introduction to Nelson Mathematics 9

Nelson Mathematics 9 is designed to help you develop your skill at solving real problems using mathematical skills and logical reasoning. There are questions that give you a chance to practise familiar mathematical skills like solving equations and graphing data. You will also have opportunities to tackle problems that require you to develop your own strategy for solving them. Throughout the book, you will be encouraged to use a variety of methods to communicate what you have learned to others.

Inquiry

When you are faced with a new situation or problem, you have to examine the problem and figure out how to solve it. This might involve analyzing the information you have, deciding if you need more information, and figuring out how you can get that information. You also need to develop a plan for working through the problem.

Problem-Solving

In your life, you have dealt with many situations in which you had to figure out the best solution to a problem. You have also been asked to solve problems in mathematics that are a bit different from anything you have done before. In either case, it is important for you to make sure you understand the problem, develop a plan for solving the problem, try applying your plan to the problem, and modify your plan as necessary in order to eventually solve the problem.

Reasoning

As you work at solving a problem, you have to keep questioning whether you are on the right track. You may have collected information that is not useful or it may be necessary to completely change your approach because it is not working. It is important to take time to reflect on what you are doing and change your approach if necessary.

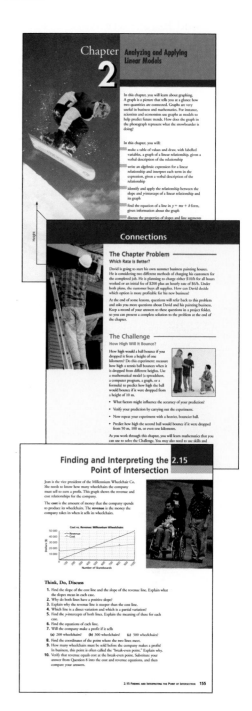

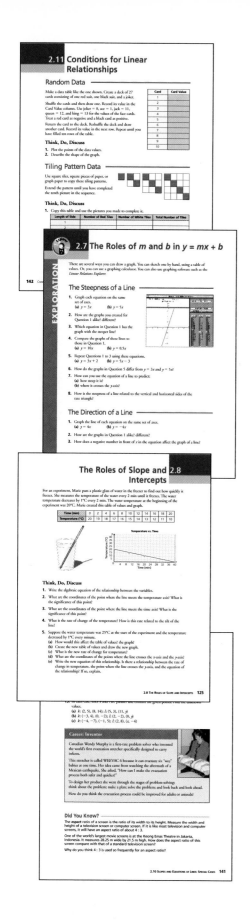

Mathematical Modelling

An important skill for you to develop is your ability to develop a mathematical model for a real situation. The model can take the form of a physical model, a computer model, a diagram, a graph, a table of values or an equation. Models help you to analyze a situation or information, predict patterns or trends, and also communicate that information in a form others can understand.

Technology

Advances in computer technology have made it possible for people to solve complex problems more easily and quickly than in the past. Graphing calculators, graphing software, spreadsheets, and geometry software can all be used to explore ideas and analyze data. You can also use computers to do research on the internet.

Communication

Throughout the chapters in *Nelson Mathematics 9*, you will be encouraged to discuss, present, write about, and report on what you are learning. This gives you the opportunity to reflect on your understanding of topics and share your ideas with other students. It also gives you a chance to develop your skill at communicating your ideas clearly to others and listening or thinking carefully about the ideas you hear or read.

Connections

Mathematics is not just something you do in mathematics class. You use it in other classes and your daily life. It will also be important as you make a career choice. Mathematicians and teachers are not the only people who use mathematics in their careers. Mathematics is used by fashion designers, bankers, tool and die makers, computer programmers, engineers, and plumbers. No matter what you choose to do in life, you will need a background in mathematics.

Features of Nelson Mathematics 9

Technology Lessons

These lessons provide guidance on using a variety of technologies, including graphing calculators, graphing software, scientific probes, geometry software, spreadsheets, and Nelson *Explorers*.

Concept Lessons

Some lessons help you to develop your understanding of mathematics through examples and questions. Others give you a chance to explore and investigate a problem. Problems are presented in a real-life context.

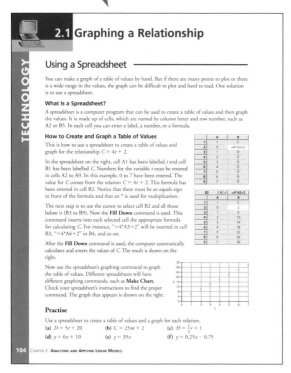

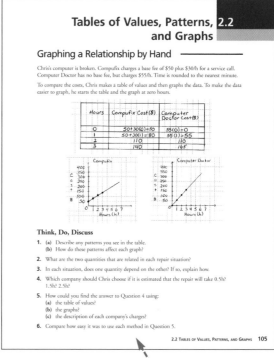

Icons

These three icons identify an opportunity to use technology.

 You will be using a graphing calculator and you will be using a data probe to collect data.

 You will be using a computer to develop a spreadsheet or graph.

 You will be using the TLE *Explorer* disk to investigate a mathematical idea.

Think, Do, Discuss

These questions help you to develop an understanding of the main ideas in a lesson and make connections between them.

Key Ideas

The Key Ideas present the important ideas and skills introduced in the lesson. They provide definitions of mathematics terms and ideas to remember.

Examples

Sample problems with solutions and notes provide examples of how to do the *Practise, Apply, Solve* questions. The example ties together the key ideas of the lesson.

Practise, Apply, Solve

These problems and questions give you a chance to practise what you have just learned. There are a variety of types of questions, from simple practice questions that emphasize skill and knowledge development to problems that require you to think, reason, and problem-solve.

Focus

Key Ideas

- When two quantities are related in some way, they form a **relationship**.
- Values that can change in a relationship are called **variables**.
- In a relationship, the variable that depends on the other variable is the **dependent variable**.
- The variable that does not depend on the other is the **independent variable**.
- In a table of values, the independent variable is placed in the left-hand column and the dependent variable in the right-hand column.
- In a graph, the dependent variable is placed on the vertical axis and the independent variable on the horizontal axis.
- When the graph of a relation is a straight line, the relationship is called **linear**.

Example

The cost of a banquet at Juan's Banquet Hall is $450 for the room rental, plus $15 for each person served. Create a table of values and draw a graph to see if this relationship is linear.

Solution

The cost of the banquet depends on the number of people who attend. Cost must be the dependent variable and number of people the independent variable.

It costs $450 to rent the hall. In addition, there is a $15 charge for each person served.

Cost is the dependent variable, so it is plotted vertically. The number of people is the independent variable, so it is plotted horizontally. The points that are plotted line up in a straight line. In this case, the relationship between cost and people is linear.

People	Cost ($)
0	450 + 15(0) = 450
10	450 + 15(10) = 600
20	450 + 15(20) = 750
30	450 + 15(30) = 900
40	450 + 15(40) = 1050
50	450 + 15(50) = 1200

Cost vs. Number of People

106 CHAPTER 2 ANALYZING AND APPLYING LINEAR MODELS

Practise, Apply, Solve

A

1. If a relationship between two variables is linear, then what shape is formed by the data points that are plotted on a graph?

2. Which of these describe a relationship?
   (a) the distance Angel swims and the time she takes
   (b) the distance Angel swims and the time Dolores spends studying
   (c) the temperature and the amount of clothing people wear
   (d) the number of cats a dog sees and how loudly it barks
   (e) the temperature in Vancouver and the temperature in Toronto

3. Identify the dependent variable.
   (a) The distance a jogger runs depends on the length of time she runs.
   (b) A recipe for 24 cookies requires 4 cups of flour.
   (c) A building must have 6 fire alarms on each floor.

4. Identify the independent variable.
   (a) A knitter needs to know how much wool is required to make ten sweaters. Twenty metres of wool are needed to make one sweater.
   (b) The printing cost for the school newspaper drops 1¢ for every page over 50.
   (c) The manager wants to know how many cartons are needed to package orange juice. Each carton holds 24

---

14. This graph represents the cost of renting a Rototiller for different lengths of time. It is called a step graph.
   (a) Is this relationship linear? Explain.
   (b) Find the cost of renting the Rototiller for two days.
   (c) Find the cost of renting the Rototiller for $3\frac{1}{2}$ days.
   (d) How long can you rent the Rototiller for $40?
   (e) Is the cost per day always the same?

Cost vs. Length of Rental

15. Write a problem that represents a linear relationship. Give your problem to a classmate to solve.

The Chapter Problem — Which Rate Is Better?

Refer back to the Chapter Problem at the beginning of this chapter.
1. Make the table of values for both of David's pricing options.
2. Describe any patterns you see in the table.
3. What are the dependent and independent variables?

Career: Furniture Making

A calculator is a common tool in many professions, and furniture making is no exception.

For instance, when raw lumber comes into the factory, the amount of usable wood must be calculated. Sometimes only 50 percent of the wood ends up in the finished product. The planning involved for some tasks is more challenging than for others, like trying to fashion rectangular planks efficiently into round tables or ornate legs.

Costing is another area where calculator skills are useful. When new furniture is designed, several prototypes of the items are made. These are examined to figure out the cost of mass-producing the item. Accurate costing is important.

Repeating fabric patterns also require calculation. In upholstering (and in wallpapering), if a fabric has a repeating pattern, the pattern on different pieces often has to be matched up so more material is required than with plain fabric.

Furniture making is an old and honoured profession that today involves both skill and modern techniques.

2.2 TABLES OF VALUES, PATTERNS, AND GRAPHS 109

Chapter Problem

As you work through the sections of the chapter, there are questions to help you solve the Chapter Problem on the Connections page.

People of Mathematics

These brief biographies tell you about women and men who have made a contribution to the world and work of mathematics. You may want to do further research (not shown).

Careers

Read these to find out how mathematics is used in the world of work.

11

Chapter Review

The concepts and skills you have developed through the work of the chapter are summarized and supported by examples and questions you can do to practise.

You can use this section to review and study.

Chapter Review Test

You can use this test to review and find out if you are ready for a class test or exam.

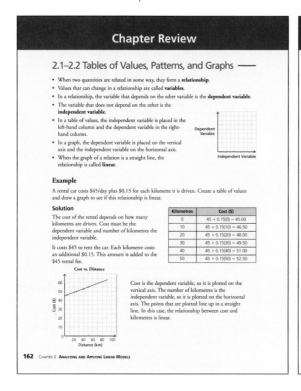

Chapter Review

2.1–2.2 Tables of Values, Patterns, and Graphs

- When two quantities are related in some way, they form a **relationship**.
- Values that can change in a relationship are called **variables**.
- In a relationship, the variable that depends on the other variable is the **dependent variable**.
- The variable that does not depend on the other is the **independent variable**.
- In a table of values, the independent variable is placed in the left-hand column and the dependent variable in the right-hand column.
- In a graph, the dependent variable is placed on the vertical axis and the independent variable on the horizontal axis.
- When the graph of a relation is a straight line, the relationship is called **linear**.

Example

A rental car costs $45/day plus $0.15 for each kilometre it is driven. Create a table of values and draw a graph to see if this relationship is linear.

Solution

The cost of the rental depends on how many kilometres are driven. Cost must be the dependent variable and number of kilometres the independent variable.

It costs $45 to rent the car. Each kilometre costs an additional $0.15. This amount is added to the $45 rental fee.

Kilometres	Cost ($)
0	45 + 0.15(0) = 45.00
10	45 + 0.15(10) = 46.50
20	45 + 0.15(20) = 48.00
30	45 + 0.15(30) = 49.50
40	45 + 0.15(40) = 51.00
50	45 + 0.15(50) = 52.50

Cost is the dependent variable, so it is plotted on the vertical axis. The number of kilometres is the independent variable, so it is plotted on the horizontal axis. The points that are plotted line up in a straight line. In this case, the relationship between cost and kilometres is linear.

Chapter Review Test

1. An experiment showed how much an elastic band stretched when various masses were hung from it. The results are recorded in the table.

Mass (g)	5	10	15	20	25	30
Stretch (cm)	1	2	3	4	5	6

   (a) Which quantity is the independent variable and which is the dependent variable?
   (b) Plot the ordered pairs on a graph.
   (c) Explain why this relationship is linear.
   (d) Is this an example of a direct or partial variation?
   (e) Estimate how far the elastic will stretch if these masses are attached: 12 g, 40 g, and 45 g.
   (f) Estimate the mass attached if the elastic band stretched 3.5 cm, 5.5 cm, and 7.8 cm.
   (g) Find the slope and the y-intercept of this line and interpret their meaning in this situation.
   (h) Find the equation of this line.

2. A line passes through the points $A(1, -3)$ and $B(3, 5)$. Find:
   (a) the slope of the line;
   (b) the equation of the line in the form $y = mx + b$;
   (c) the slope of a line parallel to AB; and
   (d) the slope of a line perpendicular to AB.

3. Manatees are large, gentle sea creatures that live along the Florida coast. The manatee is in danger of extinction. Powerboats have contributed to the demise of the manatee. Environmentalists have collected this data over a 16-year period to see if there is a relationship between the number of registered powerboats and the number of manatees killed each year.

Boats (thousands)	Manatees Killed	Boats (thousands)	Manatees Killed
447	13	585	33
460	21	614	33
481	24	645	39
498	16	675	43
512	24	711	50
513	20	719	47
526	15	727	54
559	34	730	51

   (a) Construct a scatter plot and find the line of best fit.
   (b) What type of correlation exists in this data? Can the environmentalists claim that powerboats are killing the manatee population?

There are also three Cumulative Review Tests (not shown).

Number Sense and Numeracy: Decimals

Example 1

Round to the nearest ten.

632 → 630
635 → 640
638 → 640

Example 2

Round to the nearest tenth.

6.32 → 6.3
6.35 → 6.4
6.39 → 6.4

Example 3

Add. Round to the nearest tenth.

$$6.37$$
$$\underline{+\ 12.21}$$
$$18.58$$

The answer, to the nearest tenth, is 18.6.

Practise

1. Round to the accuracy indicated.

   (a) 263 (tens)
   (b) 269 (tens)
   (c) 1338 (hundreds)
   (d) 1358 (hundreds)
   (e) 19 255 (thousands)
   (f) 19 651 (thousands)

2. Round to the number of decimal places shown in brackets.

   (a) 1.37 (1)   (b) 1.33 (1)
   (c) 1.35 (1)   (d) 0.236 (2)
   (e) 0.233 (2)   (f) 1.236 (1)
   (g) 7.276 (1)   (h) 2.393 (2)

3. Add. Round your answers to one decimal place.

   (a)   0.41   (b)   71.07
          1.68   16.47
        $\underline{+\ 7.37}$ $\underline{+\ 21.87}$

   (c) 4.9 + 1.09 + 4.069
   (d) 3.7 + 7.48 + 6.96
   (e) 14.08 + 2.3 + 4.65

4. Subtract. Round your answers to the nearest tenth.

   (a)   17.38   (b)   17.38
        $\underline{-\ 5.46}$ $\underline{-\ 12.49}$

   (c) 74.78 − 38.8   (d) 89.8 − 18.98

5. Multiply. Round your answers to the nearest tenth.

   (a)   17.4   (b)   10.5   (c)   9.73
        $\underline{\times\ 6.9}$ $\underline{\times\ 16.3}$ $\underline{\times\ 6.4}$

   (d) 8.06 × 8.7   (e) 1.08 × 70.9

6. Divide. Round your answers to one decimal place.

   (a) $\frac{3.75}{25}$ (b) $\frac{118.8}{72}$
   (c) $\frac{21.984}{3.2}$ (d) 0.648 ÷ 1.8
   (e) 1.764 ÷ 0.35   (f) 0.264 ÷ 0.48

7. Copy and complete the chart. Multiply the top row by the numbers in the left-hand column.

×	1.0317	1.043	8.07	0.18
10				
10^2		104.3		
0.1				

8. Copy and complete the chart. Divide the top row by the numbers in the left-hand column.

÷	134.1	71.43	8.31	0.45
10				
10^2		0.7143		
0.1				

13

Number Sense and Numeracy: Fractions

Example 1

Add: $\frac{7}{10} + \frac{2}{15}$

Example 2

Subtract: $2\frac{1}{4} - \frac{1}{2}$

Example 3

Multiply: $\frac{3}{5} \times 1\frac{1}{9}$

Example 4

Dvide $1\frac{2}{3} \div \frac{3}{10}$

Solution

$\frac{7}{10} + \frac{2}{15} = \frac{21}{30} + \frac{4}{30}$

$= \frac{25}{30}$ ⎰ Find a common denominator.

$= \frac{5}{6}$ ⎱ Express in lowest terms.

Solution

$2\frac{1}{4} - \frac{1}{2} = 2\frac{1}{4} - \frac{2}{4}$

$= 1\frac{5}{4} - \frac{2}{4}$

$= 1\frac{3}{4}$ ⎱ Regroup.

Solution

$\frac{3}{5} \times 1\frac{1}{9} = \frac{3}{5} \times \frac{10}{9}$

$= \frac{\cancel{3}^1}{\cancel{5}^1} \times \frac{\cancel{10}^2}{\cancel{9}^3}$

$= \frac{2}{3}$ ⎱ Express in lowest terms. Then multiply.

Solution

$1\frac{2}{3} \div \frac{3}{10} = \frac{5}{3} \div \frac{3}{10}$

$= \frac{5}{3} \times \frac{10}{3}$

$= \frac{50}{9}$ ⎰ Multiply by the reciprocal.

$= 5\frac{5}{9}$

Practise

1. Write the missing information to form equivalent fractions.

(a) $\frac{1}{3} = \frac{\blacksquare}{18}$ (b) $\frac{\blacksquare}{36} = \frac{1}{9}$ (c) $\frac{\blacksquare}{28} = \frac{4}{7}$

(d) $\frac{1}{5} = \frac{7}{\blacksquare}$ (e) $\frac{3}{8} = \frac{15}{\blacksquare}$ (f) $\frac{18}{\blacksquare} = \frac{2}{9}$

(g) $\frac{1}{\blacksquare} = \frac{9}{36}$ (h) $\frac{3}{\blacksquare} = \frac{15}{55}$ (i) $\frac{5}{35} = \frac{\blacksquare}{7}$

2. Add.

(a) $\frac{1}{7} + \frac{3}{7}$ (b) $\frac{2}{9} + \frac{5}{9}$ (c) $\frac{3}{8} + \frac{1}{8}$

(d) $\frac{1}{3} + \frac{1}{9}$ (e) $\frac{1}{3} + \frac{1}{6}$ (f) $\frac{1}{3} + \frac{5}{12}$

3. Subtract.

(a) $\frac{5}{9} - \frac{1}{9}$ (b) $\frac{14}{15} - \frac{7}{15}$ (c) $\frac{7}{15} - \frac{2}{5}$

(d) $\frac{5}{6} - \frac{3}{8}$ (e) $\frac{3}{4} - \frac{1}{6}$ (f) $\frac{1}{3} - \frac{1}{6}$

4. Add.

(a) $1\frac{1}{6} + 2\frac{1}{6}$ (b) $2\frac{3}{10} + 1\frac{3}{10}$

(c) $3\frac{3}{4} + 1\frac{3}{4}$ (d) $1\frac{3}{4} + 2\frac{5}{12}$

(e) $2\frac{1}{6} + 1\frac{5}{6}$ (f) $4\frac{2}{5} + 3\frac{1}{5}$

5. Subtract.

(a) $3\frac{5}{9} - 1\frac{2}{9}$ (b) $4\frac{7}{16} - 2\frac{3}{16}$

(c) $3\frac{3}{10} - 1\frac{7}{10}$ (d) $2 - 1\frac{1}{4}$

(e) $5\frac{1}{11} - 4\frac{9}{11}$ (f) $2\frac{3}{7} - 1\frac{6}{7}$

6. Multiply.

(a) $\frac{1}{2} \times \frac{3}{5}$ (b) $\frac{3}{4} \times \frac{7}{10}$

(c) $\frac{3}{5} \times 15$ (d) $\frac{2}{3} \times \frac{9}{11}$

(e) $\frac{3}{4} \times \frac{8}{15}$ (f) $2\frac{1}{3} \times \frac{3}{14}$

7. Divide.

(a) $\frac{3}{7} \div \frac{4}{5}$ (b) $\frac{2}{11} \div \frac{3}{5}$

(c) $\frac{3}{4} \div \frac{7}{8}$ (d) $\frac{5}{8} \div \frac{13}{16}$

(e) $2 \div \frac{2}{3}$ (f) $4 \div \frac{8}{9}$

(g) $\frac{3}{4} \div 9$ (h) $\frac{5}{7} \div 10$

8. Arrange the fractions in order from least to greatest in value.

(a) $\frac{3}{4}, \frac{5}{8}, \frac{1}{2}$ (b) $\frac{7}{8}, \frac{3}{4}, \frac{13}{16}$

(c) $\frac{3}{5}, \frac{9}{10}, \frac{3}{4}$ (d) $\frac{5}{6}, \frac{8}{9}, \frac{2}{3}$

Number Sense and Numeracy: Ratio and Rate

Quantities are often compared in mathematics. A comparison of one number to another is a ratio.

Example 1

Write as a ratio in lowest terms:
15 basketball players to 18 football players

Solution

Write the ratio in symbols.

$15 : 18 = 5 : 6$

[15 is compared to 18.]

Example 2

If 2 people earn a total of $23, how many people will earn a total of $92?

Solution

Write the ratio in fraction form and find the missing term.

$$\frac{2}{23} = \frac{\blacksquare}{92}$$

Since $\frac{2}{23} = \frac{2 \times 4}{23 \times 4} = \frac{8}{92}$

Then $\blacksquare = 8$.

Therefore, 8 people will earn a total of $92.

Practise

1. Express each as a ratio.
   (a) 3 pucks to 7 sticks
   (b) 5 pens to 6 pencils
   (c) 7 boys to 3 girls
   (d) 7 foxes to 4 coyotes
   (e) 6 perch to 5 pike
   (f) 4 bears to 7 cougars

2. Write each ratio in lowest terms.
   (a) $4 : 8$　　(b) $6 : 18$　　(c) $8 : 20$
   (d) $12 : 42$　(e) $\frac{15}{25}$　　(f) $\frac{30}{42}$
   (g) $2 : 4 : 6$　　　(h) $18 : 6 : 24$
   (i) $16 : 12 : 20$　　(j) $24 : 18 : 30$

3. Write each ratio in lowest terms.
   (a) 4 fries to 7 hamburgers
   (b) 4 defence to 6 forwards
   (c) 12 min to 30 min
   (d) 8 horses to 12 pigs

4. Write each ratio. Use the same units.
   Example: 25 cm to 1 m
   Write:　　25 cm to 100 cm

The ratio is $25 : 100$, or $1 : 4$ in lowest terms.
   (a) 7 mm to 3 cm　　(b) 17 s to 1 min
   (c) 25 m to 5 cm　　(d) 15 s to 1 min

5. Write the missing term(s) for the following.
   (a) $2 : 5 = \blacksquare : 10$　　(b) $3 : 7 = \blacksquare : 21$
   (c) $\frac{4}{7} = \frac{8}{\blacksquare}$　　　　(d) $\frac{5}{8} = \frac{15}{\blacksquare}$
   (e) $1 : \blacksquare : 4 = 2 : 6 : \blacksquare$
   (f) $1 : 6 : \blacksquare = 3 : \blacksquare : 9$

6. Express as a rate.
   (a) 4 tins for $2
   (b) $75 for 8 h work
   (c) $4 for 3 novels
   (d) 79 km in 4 h
   (e) 3 goals for 4 shots

7. Write each rate as a ratio in lowest terms.
   (a) 5 stamps for 85¢
   (b) 75¢ for 3 L of gasoline
   (c) 2 records for $10.98
   (d) $1.23 for 3 rolls of tape

Number Sense and Numeracy: Percent

There are three types of percent problems.

Example 1

Find 20% of 65.

Solution

20% of 65 = 0.20 × 65
            = 13

Thus, 20% of 65 is 13.

Example 2

What percent is 38 of 95?

Solution

$$\frac{n}{100} = \frac{38}{95} \quad \left[\frac{38}{95} = \frac{2}{5} = \frac{40}{100} \right.$$

$$\frac{n}{100} = \frac{40}{100}$$

$$n = 40$$

Thus, 38 is 40% of 95.

Example 3

60% of a number is 15.
What is the number?

Solution

60% of a number is 15.

1% of a number is $\frac{15}{60}$.

100% of a number is $\frac{15}{60} \times 100$.

Thus, the number is 25.

Practise

1. Write each percent as a fraction in lowest terms.

  (a) 49%   **(b)** 75%   **(c)** 1%

  (d) $\frac{1}{2}$%   **(e)** $33\frac{1}{3}$%   **(f)** $7\frac{1}{2}$%

2. Write each fraction as a percent.

  (a) $\frac{73}{100}$ **(b)** $\frac{3}{10}$ **(c)** $\frac{7}{50}$

  (d) $\frac{1}{4}$ **(e)** $\frac{5}{8}$ **(f)** 1

3. Write each decimal as a percent.

  (a) 0.43   **(b)** 0.92

  (c) 0.225   **(d)** 1.07

  (e) 3.51   **(f)** 0.005

4. Calculate each of the following to one decimal place.

  (a) 15% of 75   **(b)** 75% of 68

  (c) 150% of 60   **(d)** $\frac{1}{2}$% of 244

  (e) $1\frac{1}{2}$% of 76   **(f)** $2\frac{3}{4}$% of 748

5. What percent is:

  (a) 73 of 100?   **(b)** 87 of 100?

  (c) 19 of 50?   **(d)** 13 of 25?

  (e) 13 of 10?   **(f)** 63 of 50?

6. Find the number:

  (a) three to the exponent 2

  (b) four to the exponent 3

  (c) two to the exponent 5

  (d) five to the exponent 1

  (e) six to the exponent 0

  (f) two to the exponent 16

7. Find the interest on $1500 for one year at the following rates of interest.

  (a) 12%   **(b)** 8.5%

  (c) $\frac{1}{2}$%   **(d)** $\frac{1}{4}$%

  (e) 3%   **(f)** $6\frac{1}{4}$%

8. Write the rate of discount to one decimal place on a purchase of $150 if the discount is:

  (a) $15   **(b)** $30   **(c)** $22.50

  (d) $50   **(e)** $67.50   **(f)** $18.75

Number Sense and Numeracy: Factors and Exponents

Example 1

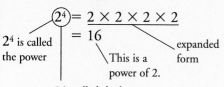

$2^4 = 2 \times 2 \times 2 \times 2$

$= 16$

2^4 is called the power

This is a power of 2.

expanded form

2 is called the base.
4 is called the exponent.

Example 2

Calculate $2^3 \times 2^2$.

Solution

$2^3 \times 2^2 = 2 \times 2 \times 2 \times 2 \times 2$
$= 32$

like bases

Example 3

Evaluate $2^2 \times 3^2$.

Solution

$2^2 \times 3^2 = 2 \times 2 \times 3 \times 3$
$= 36$

unlike bases

Practise

1. Write the value of each.

   (a) 2^2 **(b)** 2^3 **(c)** 2^4

   (d) 3^2 **(e)** 3^3 **(f)** 3^4

   (g) 4^2 **(h)** 4^3 **(i)** 5^3

2. Simplify.

   (a) 3×2^2 **(b)** 3×2^3

   (c) 2×4^2 **(d)** 2×4^3

   (e) $2^2 \times 3^2$ **(f)** $2^2 \times 3^3$

   (g) $3^2 \times 2^3$ **(h)** $2^2 \times 4^2$

   (i) $2^3 \times 4^2$ **(j)** $5^2 \times 3^2$

3. For each power, what is the base? the exponent?

   (a) 2^3 **(b)** 3^2 **(c)** 2^4

   (d) 3^4 **(e)** 5^2

4. Write each expression as a power.

   (a) $3 \times 3 \times 3 \times 3 \times 3$

   (b) $2 \times 2 \times 2 \times 2$

   (c) $5 \times 5 \times 5$

   (d) $4 \times 4 \times 4 \times 4 \times 4 \times 4$

5. Write in expanded form.

   (a) 5^2 **(b)** 2^5 **(c)** 6^4

   (d) x^3 **(e)** y^4 **(f)** $(2m)^3$

   (g) $(3n)^2$ **(h)** 4^3 **(i)** 3^4

6. Evaluate:

   (a) the third power of 2

   (b) the fourth power of 3

   (c) the second power of 5

   (d) the fifth power of 1

   (e) the sixth power of 0

   (f) the second power of 16

7. Write each number as a power of 10.

   (a) 100   **(b)** 1000

   (c) 100 000   **(d)** 1 000 000

   (e) 10   **(f)** 10 000 000

8. Write as a power of 2.

   (a) 4   **(b)** 16

   (c) 64   **(d)** 256

9. Evaluate.

   (a) $7^2 + 2^2$ **(b)** $4^3 - 2^5$

   (c) 3×2^3 **(d)** $3^2 \times 2^2$

10. Evaluate for $x = 2$.

   (a) $2x$ **(b)** x^2 **(c)** x^3

   (d) $3x^2$ **(e)** $2x^2 + 3$ **(f)** $x^3 - x^2$

11. Express each number as a product of two powers. (For instance, $36 = 2^2 \times 3^2$.)

   (a) 100   **(b)** 12   **(c)** 108

   (d) 2500   **(e)** 18   **(f)** 72

Number Sense and Numeracy: Integers—Addition and Subtraction

A number line can be used to show how to add integers.

Example 1

Find $(+5) + (-3)$.

Solution

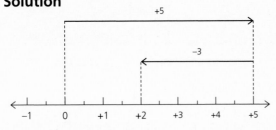

$(+5) + (-3) = 2$ —— The positive sign is often not used.

To subtract an integer you add its opposite.

Example 2

Subtract: **(a)** $5 - (-2)$ **(b)** $-8 - (+3)$

Solution

(a) $5 - (-2) = 5 + (+2)$
$= 7$

(b) $-8 - (+3) = -8 + (-3)$
$= -11$

To subtract an integer, you add its opposite.

Practise

1. Find each sum.
(a) $-3 + (-2)$ (b) $2 + (-3)$
(c) $-8 + (+8)$ (d) $-6 + (+4)$
(e) $-4 + (-5)$ (f) $2 + (-6)$

2. Add.
(a) $\begin{array}{r} 5 \\ -7 \\ \hline \end{array}$ (b) $\begin{array}{r} -3 \\ 4 \\ \hline \end{array}$ (c) $\begin{array}{r} -9 \\ 2 \\ \hline \end{array}$

(d) $\begin{array}{r} -4 \\ -6 \\ \hline \end{array}$ (e) $\begin{array}{r} 7 \\ -7 \\ \hline \end{array}$ (f) $\begin{array}{r} 7 \\ -2 \\ \hline \end{array}$

(g) $\begin{array}{r} -8 \\ -4 \\ \hline \end{array}$ (h) $\begin{array}{r} -4 \\ 3 \\ \hline \end{array}$ (i) $\begin{array}{r} -5 \\ -5 \\ \hline \end{array}$

3. Find each difference.
(a) $4 - (-3)$ (b) $-5 - (-2)$
(c) $5 - (-3)$ (d) $-4 - (-7)$
(e) $6 - (-6)$ (f) $4 - (4)$
(g) $-7 - (-3)$ (h) $-7 - (-9)$

4. Subtract.
(a) $\begin{array}{r} -4 \\ -2 \\ \hline \end{array}$ (b) $\begin{array}{r} 5 \\ -3 \\ \hline \end{array}$ (c) $\begin{array}{r} -7 \\ -3 \\ \hline \end{array}$

(d) $\begin{array}{r} -5 \\ 5 \\ \hline \end{array}$ (e) $\begin{array}{r} -7 \\ -8 \\ \hline \end{array}$ (f) $\begin{array}{r} 7 \\ -3 \\ \hline \end{array}$

(g) $\begin{array}{r} -7 \\ -3 \\ \hline \end{array}$ (h) $\begin{array}{r} -7 \\ 3 \\ \hline \end{array}$

5. Simplify.
(a) $3 - (-4)$ (b) $-7 + 2$
(c) $5 - 3$ (d) $3 - 5$
(e) $-4 - (-4)$ (f) $-4 - 4$
(g) $5 - (-3) + 4$ (h) $-4 - (-3) + 5$
(i) $-6 - 4 - 3$ (j) $-4 + 7 - 5$

6. Which choice would make each statement true: >, <, or =?
(a) $-3 - 4 - 5 + 3 \ \blacksquare \ -4 - 3 - 1 - (-2)$
(b) $4 - 7 + 6 - 8 \ \blacksquare \ -3 - 5 - (-7) - 4$
(c) $9 - 6 - (-4) - 5 \ \blacksquare \ 5 - 13 - 7 - (-8)$
(d) $5 - 13 + 7 - 2 \ \blacksquare \ 4 - 5 - (-3) - 5$
(e) $7 - 3 - (-15) - 11 \ \blacksquare \ -7 - 3 - (-11) - 1$

7. In each row, which expression has the greatest value? the least value?
(a) $-5 - 3 + 4, 4 - 3 - (-4), 5 - (-3) - 10$
(b) $4 - 3 - 1, -5 - (-2) + 4, -14 + 5 + 6$
(c) $9 - (-2) - 7, 5 - (-7) + (-9), -5 - 3 + 6$
(d) $-6 + 4 + 3 - 2, 4 - (-3) - 7, 5 - (-2) -$
(e) $-5 - 2 + 4, 3 - 12 + 2, -7 - (-2) + 1$

Number Sense and Numeracy: Integers—Multiplication and Division

Use a pattern to remember how to multiply or divide integers.

The $+$ and $-$ signs are shown here to remember the rules. In the examples and practise questions, $+5$ is written as 5.

$(-5)(-2) = +10$ $(-10) \div (-2) = +5$ $(+5)(-2) = -10$ $(-10) \div (+2) = -5$

$(+5)(+2) = +10$ $(+10) \div (+2) = +5$ $(-5)(+2) = -10$ $(+10) \div (-2) = -5$

same signs   positive integer   different signs   negative integer

Example 1

Find $3(-2)$.

Solution

$3(-2) = -6$

Example 2

Calculate $(-2)^3$.

Solution

$(-2)^3 = (-2)(-2)(-2)$
$\quad\quad = -8$

Example 3

Find $(-18) \div (-3)$.

Solution

$(-18) \div (-3) = 6$

Practise

1. Find each product.
   (a) $(-3)(2)$ **(b)** $(-4)(-9)$
   (c) $(4)(-3)$ **(d)** $(-7)(-3)$
   (e) $(5)(4)$ **(f)** $(-2)(7)$

2. Simplify.
   (a) $-2(-7)$ **(b)** $-3(8)$ **(c)** $5(-7)$
   (d) $-5(-7)$ **(e)** $-4(-9)$ **(f)** $-4(9)$

3. Find each quotient.
   (a) $-18 \div (-6)$ **(b)** $-24 \div 6$
   (c) $51 \div (-17)$ **(d)** $-42 \div (-14)$
   (e) $-18 \div (18)$ **(f)** $-24 \div (-6)$
   (g) $60 \div (-12)$ **(h)** $-30 \div (-15)$

4. Simplify.
   (a) $\frac{-50}{5}$ **(b)** $\frac{-15}{-5}$ **(c)** $\frac{30}{-6}$
   (d) $\frac{48}{-6}$ **(e)** $\frac{16}{-16}$ **(f)** $\frac{-16}{-8}$
   (g) $\frac{18}{-9}$ **(h)** $\frac{-81}{27}$ **(i)** $\frac{-18}{-9}$

5. Evaluate.
   (a) $(-4)^2$ **(b)** $(-2)^4$ **(c)** $(-3)^4$
   (d) $(-5)^2$ **(e)** -5^2 **(f)** 4^3
   (g) -4^3 **(h)** $(-2)^5$ **(i)** $(-3)^2$

6. Simplify.

   Example:
   $-3(-2)^4 = -3(16)$ ⎯⎯ ⎡ Calculate
   $\quad\quad\quad = -48$ ⎣ powers first.

   (a) $-2(-3)^2$ **(b)** $4(-2)^3$
   (c) $5(-3)^3$ **(d)** $(-3)^2(-2)^2$
   (e) $-3^2(-2)^3$ **(f)** $(5)^2(-2)^2$
   (g) $-5^2(-3)$ **(h)** $(-5)^2(-3)$

7. Calculate.
   (a) $(-6)^2 \div (-3)$ **(b)** $-6^3 \div (-3)$
   (c) $-3^4 \div (-3)^2$ **(d)** $(-4)^3 \div (-2)^3$
   (e) $6^2 \div (-3)^2$ **(f)** $-4^2 \div (-2)^3$
   (g) $2(-4)^2 \div (-8)$ **(h)** $-8 \div [(-2)(4)]$
   (i) $-8(-3) \div (-2)^2$

8. Calculate.
   (a) $(5^2 \div 5) \times (7^2 \div 7)$
   (b) $(4^3 \div 2^2) \div (2 \times 2^2)$
   (c) $(-4^3 \times 3) \times (3^2 \div 3)$

Number Sense and Numeracy: Order of Operations

When calculating expressions, we follow the order of operations:

Order of Operations
1. Simplify brackets.
2. Then simplify powers.
3. Multiply and divide.
4. Then add and subtract.

Example 1

Simplify
$-3(2 - 4) - (-2 + 4)$.

Solution

$-3(2 - 4) - (-2 + 4)$
$= -3(-2) - (2)$
$= 6 - 2$
$= 4$

Example 2

Add $(-3)^2$ to the product of -2 and 4.

Solution

$(-2)(4) + (-3)^2$
$= (-2)(4) + 9$
$= -8 + 9$
$= 1$

Practise

1. Simplify. Use the order of operations.
   (a) $5 - (3 - 4)$
   (b) $(5 - 7) - (3 - 4)$
   (c) $-3(-4) - (5 - 7)$
   (d) $(3)(2) - (3 + 5)$
   (e) $-(5 - 9) - (-2)(2)$
   (f) $(4 - 3) - 2(3 - 4)$
   (g) $4(-2) - (-8 + 4)$

2. Simplify.
   (a) $2(-3)^2 - 4(-2)$
   (b) $-4(-2)^3 - 3(-4)^2$
   (c) $(-3 - 2)^2 - (2 + 4)^2$
   (d) $3(-2 + 4)^3 - 2(-4 + 1)^2$
   (e) $2(-1 - 3)^2 - (1 + 3)^2$
   (f) $5(-2)^2 - 3(-1 - 2)^3$
   (g) $3(-1 - 2) - (5 - 7)^3$
   (h) $5(-2 + 1)^3 - (-3 - 2)^2$
   (i) $4(1 - 3)^3 - (4 - 7)^2$
   (j) $-2(1 - 4)^3 - 3(1 - 5)^2$

3. Match each expression with the corresponding sentence.
   (a) Find the sum of -3, -8, and -2.
   (b) -8 is added to the product of -3 and -2.
   (c) Subtract -8 from the product of -3 and -2.
   (d) Divide -8 by -2 and add -3.
   (e) Decrease the quotient of -8 and -2 by -3.
   i. $-3(-2) + (-8)$
   ii. $-8 \div (-2) + (-3)$
   iii. $-8 \div (-2) - (-3)$
   iv. $-8 + (-3) + (-2)$
   v. $(-3)(-2) - (-8)$

4. Increase the sum of -3 and 5 by -6.
5. Divide the sum of 7 and -16 by -3.
6. By how much is the sum of -8 and 6 more than -4?
7. How much less is the sum of -8 and -4 than the product of 4 and -2?
8. Divide -4^2 by $(-2)^2$.
9. Add -3^2 and 4^2 to the product of 6 and -2.
10. Increase the product of -7 and -3 by -18.
11. By how much is $(-3 + 5)^2$ more than $-(-3 + 5)^2$?
12. Divide the sum of -8, -11, 7, and -3 by 5.
13. Divide the sum of -4^2 and 2^4 by -7^2.

Number Sense and Numeracy: Square Roots

A square has an area of 25 m². Find the length of each side.

$A = l \times w$ In a square, $l = w$, so

$A = l \times l$
$A = l^2$
$25 = l^2$

What number multiplied by itself equals 25?

$5 \times 5 = 25$

$\therefore l = 5$ m

The **square root** of a number is the number that multiplies by itself to give a required value. The square root symbol is $\sqrt{}$. For instance, the square root of 25 is written as $\sqrt{25}$.

$\sqrt{36} = 6$, since $6 \times 6 = 36$ $\sqrt{0.25} = 0.5$, since $0.5 \times 0.5 = 0.25$

Example 1

Is the square root of 17 closer to 5 or to 4? Do not use technology to find the square root.

Solution

$5 \times 5 = 25$ and
$4 \times 4 = 16$

17 is closer to 16 than to 25, so $\sqrt{17}$ is closer to 4.

Example 2

Which is the better estimate of the square root of 50: 7.1 or 7.5?

Solution

$\sqrt{49} = 7$, so 7.1 is the better estimate.

Example 3

Is the square root of 35 closer to 5 or to 6? Do not use technology to find the square root.

Solution

$5 \times 5 = 25$ and
$6 \times 6 = 36$

35 is closer to 36 than to 25, so $\sqrt{35}$ is closer to 6.

Example 4

If $\sqrt{121} = 11$, what is $\sqrt{1.21}$?

Solution

$1.1 \times 1.1 = 1.21$, so $\sqrt{1.21} = 1.1$

Practise

1. Select the best answer from those given. Do not use a calculator.

   (a) $\sqrt{27}$ 4.8, 5.2, 6.3
   (b) $\sqrt{41}$ 5.9, 6.4, 7.1
   (c) $\sqrt{92}$ 9.6, 10.1, 11.5
   (d) $\sqrt{103}$ 8.9, 9.8, 10.1
   (e) $\sqrt{12}$ 2.8, 3.5, 4.2
   (f) $\sqrt{65}$ 8.1, 9.4, 10.2

2. Select the better answer from those given. Do not use a calculator.

(a) $\sqrt{34}$ 5.2, 5.9

(b) $\sqrt{8}$ 2.3, 2.8

(c) $\sqrt{50}$ 7.1, 7.8

(d) $\sqrt{79}$ 8.2, 8.8

(e) $\sqrt{109}$ 10.3, 10.9

(f) $\sqrt{5}$ 2.1, 2.9

3. State the value of each square root. Do not use a calculator.

(a) $\sqrt{0.09}$

(b) $\sqrt{0.36}$

(c) $\sqrt{1.44}$

(d) $\sqrt{0.25}$

(e) $\sqrt{0.81}$

(f) $\sqrt{1.69}$

(g) $\sqrt{0.64}$

(h) $\sqrt{1.96}$

4. Determine all of the prime factors of each number. Use these to write the square root of the number.

(a) 225

(b) 324

(c) 484

(d) 1296

(e) 441

(f) 289

5. A day care centre has a square play area that is 144 m². What are its dimensions?

6. The area of a square envelope is 68 cm². Find the measure of each side. Round to one decimal place.

7. Determine the length of each side of square with these areas.

(a) 169 cm²

(b) 600.25 cm²

(c) 204.49 mm²

(d) 5595.04 cm²

(e) 1296 cm²

(f) 6099.61 m²

8. This diagram shows the front profile of three square buildings. What is the length of the sidewalk along the front of the buildings?

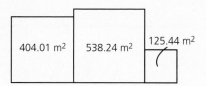

404.01 m²   538.24 m²   125.44 m²

Patterning and Algebra: Variables and Substitution

To simplify expressions, operations must be performed in a certain order. The order of operations is:

1. Simplify calculations in brackets.
2. Calculate powers.
3. Do $\times$ and $\div$ in the order in which they appear.
4. Do $+$ and $-$ in the order in which they appear.

Example 1

Simplify $8 \div 2 + 16 \div 4$.

Solution

$$8 \div 2 + 16 \div 4 = 4 + 4$$
$$= 8$$

Do multiplication or division before adding or subtracting.

Example 2

Simplify $(3 + 2) \times 3^2$.

Solution

$$(3 + 2) \times 3^2 = 5 \times 3^2$$
$$= 5 \times 9$$
$$= 45$$

Do the calculations in brackets first.

Example 3

Evaluate $4k - 3$ if $k = 2$.

Solution

$$4k - 3 = 4(2) - 3$$
$$= 8 - 3$$
$$= 5$$

Substitute 2 for k.

Practise

1. Use the order of operations to simplify each of the following.

   (a) $3 \times 5 + 6$
   (b) $18 \div 3 - 4$
   (c) $2 \times 8 + 16 \div 4$
   (d) $36 \div 3 - 2 \times 6$
   (e) $16 - 8 \div 4 \times 2$
   (f) $(3 \times 4 + 2) \div 7$
   (g) $(8 + 4) \times 6 \div 9$

2. Simplify the following.

   (a) $3^3 - 2^2$
   (b) $3 + 2^3$
   (c) $\dfrac{5 + 8 \times 2}{4 + 3}$
   (d) $\dfrac{(3 + 4) \times 6}{3 \times 4 + 2}$
   (e) $\dfrac{5 \times 2 + 7 \times 8}{3 \times 2 + 15 \div 3}$
   (f) $\dfrac{4 \times (17 - 5)}{1 + 45 \div 3}$

3. Find the value of each expression if $k = 3$.

   (a) $5(k - 1)$
   (b) $5k - 1$
   (c) $5k^2 - 1$
   (d) $5(k + 1)$

4. Evaluate each expression if $k = 3$, $h = 2$.

   (a) $7k + h$
   (b) $2h + k$
   (c) $3(k + h)$
   (d) $12(k - h)$
   (e) $k^2 + h$
   (f) $h^2 + k$
   (g) $3(k + h)^2$
   (h) $5(k - h)^3$

5. (a) Evaluate each expression if $a = 3$, $b = 2$.
   - $4a^2b^2$
   - $(2ab)^2$

   (b) Comment on the results.

6. Match the figure to the formula.

   (a) $A = l \times w$
   (b) $A = \dfrac{1}{2} \times b \times h$
   (c) $A = b \times h$
   (d) $A = s^2$

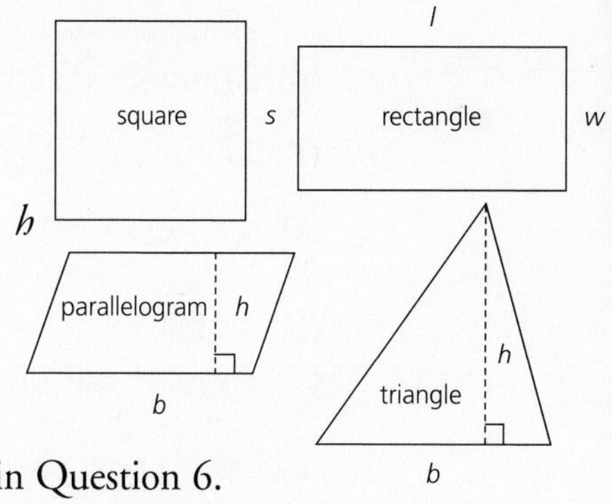

7. Use the formulas in Question 6. Find the area of the following figures. Round your answers to one decimal place.

   (a) rectangle: $l = 8$ cm, $w = 3$ cm
   (b) triangle: $h = 5.3$ cm, $b = 7.2$ cm
   (c) square: $s = 9.3$ cm
   (d) parallelogram: $b = 9.4$ cm, $h \doteq 5.2$ cm

8. The area of a circle is given by $A = \pi r^2$. Use $\pi \doteq 3.14$. Find A if r is:

   (a) 1
   (b) 2
   (c) 4

Patterning and Algebra: Language in Mathematics

To solve a problem, you may need to translate from English into the language of mathematics. A variable expression can be written using the symbols of arithmetic.

Example 1

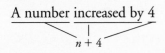

A number increased by 4

$n + 4$

Example 2

The cost in dollars of k radios each worth $15

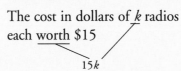

$15k$

Example 3

the symbol for year(s)

Lorraine is m a old today. How old will she be in 3 a?

Years old today: m
In 3 a: $(m + 3)$ a

Practise

1. Write a mathematical expression for each of the following, where a number is k.

  (a) a number doubled
  (b) a number decreased by 3
  (c) a number divided by 6
  (d) a number doubled and increased by 3
  (e) 3 decreased by a number doubled
  (f) a number increased by itself
  (g) a number squared

2. If Peter is now c a old, express his age:

  (a) 1 a from now
  (b) 2 a ago
  (c) doubled
  (d) doubled and decreased by 3

3. If Lorna is now $(m - 2)$ a old, express her age:

  (a) 2 a ago
  (b) tripled
  (c) 3 a from now

4. How much will Alice pay for k stamps if each is worth:

  (a) 8¢?   (b) 17¢?
  (c) 50¢?   (d) 46¢?
  (e) 75¢?   (f) 1¢?
  (g) $1.00?   (h) n¢?

5. How many cents does Jeanette have if she has $(d + 3)$ coins or bills each worth:

  (a) 10¢?   (b) 25¢?
  (c) t¢?   (d) $1?
  (e) $2?   (f) $$m$?

6. The wind is blowing at p km/h. Write the speed of the wind later in the day if it:

  (a) increases by 20 km/h
  (b) decreases by 3 km/h
  (c) doubles in velocity
  (d) decreases by $\frac{1}{3}$ of its velocity

7. If I have $(2n - 5)$ tickets and Pierre has 2 more, how many does he have?

8. At a certain intersection there are e accidents per month. In June, there were 2 fewer accidents than normal. How many occurred?

9. Mona bought $(z + 3)$ cans of soup at 49¢ per can. Find the increase in the total cost if each can now costs 51¢.

10. Elle bought $(2c - 3)$ CDs for $14.95 per CD. Find the decrease in the total cost if each CD goes on sale for $10.99.

Patterning and Algebra: Solving Equations

To solve equations by inspection, write equivalent equations using the operations: $+$, $-$, $\times$, and $\div$.

Example 1

Solve $3n - 5 = 13$.

Solution

Something minus 5 must equal 13.

$18 - 5 = 13$

This means that $3n = 18$.
Three times what gives eighteen?

$3 \times 6 = 18$

Therefore, the solution is $n = 6$.

Example 2

Verify than $n = 6$ is a solution of
$3n - 5 = 13$.

Solution

$$\begin{aligned} \text{L.S.} &= 3n - 5 & \text{R.S.} &= 13 \\ &= 3(6) - 5 \leftarrow \text{Substitute 6 for } n. \\ &= 18 - 5 \\ &= 13 \end{aligned}$$

L.S. = R.S.

Therefore, 6 is a solution of the equation.

Practise

1. Solve by inspection.

   (a) $n + 3 = 7$ **(b)** $f + 5 = 2$
   (c) $9 = 3 + x$ **(d)** $9 + g = 3$
   (e) $n - 4 = 7$ **(f)** $z - 2 = 13$

2. Solve by inspection.

   (a) $2x = 6$ **(b)** $3n = 18$
   (c) $4c = -16$ **(d)** $-4m = 20$
   (e) $-30 = 6h$ **(f)** $-25 = -5a$

3. Solve by inspection.

   (a) $2k + 1 = 7$ **(b)** $6 + 3k = 27$
   (c) $18 = 4a - 2$ **(d)** $11 = 2 - 3y$
   (e) $3 - 4z = -5$ **(f)** $4p - 3 = 9$
   (g) $-6 = 8 - 7v$ **(h)** $3h - 4 = -4$
   (i) $8 = 2 - 3y$ **(j)** $4y - 2 = 2$

4. Find the solution set for each equation.

   (a) $\frac{1}{3}m = 4$ **(b)** $\frac{3}{4}e = 15$

   (c) $-6 = \frac{3}{4}h$ **(d)** $20 = \frac{-5}{8}a$

   (e) $\frac{-5}{8}y = -30$ **(f)** $\frac{-3}{11}c = 0$

5. Solve. Verify your answers.

   (a) $\frac{1}{3}m + 1 = 3$ **(b)** $\frac{1}{5}k + 5 = 2$

   (c) $\frac{2}{5}n - 5 = 3$ **(d)** $3 = \frac{3}{4}e - 18$

   (e) $\frac{3}{4}h - 4 = 2$

6. Match each sentence with the correct equation.
   (a) Three times a number is equal to twenty-one.
   (b) A number increased by three is ten.
   (c) A number divided by five is twenty.
   (d) Jim's age five years ago was fifteen.

   i. $n + 3 = 10$ **iii.** $3x = 21$

   ii. $a - 5 = 15$ **iv.** $\frac{m}{5} = 20$

7. Write an equation for each sentence, and then solve it.

   (a) Two times a number is twenty-six.
   (b) Five less than a number is two.
   (c) A number decreased by four is negative nine.
   (d) Three more than twice a number is 19.

Patterning and Algebra: Working with Right Triangles

One of the many important relationships in mathematics is known as the Pythagorean property of a right-angled triangle. The area of the square of the hypotenuse is equal to the sum of the areas of the squares of the other two sides.

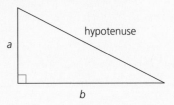

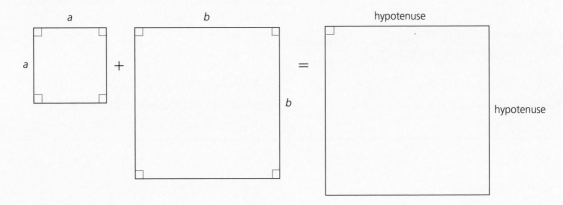

Example

Find the value of *g*.

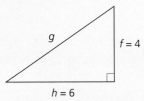

Solution

$$g^2 = f^2 + h^2$$
$$g^2 = 4^2 + 6^2$$
$$= 16 + 36$$
$$= 52 \qquad \text{Use your calculator.}$$
$$g \doteq 7.2 \qquad \text{The positive square root of 52 is rounded to one decimal place.}$$

Practise

Round your answers to one decimal place.

1. Calculate to the number of decimal places indicated in brackets.

  (a) $\sqrt{65}$ (2)   **(b)** $\sqrt{43}$ (2)

  (c) $\sqrt{359}$ (1)   **(d)** $\sqrt{262}$ (1)

  (e) $\sqrt{5.52}$ (2)   **(f)** $\sqrt{0.89}$ (2)

2. For each right-angled triangle, write the equation for the Pythagorean property.

(a)

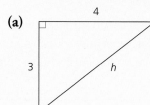

(b)

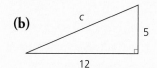

(c)

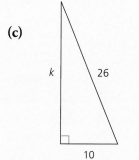

(d)

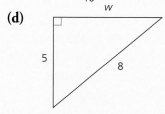

3. Calculate the length of the missing side for each part of Question 2.

  (a) $h = \blacksquare$ **(b)** $c = \blacksquare$

  (c) $k = \blacksquare$ **(d)** $w = \blacksquare$

4. For each equation find the value of the missing measure.

  (a) $a^2 = 8^2 + 6^2$ **(b)** $g^2 = 7^2 + 10^2$

  (c) $14^2 = c^2 + 8^2$ **(d)** $13^2 = n^2 + 5^2$

  (e) $16^2 = 9^2 + y^2$ **(f)** $h^2 = 1.4^2 + 4^2$

5. A rectangular park is crossed from A to B using the diagonal path. How many metres are saved by not going from A to C to B?

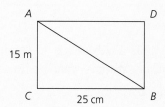

6. A support cord is fastened to a pup tent and to the ground. If the tent is 1.2 m high and the cord is 2.3 m long, how far is the end of the cord from the tent?

7. A shadow is cast by a building. The distance from the tip of the shadow to the top of the building is 85 m. The tip of the shadow is 55 m from the base of the building. How tall is the building?

Data Management: Working with Statistics

Statistics is a branch of mathematics that involves

A: gathering data (numerical figures and so on);

B: organizing and analyzing the data;

C: interpreting the data; making inferences, predictions, or decisions about the data.

To work with statistics, you need to learn the vocabulary. This example illustrates some important terms.

If you ask each student at your school to answer a question such as "What is your favourite sport?," then the students are called the **population**. If you make a selection of students instead, the group of students selected is called a **sample**. The students should be chosen randomly, and are called a **random sample.**

To gather data, you can use a variety of methods such as questionnaires, telephone responses, personal interviews, and so on. Once the data has been gathered, it can be organized using graphs, charts, and so on. Then you can make observations about the information and answer questions.

Practise

1. The possible disadvantages of certain methods of gathering data are listed.

A: time-consuming
B: limited return of information
C: difficult to contact all the people
D: high cost
E: difficulty in interpreting questions
F: limited choice of responses

From the above list, select the disadvantages that may be related to each of the following data-gathering techniques.

(a) A telephone survey across Canada to find the number of people watching the Grey Cup Parade.

(b) A personal interview of each student at Northmount High to find out which foods were preferred for lunch.

(c) A questionnaire mailed to the people in several cities across Canada to obtain an opinion on municipal policies.

2. To predict the outcome of the Grey Cup (the Canadian Football League championship game), which of the following methods would most likely provide data on which to base a decision?

A: interviews with the members of either team
B: 100 people randomly surveyed in Florida
C: 100 phone calls randomly placed across Canada
D: 20 sportcasters and writers interviewed at random
E: 1000 questionnaires sent to Moscow

3. To test the quality of its paper clips, a manufacturer randomly selects 100 paper clips from each batch. After 10 random samples, the following results are obtained.

Sample	A	B	C	D	E	F	G	H	I	J
Defective	2	1	2	0	1	2	1	4	2	3

(a) What percent of the paper clips are defective in sample A?

(b) What percent of the paper clips are defective in the total of samples A to J?

(c) If sample K is taken, how many defective paper clips might you expect? Select the best answer for each number.
- 6: yes, no, maybe
- 3: yes, no, maybe
- 2: yes, no, maybe
- 0: yes, no, maybe

4. For each of the following, indicate whether you would use a sample, S, or all of the population, P, to make a decision.

(a) Testing the quality of the carbon on computer printer tapes.

(b) Determining the amount of silver in a new mineral discovery.

(c) Deciding on the number of bears in a forest.

(d) Determining the workability of new engines for 747 jet liners.

(e) Testing the parachutes in a shipment.

(f) Checking that pages of a book are numbered.

(g) Testing the quality of a shipment of ballpoint pens.

(h) Testing the light bulbs made in one shift.

5. Some formats for a survey questionnaire are yes/no response (Y), short answer (S), numeric response (N), multiple choice (M), check-mark response (C), or a rating scale (R). For each of the following survey questions, indicate which type of format you would use.

(a) Which colour do you like the most?

(b) Which high school subject do you like best?

(c) How many hours do you study each week?

(d) How much did you like this movie?

(e) Check all the foods that you eat each day.

(f) Do you play video games?

(g) Are you going to the dance?

(h) Which of the following costumes would you wear at Halloween?

(i) How would you rate the cafeteria food?

(j) What is your favourite hobby? Why?

(k) How often did you go to the movies last month?

Data Management: Organizing and Representing Data

A chart can be used to show the frequency for data. Twenty-eight students stated the type of vehicle they liked.

The tally shows how many liked each vehicle.

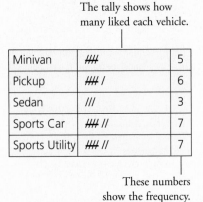

Minivan	////|	5
Pickup	////| /	6
Sedan	///	3
Sports Car	////| //	7
Sports Utility	////| //	7

These numbers show the frequency.

A bar graph can be created for the data.

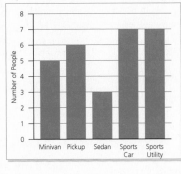

A circle graph can be created for the data.

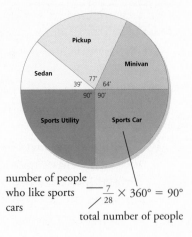

number of people who like sports cars
$\dfrac{7}{28} \times 360° = 90°$
total number of people

This data shows the heights of students (rounded to the nearest centimetre).

Class	Frequency	Class	Frequency
161–165 cm	2	176–180 cm	7
166–170 cm	5	181–185 cm	6
171–175 cm	7	186–190 cm	4

A histogram can be drawn for the data.

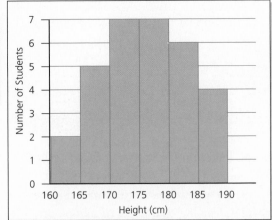

Practise

1. This tally sheet records the number of students who took part in various Friday night activities.

Activity	Tally	Frequency
Movie	ℋℋ ℋℋ ℋℋ //	
Party	ℋℋ ℋℋ ℋℋ	
Bowling	ℋℋ //	
Skating	ℋℋ ℋℋ ℋℋ ℋℋ	
Hockey	ℋℋ ℋℋ ℋℋ ////	

   (a) Copy this table and write the frequency for each activity.
   (b) Copy this bar graph and use the above data to complete it.

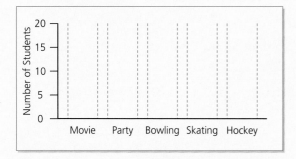

2. Students were asked what type of movie they enjoyed. This table shows the data.

Movie	Tally	Frequency
Action	ℋℋ	5
Comedy	ℋℋ //	7
Drama	///	3
Science Fiction	ℋℋ	5

   (a) How many students were interviewed?
   (b) What percent prefer action movies?
   (c) To draw a circle graph of the data, what size angle do you need for drama?

3. Students were asked the sport they most often participate in. This table shows the data.

Activity	Tally	Frequency
Basketball	ℋℋ ℋℋ ℋℋ //	17
Volleyball	ℋℋ ℋℋ ℋℋ ℋℋ //	22
Football	ℋℋ ℋℋ ///	13
Badminton	ℋℋ ///	8

   (a) How many students were interviewed?
   (b) What percent of the students participate in basketball? in volleyball? Express your answers to one decimal place.
   (c) To draw a circle graph for the data, what size angle do you require for football? for badminton?

4. Using a survey, data was gathered for the hourly rates of students doing part-time jobs.

$1.50	///	$4.00	ℋℋ ℋℋ ℋℋ ℋℋ /
$2.00	ℋℋ //	$4.50	ℋℋ ℋℋ ℋℋ
$2.50	ℋℋ ℋℋ ℋℋ //	$5.00	ℋℋ //
$3.00	ℋℋ ℋℋ ℋℋ	$5.50	ℋℋ
$3.50	ℋℋ ℋℋ /	$6.00	///

For each dollar amount, state its frequency and the size angle it would have in a circle graph.

Data Management: Graphing Relationships

This table shows a **relation** for the amount of gasoline a motorcycle needs when travelling at a steady rate.

From the data, you can write the ordered pairs and graph the relation as shown below. To show the amount of gasoline consumed, V, at any time, you then draw a line through the ordered pairs.

Gas Consumption - Motorcycles

Time taken, t, in hours	Gas consumed, V, in litres	Ordered Pairs
0	0	(0, 0)
1	0.5	(1, 0.5)
2	1.0	(2, 1.0)
3	1.5	(3, 1.5)
4	2.0	(4, 2.0)

This graph shows the five ordered pairs.

To show all the values of t, you draw a line.

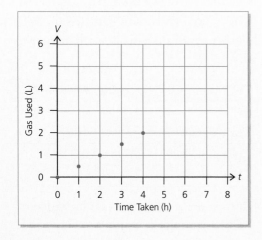

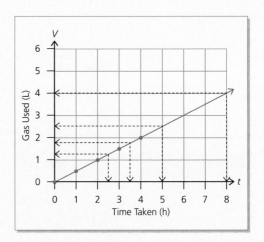

From the graph, you can make estimates and predictions of gas consumed at different times.

Example

(a) Estimate the time it took for 1.25 L of gasoline to be consumed.
(b) Estimate the amount of gasoline consumed in 3.5 h.
(c) Estimate the time it took for 4.0 L of gasoline to be consumed.
(d) Estimate the amount of gasoline consumed in 5 h.

Solution

(a) 2.5 h ⎯ In these questions, you choose two
(b) 1.75 L ⎯ known values on a graph and
estimated a value between them.
This is called interpolating.

(c) 8 h ⎯ In these questions, you estimate a
(d) 2.5 L ⎯ value which was beyond the values
given. This is called extrapolating.

Practise

1. John and Marianne recorded measurements for stretching a spring. They recorded the mass and the length of the spring as follows: (5, 1), (10, 2), (15, 3), (20, 4), (25, 5), (30, 6). What might the missing values be?

    (a) (35, ■)   **(b)** (40, ■)   **(c)** (45, ■)

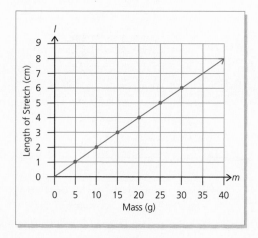

2. John and Marianne continue recording measurements for stretching a spring as in Question 1. What might the missing values be?

    (a) (18, ■)   **(b)** (28, ■)   **(c)** (22, ■)
    (d) (50, ■)   **(e)** (77, ■)   **(f)** (65, ■)

3. An experiment showed the amount of stretch resulting from adding mass to an elastic band.

Mass (g)	5	10	15	20	25	30
Stretch (cm)	1	2	3	4	5	6

(a) Plot the ordered pairs on a graph.
(b) Estimate how far the elastic band would stretch if these masses were attached: 12 g, 40 g, and 45 g.
(c) Estimate the mass attached if the elastic band were stretched 3.5 cm, 5.5 cm, and 7.8 cm.

Data Management: Measures of Central Tendency

Three measures of central tendency are mean, median, and mode.

Example 1

Find the mean of these heights: 163 m, 160 m, 165 m, 165 m, 161 m

Solution

The mean is the average.

Mean

$$= \frac{163 + 160 + 165 + 165 + 161}{5}$$

$$= \frac{814}{5} = 162.8$$

Thus, the mean is 162.8 m.

Example 2

Find the median for the heights in Example 1.

Solution

The median is the middle measurement when the numbers are arranged from the least to greatest.

160 161 163 165 165
↑ least   ↑ median   ↑ greatest

Thus, the median is 163 m.

Example 3

Find the mode of the heights in Example 1.

Solution

The mode is the measure that occurs most frequently.

160 161 163 165 165

Thus, the mode is 165 m.

Practise

1. The mass, in kilograms, of ten people randomly chosen from a crowd is listed below.

    74 71 68 84 54
    60 64 68 68 65

    (a) Find the mode of the data.
    (b) Find the median of the data.
    (c) Find the mean of the data, to one decimal place.
    (d) If another person were randomly chosen from the same crowd, what would be your best estimate of this person's mass?

2. A group of ten girls had the following ages, in years.

    16 15 15 16 14
    16 16 15 15 15

    (a) Find the mean, median, and mode of the data.
    (b) Two grandmothers, one aged 65 and the other 72, joined the group. Which measure(s) of central tendency remained unchanged?
    (c) Calculate the mean for the combined data of (a) and (b). (Why has it changed from your answer in (a)?)

3. Students of City High had a frisbee-throwing contest. These distances, in metres, were recorded for the frisbee throws.

    45 52 47 55 62 80 71
    60 84 57 46 50 48 61
    49 63 54 63 49 72

    (a) Calculate the mean, median, and mode for the data, to one decimal place.
    (b) Why is the mode not a good measure of central tendency for the above data?

4. Smokie's Sport Shop recorded the following sales on running shoes: court 17, basketball 4, tennis 14, volleyball 8, crosstrainers 17.

    (a) Can you calculate the mean type of shoe? Why or why not?
    (b) Can you calculate the median type of shoe? Why or why not?
    (c) You are in charge of ordering stock for the store. Which type would you order most? least?

Rounding Up/Rounding Down ———————

Fred wants to buy these items at the corner store.

- juice $1.79
- milk $2.39
- newspaper $0.75
- pop $0.69
- potato chips $1.89
- gum $0.89
- candy $0.35

He has $10 in his pocket. Does he have enough money to buy the items?

Rounding up or **rounding down** are strategies for estimating.
Round amounts of $0.50 or more up to the nearest dollar.
Round amounts of less than $0.50 down to the nearest dollar.

Item	juice	milk	paper	pop	chips	gum	candy
Actual Amount	1.79	2.39	0.75	0.69	1.89	0.89	0.35
Rounded Amount	2.00	2.00	1.00	1.00	2.00	1.00	0.00

The estimated amount is the sum of the rounded amounts, or $9.00. Fred should have enough money. The actual amount is $8.75.

Round up or round down to estimate the totals. Predict whether your answer will be more than or less than actual value. How do you know which it will be? Calculate the actual value. Were you close enough?

(a) $2.75, $3.18, $1.82, $5.01, $0.24

(b) $0.42, $1.09, $4.21, $3.85, $0.94

(c) $6.61, $5.19, $7.05, $7.92

Flexible Rounding ————————————————

Sasha earns $679 per week. About how much does he earn per year?

To find the amount Sasha earns in one year, multiply his weekly salary by the number of weeks in one year: $679 × 52.

Flexible rounding is a strategy for estimating this amount. Round to numbers that are close to the given values but easier to work with.

$679 is about $700. 52 weeks is about 50 weeks.

Then, 679 × 52 is about 700 × 50 = 35 000.

Sasha earns about $35 000/a. The actual amount is $35 308/a.

Use **flexible rounding** to estimate the weekly earnings. Predict whether your estimate will be more or less than the actual value. How do you know which it will be? Calculate the actual value. Were you close enough?

(a) $8.37/h for 21 h   **(b)** $11.12/h for 28 h   **(c)** $19.06/h for 42 h

Compatible Numbers ————————————————

Naomi has $512 in her bank account. She wants to withdraw the same amount every week for 24 weeks. About how much can she withdraw each week?

To find the amount she can withdraw each week, divide the total amount by the number of weeks: $512 ÷ 24.

Using compatible numbers is a strategy for estimating this amount.

$512 is about $500. 24 weeks is about 25 weeks.

The numbers 500 and 25 are compatible numbers because 25 divides into 500 to give exactly 20. Naomi can withdraw about $20 per week. The actual amount is $21.33 per week.

Use compatible numbers to estimate the average value. Predict whether your estimate will be more than or less than the actual value. How do you know which it will be? Calculate the actual value. Were you close enough?

(a) $611 averaged over 29 weeks
(b) $1263 averaged over 41 weeks
(c) $2627 averaged over 52 weeks

Convenient Decimals ————————————————

Ethel wants to buy a hamburger, fries, and milk. This combination costs $4.89. Sales tax is an additional 15%. Ethel has $6. Can she afford this meal?

Using numbers like 10, 100, 0.1, or 0.01 is a strategy for estimating.

15% of $4.89 is about 10% of $5.00, or $0.50, plus an additional half of 10%, or $0.25.

The tax is about $0.50 + 0.25 = $0.75.

The total estimated bill is about $5.00 + $0.75 = $5.75.

Ethel should have enough money. The actual amount is $5.62.

Use 10, 100, 0.1 or 0.01 to estimate the values. Predict whether your estimate will be more than or less than the actual value. Calculate the actual value. Were you close enough?

(a) 15% of $38.11   **(b)** 20% of $97.38   **(c)** 1.5% of $42.11

Clustering

Swapan knows his boat will safely carry about 400 kg. The mass of Swapan and each of his friends is shown.

53 kg, 45 kg, 49 kg, 55 kg, 52 kg, 45 kg

Will the boat carry Swapan and his friends safely?

Clustering is a strategy for estimating. In this example, masses with sums of about 100 kg are paired.

53 + 45 is about 100. 45 + 55 is about 100. 49 + 52 is about 100.

The total is about 100 kg + 100 kg + 100 kg = 300 kg.

Swapan should be able to safely accommodate his friends in the boat. The actual mass is 299 kg.

Use clustering as a strategy for estimating the totals. Predict whether your estimate will be more than or less than the actual value. Calculate the actual value. Were you close enough?

(a) 7 L, 4 L, 2 L, 9 L, 6 L, 2 L

(b) $8.25, $4.15, $1.70, $6.02, $9.65

(c) 593 kg, 632 kg, 391 kg, 407 kg, 284 kg, 753 kg

Rounding to the Nearest Half

Rossana is a biologist studying samples of fruit flies. She is counting the number of flies with a particular generic trait. In Sample A, 18 out of 99 flies have the trait. In Sample B, 43 out of 87 flies have the trait. In Sample C, 93 out of 104 flies have the trait. She knows the trait shows up about one quarter of the time under normal conditions. She wants to study the samples in which the trait occurs more often than usual. She rounds to see which samples these are.

Rounding to 0, $\frac{1}{2}$, or 1 is a strategy for estimating fractions.

In Sample A, the denominator of $\frac{18}{99}$ is much larger than the numerator. Round this fraction to 0.

In Sample B, the denominator of $\frac{43}{87}$ is about twice the numerator. Round this fraction to $\frac{1}{2}$.

In Sample C, the denominator of $\frac{93}{104}$ is about the same size as the numerator. Round this fraction to 1. The fractions for Samples B and C are both greater than one quarter $\left(\frac{1}{4}\right)$, which means that in these samples the trait happens more often than one quarter of the time. Therefore, Rossana will study Samples B and C.

Use **rounding** to 0, $\frac{1}{2}$, or 1 as a strategy for estimating the totals. Predict whether your estimate will be more than or less than the actual value. Use a calculator and decimals to calculate the value. Were you close enough?

(a) $\frac{21}{157} + \frac{93}{182} + \frac{55}{56}$ **(b)** $\frac{97}{111} - \frac{512}{1121} + \frac{323}{351}$

(c) $\frac{17}{241} - \frac{81}{78} + \frac{123}{135} + \frac{48}{91}$

Front End Loading

Chester and his parents go on a driving trip for summer vacation. They travel 506 km from Nipigon to Kapuskasing, 254 km from Kapuskasing to Kirkland Lake, 233 km from Kirkland Lake to North Bay, 130 km from North Bay to Sudbury, 552 km from Sudbury to Sault Ste. Marie, and 594 km from Sault Ste. Marie to Nipigon. Chester tells his friend he travelled over 2000 km. Did he really go that far?

Looking at the **front end** of numbers is a strategy for estimating. The numbers that Chester is using are all in the hundreds.

Here are the numbers with the front digits shown in blue:

$$506, 254, 233, 130, 552, 594$$

Adding the front digits gives $5 + 2 + 2 + 1 + 5 + 5 = 20$.

That means there are 20 hundreds or 2000. **Front end** estimating always gives a value that is lower than the actual value. Since 2000 km is a low estimate, Chester did travel over 2000 km.

Use the **front end** strategy to estimate the following totals. Predict whether your estimate will be more than or less than the actual value. Calculate the actual value. How could you modify this strategy to get a closer estimate of the actual value? Are you close enough now?

(a) 3722, 4107, 5234, 7802
(b) 684, 9283, 794, 8103
(c) 21 293, 36 107, 9214, 632, 11 641

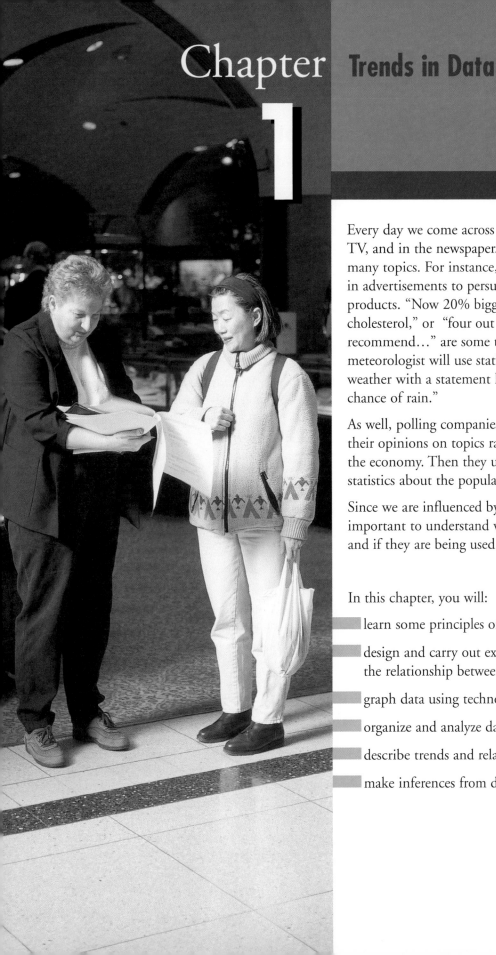

Chapter 1

Trends in Data

Every day we come across statistics on the radio and TV, and in the newspaper. These statistics cover many topics. For instance, companies use statistics in advertisements to persuade us to buy their products. "Now 20% bigger," or "15% less cholesterol," or "four out of five dentists recommend…" are some typical examples. Or, a meteorologist will use statistics to predict the weather with a statement like, "There is a 50% chance of rain."

As well, polling companies survey individuals for their opinions on topics ranging from politics to the economy. Then they use the results to generate statistics about the population as a whole.

Since we are influenced by these statistics, it is important to understand where they come from, and if they are being used properly.

In this chapter, you will:

- learn some principles of sampling and surveying
- design and carry out experiments to investigate the relationship between variables
- graph data using technology
- organize and analyze data
- describe trends and relationships in data
- make inferences from data.

Connections

The Chapter Problem

How Are Shoes Designed?

Edith Harmon is the Advanced Concepts Manager, research and development, for New Balance shoes.

"Let's assume that we are creating a new basketball shoe. There are three steps in conducting the research."

- *Identify market needs: Working with our marketing department, we might establish a focus group of basketball players. We'd have to be careful who is selected to ensure that the group would provide useful data. One thing we want to find out is the price point – the amount people will pay for the product. We don't want to design a shoe that is too expensive for the market.*

- *Create a design and prototype: We'd use the information collected from a focus group to design a prototype. We must develop a product that is user-friendly, attractive, and functional.*

- *Evaluate the product idea: The next step is to go back to the focus group and ask them if our prototype meets their needs. We might even give them the product to test. We'd do extensive testing to make sure that the product did what we said it could do.*

To design a shoe that really works, it is important to know if there is a relationship between a person's foot size and height or weight. Edith's company has just hired you. Design and carry out a process to see if such a relationship exists. Keep accurate records and make a report to present to the product development team.

At the end of some lessons in this chapter, questions will refer you back to this problem, and you will be able to use what you have learned to answer them. Keep your notes in a folder, so that at the end of the chapter you can provide a full solution to this problem.

The Challenge

Is There a Trend?

Is there a trend in the population growth of your school? Use data and an appropriate model to assist the school administration in planning future expansion. Discuss the strength of any trend in the data and the confidence you have in any predictions you make. To complete this Challenge, you may need to discuss a research plan with your teacher or with other students. You may also need to research outside the classroom.

Getting Ready

The work in this chapter requires you to know some basic statistical concepts and terms. These exercises will help you warm up for the work you will be doing in this chapter.

1. What is the mode? If there is no mode, write "does not exist."
   (a) 2, 2, 3, 2, 4, 5, 3, 5
   (b) 76, 78, 79, 57, 78, 22
   (c) 14, 19, 23, 19, 24
   (d) 56, 0, 25, 0, 67, 35, 82
   (e) 4, 95, 33, 68, 40, 84
   (f) 23, 23, 56, 67, 87, 23, 71

2. What is the median?
   (a) 1, 2, 3, 4, 5, 6, 7
   (b) 7, 5, 6, 4, 3, 2, 1
   (c) 12, 10, 8, 9, 6, 14
   (d) 13, 11, 9, 10, 7, 15
   (e) 73, 68, 76, 62, 80, 78
   (f) 100, 1, 10 000, 1000, 10

3. What is the mean? Round to one decimal place if necessary.
   (a) 6, 6, 6, 6, 6, 6, 6, 6
   (b) 7, 6, 7, 7, 6, 7, 8, 8
   (c) 12, 24, 13, 26, 16, 28
   (d) 23, 74, 51, 78, 49, 30, 65
   (e) 49, 51, 0, 17, 100, 83
   (f) 12, 7, 4, 29, 15, 1, 21, 2, 25

4. What are the mode, median, and mean? If there is no mode, write "does not exist."
   (a) 13, 14, 15, 13, 14, 16, 13
   (b) 21, 20, 0, 7, 90, 66, 20
   (c) 102, 602, 1002, 1202
   (d) 0, 0, 0, 0, 0, 0, 91
   (e) 61, 12, 89, 50, 36, 12
   (f) 5, 4, 5, 4, 99, 99, 35, 99

5. What are the mode, median, and mean? If there is no mode, write "does not exist."
   (a) 4.5, 4.2, 4.4, 4.5, 4.5, 4.9
   (b) 3, 3, 6, 3, 3, 9, 3, 3, 12

(c) 789, 425, 367, 616
(d) 32, 0, 47, 56, 84, 0, 5
(e) 0.3, 1.6, 0.7, 2.3, 0.8, 0.3
(f) 76, 25, 163, 98, 39, 84, 12

6. Suppose you want to know the name of the best-selling computer in Canada. You decide to survey every computer store in Canada.
   (a) Why would you collect data in this way?
   (b) What are the advantages of this method? the disadvantages?
   (c) How else could you collect this data?
   (d) Surveying an entire population is called a **census**. When would this method be necessary?
   (e) Is this sampling procedure biased? Explain.

7. Graph the data.
   (a)

Cost ($)	5	10	15	20	25	30	35
Time (h)	1	2	3	4	5	6	7

(b)

Age (years)	1	2	3	4	5	6	7	8
Height (cm)	70	82	93	98	106	118	127	135

(c)

Length (m)	3	3.5	4	4.5	5	5.5	6	6.5
Mass (kg)	450	525	600	675	750	825	900	975

(d)

Speed (m/s)	4	8	12	16	20	24	28	32
Time (s)	800	400	270	200	160	135	115	100

(e)

Width (cm)	3	7	11	15	19	23	27
Volume (cm³)	24	56	88	120	152	184	216

(f)

Height (m)	500	440	380	320	260	200	140	80
Time (s)	0	1	2	3	4	5	6	7

1.1 Analyzing Survey Data

Statistics can be used to educate people. They can also be manipulated so that false things appear to be true. Analyze and question the statistics you hear and read.

Analyzing Data

A music store advertises the week's "Top Ten" CDs.

Think, Do, Discuss

1. Does the store have the credibility to make this claim?
2. How would the data have been collected to find the Top Ten list?
3. Why would the store advertise this list?
4. Is it important to know what the population is for the data? Why?
5. Would it help sales to have more than one kind of Top Ten list? Why?
6. What other kinds of lists could be developed?

the Top 10 List

1. Siobhan Shines Sharp
2. Rodrigues Roadrunners
3. Burns and the George Group 2
4. Palmer's Plants
5. Bill and the Bronze Bucket Band III
6. Tea Cup Trails
7. QED - The Sounds of Rap
8. Davide and the Puffer Fish
9. Newfoundland Nash
10. London Larriot

Conducting a Survey

You are responsible for selecting the music for the next school dance. How can you do this and satisfy the majority of students at your school?

Think, Do, Discuss

1. Design a questionnaire to discover the students' favourite type of music.
2. Examine your questionnaire for bias. Remove any bias you find.
3. How could you select a sample from your school to complete the questionnaire?
4. Discuss your selection method with other groups. How are the methods alike? different?
5. Reduce the bias in your method.
6. Randomly select students and ask them to complete the questionnaire. What conclusion can you draw from the responses?
7. Have other students complete the questionnaire. Compare your conclusions from this second survey with those in your first survey.
8. Combine the data from these two surveys and draw a conclusion for the entire school. Compare this conclusion with conclusions from your first two surveys.
9. Were the conclusions from the first two samples accurate? Explain.

Recognizing and Reducing Bias

Selecting a Sample

The editor of the school newspaper asks four reporters to find out what sport the students like to watch most.

- Ted interviews his soccer mates.

- Winston posts a notice in the gym asking students to check off their favourite sport.

- Cal and Nancy ask the vice-principal to use the school computer to randomly generate a list of names of students to ask.

Think, Do, Discuss

1. Whose input is needed to find out what sport students like to watch most?

2. Name some advantages for each of the three data collection techniques.

3. Name some disadvantages for each of the three data collection techniques.

4. Who collected data that allowed more than one response for each person surveyed? How will this affect the results of the survey?

5. Who had the best data? the weakest data? Why?

6. If you were a school reporter, how would you collect this data?

Focus

Key Ideas

- Each member of a population must have an equal chance of being selected to be in the sample group. Otherwise, the sample is biased.
- For a good survey:
  - aim for a good cross-section of the population
  - eliminate chances of more than one response per person
  - ensure that every member of the population has an equal chance of being chosen.

Example

1. Fred and his group want to survey 25 out of 512 people in the school to see if the cafeteria should change its menu. Which plan should they use?
   Plan 1: Select 25 of the students in the cafeteria at lunch.
   Plan 2: Choose a class in the school that has 25 students and survey them.
   Plan 3: Assign each student in the school a number from 1 to 512. Have a computer select 25 numbers and then interview those students.

2. Jordan wants to survey students at school to see if the school radio station should change its playlist. Which plan should he use?
   Plan 1: Ask some of his classmates.
   Plan 2: Assign each student in the school a number and have a computer select the students to be interviewed.

3. A computer games developer wants to know what games teens like. Which plan should be used?
   Plan 1: Publish a checklist of games in a teen magazine and ask respondents to mail their completed list to the manufacturer.
   Plan 2: Use a computer to randomly select households from across the country and ask teens what kind of games they like.

Solution

1. *Plan 1* is biased because students who do not eat lunch in the cafeteria won't be selected. *Plan 2* is biased because students whose class has more than or less than 25 students won't be selected. *Plan 3* is non-biased because each student has an equal chance of being selected.

2. *Plan 1* is biased because students who are not in Jordan's class cannot be selected. The sample may be too small. *Plan 2* is non-biased because each student has an equal chance of being selected.

3. *Plan 1* is biased because it does not include teens who did not buy that magazine. Also, respondents might complete more than one checklist, and some games may have been excluded from the list. *Plan 2* is non-biased because all teens across the country have an equal chance of being selected.

Practise, Apply, Solve

A

1. Which samples are biased? Why?
   (a) To find how long it takes to travel to school, students on a school bus are interviewed.
   (b) A pollster in a mall asks shoppers who will win the Stanley Cup.
   (c) All teachers' names are put into a hat and two are drawn to be supervisors of a student ski trip.
   (d) A TV news show invites viewers to vote on a news topic. Viewers telephone one number to vote "yes" and another to vote "no."

2. To discover students' attitudes toward homework, these methods are suggested. What bias is in each method?
   (a) Survey the first 50 students to arrive at school on Monday morning.
   (b) Interview students in the library on Friday night.
   (c) Ask a number of students from each class.
   (d) Phone students when they are most likely doing their homework.
   (e) Ask students at the school dance.
   (f) Poll all of the teachers in the school.
   (g) Ask students who are peer tutors.

B

3. Which samples are biased? Why?
   (a) To predict the winner in an upcoming election, an ice cream shop sets up photographs of the candidates. Patrons get one vote for each cone they buy. A vote is recorded by putting a check mark below the candidate's photo.
   (b) Student representatives from each class in a school decide which charity should receive money from a school fundraiser.
   (c) A telephone survey is conducted on a Wednesday morning to see if more day-care facilities are needed.

4. To find which band to hire for a school dance, the student council tries these methods. Which have bias? Explain.
   (a) They ask members of the school band and music department.
   (b) They ask the teachers.
   (c) They ask ten students randomly selected from each grade.

5. Suppose you want to collect data about which television shows teenagers like.
   (a) What is the easiest way to collect this data?
   (b) Who would be in your sample group? Is your sample group readily available? Would you survey everyone in the group?
   (c) This procedure is called **convenience sampling**. Write a definition of convenience sampling.
   (d) What are the advantages of this method? the disadvantages?
   (e) Is this sampling procedure biased? Explain.

6. Place the name of everyone in your class into a hat. Then select ten names.
  (a) Did everyone in the class have an equal chance of being selected? Explain.
  (b) Explain why this sample is a **random sample**. Write a definition of random sampling.
  (c) Suppose each person in your class is given a number 1, 2, 3, and so on. The principal selects ten of these numbers. Is this random sampling? Explain.
  (d) How else could you take a random sample?
  (e) What are the advantages of this method? the disadvantages?
  (f) Is this sampling procedure biased? Explain.

7. Write the name of everyone in your class on a different piece of paper. Group the papers into boys' names and girls' names.
  (a) How might you use the number of boys' names and the number of girls' names to create a representative sample of your class?
  (b) How else could you group the class so that each group is represented fairly?
  (c) A sample in which all groups of the population are represented fairly is a **stratified sample**. What are the advantages of this method? the disadvantages?
  (d) Write a paragraph to tell how you would take a stratified sample of the groups that are working on this activity.

8. A publisher wants to know which type of book high school students like best. The publisher chooses ten high schools at random and surveys every student in each school.
  (a) Why would the publisher collect the data this way?
  (b) Is this sampling procedure biased? Explain.
  (c) What are the advantages of this method? the disadvantages?
  (d) How else could you collect the data?
  (e) This procedure is called **cluster sampling**. Write your own definition of cluster sampling.
  (f) Tell two ways you could take a cluster sample of the students in your school.

9. How would you choose a sample of students from your school to develop conclusions about:
  (a) the academic success of the school?
  (b) the school's success in fine arts?
  (c) the athletic success of the school?

10. Explain why each sample in Question 9 is biased or non-biased.

11. Using your class as the population, describe how to select a biased sample and a non-biased sample to find:
  (a) the average height of your classmates.
  (b) the favourite hairstyle.
  (c) the shoes teenagers like most.
  (d) the concerns of teenagers.

12. Your principal wants to change some school policies. A meeting is called to discuss possible changes and to get feedback. Who should be at the meeting? Explain.

13. Decide how to fairly select a person in each case. Compare answers with a partner.
  (a) A member of Canada's Olympic team to carry the flag.
  (b) A member of a team for the Most Improved Player trophy.
  (c) A bank teller as Employee of the Month.

14. You are conducting research on traffic accident rates for different groups of drivers. Explain how to select a biased sample that would lead to each conclusion.
  (a) Young male drivers have the highest traffic accident rate.
  (b) Young male drivers have the lowest accident rate.
  (c) The traffic accident rate for young male drivers is about the same as the national average.

C

15. You are in charge of finding out if people like sugarless gum better than gum with sugar.
  (a) What questions would you ask?
  (b) How many people would you survey? How would you select them?
  (c) How would you collect the data?
  (d) How would you present the data that you collected?
  (e) Collect some of the data that you need. What conclusions can you draw?

16. You have just developed a new gum that is tastier than any other gum. However, the gum contains sugar. You are in charge of gathering data and developing an advertising campaign for the gum.
  (a) List questions you might ask.
  (b) Who would you survey?
  (c) How would you collect your data – in questionnaires, personal interviews, or by telephone?

17. Make up a set of data that you might get from your survey in Question 16. Set up an advertising campaign for the gum. Present your campaign to the rest of the class. What math skills did you need to develop your campaign? Write the skills in your journal.

The Chapter Problem — How Are Shoes Designed?

Refer to the Chapter Problem at the beginning of this chapter.

1. How would you select a **non-biased** basketball shoe focus group from:
  (a) your class?
  (b) all of the Grade 9 students at your school?

2. You will need to ask the focus group questions that provide useful data. Write questions that you might ask the focus group. Try out your questions on several other students.

3. How could you collect data about weight, height, and foot size? How would you avoid bias in your sample?

Did You Know?

EXPLORATION

These pictures are by Swiss artist Sandro Del Prete.

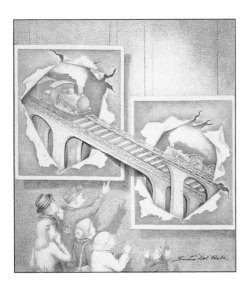

Think, Do, Discuss

1. Look at each picture quickly to obtain an idea of what the image is portraying. Describe what you see.
2. Look at each picture again. Do you see something that you didn't see the first time? If so, describe it.
3. Is it safe to conclude that what you observe on first inspection is always correct? Explain.

Drawing Conclusions from Data 1.4

Judging Validity of Data

Different people can draw different conclusions from the same data. To judge the validity of a conclusion based on data, you need to know the following:

Motivation: Why the data was collected.
Method: The sampling procedure or data collection process.
Observations: The actual data.
Reasoning Process: The logical steps that lead from the data to the conclusion.
Error: Any sources of error, such as bias or false assumptions.

The following table gives the number of car accidents for different age groups and the ratio of that number compared to the national population.

Age Group	Number of Accidents	Ratio
16–19	6 382	1 : 12
20–24	7 183	1 : 13.5
25–34	11 733	1 : 14
35–44	8 990	1 : 15.25
45–54	5 517	1 : 15.7
55–64	3 307	1 : 14.6
65–74	2 308	1 : 14

Think, Do, Discuss

1. How could you use this data to show that:
   (a) young drivers are more likely to have an accident?
   (b) young drivers are less likely to have an accident?
   (c) older drivers are more likely to have an accident?
   (d) older drivers are less likely to have an accident?

2. Why would this data have been collected? Who would need this information?

3. How would this data have been collected?

4. Explain why the data in the table is presented in a biased way. How did you overcome this bias as you answered each of the questions above?

Focus

Key Ideas

- Different conclusions can be drawn from the same data. To judge the validity of a conclusion based on data, ask yourself:

    - **Why** was the data collected?
    - **How** was the data collected?
    - **What** data was collected?
    - What **reasoning** was used to draw the conclusion?
    - Are there any sources of **error**, such as bias or false assumptions?

- The conclusions drawn from data can be wrong or misleading. Think about what you read. Make sure conclusions follow reasonably from the data. Watch for bias, false assumptions, and inaccurate wording.

Example

The manager of a jeans store does a survey on the Internet asking teens to vote for the brand of jeans they like best. The manager then advertises the five most popular brands for teens. No data is supplied. Is this conclusion valid?

Solution

Why was the data collected?
The store manager must already know which brands sell the best in the store. The manager may want to influence teens to buy more expensive brand names.

How was the data collected?
It was collected over the Internet from teens who were interested in responding.

What data was collected?
No data is given. You do not know how many votes each brand got or if teens voted for other brands that were not in the top five.

What reasoning was used?
The manager reasons that the brands that receive the most votes are the most popular.

Are there any sources of error?
The selection method is biased because:

- only teens with access to a computer were able to respond
- people may have voted more than once
- people other than teens may have responded.

Since the possibility of error exists, we cannot say the conclusion is valid.

Practise, Apply, Solve

1. **(a)** What do you see in this picture? Does everyone see the same thing?

   (b) There are two women in this picture. Try to see both of them. Why would some members of the group see the old woman first? Why would some see the young woman first?

2. Identify the error or bias.

   (a) An advertisement says 80% of dentists use Brand A toothpaste.

   (b) A council member says, "A great majority votes to move the homeless off the streets."

   (c) You conduct a survey regarding cafeteria food. Two people answer. Both say changes are needed. You report, "100% of students vote for change."

   (d) A commercial for sugar-free gum says three out of five people prefer sugar-free gum.

B

3. Find an example in the media (newspapers, magazines, radio, or TV) of conclusions drawn from data. Then answer these questions.

   (a) Why is the information being presented?

   (b) How was the sample selected? Is it appropriate?

   (c) Is there enough data? Is the data clear? honest?

   (d) Do the conclusions follow logically from the data? Are questions left unanswered? Is this deliberate?

   (e) Is there any evidence of bias or assumptions? Explain.

   (f) Is the conclusion valid? Explain.

4. How could the conclusion in each situation be biased?

   (a) A taste test urges you to try a new product and rate it against similar products that you already buy. However, the other product samples are not available for tasting.

   (b) A certain lobby group presents to city council the results of a survey they conducted.

5.
   > The US Kidney Foundation found that 48% of those surveyed would not take offence to moderate reimbursement (such as funeral costs) in exchange for donating vital organs upon death.
   >
   > *Source: 60 Minutes, Sun. Nov. 26, 1995.*

   (a) With a partner, discuss possible reasons for this statement.

   (b) Explain the possibility of bias.

6. Identify the assumptions in each example. Is the sample size appropriate? Explain.

   (a) In a survey, 485 out of 513 people preferred comics to be at the end of the newspaper.

   (b) Two out of three dentists surveyed recommend baking soda in toothpaste.

7. Of 28 teens, 43% could not name one Canadian they considered to be a hero. This means that 1.2 million teens in Canada are without a hero.

    (a) Does this conclusion follow logically from the data? Explain.

    (b) What assumption is being made?

    (c) Conduct this survey with your class. Do you get the same results?

    (d) If you conducted this survey with teens in the entire school, would you get the same results? Explain.

Canadian astronaut
Julie Payette

8. Analyze the data and conclusions in this article.

What Do You Want To Be?

Most children want to be more like their mother than their father, according to a recent survey of over two thousand children aged from 5 to 12 years old. Thirty-five percent of the ten-year-olds wanted to have the same jobs as their mothers. Only 5 percent wanted their fathers' jobs. Twenty-five percent of all the boys surveyed wanted jobs like their mothers had, but 10 percent of them wanted their fathers' jobs. The other children wanted different careers than their parents had.

    (a) What external influences could be affecting these results?

    (b) How could the neighbourhood where the survey was conducted affect the results?

    (c) Would children of different ages have similar or different opinions? Why?

9. Work in groups to analyze this advertisement.

According to recent health studies, up to 80% of Canadian women are not getting enough iron in their diet. Iron is important for several reasons, but its most vital function is carrying oxygen to the blood. Simply put, if you don't get enough iron, your muscles don't get enough oxygen and that can leave you feeling run down, lethargic, worn out.

You could take a supplement, but most nutrition experts agree it's far better to get iron from food. There are two different types of iron: heme and non-heme. Heme iron, found only in red meat, fish, and poultry, is absorbed 5 to 10 times more readily than non-heme iron found in vegetables, cereals, and grains.

For your body to absorb the same amount of iron as in a 3-oz. broiled sirloin steak, you'd have to eat an entire bag of raw spinach or three 3-oz. roasted chicken breasts or eleven 3-oz. fillets of baked sole.

Today's lean beef can help you meet your daily iron needs without contributing excess fat. So you can enjoy its great taste more often.

Source: Flare magazine, December 1995, p. 63.

(a) Who do you think sponsored this advertisement?

(b) Is the data presented honestly and clearly? Explain.

(c) Do you agree with the information presented? Explain.

(d) How is your analysis of the ad like those of other groups? different?

C

10. In a recent stratified random sample, 1501 adult Canadians who recently purchased a new car were surveyed. They were asked, "How satisfied are you with your new vehicle?" This is a graph of the data collected.

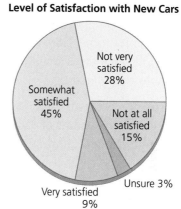

Level of Satisfaction with New Cars

Write two newspaper articles using this data. In one article, show that people are satisfied with their purchase. In the other, show they are dissatisfied.

Reasons given for dissatisfaction included:
- poor quality of the vehicle in general (12%)
- noisy and uncomfortable ride (15%)
- poor fuel effeciency (8%)
- unreliable/mechanical breakdowns (17%)
- high cost of service (26%)
- not enough room for passengers (18%).

11. Does this graph present data reliably? How could it be improved?

12. (a) Write a question that you would like to know the answer to – one that could be answered by conducting a survey.

(b) Conduct the survey, analyze the data, and write a concluding statement.

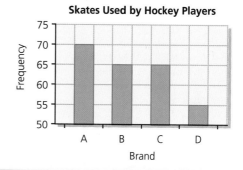

Skates Used by Hockey Players

Career: Journalist

Journalists play a vital role in society. They inform people about events in their community, their country, and the rest of the world.

The main responsibility of journalists is to provide reports that will help people form opinions about current affairs. Journalists communicate through print materials, such as newspapers and magazines, or through electronic media like television, radio, and the Internet.

People believe the statistics that journalists report. Therefore, it is important for journalists to understand how surveys are done and how statistics are produced.

People rely on journalists to provide fair and truthful reporting of current events. In some countries, the news media is controlled by the state. How would the political system in these countries affect the information received by the public through the media?

1.5 Surveys and Television Ratings

Daphne Hubble, Director of Marketing Research, works for MuchMusic and Bravo! TV stations. She uses TV survey data to help advertisers and station programmers make decisions.

For example, programmers may want to know when to air a program for teens. Daphne can use survey data to help them find when teens are likely to watch TV and what programs they watch.

The size of a program's audience is expressed either as the total number of viewers or as a percent of the population. These numbers are called ratings.

Daphne Hubble

Nielsen Week/Semaine
Oct 19 Oct., 1998

Day Jour	Start Début	Program Emission	Dur Min	# Stns	Total 2+ (000)
Sun/Dim	6.00A	Muchcombatzone	210	1	23
Sun/Dim	9:30A	Da Mix	60	1	20
Sun/Dim	10:30A	The Monkees	30	1	18
Sun/Dim	11:00A	Muchondemand	60	1	35
Sun/Dim	12:00A	Pop-up Video	180	1	40
Sun/Dim	1:00A	Fax	30	1	62
Sun/Dim	4:00A	Muchondemand	30	1	92
Sun/Dim	4:30A	Muchmegahits	60	1	81
			60	1	65
			60	1	59

A sample ratings sheet

When a program like *Electric Circus* has a 5 teen rating, it means that on average five percent of teens were watching the program at the time of the survey. A 20 percent share means that one-fifth of all the teens watching TV at that time were tuned to *Electric Circus*.

Think, Do, Discuss

1. Why do television and radio stations keep close track of the number of viewers or listeners?
2. Design a process Daphne could use to get data about the ratings of *Electric Circus* among different age groups.
3. How could the station use this data to set advertising rates for the show?
4. What evidence might an advertiser want to justify the cost of advertising during a particular program?
5. Why can television networks demand huge advertising fees for events like the Grey Cup, the Stanley Cup final game, the Academy Awards, and the Three Tenors concert?

The Process of Designing 1.6 an Experiment

In Grade 8, Omid learned that the formula for calculating the circumference of a circle is $C = \pi d$.

He wondered where this formula came from and decided to design an experiment to see if he could prove this relationship on his own. He collected about 20 round objects, including cans, jar lids, balls, and coins.

Think, Do, Discuss

1. What other materials does Omid need for this experiment?
2. How can he find out if there is a relationship between circumference and diameter using the objects he has collected?
3. What information should Omid be finding out about each object?
4. How should Omid organize the information he collects?
5. What would be the best method for Omid to use to display his findings?
6. Once he has completed the experiment, recorded and displayed his data, what does he need to do to prove the relationship?

Focus

> ## Key Ideas
>
> - To design an experiment to find a relationship between two variables:
>   - decide what data is needed
>   - decide on a method to collect the data (survey, experiment, research)
>   - collect the data and organize it in a table
>   - graph the data
>   - look for a pattern.

Example

Design an experiment to find out how effective an exercise class is in improving a person's fitness level.

Solution

Step 1: Decide what data is needed.
When a person exercises, the heart beats faster than when the person is at rest. After exercise, the heart beat returns to its resting rate. Usually, the more quickly a person's heartbeat returns to its resting rate, the fitter that person is. Use the length of time it takes for a person's heartbeat to return to its resting rate as a level of fitness.

Step 2: Decide on a method to collect the data. Then collect the data and organize it in a table.
Select a sample of ten students from the class and number them from 1 to 10. Measure the resting heart rate of each student before exercise. After each exercise class, measure how long it takes the heart rate of each student to return to its resting rate. Organize the data for each student in a separate table as shown.

Exercise Class Number	Time to Return to Resting Heart Rate

Step 3: Graph the data and look for a pattern.
Graph the data in each table, with "Exercise Class Number" on the horizontal axis and "Time to Return to Resting Rate" on the vertical axis, as shown. If the exercise class is improving student fitness, then there should be a pattern among the points on the graph.

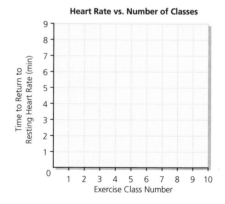

Step 4: Draw a conclusion from the data you have collected.
By examining the graph you have drawn, you should be able to see if there is a relationship between the students' fitness level before and after the exercises. For instance, if the fitness level is improving, then the heart rate will return to its resting rate more quickly as more exercise classes are done.

Step 5: Analyze your experiment and comment on any bias.

Practise, Apply, Solve ——————————————————

A

1. Which step of an experiment is each example? Explain.
   (a) A questionnaire is to be used.
   (b) The data is organized in a chart.
   (c) A graph is used to display data.
   (d) Questions are being asked at a video arcade.
   (e) Comments on bias are presented.
   (f) A sampling strategy is to be used.

2. Design an experiment that will find if there is a relationship between people's height and their "arm stretch."
   (a) State your hypothesis (what you expect your results to be).
   (b) How will you collect your data?
   (c) What kind of sampling method will you use?
   (d) What procedures will you use to get your results?
   (e) How much data will you collect? How will you organize your data?
   (f) How will you present your findings? What type of graph or diagram is appropriate?
   (g) How will you represent each variable clearly? How does this make reporting easier?
   (h) What conclusions can you make from your experiment?
   (i) What are the advantages of your data collection procedures? disadvantages?
   (j) Comment on how you avoided bias in your experiment.

B

3. Design an experiment to find each relationship:
   (a) the length of time someone can hold his or her breath versus the body mass of that person.
   (b) the length a spring stretches versus the mass of weight used.
   (c) the strength of your grip versus your body mass.
   (d) recycling awareness versus action.
   (e) peer pressure versus decision making by teens.
   (f) grades versus time spent on homework.
   (g) the number of pages in a book versus interest in reading it.
   (h) interest in music versus a person's age.
   (i) the time spent practising versus performance.

4. Design an experiment to show the effect of music on heart rate. How could doctors use this information? Who else might be interested in the results?

5. Suppose you wish to accumulate $1 million by investing $30 each month starting at age 18 and continuing to age 65. How could you investigate the relationship between the number of years it takes to reach $1 million and the annual rate of return?

6. Design an experiment to find how residents of Tuktoyaktuk feel about plans to tap into the oil and natural gas reserves in that area. To do research on Tuktoyaktuk, you could use the Internet. There are several Web sites, including one for Mangilaluk School.

(a) What sampling procedures will you use?

(b) How much information will you collect?

(c) How will you get your results?

(d) How will you use the information you collect?

7. There is a growing concern about the condition of the world's water. Third World countries have a shortage of clean water. England has considered rationing water. Speak to a civil engineer who works with water resources. What kind of experiments do they design, conduct, and report on? How might the information they collect affect your life?

8. Research MADD (Mothers Against Drunk Driving). (There are several Web sites on the Internet, including MADD's Idea Library.)

(a) How and why was the organization created?

(b) What data was collected to bring attention to the organization?

(c) Describe the reports that were generated.

9. What method of collecting data would you use to determine:

(a) the most common reasons for exercising?

(b) which of three kinds of paint is most weatherproof?

(c) the amount of snow that falls in Sudbury in January?

C

10. (a) List the most popular fast foods in your neighbourhood.

(b) Choose a method of collecting data to find which fast food is most popular. Then gather the data.

(c) What percent of the sample chose the most popular food? the least popular?

(d) Suppose you are going to invest in a fast-food outlet near your school. Which foods would you sell?

(e) Based on the success of your outlet in (d), you decide to build another outlet. What is your first step in finding out where the outlet should be built? Where would you build it?

11. Checking your pulse as you exercise gives you useful information about your fitness level.

(a) Find different methods of taking your pulse.

(b) Take your pulse using one of the methods in (a).

(c) Complete some activities, like running on the spot, push ups, or sit ups for about 5 min. Check your pulse rate using the same method you used in (b).

(d) Now sit down and rest for 3 min. Find your pulse rate using the same method you used in (b).

(e) Compare your pulse rate to others in the class after exercise and at rest. Display your data to compare the pulse rates of your classmates.

(f) Interpret your data. What conclusions can you make?

12. Your school is interested in finding the fitness level of the student body as part of the prime minister's annual report on fitness.

(a) Design an experiment that would test one aspect of student physical fitness. Discuss likely sources of error.

(b) How would you conduct the experiment so that you collect enough data to make valid conclusions about the student body's fitness level?

(c) How would you present this data graphically as part of a report to the student council and staff? Draw up a sample presentation.

13. Design an experiment to find if there is a relationship between the height of a certain type of plant and the amount of water given to the plant each day.

(a) State your hypothesis (what you expect your results to be).

(b) Many factors affect the growth of a plant. List as many as you can think of.

(c) Which of the factors in (b) are you studying in your experiment?

(d) Which of the factors in (b) are you ignoring in your experiment?

(e) What should you do to make sure that the factors in (d) do not interfere with the results of your experiment?

(f) Describe the procedure that you will follow to collect your data.

(g) How will you organize your data?

(h) What type of graph or diagram is appropriate for presenting your data?

(i) Discuss the advantages and disadvantages of your experiment design with a classmate. Comment on how you avoided bias in your experiment.

The Chapter Problem — How Are Shoes Designed?

Refer back to the Chapter Problem at the beginning of this chapter.

1. Design a process that you can use to collect data on height and shoe size for each person in your class.

2. Determine how you will organize your findings and display the results.

Colin Percival

As long as 4000 years ago, people had discovered that the ratio of the circumference to the diameter of a circle was about 3 to 1. The ancient Egyptians used $\frac{256}{81}$ and the Babylonians used $\frac{25}{8}$ as values for π. The Chinese found a value that was used for over one thousand years.

In 1997, the mathematician Kanada computed π to 50 billion digits using a 1024 processor Hitachi SR2201 supercomputer at the University of Tokyo. In 1998, Colin Percival, of Burnaby, BC, (shown here) used a network of computers and an algorithm discovered in 1995 at Simon Fraser University by Bailey, Borwein, and Plouffe to set a new record. In base-2 format, a number is represented by a combination of 0s and 1s. Each 0 or 1 in the number is called a bit. Colin computed the five trillionth bit of π without computing all the previous bits. At the time he was 17. He also is an accomplished musician.

1.7 Creating Scatter Plots

Anthropologists use the length of the humerus, or upper arm bone, to estimate the height of the humans whose bones they discover. They developed this method by collecting data from living subjects.

They measure the length of the humerus of each subject and the subject's height. Then they model the relationship between height and humerus length.

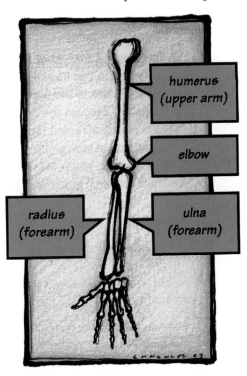

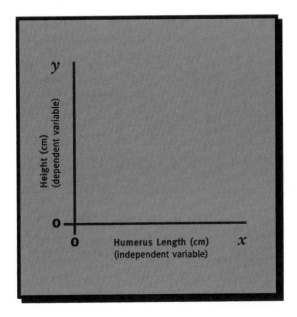

Think, Do, Discuss

1. Collect data on the relationship between the height of a person and the length of the humerus among your classmates.
2. Plot your data by creating a data table with a spreadsheet or by entering the information into your graphing calculator or the *Line of Best Fit Explorer*. Enter the data for the length of the humerus first and the height of the person second. Refer to the instruction manual for the calculator if you are not sure how to do this. For the *Explorer*, enter the length of the humerus in the *x*-column and the height in the *y*-column. Use the graphing capabilities of the technology to create the scatter plot.
3. Is there a strong relationship between height and humerus length? Use the data and the graph of the data to answer this question.
4. Is it enough to record each person's height and humerus length once, or do you need to do it again? Explain.
5. Can you use your data to predict the height of an adult? Why?

EXPLORATION

Drawing and Interpreting Scatter Plots 1.8

Kathleen Heddle and Marnie McBean were two of the 10 744 athletes who competed in the 1996 Summer Olympics in Atlanta, Georgia. All of these athletes stayed in the Olympic Village. An Olympic Village has to be built at the site of each Olympic games. Organizers need to predict in advance how many athletes need to be housed. The size of the Olympic Village depends on two factors: the number of nations attending the games and the number of athletes participating. Organizers collected this data:

Kathleen Heddle and Marnie McBean

Location	Year	Nations Represented	Athletes
Tokyo	1964	93	5 140
Mexico City	1968	112	5 531
Munich	1972	122	7 147
Montreal	1976	92	6 085
Moscow	1980	81	5 353
Los Angeles	1984	141	7 078
Seoul	1988	160	9 581
Barcelona	1992	172	10 563
Atlanta	1996	197	10 744

Think, Do, Discuss

1. Use the table to make a graph of the years from 1964 and the number of nations at the Summer Olympic games. Put years on the horizontal axis and nations represented on the vertical axis, then plot the points.
2. Usually the points you have plotted are related in some way. What difficulty are you faced with here?
3. Can you see a pattern in these points? Explain.
4. Can you use the graph you have drawn to make an accurate prediction of the number of nations that will attend the next Summer Olympics? Explain.
5. Use the table to make a graph of the years from 1964 and the number of competitors at the Summer Olympic games. Put years on the horizontal axis and competitors on the vertical axis, then plot the points.
6. Explain how these points are related.
7. Can the organizers predict with confidence how many athletes have to be housed? Explain.

Focus

Example

The table shows what a traveller paid for a hotel room and dinner in nine different cities.

(a) Draw a scatter plot to examine the relationship between the cost of the hotel and the cost of dinner.

(b) Describe any trends in the data.

City	Cost of Hotel ($)	Cost of Dinner ($)
1	47.88	20.33
2	50.19	21.40
3	69.54	19.68
4	67.26	11.24
5	91.20	38.52
6	71.82	44.94
7	57.00	29.74
8	125.40	19.59
9	62.70	32.58

Solution

(a) Graph the data. Neither variable depends on the other, so it does not matter which one is on which axis.

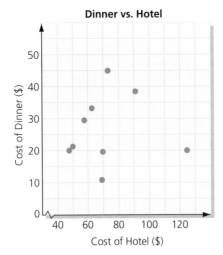

(b) The points incline up and to the right. It appears that as the hotel cost increases, the dinner cost also increases. The point representing city 8 is odd because the cost of dinner ($19.59) is low compared to the hotel cost ($125.40). Perhaps the traveller ate at a less expensive restaurant, or the hotel gives guests a discount on meals.

Practise, Apply, Solve

A

1. Suppose you survey your classmates to see if there is a relationship between a student's math mark and the amount of TV watched.
   (a) How would you set up a table to help in your data collection?
   (b) How would you label each axis of the scatter plot?
   (c) Give an example of an ordered pair that reflects how you would plot the data.
   (d) What do you think the finished scatter plot would look like? Why?

2. Jodi and Jeffrey conduct an experiment and gather this data from six students.

Height (cm)	Arm Length (cm)
159	43
157	41
160	45
159	43
160	46
157	41

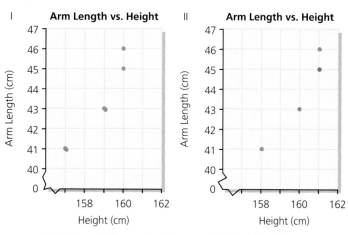

Jodi draws scatter plot I; Jeffrey draws scatter plot II.
   (a) Who is correct? Explain.
   (b) Write a note to correct the other student.

B

3. Graph this data on the percentage of women in the Canadian work force.
   (a) What will be on the horizontal axis? the vertical axis?
   (b) Describe any trends that you see.
   (c) What is the relationship between year and percentage of women in the Canadian work force?
   (d) What percentage of women do you predict will be in the work force in 2010?

Year	Percentage of Women in the Canadian Work Force
1950	30
1955	33
1960	30
1965	37
1970	38
1975	39
1980	41
1985	45
1990	47
1995	49

4. Draw a scatter plot of this data. Give your scatter plot a title.

Age of Car (year)	Value ($)
7	3 000
5	3 500
4	9 950
3	8 950
2	13 500

5. The fuel a car consumes is measured at various speeds. The data is recorded as ordered pairs (speed in kilometres per hour, gas consumed in litres per 100 km).
(10, 8.2), (20, 7.9), (30, 7.5), (40, 6.9), (50, 6.7), (60, 6.4), (70, 6.2), (80, 5.9), (90, 6.1), (100, 6.7), (110, 7.8), (120, 8.4), (130, 9.9)
(a) Draw a scatter plot of this data.
(b) Does the scatter plot seem reasonable? Explain.
(c) Describe any trend that you see.
(d) Who would want this information? Why?

6. What might a scatter plot that shows a relationship between allergies and the cleanliness of the air we breathe look like? Explain the relationship.

7. **(a)** Copy these axes.

(b) Predict a scatter plot for the data and draw it.
(c) Describe the relationship shown. Explain.

8. A basketball coach recorded the length of time each player was in a game and the number of points the player scored as an ordered pair (time in minutes, points scored). The data was collected over ten games.
(151, 51), (18, 10), (164, 38), (86, 28), (136, 39), (110, 40), (55, 8), (163, 62), (192, 50), (98, 32), (71, 25)
(a) Make a scatter plot.
(b) Describe the relationship between points scored and minutes played.

C

9. Family doctors record the growth of their young patients. As you continue to grow, regular medical exams will include measuring your height and weight. Use the table to see if there is a relationship between height and weight.
(a) Graph the data in the table.
(b) Does your graph consist of scattered points or a line? Why?
(c) From your graph, what can you say about the relationship between height and weight?
(d) Would it be a concern if your height stayed the same for three years? Explain.

Height (cm)	Weight (kg)
58	5.0
60	6.3
64	7.3
68	8.1
73	8.8
74	8.2

10. (a) Draw scatter plots of the data.
(b) Describe any patterns you see.
(c) What would happen if the trend continued?
(d) Do you expect this trend to continue? Why?

Birth Rates Per 1000 People				
Year	Ontario	NF	PE	NS
1994	13.5	11.2	12.9	12.2
1995	13.4	10.8	12.5	11.6
1996	12.9	10.4	13.1	11.6
1997	12.5	10.0	12.0	11.0
1998	12.1	9.7	12.4	10.9

11. Teachers record how many days of school students have missed. The other important item that teachers record is the mark for each student. Use the table to see if there is a relationship between attendance and marks.
(a) Graph the data in the table.
(b) Describe the relationship between attendance and marks using your graph.

Days of School Missed	Mark
0	95
3	86
4	83
8	74
12	67

The Chapter Problem — How Are Shoes Designed?

Refer back to the Chapter Problem at the beginning of this chapter.

1. Collect data on height and shoe size of each person in your class.
2. Draw a scatter plot of your findings. How will the horizontal axis be labelled?
3. Describe the trend in your graph.

Did You Know?

The earliest known use of negative numbers was by Chinese mathematicians during the Chou period (1030–221 BCE). Red rods on a counting board were used to represent negative numbers.

The Chinese scholar Li Yeh (circa 1300) was the first to introduce a notation for negative numbers.

When a number is written in the Chinese **Scientific** or **Rod System**, a diagonal stroke through the right-hand digit indicates that the number is negative.

$$\bigcirc\ulcorner\equiv\text{╫} = -10\ 724$$

This system was different from the positional number system that is in current use with Hindu-Arabic numerals.

The following are the symbols for the numbers 1 to 9 under the Chinese Scientific or Rod System.

$$— = \equiv \equiv \overline{\equiv} \perp \underline{\perp} \overline{\underline{\perp}} \overline{\equiv}$$

EXPLORATION

Responding to Stimuli

When it's cold, you shiver. When it's hot, you perspire. When it's dusty or there is bright light, you blink. In each case your body's response is activated by your nervous system to help you adjust to change. How does your body respond to stimuli? Try this investigation to find out.

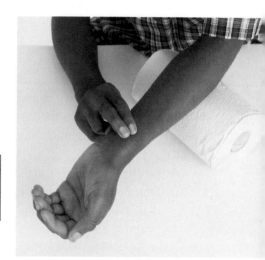

Resting Pulse	10-s Jog	15-s Jog	30-s Jog	45-s Jog	60-s Jog

Think, Do, Discuss

1. Take your pulse by placing two fingers on your wrist. Once you feel the beating under your fingertips, look at your watch and count the number of beats you feel in 10 s. Multiply the number of beats by 6 to obtain the number of beats per minute. This is your resting pulse rate. Copy the table and enter your resting pulse rate.
2. Jog on the spot for 10 s, then take your pulse. Record it in the table. Rest until your heart rate returns to its resting value.
3. Repeat Step 2 for 15 s, 30 s, 45 s, and 60 s.
4. Create a scatter plot of the data you have collected.
5. Describe any patterns that you see.
6. On the scatter plot, draw a straight line that will represent the relationship in the data. Explain how you can do this.
7. What would you expect your pulse to be if you jogged for 50 s? 90 s?
8. Consult with five other students and find out their results. Do their lines look the same as yours? Why or why not?
9. Take their data and add these points to your scatter plot. Does your original line represent the new data? Explain.
10. Draw a new line to represent the data you have collected from all six students (including yourself).
11. What will happen to your line if you add the data from everyone in the class?

The Line of Best Fit

Students in Mr. Chan's social science class conducted an experiment to determine if marks scored on a test were related to the number of hours of television watched.

This data was collected for ten students.

Student	1	2	3	4	5	6	7	8	9	10
Mark (%)	82	64	84	70	74	76	85	73	94	90
Hours of TV	2	4	0	3	2	2	1	3	1	2

Television/Marks Survey

1. How many hours of television did you watch the night before your science test? Answer to the nearest hour.

2. What was your score on the science test?

3. What was

Think, Do, Discuss

1. Create the scatter plot for this data. Does the data show a trend?
2. How would you describe the relationship between hours of TV watched and test score?
3. Draw a straight line that passes close to the data points. How many data points lie on your line? above your line? below your line?
4. Compare your line with two other students' lines. Are all three lines the same? Why or why not?
5. Using the line that you drew, predict the test score of a student who watched 2.5 h of TV.
6. Will the rest of the students get the same answer to Question 5 as you do? Explain.
7. Create some rules that everyone can follow so that they all create a similar line.

Focus

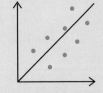
Example

This table shows the sales of bottled water at a refreshment booth at the Canadian National Exhibition in Toronto for different days during a heat wave one summer.

Temperature (°C)	23	25	28	29	24	28	27	30	32	35	35	37	36	37
Bottles Sold	32	50	112	147	193	223	312	376	286	250	357	364	321	335

Predict how many bottles of water will be sold on a day when the temperature reaches:

(a) 25°C **(b)** 42°C

(a)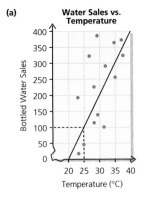

Water Sales vs. Temperature

Solution

First draw a scatter plot and a line of best fit.

(a) 50 bottles were sold the last time it was 25°C. This is no guarantee that 50 bottles will be sold the next time that it is 25°C. (Different numbers of bottles were sold on the two days when it was 35°C.) It is better to use the trend shown by the line of best fit to make the prediction.

Draw a vertical line from 25°C to the line of best fit. Draw a horizontal line to determine the number of bottles sold. About 100 bottles of water will be sold.

(b) Extend the line. Then find where 42°C meets the line and read the corresponding number of bottles sold. About 410 bottles of water will be sold.

(b)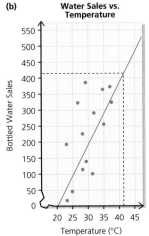

Water Sales vs. Temperature

Practise, Apply, Solve

Ⓐ

1. Draw a scatter plot for this data. Draw the line of best fit.

x	10	4	2	5	7	3	8	8
y	6	10	19	16	15	21	12	10

2. Compare your results for Question 1 with a classmate. How are the lines alike? different? Explain any differences.

3. Data for ten more students in Mr. Chan's social science class was collected.

Student	11	12	13	14	15	16	17	18	19	20
Mark	75	81	69	62	88	83	90	77	89	60
Hours of TV	3	3	1	5	1	3	0	3	1	4

(a) Plot the points. What is the relationship between hours of TV watched and test mark?

(b) Draw a straight line that passes close to the data points. How many data points lie on your line? above your line? below your line?

(c) Compare your line with the line for the first ten students on page 67. Are the lines the same?

(d) Draw the line that best fits both sets of data.

Ⓑ

4. (a) Copy this scatter plot in your notebook.

(b) Draw the line of best fit. How many points are on your line? How did you estimate the line of best fit?

(c) Describe any trends you see.

Height vs. Age

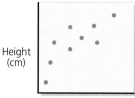

Height (cm)

Age (years)

5. (a) Copy these scatter plots in your notebook.

(b) Draw the line of best fit on each graph. Compare your lines with another student's.

(c) Which lines were least similar?

6. Draw the scatter plot and the line of best fit.
(a) (1, 1), (1, 3), (3, 1), (2, 5), (3, 3), (3, 5), (4, 4), (5, 6), (5, 5)
(b) (1, 2), (1, 3), (2, 3), (2, 4), (3, 4), (3, 5), (4, 5), (4, 6), (5, 6)
(c) (1, 5), (2, 6), (2, 4), (3, 5), (4, 3), (5, 4), (5, 1), (5, 2), (6, 1)
(d) (1, 5), (1, 4), (2, 4), (2, 3), (3, 3), (3, 2), (4, 2), (4, 1), (5, 1)

7. A basketball coach recorded the amount of time each player played and how many points the player scored in one game.

Time (min)	20	5	10	18	15	14	15
Points Scored	12	2	4	14	8	6	7

(a) Char's data is not recorded, but she scored 9 points. Estimate how long she played.

(b) Predict the number of points she would score if she played for 25 min.

8. The basketball coach at Chippewa High School appointed a student to act as team statistician. Her job was to compile data on each member of the team. Her data sheet for one game is given. Field goals score two points. Free throws score one point.

Player	Minutes Played	Field Goals Made – Attempted	Free Throws Made – Attempted	Points Scored
Anne	32	5–13	4–6	14
Beth	30	4–10	3–3	11
Cecile	24	2–6	1–1	5
Dawn	29	1–3	2–4	4
Eliza	36	3–6	0–1	6
Fran	19	5–11	2–2	12
Gerry	12	0–3	0–4	0
Helen	21	1–5	1–2	3
Irene	18	3–5	1–5	7
Jane	19	3–7	2–6	8
Totals	**240**	**27–69**	**16–34**	**70**

(a) Make a scatter plot showing field goals made, *FG*, and field goals attempted, *A*.

(b) If a player attempted 9 field goals, about how many would be successful?

(c) Make a scatter plot showing time played and points scored by each player.

(d) If a player played for 40 min, about how many points might she be expected to make?

9. (a) Copy this graph in your notebook.

(b) Draw the line of best fit.

(c) Predict the distance needed between plants that grow to 8 cm.

(d) Predict the distance needed between plants that grow to 12 cm.

(e) Compare your answers to (c) and (d) with another student. Are there any differences?

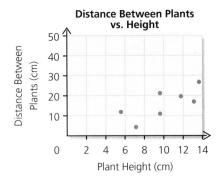

10. Doug drew this line of best fit through his data. Is his line reasonable? What would your line look like? Explain how you would draw the line.

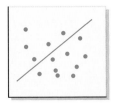

11. Alex is a member of the school track and field team. His times for running various distances are shown.
(a) Predict the distance Alex can run in 20 s.
(b) Estimate the time it will take Alex to run 280 m.
(c) If a graph was drawn based on the above data, would it be reasonable to use the graph's line of best fit to estimate how long it would take Alex to run 3000 m? Why or why not?

Distance (m)	Time (s)
50	6.1
100	12.0
150	18.3
200	25.2
250	31.7

12. A company that specializes in building chairs has a contract to make all of the seats in a 1790-seat concert hall. Their progress over the first week of work is shown.
(a) About how many seats are built after 9 days? by the middle of day 5?
(b) Estimate the number of days needed to build 1252 seats.
(c) The company gets a bonus if they are able to finish all of the seats in 2 weeks or less. If the workers, in the second week, continue to make chairs at about the same rate, will the company be able to collect the bonus?

Number of Days	Number of Seats Completed
1	97
2	204
3	327
4	443
5	539
6	661
7	795

The Chapter Problem — How Are Shoes Designed?

Refer back to the Chapter Problem at the beginning of this chapter.
1. Draw a line of best fit on your height-and-shoe-size scatter plot. Use it to predict:
(a) the shoe sizes of the tallest and shortest people in your class.
(b) the heights of the people with the largest and smallest shoe sizes.
2. Compare your results to actual student heights and shoe sizes. What information can you give Edith?

Aristotle

The Greek philosopher Aristotle (384–322 BCE) was one of the greatest thinkers of Western culture. Aristotle developed a style of reasoning we now call logic. Here is a typical example:

If: **1.** All cats have whiskers.

And: **2.** Sylvester is a cat.

Then: **3.** Sylvester has whiskers.

Aristotle would say that, given the truth of statements 1 and 2, you are forced by logic to accept that statement 3 is true. He called this pattern of reasoning a **syllogism**.

1.11 Predictions from Data

This activity will allow you to collect data about how quickly you can print words of different lengths. You will be able to use this data to make predictions about the performance of others in your class.

Think, Do, Discuss

1. Determine how many times you can print the word "RED" completely and correctly in exactly 15 s.
2. Repeat Step 1 nine more times to collect a total of ten data points. Find the median of the number of times. This represents your "typical" performance.
3. Repeat Steps 1 and 2 for each of these longer words: "GREEN," "MAGENTA," "TURQUOISE," and "ULTRAMARINE."
4. Prepare a scatter plot to show the relationship between the number of letters in a word and the median number of times you can print it in 15 s.
5. Describe the pattern in the scatter plot. What does this tell you about the relationship between word length and the number of times a word can be printed in 15 s?
6. Predict how many times you could print a six-letter word in 15 s. How confident are you that your prediction is reasonable?
7. Predict how many times you could print a two-letter word in 15 s and a 12-letter word in 15 s. How confident are you that your predictions are reasonable? Explain.
8. Add the data from four other randomly selected students to your scatter plot. Can you use the existing line of best fit? Explain.
9. Draw the new line of best fit and repeat Steps 6 and 7. This time you will be making predictions about the entire class.
10. Compare your confidence in the predictions you made about your own performance to those you made about the class using the combined data.

Interpreting Correlation Value 1.12

Scatter plots give visual clues about the relationship between two quantities. Some relationships are stronger than others, so you can make predictions more confidently.

Use the *Line of Best Fit Explorer* to investigate correlation.

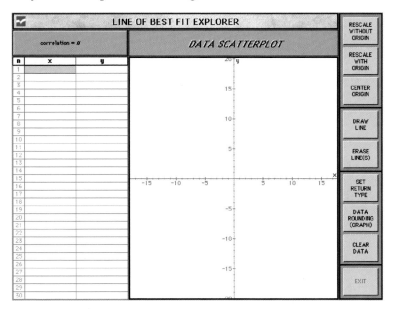

Think, Do, Discuss

1. Plot these points by entering them in the spreadsheet window. Press ENTER to record each coordinate.

x	y
0	3
1	5
2	7
3	9

2. Record the correlation value found in the top left of the spreadsheet window.
3. Move the points around so that they occupy different positions. To "grab" a point, move the cursor pointer over it and hold down the left mouse button. Then you can drag it to a new position. Release the left button to drop the point.
4. Move the points around so that the correlation value is:
   (a) the largest positive number possible. Describe any pattern in the points.
   (b) the smallest negative number possible. Describe any pattern in the points.
   (c) as close to 0 as possible. Describe any pattern in the points.

Focus

Key Ideas

- A scatter plot of the relationship between two variables shows:
  - positive correlation when the pattern slopes up and to the right. The two quantities increase together.
  - negative correlation when the pattern slopes down and to the right. As one quantity increases, the other decreases.
  - no correlation when no pattern appears.
- If the points nearly form a line, then the correlation is strong.
- If the points are dispersed more widely, but still form a rough line, then the correlation is weak.

Example

Describe the type of correlation that exists for each of the following scatter plots. Where possible, describe the relationship that exists between the two quantities.

(a)

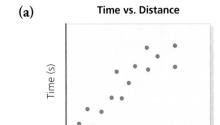

Time vs. Distance

(b)

Pages Left vs. Days Attended

(c)

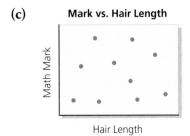

Mark vs. Hair Length

Solution

(a) The scatter plot slants up and to the right. As the distance increases, the time also increases. This is a positive correlation.

(b) The scatter plot shows a slant down and to the right. As the number of school days attended increases, the number of pages left in your math text decreases. This is a negative correlation.

(c) The scatter plot points are widely dispersed, showing no pattern. This is an example of no correlation.

Practise, Apply, Solve

1. Does each scatter plot show a positive correlation, a negative correlation, or no correlation? Explain.

(a)

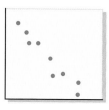

(b)

(c)

(d)

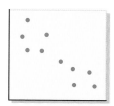

2. Find out from your classmates how far they live from school and how long it takes them to get to school.
   (a) Make a table of distance and time.
   (b) Draw a scatter plot.
   (c) Is there a relationship? If so, describe it.
   (d) What correlation is there? Explain.
   (e) What conclusions can you draw from your scatter plot?

3. Does each set of variables show a positive correlation, a negative correlation, or no correlation? Explain your reasoning.
   (a) temperature and snow-ski sales
   (b) the size of a person's hand and the amount in that person's savings account
   (c) outside summer temperature and the sales of cold drinks
   (d) length of a student's nails and final grade in English
   (e) the number of pages left to be read in a book and the number already read

4. Does each set of variables show a positive correlation, a negative correlation, or no correlation? Explain your reasoning.
   (a) hours of study and marks scored on an exam
   (b) distance from Earth and force of gravity
   (c) hours of typing practice and typing speed
   (d) altitude and air pressure
   (e) speed and air resistance

5. A set of data points is plotted. Three students draw these graphs below so that they can make predictions about the data.
(a) Who is correct? Explain.
(b) What errors did the other two students make?

i. 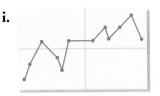 ii. 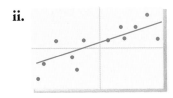 iii.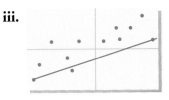

6. Identify a variable that has:
(a) a positive correlation with age
(b) a negative correlation with age
(c) no correlation with age.

7. For each situation in Question 6, sketch and label scatter plots to show your ideas. Have a classmate interpret each scatter plot.

8. Identify a variable that has:
(a) a positive correlation with marks
(b) a negative correlation with marks
(c) no correlation with marks.

9. For each situation in Question 8, sketch and label scatter plots to show your ideas. Have a classmate interpret your scatter plots.

10. Sketch a scatter plot showing heart rate versus minutes of exercise. Identify the limits on each variable.

11. Compare the correlations shown in Figures A and B. Are they positive or negative? Which is stronger?

Figure A

Figure B

12. Examine scatter plots i–iv.
(a) Which scatter plot shows the strongest correlation?
(b) How many scatter plots show a negative correlation?
(c) Which scatter plot shows no correlation?
(d) Which scatter plot shows a weak negative correlation?
(e) Which scatter plot shows a strong positive correlation?

i. 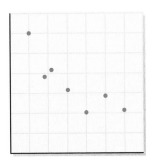 ii.

iii.  **iv.**

C

13. Research the average temperature and the latitude of ten cities that are north of the equator. Use the Internet or the library.
  (a) Draw a scatter plot of the data.
  (b) What kind of correlation does the scatter plot show?
  (c) Write a question that could be answered using your scatter plot.

14. (a) For each student in your class, find his or her:
  • height, in centimetres, and
  • hand span (distance between thumb and little finger when stretching).
  (b) Complete a table of values for the data.
  (c) What conclusions can you make from your data?

The Chapter Problem — How Are Shoes Designed?

Refer back to the Chapter Problem at the beginning of this chapter.

What kind of correlation exists between the shoe size and height data you collected? Why?

Career: Seismologist

Seismologists study earthquakes to find how they are caused and how to predict them. They collect data about the longitude, latitude, and depth of the epicentre of each earthquake within a certain area. Until recently, only the first two variables could be plotted on a scatter plot; the depths of the earthquakes were missing from the plots. In the 1980s, Dr. Peter Huber designed a computer program that could present all three variables in a three-dimensional scatter plot. This perspective has helped seismologists to interpret their earthquake data.

1.13 Finding the Mean Fit Line

TECHNOLOGY

Using the *Line of Best Fit Explorer*

The test marks of 20 students are compared with how long they studied. The results are shown.

Study Time (h)	Marks (out of 20)
0	8, 10
0.5	7, 10, 12, 16
1.0	8, 12, 13, 14, 16, 18
1.5	10, 12, 16, 18
2.0	13, 16, 18, 19

Use the *Line of Best Fit Explorer* to make a scatter plot of the students' marks.

How to Use the *Explorer*

1. Enter the data into the spreadsheet. Press ENTER after each value. Use study time for the *x*-values and marks for the *y*-values.

2. Adjust the scales by using the "Rescale with Origin" button.

3. To draw a line of best fit, click on the "Draw Line" button. Move the cursor to where you want to position point *A*. Place point *A* on the graph by left-clicking the mouse. To draw the line, keep holding the left button down and move the cursor to the location for point *B*. Letting go of the mouse button places the line on the scatter plot.

4. Use the line you made in Step 3 to predict the mark a student will get if he or she studies for 1.75 h.

5. The red cross on the screen gives an estimate of the centre of the data. Click on the "Draw Line" button. Then redraw the line of best fit by positioning point *A* on the red cross.

6. Copy this graph into your notebook. Be sure to indicate all coordinates on the line.

7. Use the new line to make the same prediction as in Step 4.

8. Which line would you feel more confident using to make predictions? Explain.

Practise

Create a scatter plot for each set of data. Draw the mean fit line.

(a)
x	1	4	2	3	1	6	5	2	4
y	3	6	5	6	2	10	3	2	3

(b)
c	2	3	2	3	1	6	5	2	4
t	10	7	6	8	12	2	4	5	1

Drawing the Mean Fit Line

Zach's class developed a recycling program to encourage students to put pop cans in the recycling bin. The students wanted to find out if their program was working, so they collected this data for the first two weeks.

	Mon.	Tue.	Wed.	Thu.	Fri.	Mon.	Tue.	Wed.	Thu.	Fri.
Cans of Pop Consumed	24	26	32	21	18	25	27	19	20	22
Cans in Recycling Bin	8	10	20	16	15	22	24	17	19	21

Think, Do, Discuss

1. Plot the data and draw the line of best fit. What type of correlation exists?
2. What is the average number of cans that were recycled? What is the average number of cans of pop consumed?
3. Plot the coordinates of the averages. Redraw the line of best fit through this point.
4. How does this new line of best fit compare with the first line you drew?
5. Which line of best fit would be best for making predictions? Explain.
6. What relationship exists between the number of cans of pop consumed and the number of cans recycled?
7. Has the recycling program been a success? What evidence supports your answer?

Focus

Example

A mathematics teacher wants to know if the hours her students study for an exam is related to their marks. This data is collected. Draw a scatter plot and a line of best fit. What predictions can you make?

Student	A	B	C	D	E	F	G	H	I	J	K	L
Hours of Study	4	1	4	1	0	2	3	0	2	3	3	1
Exam Mark (%)	88	71	87	80	68	76	70	58	84	90	93	74

Solution

Draw the scatter plot.
The teacher wants to know if the mark depends on the hours of study, so place "Hours of Study" on the *x*-axis and "Mark" on the *y*-axis. If you use the *Line of Best Fit Explorer,* enter hours in the *x*-column and marks in the *y*-column.

Write a summary.
The points rise to the right, which indicates a positive correlation. As the hours of study increase, the marks also increase.

Draw a line of best fit.
Look at the points on the scatter plot and by inspection draw a line that seems to fit the data. If you use the *Line of Best Fit Explorer* to draw a line of best fit, try positioning point *A* over the cross that represents the centre of the data.

What limitations does the graph have?
No matter how long you study, you cannot get a mark greater than 100% or less than 0%, so you cannot extend the line of best fit beyond 0% or 100%. Data is plotted for only 12 students. If more points were plotted, the position of the line of best fit would likely change.

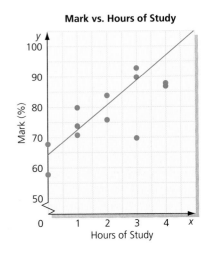

What predictions can you make?

Since many factors other than study time influence exam marks, you cannot use the graph to predict exact marks based on study time. However, it seems reasonable that most students will get better marks if they study longer.

Practise, Apply, Solve

A

1. For each set of data, calculate the coordinates of the point that the mean fit line will pass through.
   (a) (3, 7), (9, 12), (8, 5), (7, 10)
   (b) (1, 1), (2, 4), (3, 5), (3, 7), (4, 10), (5, 13)
   (c) (320, 200), (310, 300), (325, 280), (500, 70)

2. (a) Draw a scatter plot for each set of data in Question 1. Draw the mean fit line. Describe the correlation for each scatter plot.
   (b) Compare your scatter plots with a partner. Explain any differences.

3. (a) This table shows the number of successful jump shots Dawn made at various distances from the basket. Draw a scatter plot and the mean fit line.

Distance from Basket (m)	Shots Made
3	22
5	17
7	17
8	10
9	2
10	3

   (b) What conclusions can you draw? What is the relationship between the distance from the basket and the number of successful shots made?
   (c) Interpret the data and make some predictions.

B

4. (a) Measure the wrist circumference and shoe length of each student in your class. Draw a scatter plot for your data.
   (b) What are the mean coordinates of the data you used? What does this point represent?
   (c) Plot the mean coordinates and draw the mean fit line though this point.
   (d) How many data points are on the line? above it? below it?
   (e) What does this line represent?

5. Write a paragraph on how to draw the mean fit line. Include any strategies you have discovered.

6. Is it easier or harder to see a correlation when the number of data points increases? Is it then easier or harder to draw the mean fit line? Explain.

7. This table shows the average number of kilometres driven per litre of gasoline for cars. Write some questions about car efficiency. Have a classmate answer your questions and check the solutions.

Year	1985	1986	1987	1988	1989	1990
Fuel Consumption (km/L)	7.04	7.24	7.4	7.81	8.77	9.17

8. Find some data on any topic and use it to draw a scatter plot. Find the mean fit line. Make predictions from your data.

9. Use diagrams to tell how to use a mean fit line to make predictions from a scatter plot.

10. What is meant by a strong correlation and a weak correlation? Draw one graph of a strong correlation and another of a weak correlation.

11. Explain how to use a scatter plot. Find real-life examples of how scatter plots are used and include these in your notes.

12. This data represents the time period (in hours) and the total number of soft drinks sold at a baseball game: (1, 200), (1.5, 300), (2, 400), (2.5, 500), (3, 600).
   (a) Draw a scatter plot.
   (b) Draw the line of best fit.
   (c) Use interpolation to predict the number of soft drinks sold in $2\frac{3}{4}$ h.
   (d) Use extrapolation to predict the number of soft drinks sold in 3.5 h.

13. In a laboratory, an experiment was carried out on nine groups of people, each group containing 120 people. The people were exposed to perfume of different strengths and the number of people who could smell the perfume was recorded.

Strength	1.2	1.3	1.4	1.5	1.6	1.7	1.8	1.9	2.0
Number Who Smelled Perfume	38	45	52	49	46	58	76	69	66

   (a) Draw a scatter plot of the data.
   (b) Draw the line of best fit.
   (c) Use extrapolation to predict the number of people who would smell the perfume if the strength of the perfume was 2.2.
   (d) Use interpolation to predict the number of people who would smell the perfume if the strength of the perfume was 1.55.

14. (a) Think of an example of a positive correlation. Draw a scatter plot to show this.
   (b) Think of an example of a negative correlation. Draw a scatter plot to show this.
   (c) Think of a situation you would like to test for a correlation. How might you gather the data? What type of correlation do you think you would get?

15. Doctors measured the ages, x, in months, and the heights, y, in centimetres, of a sample of baby boys. The results were recorded as follows.

x	0	15	18	9	1	3	6	10
y	56	84	85	76	54	46	70	66

(a) Make a scatter plot of the data.
(b) Draw the line of best fit.
(c) Predict the height of a baby boy who is 12 months old.

16. (a) Manually, find the mean fit line for the mark data in the Example on page 80.
(b) Compare this line of best fit and the line you found with the *Line of Best Fit Explorer*.
(c) Use the line to predict the mark of someone who studied 1.75 h.
(d) Add the point (0, 0) to the data set. Which line of best fit now provides the better prediction? Why?

The Chapter Problem — How Are Shoes Designed?

Refer back to the Chapter Problem at the beginning of this chapter.

1. Find the mean height and shoe size for your data. Plot this point and now draw the line of best fit.
2. How could Edith use this model for shoe production?

Did You Know?

When a study is carried out, two principal points must be kept in mind: the validity and the reliability of the data. Validity means that the data is an accurate measure of the variables involved in the study. Reliability means that if the same study were run a number of times, the results would be consistent.

These points should have been kept in mind by a well-known psychologist who was knighted for his work with twins and IQ scores. In his work, he found a strong correlation in the IQ scores of identical twins, but a weak correlation for non-identical twins. His studies consistently found such values. Independent research carried out after his death did not produce the same results. Although IQ scores may have been a valid measure of intelligence, the data was not reliable.

1.15 Collecting Bounce Data Using Digital Probes

What Are Digital Probes?

Digital probes are small machines that you can use to collect data directly from an experiment. These probes translate the data into digital form and send it to a computer or graphing calculator. Then you can analyze the data, just as you would analyze data you entered yourself.

A digital probe

Experiment: The Bouncing Ball

What is the relationship between the height from which a ball is dropped and how high it bounces?

The following experiment will use the motion detector and Computer Based Laboratory (CBL) to record data obtained by bouncing a ball. Use the BOUNCE program to collect and graph the data.

Set-Up and Operation of the CBL Unit

1. Make sure that the CBL and calculator are both OFF.

2. Connect the CBL to the calculator using the unit-to-unit connector cable. Connect the cable firmly to the input/output port on the bottom of the calculator (see diagram below).

3. Connect the motion detector to the SONIC port on the CBL. This port is on the left side of the unit.

4. Turn the CBL unit and the calculator ON.

5. Secure the motion detector to the ring stand. Be sure that the motion detector is level and facing a hard surface.

6. Make sure the CBL is turned on. Start the BOUNCE program on the calculator. (Stop at the display message, "PRESS ENTER TO START COLLECTING DATA.")

7. Hold the ball at least 50 cm away from the detector. When you are ready to start collecting data, press `ENTER` on the calculator to start the motion graph.

8. When the motion detector starts clicking, release the ball from rest and allow it to bounce up and down directly below the detector. The distance (in metres) is stored in **L1** and the time (in seconds) is stored in **L2**.
   Note: If the ball bounces out of the detector's range, check to see if the surface on which the ball is bouncing is level, and then restart the experiment.

9. If you are satisfied with your graph of Distance vs. Time, save it to a PIC variable to be printed later.

10. On the calculator, press `2nd` `DRAW` `3` to add a horizontal line to the display. Use the arrow keys to move the line up and down until it aligns with the portion of the graph corresponding to the ball's release position. The displayed *y-value* gives an estimation of the ball's initial height. Record this data in a table with the corresponding bounce number — zero.

11. Adjust the horizontal line so that it aligns with the ball's rebound height after one bounce. Record the displayed *y-value* in your data table with the corresponding bounce number — one.

12. Repeat Step 11 until you have collected data for at least six bounces. Each time adjust the horizontal line for the current bounce number.

Analysis of Collected Data

Put a copy of the graph in your notes, if you have the technology. It is also possible to copy the graph to a computer and then print it.

Press `STAT` and select **EDIT** to get to the List editor on your calculator. Use the arrow keys to move to the top of lists **L1** and **L2** and press `CLEAR`, then `ENTER` to clear the existing data. Enter the bounce data in list **L1** and the corresponding height data in list **L2** from the data table that you constructed earlier.

Create a scatter plot for the data in **L1** and **L2** using the `STAT` `PLOT` options.

Does the ball's rebound height decrease by the same factor with each bounce? How can you tell?

Practise

1. Repeat this experiment at least two more times and record all relevant data in your lab notebook. For one of the trials, change the ball's release height. To what extent does the initial height affect the rebound rate? Explain your answer.

2. For another trial, use a different type of ball, such as a tennis ball or a basketball. List several physical characteristics of the balls that you suspect might have an effect on the rebound height.

1.1–1.2 Recognizing and Reducing Bias

- Each member of a population must have an equal chance of being selected to be in the sample group. Otherwise, the sample is biased.
- For a good survey:
  - aim for a good cross-section of the population
  - eliminate chances of more than one response per person
  - ensure that each member of the population has an equal chance of being chosen.

Example

The dress code in Yolanda's school requires that no students can wear jeans. Yolanda and her group want to survey 35 out of 850 people in the school to see if the administration should change its policy on the dress code. Which plan should they use?

Plan 1: Select 35 of the students in the cafeteria at lunch.

Plan 2: Choose a class in the school that has 35 students and survey them.

Plan 3: Assign each student in the school a number from 1 to 850. Have a computer select 35 numbers at random and then interview those students.

Solution

Plan 1 is biased because students who do not eat lunch in the cafeteria won't be selected. *Plan 2* is biased because students from other classes won't be selected. *Plan 3* is non-biased because each student has an equal chance of being selected.

Extra Practice

1. From a group of 100 people, a sample of ten are to be interviewed. How can you select the ten people to minimize bias?
2. Use students in your school as the population. Tell how to select biased and unbiased samples to find:
   (a) the favourite topping on pizza.
   (b) who does more homework on a daily basis, female or male students.
   (c) which sport students most enjoy playing.
3. "Four out of five dentists recommend Glow toothpaste."
   (a) Would you buy Glow because of this ad? Explain.
   (b) What questions would you ask the advertiser?
   (c) Under what conditions would this ad be valid?
4. Why is there bias in each sample? Choose an appropriate sample.
   (a) Parents at a school meeting are asked if the school day should be longer.
   (b) The lead in the school play is to be selected from students who are not bused to school.

1.3–1.4 Drawing Conclusions from Data

- Different conclusions can be drawn from the same data. To judge a conclusion based on data, ask:
  - **Why** was the data collected?
  - **How** was the data collected?
  - **What** data was collected?
  - What **reasoning** was used to draw the conclusion?
  - Are there any sources of **error**, such as bias or false assumptions?

- The conclusions drawn from data can be wrong or misleading. Think about what you read. Make sure conclusions follow reasonably from the data. Watch for bias, false assumptions, and inaccurate wording.

Example

Read the following information. Analyze the data and conclusions.

> The caffeine in soft drinks can harm children more than you think. Although little research has been done in this area, some experts say that drinking too much caffeine will slow children's natural growth and development. Caffeine is found primarily in coffee, tea, soft drinks, and chocolate. Most children consume some caffeine in their diet – but how much is too much? An 18-kg child who drinks just one can of cola per day is consuming proportionately about as much caffeine as a 68-kg adult who drinks two cups of coffee daily. An informal survey of 30 children in a Grade 2 class showed that 30% of the children drink pop five or more times per week, and another 50% drink pop at least once a week. Since caffeine reduces appetite, this means that these children are likely missing out on more wholesome foods that would help them grow.

Solution

Motivation: The article is likely intended to inform parents about the negative effects of caffeine in soft drinks. The author may hope that the article will prompt parents to encourage children to drink less cola and to eat healthier snacks.

Method: The article refers to an informal survey of 30 children in a Grade 2 class. This type of survey is called a cluster sample, so the results cannot be taken to represent all children reliably. It is biased because of the ages of the children and because they are all in the same school.

Observations: The author presents many conclusions as facts, but fails to support them. For example, the author says that a child who drinks one cola per day is consuming as much as an adult who drinks two cups of coffee, but fails to give any evidence that this amount is harmful.

Reasoning Process: It is asserted that "some experts" say drinking cola is harmful. We do not know how many experts feel this way, nor are we given any reasons for this opinion. The author says that "most children" consume some caffeine, but gives no evidence other than the cluster sample of Grade 2 students.

Error: The writer makes several assumptions, such as:

• Most children drink soft drinks that contain caffeine, no matter where they live.

This assumption may be true, but it is not supported in the article.

Extra Practice

5. (a) Do you agree with the conclusion in this article? Explain.

> The most successful film of 1996 was **Independence Day**, which earned over $300 million. It looks like movie-goers still prefer action and suspense over comedy or romance! The best movies of the year are listed here in order:
>
> **Independence Day** (action/suspense): cost $75 million, gross $300 million
> **Twister** (action/suspense): cost $92 million, gross $240 million
> **Mission Impossible** (action/suspense): cost $75 million, gross $180 million
> **The Rock** (action/suspense): cost $70 million, gross $135 million
> **The Nutty Professor** (comedy): cost $54 million, gross $125 million
> **A Time to Kill** (action/suspense): cost $40 million, gross $100 million
>
> **Data is from September, 1996.**

(b) Show another way to present the data.

6. (a) Do you agree with the conclusion in this article? Explain.

> Do you believe in Unidentified Flying Objects (UFOs)? Statistics suggest that if you do, you are in the majority of Canadians. In a recent poll, more than half of the respondents said that it is at least somewhat likely that intelligent beings from another planet have already visited Earth. Many Canadians even say they expect aliens to visit during their lifetimes. Albertans are the most willing to accept the possibility of aliens, with 38% of respondents convinced that aliens exist. Prairie-dwellers seem more skeptical. Only 18% of the respondents in Manitoba and 33% in British Columbia are prepared for the sight of a flying saucer.
>
> **Data source: exoScience UFO Web site.**

(b) This article presents data in different ways. Which presentation is most convincing? Why?

1.5–1.6 The Process of Designing an Experiment —

• To design an experiment to find a relationship between two variables:
  ◆ decide what data is needed
  ◆ decide on a method to collect the data
  ◆ collect the data and organize it in a table
  ◆ graph the data
  ◆ look for a pattern.

Example

Design an experiment to determine how smoking cigarettes can affect a person's fitness level.

Solution

Step 1: Select a measure of fitness, such as resting heart rate.
Step 2: Select a sample.
Step 3: Design a data collection process and proceed to collect the data.
Step 4: Represent the data graphically and examine it for trends.
Step 5: Make conclusions for your data.
Step 6: Analyze your procedure and comment on any bias.

Extra Practice

7. Design an experiment to find:
   (a) the effect of increasing the size of an inflated balloon on the speed with which it falls.
   (b) the effect of the length of a pendulum on the speed of its swing.
   (c) the relationship between nutrition and school performance.
   (d) the relationship between toothbrush design and tooth decay.

1.7–1.8 Drawing and Interpreting Scatter Plots ——

- A scatter plot is a graph that shows the relationship between two sets of numeric data.
- The points in a scatter plot often show a general pattern, or **trend**. From the pattern or trend, you can describe a relationship, if it exists.
- To create a scatter plot:
  - ♦ collect the data and organize it in a table or as ordered pairs
  - ♦ present the data points on a graph with labelled axes.
- Use the scatter plot to:
  - ♦ analyze the data by looking for a pattern
  - ♦ describe the pattern if one exists.

Example

This table shows the height of trees (of the same type) over several years.

Age (years)	4	6	8	10	12	8	6	13	13	12	10	10	9	11
Height (m)	2	4	3	6	5	4	2	5	6	7	4	5	3	6

Create a scatter plot and describe any trends that exist.

Solution

Plot the data with age on the horizontal axis and height along the vertical axis.

The graph at the right shows that, as a tree's age increases, its height also increases.

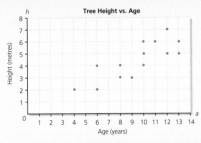

Extra Practice

8. The data on the right is collected from students with part-time jobs. Each student works an average of 16 h per week.
   (a) Draw a scatter plot.
   (b) Write a summary of your findings.

Student	Wage ($/h)	Average Savings ($/wk)
1	9.00	14
2	7.50	10
3	7.75	9
4	7.10	10
5	8.50	9
6	7.25	8
7	7.75	11
8	8.00	11
9	7.40	10
10	7.60	9

9. Some colleges and universities give entrance tests so they can place students in the appropriate courses. One college wants to know if there is a relationship between a student's test mark and course grade.

Test Mark (%)	88	91	79	68	94	73	65	77	84	80
Course Grade (%)	92	98	78	71	100	72	69	80	90	85

   (a) Draw a scatter plot.
   (b) Write a summary of your findings.

10. Here is data for 12 professional basketball players.
    (a) Draw a scatter plot.
    (b) Write a summary.

11. The daily practice habits of music students is shown as ordered pairs (years of lessons, hours of daily practice). (0.5, 0.5), (1, 0.75), (1, 1), (2, 1), (2, 1.5), (2.5, 0.75), (3, 0.5), (3, 1.25), (4, 0.75), (4, 1), (5, 2), (6, 1), (6, 0.5), (7, 1), (8, 3)
    (a) Draw a scatter plot.
    (b) Describe the trend.

Most Points in One Game	Disqualifications in One Season
55	0
33	1
27	0
19	0
19	3
27	1
14	5
16	0
11	0
14	1
14	0
16	0

12. This table shows the budget and gross for six movies.

Budget ($ millions)	Gross ($ millions)
50	$90.0
30	$75.0
25	$35.0
9	$32.0
7	$25.4
50	$10.5

(a) Predict what the relationship might be and then draw a scatter plot.
(b) Describe the trend you see in your graph.
(c) Does your graph support your prediction? Explain.

1.9–1.10 The Line of Best Fit

- A line that approximates a trend for the data in a scatter plot is called a **line of best fit**.
- The line of best fit can help you to make predictions.
- A line of best fit shows the pattern and direction of the points on a scatter plot.
- A line of best fit passes through as many points as possible, with the remaining points grouped equally above and below the line, and spread out along the line rather than concentrated at one end.
- A line of best fit can be used to make predictions for values not actually recorded and plotted. When the prediction involves a point within the range of values of the independent variable, this is called **interpolating.** When the value of the independent variable falls outside the range of recorded data, it is called **extrapolating**.

Example

This table shows the life expectancy for people born in different years.

Year of Birth	1900	1910	1920	1930	1940	1950	1960	1970	1980	1990
Life Expectancy (years)	47.3	50.0	54.1	59.7	62.9	68.2	69.7	70.8	73.7	75.4

(a) Make a scatter plot for the data. Draw the line of best fit on the scatter plot.

(b) Predict the life expectancy for people born in 1978, 1994, and the year in which you were born.

Solution

(a)

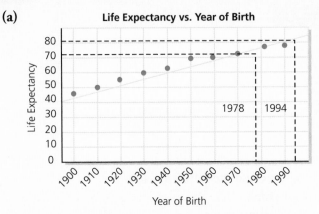

Life Expectancy vs. Year of Birth

(b) 1978: about 73 years; 1994: a bit over 80 years

Extra Practice

13. This data is the height (in metres) and age of each student in a sample.
(1.6, 15), (1.5, 16), (1.8, 15), (1.9, 16), (1.7, 13), (1.5, 14).
(a) Draw a scatter plot.
(b) Draw a line of best fit.
(c) Can you use this graph to extrapolate data? Explain.

14. This scatter plot shows how the distance driven changes with the volume of gasoline used.
(a) Copy the graph. Draw a line of best fit.
(b) Use the line of best fit to predict the distance driven on 70 L of fuel.
(c) Use the line of best fit to predict the distance driven on 25 L of fuel.
(d) Did you interpolate or extrapolate in (b) and (c)? Give reasons for your choices.
(e) Suggest reasons why the data points in the graph do not lie exactly in a straight line.

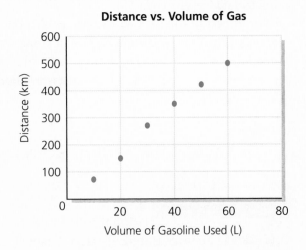

Distance vs. Volume of Gas

15. For an experiment, some students place measured volumes of water in a glass cylinder and read the height of water in the cylinder. The results are shown.

Volume (mL)	10	20	30	40	50	60
Height (cm)	1.2	2.4	3.6	4.8	6.0	7.2

(a) Draw a scatter plot. Place volume on the horizontal axis.
(b) Draw a line of best fit.
(c) Use the line of best fit to predict the height of water in the cylinder if it contains 25 mL of water.
(d) Use the line of best fit to predict the volume of water in the cylinder when the height of the water is 3.6 cm.
(e) Use the line of best fit to find the height of water in the cylinder when the volume is 75 mL.

16. Every year since she was born, her mother has recorded Mary's height.

Age (years)	Height (cm)
0	50
1	64
2	75
3	90
4	105
5	120
6	128
7	135
8	141
9	146
10	149
11	153
12	157

(a) Draw a scatter plot of Mary's height.
(b) Draw a line of best fit.
(c) Use the line of best fit to predict Mary's height when she was four-and-a-half years old.
(d) Would you use the line to predict Mary's height when she turns 18? Explain.
(e) Are there any limitations on how you can use the line of best fit?

1.11–1.12 Interpreting Correlation Value

- A scatter plot of the relationship between two variables shows:
  - ◆ positive correlation when the pattern slopes up and to the right. The two quantities increase together.
  - ◆ negative correlation when the pattern slopes down and to the right. As one quantity increases the other decreases.
  - ◆ no correlation when no pattern appears.

- If the points nearly form a line, then the correlation is strong.

- If the points are dispersed more widely, but still form a rough line, then the correlation is weak.

Example

The scatter plot shows gold medal throws in the discus competition for the Summer Olympics from 1908 to 1992. Describe the correlation and your confidence in making predictions based on this data.

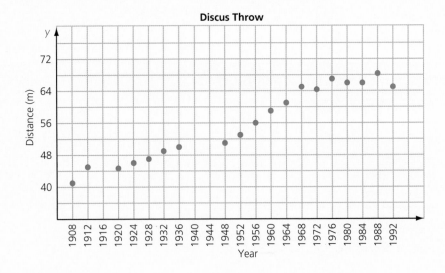

Solution

As the year increases, the distance of winning throws also increases, so the correlation is positive. The data points are tightly clustered around a line, so the correlation is strong. As a result, your confidence will be high that predictions based on this data are reliable.

Extra Practice

17. Julie is an usher in a theatre. She records the number of people at each performance. Here is her record of the number of people at each performance of *Guys and Dolls.*

Performance	1	2	3	4	5	6	7
Attendance	250	385	521	634	802	901	995

   (a) Draw a scatter plot.

   (b) Draw a line that best fits the data. Describe the line.

   (c) Does the data have a positive correlation, a negative correlation, or no correlation?

18. (a) Visualize a line of best fit for each scatter plot.

   i.

   ii.

   iii.

   iv.

   (b) List these scatter plots in order of your confidence that the line of best fit can be used to make accurate predictions.

   (c) Why would you have more confidence in some than in others?

19. Explain each term.
  (a) positive correlation
  (b) negative correlation
  (c) no correlation

20. Sketch a pattern of points to show each relationship in Question 19.

21. Two points are graphed as shown.

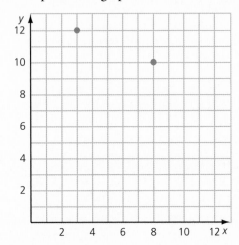

Which of these points would be the best choice to include on the scatter plot if you wanted to show:
  (a) a strong negative correlation: (10, 12), (13, 8), or (10, 2)?
  (b) a weak negative correlation: (10, 7), (1, 6), or (10, 12)?
  (c) no correlation: (13, 8), (10, 7), or (4, 3)?

22. What type of correlation would you expect to find if you compared:
  (a) the volume of gasoline remaining in your gas tank with the distance driven since the tank was filled?
  (b) the average outdoor temperature with the number of kites sold by a store?

1.13–1.14 Drawing the Mean Fit Line ────────

- The mean fit line gives a better model for a set of data, compared to a line drawn freely.

- To draw a mean fit line, find the mean coordinates of a set of points by calculating the mean of the first set of values and then the second set of values. Plot this point and then draw a line through it so that about the same number of points are on each side of the line.

- The mean fit line allows everyone to make similar predictions about the same set of data.

Example

A hockey team is interested in the relationship between the number of shots on goal they make and the number of goals they score. Plot the data and construct the mean fit line. Use it to predict the number of goals they will score if they take 35 shots.

Shots	11	20	22	24	28	32	32	40
Goals	1	6	2	7	6	4	8	11

Solution

Plot the data.

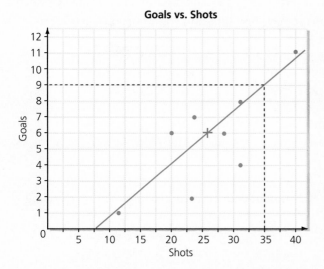

Calculate the mean number of shots and the mean number of goals.

$$\text{mean number of shots} = \frac{11 + 20 + 22 + 24 + 28 + 32 + 32 + 40}{8}$$

$$= \frac{209}{8}$$

$$= 26.125$$

$$\doteq 26$$

$$\text{mean number of goals} = \frac{1 + 6 + 2 + 7 + 6 + 4 + 8 + 11}{8}$$

$$= \frac{45}{8}$$

$$= 5.625$$

$$\doteq 6$$

Plot the point (26, 6) and draw the line of best fit so that it passes through this point. Use the line to determine the number of goals scored on 35 shots. From the graph it appears to be 9.

Extra Practice

23. **(a)** Draw a scatter plot of the data.

x	1	2	3	4	5	6	7	8	9	10
y	100	95	80	80	75	70	75	55	45	30

(b) Is the correlation positive or negative?

(c) Is the correlation strong or weak?

(d) What are the mean coordinates for the data?

(e) Draw a line of best fit for the scatter plot.

24. The student council wants students to improve their rate of recycling empty cans. Council members record how many cans are put in recycling bins and trash bins each week.

Week	1	2	3	4	5	6	7	8
Cans in Recycling Bins	324	309	310	288	523	509	210	251
Cans in Trash	275	300	281	312	70	100	400	340

(a) How would they determine the rate of recycling per week?

(b) Calculate the rate of recycling per week and draw the scatter plot, Rate of Recycling vs. Week.

(c) Draw the mean fit line.

(d) Analyze the graph to determine if the student council is succeeding with its recycling program.

Chapter Summary

In this chapter, you have seen how to design and conduct and experiment or survey to collect unbiased data. You have also seen how to analyze the data and use it to draw reliable conclusions. One way to analyze data is to plot it on a scatter plot and to approximate it with a line of best fit. If the data points form a pattern, such as a line that slopes up to the right or a line that slopes down to the right, then the data can be used to draw conclusions. The more definite the pattern is, the more reliable the conclusions are likely to be. The correlation value is a measure of how well the line of best fit fits the data. This value ranges from -1 to 1. The closer it is to 1 (if the data points slope upward) or -1 (if they slope downward), the more accurate the predictions are likely to be. A correlation value close to 0 indicates that points are scattered with little pattern. If the data points are scattered randomly, then the data does not show a trend and cannot be used to draw reliable conclusions.

1. The scatter plot shows the number of bacteria living in a culture at various temperatures.

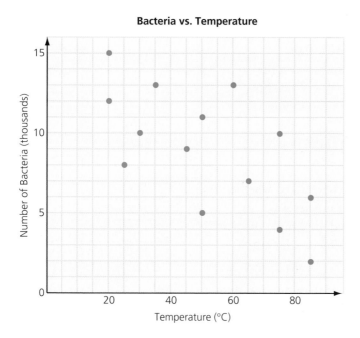

Bacteria vs. Temperature

Number of Bacteria (thousands) (y-axis)

Temperature (°C) (x-axis)

(a) Draw the line of best fit.
(b) Describe the correlation.
(c) What is the relationship between temperature and number of bacteria?

2. How might each sample described below give you false information?
Describe a better way of choosing the sample.

(a) Twenty people at the Ottawa Airport are asked which Canadian city has the best NHL team.
(b) Twenty people at a drugstore are asked which brand of toothpaste best prevents cavities.
(c) Twenty people at a subway stop are asked to comment on the proposed increase in gasoline taxes.

3. Define bias and give an example of a sample of data that would contain bias.

4. Give an example of two quantities that show each of the following:
(a) positive correlation
(b) negative correlation
(c) no correlation

Chapter Review Test

5. These measurements were taken.
   (a) Create a scatter plot.
   (b) Find the mean height of the boys.
   (c) Find the mean height of the fathers.
   (d) Draw the mean line of best fit.
   (e) Describe the relationship between the boys' heights and their fathers' heights.
   (f) Predict a boy's height if his father is 195 cm tall.
   (g) Predict a father's height if the boy is 155 cm tall.

Height of Grade 9 Boy (cm)	Height of Boy's Father (cm)
164	171
168	186
150	164
162	180
159	176
165	177
187	192
152	167
180	189
166	180
148	165
159	172

6. A random sample of people were asked whether they thought the popcorn at movies was reasonably priced. Was a random sample the best kind of sample to choose? Why or why not?

7. Explain why the mean fit line is a better line of best fit for making predictions than one you draw by visual estimation.

8. Adrienne is an author, and her popularity grows with each book that she writes. She keeps statistics on how many of her books have been sold at a local bookstore.
   (a) Predict how many copies of Adrienne's 9th book would sell at the local bookstore.
   (b) If 100 copies of one of Adrienne's books were sold, which book would it be?
   (c) Adrienne plans to write until one of her books sells at least 200 copies at the local bookstore, or until she has written her 17th book, whichever comes first. Predict how many books Adrienne will have written before she quits.

Book	Number Sold
1st	7
2nd	18
3rd	34
4th	42
5th	59
6th	74

9. A random sample of adults in a small community were asked whether they would support the construction of a small mall on the west side of the community.
   (a) Is this survey biased? How?
   (b) Describe the type of sample you would choose to obtain an accurate response.

Chapter 2

Analyzing and Applying Linear Models

In this chapter, you will learn about graphing. A graph is a picture that tells you at a glance how two quantities are connected. Graphs are very useful in business and mathematics. For instance, scientists and economists use graphs as models to help predict future trends. How does the graph in the photograph represent what the snowboarder is doing?

In this chapter, you will:

- make a table of values and draw, with labelled variables, a graph of a linear relationship, given a verbal description of the relationship

- write an algebraic expression for a linear relationship and interpret each term in the expression, given a verbal description of the relationship

- identify and apply the relationship between the slope and y-intercept of a linear relationship and its graph

- find the equation of a line in $y = mx + b$ form, given information about the graph

- discuss the properties of slopes and line segments

- with and without technology, develop and use linear models for data and discuss "goodness of fit."

Distance

Connections

The Chapter Problem

Which Rate Is Better?

David is going to start his own summer business painting houses. He is considering two different methods of charging his customers for the completed job. He is planning to charge either $10/h for all hours worked or an initial fee of $200 plus an hourly rate of $6/h. Under both plans, the customer buys all supplies. How can David decide which option is more profitable for his new business?

At the end of some lessons, questions will refer back to this problem and ask you more questions about David and his painting business. Keep a record of your answers to these questions in a project folder, so you can present a complete solution to the problem at the end of the chapter.

The Challenge

How High Will It Bounce?

How high would a ball bounce if you dropped it from a height of one kilometre? Do this experiment: measure how high a tennis ball bounces when it is dropped from different heights. Use a mathematical model (a spreadsheet, a computer program, a graph, or a formula) to predict how high the ball would bounce if it were dropped from a height of 10 m.

- What factors might influence the accuracy of your prediction?

- Verify your prediction by carrying out the experiment.

- Now repeat your experiment with a heavier, bouncier ball.

- Predict how high the second ball would bounce if it were dropped from 50 m, 100 m, or even one kilometre.

As you work through this chapter, you will learn mathematics that you can use to solve the Challenge. You may also need to use skills and knowledge you already have. You may want to discuss your plan with your teacher and with other students.

The work of this chapter requires you to be able to carry out calculations with fractions, decimals, and signed numbers and to be able to use rates and solve simple equations. These exercises will help you warm up for the work you will be doing in this chapter.

1. Evaluate.
   (a) $36 \div 6 + 3$
   (b) $8(5) \div 2$
   (c) $\dfrac{12 + 6}{9 - 3}$
   (d) $\dfrac{(4 + 6) \times 6}{12 - (8 - 2)}$
   (e) $\dfrac{(11 - 3) \div 2}{2 + (6 - 4)}$
   (f) $9(8) \div 2(6)$
   (g) $\dfrac{42 \div 3}{13 - (1 + 5)}$
   (h) $\dfrac{(1 + 6) \times 8}{9 - (2 + 3)}$

2. Evaluate.
   (a) $\dfrac{1}{3} + \dfrac{2}{5}$
   (b) $2\dfrac{1}{2} - 1\dfrac{2}{3}$
   (c) $\dfrac{9}{16} \times \dfrac{8}{21}$
   (d) $9\dfrac{2}{3} - 3\dfrac{3}{4}$
   (e) $\dfrac{6}{35} \times \dfrac{7}{9}$
   (f) $7\dfrac{2}{3} - 5\dfrac{4}{5}$
   (g) $1\dfrac{3}{5} + \dfrac{3}{4}$
   (h) $\dfrac{10}{21} \times \dfrac{7}{15}$

3. Evaluate.
   (a) $(-2) + 6$
   (b) $5 - (-3)$
   (c) $4 - 8$
   (d) $(-4)(9)$
   (e) $(-3)(-7)$
   (f) $15 \div (-5)$
   (g) $(-48) \div (-6)$
   (h) $72 \div (-9)$
   (i) $12 \div (-6) + 16 \times 2$
   (j) $\dfrac{20 + (-12) \div (-3)}{(-4 + 12) \div (-2)}$
   (k) $(6)(-8)$
   (l) $(-52) \div 4$
   (m) $(-36) \div (12 - 6) + 7$
   (n) $(-2) \times (-13) - 63 \div 9$
   (o) $21 \div (-3) + (-36) \div (-9)$
   (p) $\dfrac{19 - 5 \times (-3)}{24 \div (-4) - 11}$

4. Express as a decimal.
   (a) 8%
   (b) 15%
   (c) $7\dfrac{1}{2}\%$
   (d) 0.5%
   (e) 23.6%
   (f) 103%
   (g) $58\dfrac{3}{5}\%$
   (h) 0.04%

5. Express first in lowest terms, and then as a decimal.
   (a) $\dfrac{25}{50}$
   (b) $\dfrac{64}{80}$
   (c) $\dfrac{48}{28}$
   (d) $\dfrac{15}{24}$
   (e) $\dfrac{27}{36}$
   (f) $\dfrac{42}{48}$
   (g) $\dfrac{16}{24}$
   (h) $\dfrac{77}{56}$

6. Express as a rate.
   (a) $\$8.00$ for 4 tins
   (b) $\$75$ for 8 h of work
   (c) 79 km in 2 h
   (d) $\$21.98$ for 2 CDs
   (e) 63 m in 9 s
   (f) $\$46.06$ for 7 books
   (g) $\$56.68$ for 4 dinners
   (h) 5.1 min for 3 laps

7. Evaluate.
   (a) $6x - 3$, if $x = 4$
   (b) $2a - 3b$, if $a = 2$ and $b = -1$
   (c) $\dfrac{5c - 2}{4d}$, if $c = -2$ and $d = 1$
   (d) $2x - 3(y - 1)$, if $x = -1$ and $y = -2$
   (e) $3x - 5y + 2$, if $x = \dfrac{1}{3}$ and $y = \dfrac{2}{5}$
   (f) $17 - 3(x - 2)$, if $x = 6$
   (g) $5a + 7b + 13$, if $a = -3$ and $b = 0$
   (h) $13c - (-4d) - 7$, if $c = -3$ and $d = 11$
   (i) $\dfrac{5x + 2y}{3x}$, if $x = -2$ and $y = -4$
   (j) $4m - 7n(3 - 2m)$, if $m = \dfrac{1}{2}$ and $n = \dfrac{1}{7}$

8. Solve.
   (a) $x + 5 = 9$
   (b) $26 = -11 + b$
   (c) $-13 + y = -10$
   (d) $-63 = 29 + c$
   (e) $5b = 30$
   (f) $-2x = -10$
   (g) $\dfrac{x}{3} = 9$
   (h) $\dfrac{d}{6} = -3$
   (i) $17 - y = -23$
   (j) $43 = 15 + 4c$
   (k) $-7b = 21$
   (l) $-\dfrac{m}{13} = -6$

2.1 Graphing a Relationship

Using a Spreadsheet

You can make a graph of a table of values by hand. But if there are many points to plot or there is a wide range in the values, the graph can be difficult to plot and hard to read. One solution is to use a spreadsheet.

What Is a Spreadsheet?

A spreadsheet is a computer program that can be used to create a table of values and then graph the values. It is made up of cells, which are named by column letter and row number, such as A2 or B5. In each cell you can enter a label, a number, or a formula.

How to Create and Graph a Table of Values

This is how to use a spreadsheet to create a table of values and graph for the relationship $C = 4t + 2$.

In the spreadsheet on the right, cell A1 has been labelled t and cell B1 has been labelled C. Numbers for the variable t must be entered in cells A2 to A9. In this example, 0 to 7 have been entered. The value for C comes from the relation $C = 4t + 2$. This formula has been entered in cell B2. Notice that there must be an equals sign in front of the formula and that an * is used for multiplication.

	A	B
1	t	C
2	0	=4*A2+2
3	1	⇓
4	2	⇓
5	3	⇓
6	4	⇓
7	5	⇓
8	6	⇓
9	7	⇓

The next step is to use the cursor to select cell B2 and all those below it (B3 to B9). Now the **Fill Down** command is used. This command inserts into each selected cell the appropriate formula for calculating C. For instance, "=4*A3+2" will be inserted in cell B3, "=4*A4+2" in B4, and so on.

B2	X ✓	=4*A2+2

	A	B
1	t	C
2	0	2
3	1	6
4	2	10
5	3	14
6	4	18
7	5	22
8	6	26
9	7	30

After the **Fill Down** command is used, the computer automatically calculates and enters the values of C. The result is shown on the right.

Now use the spreadsheet's graphing command to graph the table of values. Different spreadsheets will have different graphing commands, such as **Make Chart.** Check your spreadsheet's instructions to find the proper command. The graph that appears is shown on the right.

Practise

Use a spreadsheet to create a table of values and a graph for each relation.

(a) $D = 5t + 20$ **(b)** $C = 25m + 2$ **(c)** $H = \frac{2}{3}r + 1$

(d) $y = 6x + 10$ **(e)** $y = 35x$ **(f)** $y = 0.25x - 0.75$

Tables of Values, Patterns, and Graphs

Graphing a Relationship by Hand

Chris's computer is broken. Compufix charges a base fee of $50 plus $30/h for a service call. Computer Doctor has no base fee, but charges $55/h. Time is rounded to the nearest minute.

To compare the costs, Chris makes a table of values and then graphs the data. To make the data easier to graph, he starts the table and the graph at zero hours.

Hours	Compufix Cost ($)	Computer Doctor Cost ($)
0	50+30(0)=50	55(0)=0
1	50+30(1)=80	55(1)=55
2	110	110
3	140	165

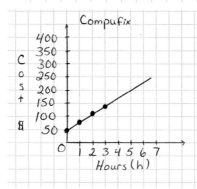

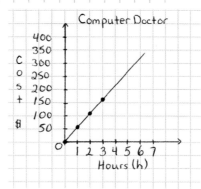

Think, Do, Discuss

1. **(a)** Describe any patterns you see in the table.
   (b) How do these patterns affect each graph?

2. What are the two quantities that are related in each repair situation?

3. In each situation, does one quantity depend on the other? If so, explain how.

4. Which company should Chris choose if it is estimated that the repair will take 0.5h? 1.5h? 2.5h?

5. How could you find the answer to Question 4 using:
   (a) the table of values?
   (b) the graphs?
   (c) the description of each company's charges?

6. Compare how easy it was to use each method in Question 5.

Focus

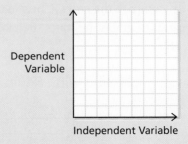
Example

The cost of a banquet at Juan's Banquet Hall is $450 for the room rental, plus $15 for each person served. Create a table of values and draw a graph to see if this relationship is linear.

Solution

The cost of the banquet depends on the number of people who attend. Cost must be the dependent variable and number of people the independent variable.

It costs $450 to rent the hall. In addition, there is a $15 charge for each person served.

Cost is the dependent variable, so it is plotted vertically. The number of people is the independent variable, so it is plotted horizontally. The points that are plotted line up in a straight line. In this case, the relationship between cost and people is linear.

People	Cost ($)
0	450 + 15(0) = 450
10	450 + 15(10) = 600
20	450 + 15(20) = 750
30	450 + 15(30) = 900
40	450 + 15(40) = 1050
50	450 + 15(50) = 1200

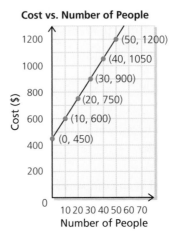

Cost vs. Number of People

Practise, Apply, Solve

A

1. If a relationship between two variables is linear, then what shape is formed by the data points that are plotted on a graph?

2. Which of these describe a relationship?
   (a) the distance Angel swims and the time she takes
   (b) the distance Angel swims and the time Dolores spends studying
   (c) the temperature and the amount of clothing people wear
   (d) the number of cats a dog sees and how loudly it barks
   (e) the temperature in Vancouver and the temperature in Toronto

3. Identify the dependent variable.
   (a) The distance a jogger runs depends on the length of time she runs.
   (b) A recipe for 24 cookies requires 4 cups of flour.
   (c) A building must have 6 fire alarms on each floor.

4. Identify the independent variable.
   (a) A knitter needs to know how much wool is required to make ten sweaters. Twenty metres of wool are needed to make one sweater.
   (b) The printing cost for the school newspaper drops 1¢ for every page over 50.
   (c) The manager wants to know how many cartons are needed to package orange juice. Each carton holds 24 cans of juice.

5. True or False? This graph is labelled correctly. Explain.

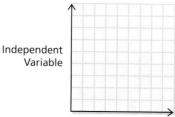

B

6. You often hear that a picture is worth a thousand words. Why do you think graphs are used to represent situations involving quantities?

7. To fix a car, Sally's Garage charges a base fee of $20, plus $40/h.
   (a) What is the dependent variable? the independent variable?
   (b) Make a table of values of the cost of fixing a car for each hour up to 4 h.
   (c) Graph the cost of fixing a car for up to 4 h.
   (d) Use the graph to find the cost for a 2.5 h repair job.

8. A small balloon is launched from a hill 1500 m above sea level. It rises at 35 m/s.
   (a) Make a table of values of the height of the balloon at each minute up to 10 min.
   (b) Graph the height of the balloon for the first 10 min.
   (c) What patterns do you see in the table and the graph?
   (d) Use the graph to find the time it takes the balloon to rise to a height of 15 000 m.

9. An author earns a royalty of 25¢ for each book sold.
  (a) Make a table of values of the author's royalties. Have one row for each 5000 books sold up to 25 000 books.
  (b) Graph the author's royalties for selling up to 25 000 books.
  (c) What patterns do you see in the table and the graph?
  (d) Use the graph to find the author's royalties on 21 500 books.

10. Marlon has $900 in his bank account. He takes $100 out of his account every week.
  (a) Make a table of values for the money in the account over nine weeks.
  (b) Graph the amount of money in the account over nine weeks.
  (c) What patterns do you see in the table and the graph?
  (d) How many weeks will it take for the bank account to reach a balance of $0?
  (e) How are the table and graph similar to those in Questions 7 to 9? different?

11. Anne earns $9/h for working a 40-h week and $13.50/h for overtime (any hours over 40 h).
  (a) Make a table of values of Anne's earnings with her hours worked for up to 50 h. Use 5-h intervals.
  (b) Use the table of values to graph this relationship.
  (c) Is this relationship linear? Explain.
  (d) Why does the line change at 40 h?

12. A submarine at sea level descends 50 m every 5 min.
  (a) Make a table of values of the submarine's depth. Have one row for every 5 min up to 30 min.
  (b) Graph the submarine's depth for 30 min.
  (c) What patterns do you see in the table and the graph?

C

13. A miniature rocket is launched and its height above ground is measured at one-second intervals.
  (a) Graph this relationship.
  (b) Is this relationship linear? Explain.
  (c) Use the graph to find the rocket's height after 1.5 s and after 4.5 s. What do you notice?
  (d) Explain why the rocket can be 80 m high at two different times.
  (e) What is the rocket's height after 7 s? How is this represented on the graph?

Time (s)	Height (m)
0	0
1	80
2	128
3	144
4	128
5	80
6	0

14. This graph represents the cost of renting a Rototiller for different lengths of time. It is called a step graph.

(a) Is this relationship linear? Explain.

(b) Find the cost of renting the Rototiller for two days.

(c) Find the cost of renting the Rototiller for $3\frac{1}{2}$ days.

(d) How long can you rent the Rototiller for $40?

(e) Is the cost per day always the same?

15. Write a problem that represents a linear relationship. Give your problem to a classmate to solve.

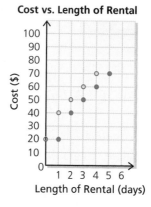

Cost vs. Length of Rental

Cost ($) vs. Length of Rental (days)

The Chapter Problem — Which Rate Is Better?

Refer back to the Chapter Problem at the beginning of this chapter.

1. Make the table of values for both of David's pricing options.

2. Describe any patterns you see in the table.

3. What are the dependent and independent variables?

Career: Furniture Making

A calculator is a common tool in many professions, and furniture making is no exception.

For instance, when raw lumber comes into the factory, the amount of usable wood must be calculated. Sometimes only 50 percent of the wood ends up in the finished product. The planning involved for some tasks is more challenging than for others, like trying to fashion rectangular planks efficiently into round tables or ornate legs.

Costing is another area where calculator skills are useful. When new furniture is designed, several prototypes of the items are made. These are examined to figure out the cost of mass-producing the item. Accurate costing is important.

Repeating fabric patterns also require calculation. In upholstering (and in wallpapering), if a fabric has a repeating pattern, the pattern on different pieces often has to be matched up so more material is required than with plain fabric.

Furniture making is an old and honoured profession that today involves both skill and modern techniques.

2.3 Graphing an Equation

TECHNOLOGY

Using a Graphing Calculator

As its name indicates, you can use a graphing calculator to graph relationships. Here are some guidelines for using a graphing calculator. Although these guidelines apply to most graphing calculators, you should check your calculator's manual for specific instructions.

The Viewing Window

A graphing calculator's display window shows part of the coordinate plane. Usually, it uses values from –10 to 10 on both the *x*- and *y*-axes as shown below. To adjust the window, press the **RANGE** or **WINDOW** key. Then you can enter new values for the window variables.

Calculator View

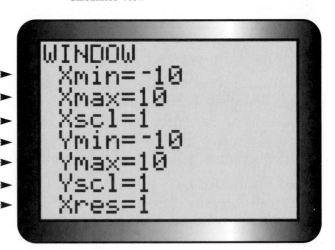

the starting point of the *x*-axis ⟶

the end point of the *x*-axis ⟶

tells how the *x*-axis is scaled ⟶

the starting point of the *y*-axis ⟶

the end point of the *y*-axis ⟶

tells how the *y*-axis is scaled ⟶

controls the resolution (affects how smooth the graph will look) ⟶

```
WINDOW
 Xmin=-10
 Xmax=10
 Xscl=1
 Ymin=-10
 Ymax=10
 Yscl=1
 Xres=1
```

Entering and Graphing a Function

To enter an equation, you must first make sure it is in the form $y = ax + b$, where a and b are numbers. For instance, to graph $y = 2x + 5$, press the Y= key. Then enter $2x + 5$.

Calculator View

Y₁ = 2X + 5

Now press the GRAPH key. The graph should appear.

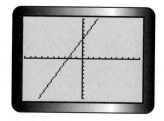

Reading a Graph

Cursor on a Point of Graph

The TRACE key lets you read points on the graph in the viewing window. If you press this key after you have graphed a relation, a flashing cursor will appear. The coordinates of the cursor's location are at the bottom of the window. Use the left and right arrow keys to move the cursor along the graph.

Use the ZOOM key to look more closely at your graph. Some calculators can zoom in and out several times. With others, you need to create a "zoom box" around the desired area. Refer to your calculator's instruction manual to see how this is done on your calculator. Repeated zooming and tracing allows more precise estimates of the location of a point.

Creating a Table of Values

If your calculator has a table feature, you can use it to create a table of values from a graph. Graph $y = 5x - 3$. Press the TABLE key. The calculator gives a table of values of points on the graph.

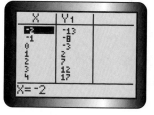

Practise

Use a graphing calculator to graph each of the following. Adjust the window if needed. Use the TRACE and ZOOM keys to find the coordinates of the points that lie on the x-axis or the y-axis.

(a) $y = 3x - 1$ **(b)** $y = \frac{1}{2}x + 5$

(c) $y = x$ **(d)** $y = -5x + 2$

(e) $y = 0.25x - 1$

2.4 Connecting Equations and Graphs

Chris's boss asks him to report on the cost of Compufix and Computer Doctor service calls. Chris decides not to use a hand-written table of values and a hand-drawn graph for a company report. (Recall that Compufix charges $50 plus $30/h. Computer Doctor charges $55/h.)

Chris is deciding whether to use a spreadsheet, graphing software, or a graphing calculator. To use these tools, he has to represent the cost-and-time relationships with algebraic expressions. He writes these equations for the Compufix charges:

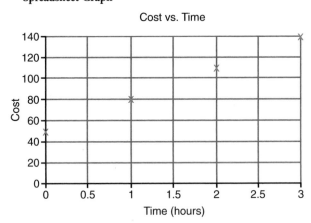

$$\text{Cost} = 50 + 30 \times \text{time in hours (word equation)}$$
$$\text{or}$$
$$C = 50 + 30t \text{ (algebraic equation)}$$

In a spreadsheet, the rows are numbered and the columns are identified by a letter. Each cell is identified by its column letter and row number.

Spreadsheet Input

	A	B
1	Time (hours)	Cost ($)
2	0	=50+30*A2
3	1	=50+30*A3
4	2	=50+30*A4
5	3	=50+30*A5

Spreadsheet Graph

Cost vs. Time

[Graph: Cost (vertical axis, 0 to 140) vs. Time (hours) (horizontal axis, 0 to 3) with plotted points]

Calculator Input

$Y_1 = 50 + 30X$

Most graphing calculators and software call the independent variable x and the dependent variable y.

Calculator Graph

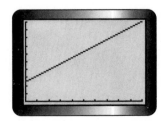

Graphing Software Input

y = 30x + 50

Graphing Software Graph

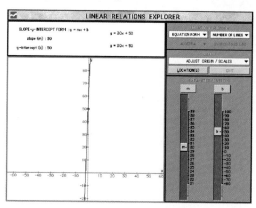

Think, Do, Discuss

1. How do the formulas for the spreadsheet, calculator, and software represent the equation $C = 50 + 30t$?

2. Chris noticed that when he went from the first row to the second row in the table of values, the time changed by one hour and the cost changed by $30. He showed this on the graph with a right triangle. Does this pattern exist for the entire table? Explain.

Compufix

Time (h)	Cost ($)
0 > 1	50 > 30
1 > 1	80 > 30
2 > 1	110 > 30
3 > 1	140 > 30
4	170

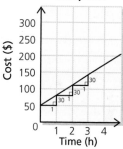

Compufix

3. Copy the table and extend it for five more rows. Copy the graph and continue it.

4. Write the word equation and the algebraic equation that describe the pricing plan for Computer Doctor.

5. Write the spreadsheet, graphing calculator, and software formulas for the Computer Doctor equation.

6. Set up a table of values for the Computer Doctor like the one in Question 2. What is the pattern in this table of values? Extend the table of values for five more rows. Continue the graph.

7. How are the patterns in the tables of values and in the graphs connected to the descriptions of the pricing plans?

8. How are these two graphs different? alike?

9. What happens when the time for a Computer Doctor service call is doubled? tripled? halved? Does the same effect happen when a Compufix service call is doubled, tripled, or halved?

Focus

Key Ideas

- A graph can be created by hand from a table of values; with computer spreadsheets or graphing software; or with a graphing calculator.

- To graph a relationship using technology, it must first be written as an algebraic equation. Traditionally, x represents the independent variable and y represents the dependent variable.

- On a linear graph, a **rate triangle** can be drawn between any two points. The shape of the rate triangle shows how steep the line is.

- A **direct variation** has an equation of the form $y = mx$. The graph of a direct variation crosses the y-axis at $y = 0$.

- A **partial variation** has an equation of the form $y = mx + b$. The graph of a partial variation does not cross the y-axis at $y = 0$, but at some other value, namely b.

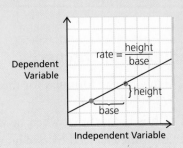

Example

Mpho sells stereos and is paid by commission. He earns a weekly salary of $300 plus 5% commission on his total weekly sales. Find the algebraic expression that represents this relationship and graph it using a spreadsheet or graphing calculator.

Graphing Calculator Solution

Mpho's earnings depend on the value of the stereos he sells. His commission is 5% of his weekly sales. The word equation that represents this relationship is:

$$\text{Earnings} = 300 + 5\% \times \text{Weekly Sales}$$

If E represents earnings and W represents the value of his weekly sales, then an algebraic equation for this relationship is:

$$E = 300 + 0.05W \quad (5\% \text{ must be changed to a decimal: } 5\% = 0.05)$$

To use a graphing calculator, enter the equation as $\boxed{\text{Y1} = 300 + 0.05\text{X}}$.

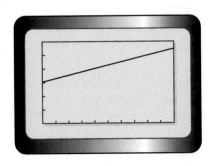

Spreadsheet Solution

Use the **Fill Down** command to create a table of values.

	A	B
1	Weekly Sales (W)	Earnings (E)
2	0	=300+0.05*A2
3	1000	⇩
4	2000	⇩
5	3000	⇩
6	4000	⇩
7	5000	⇩

⇒

	A	B
1	Weekly Sales (W)	Earnings (E)
2	0	300
3	1000	350
4	2000	400
5	3000	450
6	4000	500
7	5000	550

Once the values are entered, use the graphing feature to draw the graph.

Mpho's Weekly Earnings

Practise, Apply, Solve

A

1. Write the word equation and the algebraic equation.
   (a) The cost to cut the lawn is a flat fee of $5, plus $5/h.
   (b) The charge to walk a dog is $10/h.
   (c) Twenty baskets of apples are picked in one hour.
   (d) Hans Building Supplies sells sand for $19/t, plus $25 for delivery.
   (e) The gas tank of a van holds 75L. The van uses 0.125 L/km.
   (f) Alla earns $15/h shovelling snow.

2. Which situations in Question 1 are partial variations?
3. Write the equations needed for a graphing calculator for each situation in Question 1.
4. Which coloured line shows a direct variation? a partial variation?

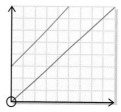

B

5. True or False?
   (a) To graph a relationship using a graphing calculator, you must first write it as a word equation.
   (b) Usually, x represents the dependent variable and y represents the independent variable.
   (c) The graph of a partial variation does not cross the y-axis at $y = 0$.
   (d) The graph of a direct variation does not cross the y-axis at $y = 0$.

6. To fix a car, Sally's Garage charges a flat fee of $20, plus $40/h.
   (a) Write the word equation and algebraic equation for this relation.
   (b) In Section 2.2, you made a table of values for this relation. Now make the spreadsheet for this table. Show the cell formulas.
   (c) Write the equations for graphing this situation with a calculator and with software. Which variable is represented by *x*? by *y*?
   (d) Is this relation a direct variation or a partial variation? Explain.
   (e) Extend the table of values for three more hours. Use the table to extend the graph.
   (f) Use the equation to find the cost of a repair job lasting 10.5 h.

7. A small rocket is launched from a hill 1500 m above sea level. It rises at 35 m/s.
   (a) Write the word equation and algebraic equation for this relation.
   (b) Write the equations for graphing this situation with a calculator and with software. Which variable is represented by *x*? by *y*? Explain.
   (c) In Section 2.2, you made a table of values for this relation. Now make the spreadsheet for the first ten rows of this table. Show the cell formulas.
   (d) Is this a direct variation or a partial variation? Explain.
   (e) Use a rate triangle to explain how the patterns in the table of values are represented in the graph.
   (f) Use the equation to find the height of the rocket after 5 min.

8. An author earns a royalty of 25¢ for each book sold.
   (a) Write the word equation and algebraic equation for this relation.
   (b) Write the equations for graphing this situation with a calculator and with software. Which variable is represented by *x*? by *y*? Explain.
   (c) In Section 2.2, you made a table of values for this relation. Now make the spreadsheet for the first ten rows of this table. Show the cell formulas.
   (d) Is this relation a direct variation or a partial variation? Explain.
   (e) Use a rate triangle to explain how the patterns in the table of values are represented in the graph.
   (f) Use the equation to find the royalties on 1 000 000 books sold.

9. Marlon has $900 in his bank account. He takes $100 out of his account every week.
   (a) Write the word equation and algebraic equation for this relation.
   (b) Write the equations for graphing this situation with a calculator and with software. Which variable is represented by *x*? by *y*? Explain.
   (c) In Section 2.2, you made a table of values for this relation. Now make the spreadsheet for the first nine rows of this table. Show the cell formulas.
   (d) Is this relation a direct variation or a partial variation? Explain.
   (e) Use a rate triangle to explain how the patterns in the table of values are represented in the graph.
   (f) Use the equation to find the amount of money Marlon will have in his bank account after six weeks.

10. A submarine at sea level dives 50 m every 5 min.
    (a) Write the word equation and algebraic equation for this relation.

(b) Write the equations for graphing this situation with a calculator and with software. Which variable is represented by x? by y? Explain.

(c) In Section 2.2, you made a table of values for this relation. Now make the spreadsheet for the first ten rows of the table of values for this relation. Show the cell formulas.

(d) Is this relation a direct variation or a partial variation? Explain.

(e) Use a rate triangle to explain how the patterns in the table of values are represented in the graph.

11. Students can choose from two different monthly cafeteria beverage plans.

Plan A: Pay $0.75 per glass; *Plan B*: Pay $10 plus $0.50 per glass

(a) Write the algebraic equations for both plans.

(b) Find the cost of 20 beverages under each plan.

(c) Find the cost of 40 beverages under each plan.

(d) Which plan is better if you drink 30 beverages a month? 50 beverages a month?

12. Create a problem with a relationship for the equation $y = 10x + 25$. Give your problem to a classmate to solve.

13. Create a problem with a relationship for the equation $y = 14x$. Give your problem to a classmate to solve.

C

14. The table shows several different heights and areas for triangles with a base of 10 cm.

(a) Graph this relationship.

(b) Write an algebraic equation that relates the area and the height of the triangle.

Height (cm)	2	5	10	20
Area (cm²)	10	25	50	100

15. Use a graphing calculator to graph each relationship. In each case, you must first change the equation to a different form.

(a) $2y = 4x - 8$ **(b)** $3y + 6 = 12x$

(c) $10x - 5 = 5y$ **(d)** $8x = 4y - 20$

16. (a) Create a problem that shows a direct variation. Give your problem to a classmate to solve.

(b) Repeat part (a) for a partial variation.

The Chapter Problem — Which Rate Is Better?

The use of technology is recommended for this activity.

Refer back to the Chapter Problem at the beginning of this chapter.

1. Graph both of David's pricing options on the same set of axes.

2. Which graph shows partial variation? direct variation?

3. Write the word equation for each pricing option.

4. Compare the rate triangle for each line to the hourly rate charged.

2.5 Developing a Coordinate System

The Battleship Game

Draw two grids on graph paper. Mark off a scale from 0 to 10 on both the horizontal and vertical axes.

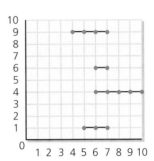

On one grid, draw four ships. Draw them using only horizontal and vertical lines. Each ship consists of several points joined by a straight line. Use these guidelines:

> Aircraft Carrier: 5 points on the grid
> Destroyer: 4 points on the grid
> Submarine: 3 points on the grid
> Battleship: 2 points on the grid

Toss a coin to decide who will go first. Take turns calling out pairs of numbers such as (2, 3), where 2 is the number on the horizontal axis and 3 is the number on the vertical axis. If you call out a point that lands on one of your opponent's ships, he or she must tell you. Record the location of the boat on your second grid, and go again. If you miss, your opponent has the next turn. Keep taking turns until one of you has eliminated the other's fleet.

Try this game a second time by extending your grids as shown.

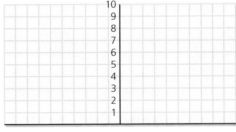

Think, Do, Discuss

1. How will the inclusion of negative numbers on the horizontal axis affect the way you locate points?
2. Describe how you would locate point $(-3, 4)$.
3. Which game will take longer to play, the first game or the second? Why?
4. Try the game a third time, but now extend both the vertical and horizontal axes from -10 to 10.
5. Set up a tournament that takes several days to play over lunch hour. Keep track of the results in a flow chart. Who will be the Ultimate Battleship Champion of your class?

EXPLORATION

Graphing in Four Quadrants

Plotting Ordered Pairs

Mathematicians have developed many powerful tools to help solve problems. One of them is the number plane, also known as the **coordinate plane**.

The numbers in an **ordered pair**, such as $(-4, 5)$, are used to locate the position of a point on the grid. The numbers are called the **coordinates** of a point.

In the diagram, the location of points $(-4, 5)$, $(3, 2)$, $(4, -4)$, and $(-6, -5)$ are shown by the points A, B, C, and D.

The grid with a horizontal axis and a vertical axis is often called the Cartesian plane after French mathematician René Descartes, who invented it.

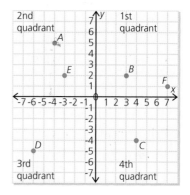

The Coordinate Plane

Think, Do, Discuss

1. Why would each section be called a quadrant?
2. Name the quadrant where both the coordinates are negative.
3. Name the quadrant where both the coordinates are positive.
4. Is point $(-2, 3)$ in the same spot as $(2, -3)$? Explain.
5. Name the coordinates of points E and F in the above diagram.
6. Must every point fall within a quadrant?

Focus

Key Ideas

- The coordinate grid is often called the Cartesian plane.
- The axes divide the plane into four **quadrants.**
- The point where the axes intersect is called the **origin**.
- The horizontal axis is called the *x*-axis.
- The vertical axis is called the *y*-axis.
- The ordered pair of numbers that identifies any point is (x, y). The *x*-value of a point is the *x*-coordinate and is always written first. The *y*-value is the *y*-coordinate and is always written second.
- The coordinates of the origin are $(0, 0)$.
- A dot is used to represent a point on the graph. A capital letter is used to name the points.

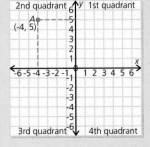

$$A(-4, 5)$$

horizontal coordinate   vertical coordinate

Example

Graph the relationship defined by $y = 2x - 1$.

Solution

Make a table of values. Choose small integers for *x*.

x	y
−2	− 5
−1	− 3
0	− 1
1	1
2	3

Substitute each number for *x* into the equation and evaluate to find *y*.

x	y
−2	$2(-2) - 1 = -5$
−1	$2(-1) - 1 = -3$
0	−1
1	1
2	3

Plot the points.

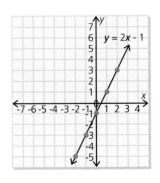

The points are in a straight line, so we join them and label the line with its equation.

Practise, Apply, Solve

A

Use the diagram on the right to answer Questions 1 to 2 and 4 to 11.

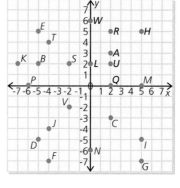

1. Name the coordinates of each point.
   (a) *U*   (b) *B*   (c) *C*   (d) *V*

   (e) *G*   (f) *K*   (g) *E*   (h) *N*

2. What is the corresponding letter for each ordered pair?
   (a) (2, 3)   (b) (−2, 2)   (c) (−4, 4)

   (d) (5, −5)   (e) (2, 0)   (f) (0, 2)

3. (a) A code using ordered pairs has been used to represent a word. To decode it, draw a grid and plot the points. Find each letter of the word.

   • Join (−7, 1) to (−7, 3) to (−6, 2).

   • Join (−6, 2) to (−5, 3) to (−5, 1).

   • Join (−4, 1) to (−2, 3) to (0, 1).

   • Join (−3, 2) to (−1, 2).

   • Join (0, 3) to (2, 3) and (1, 1) to (1, 3).

   (b) Use the method in part (a) to represent a word of your own.

B

4. (a) What are the coordinates of *P* and *Q*?
   (b) What property do these points have in common?

5. (a) What are the coordinates of *W*, *L*, and *N*?
   (b) What property do these points have in common?

6. Name all the points whose coordinates are both negative.

7. Name the coordinates of the origin.

8. Name all the points whose coordinates are equal.

9. Which point is named by (5, –5)? by (–5, 5)?

10. In which quadrant is each point found?
    (a) (2, 5)   (b) (–5, 5)   (c) (5, –7)

    (d) (–5, 2)   (e) (–4, –7)

11. Name and give the coordinates of each point on the boundary of the:
    (a) 2nd and 1st quadrants   (b) 3rd and 4th quadrants
    (c) 1st and 4th quadrants   (d) 2nd and 3rd quadrants

For Question 12, prepare a separate grid by drawing the horizontal and vertical axes, and placing the numbers along each. Have a partner check your work.

12. (a) Locate these points on the grid: (2, 4) and (–2, –4).
  (b) Use a ruler to join these points.
  (c) Through what other points does the line pass?
  (d) Mark these points on the grid: $A(2, 1)$, $B(4, 2)$, and $C(4, 1)$.
  (e) Connect AB, BC, and AC. What geometric figure have you drawn?

13. (a) Draw the grid shown on the right and plot these points.
    $A(3, 4)$, $B(5, 6)$, $C(1, 2)$, $D(4, 5)$, $E(2, 3)$, $F(6, 7)$
  (b) What relationship do these points have in common?
  (c) What are the coordinates of the two other points on this grid that fit this pattern?

14. (a) Draw a grid and plot these points on it.
    (2, 8), (10, 0), (8, 2), (6, 4), (7, 3), (3, 7)
  (b) What geometric figure is suggested by the points in part (a)?
  (c) Name two other ordered pairs that fit this pattern.

15. (a) Find the sum of the coordinates of each ordered pair. What do you notice?
    (4, 5), (3, 6), (1, 8), (0, 9), (9, 0), (5, 4), (7, 2), (2, 7)
  (b) Plot the points. What do you notice?
  (c) Write the coordinates of two other points that fit the pattern.
  (d) Write in words the relationship shown by these ordered pairs.

16. For each relationship, make a table of values. Then draw the corresponding graph. Use $-2, -1, 0, 1$, and 2 for your x-coordinates.
  (a) $y = x + 3$ **(b)** $y = 2x$ **(c)** $y = 2x - 3$
  (d) $y = 3x + 2$ **(e)** $y = -4x$ **(f)** $y = -5x + 1$
  (g) $y = \frac{1}{2}x$ **(h)** $y = \frac{1}{4}x - 4$

17. (a) On the same set of axes, graph $y = 2x$, $y = 2x + 1$, $y = 2x - 1$, and $y = 2x + 2$.
  (b) How are the graphs alike? different?

18. (a) On the same set of axes, graph $y = x + 3$, $y = 2x + 3$, $y = -x + 3$, and $y = -2x + 3$.
  (b) How are the graphs alike? different?

C

19. For an experiment, a beaker of liquid is heated and its temperature is recorded over time. It is found that the liquid's temperature, T, in degrees Celsius, is given by $T = 2.5t$, where t is the time in hours.
  (a) Choose values for the variables and draw a graph. Describe the graph.
  (b) Create two problems based on the graph. Solve your problems.

20. The cost, C, in dollars, of producing brochures is given by $C = 2n + 8$, where n is the number of brochures and 8 is the fixed cost. Fixed costs, such as design, are independent of the number of brochures.
   (a) Choose values of the variables and draw a graph. Describe the graph.
   (b) Create two problems based on the graph. Solve your problems.

21. For each relationship, make a table of values and draw the graph.
   (a) $x + y = 10$ (b) $2x + y = 8$ (c) $3x - 5y = 15$

22. These points are plotted on a graph.
       $(-4, 5), (-2, 3), (2, 3), (4, 5), (0, 7)$
   (a) Sanjay is to draw a line from each point to each other point. How many lines will he draw?
   (b) Suppose he were to add the point $(5, 5)$ to the grid. How would that change the answer in part (a)? What pattern can help you?

23. The price, P, of a pizza is given by $P = 0.75t + 9$, where t is the number of toppings and 9 is the price of a pizza without any toppings.
   (a) Make a table of values using values of t from 0 to 5.
   (b) Draw the graph. Describe any trends.
   (c) What is the price of a pizza with 6 toppings?
   (d) Is it possible to buy a pizza with 2.5 toppings? Explain.

24. For each relationship, make a table of values and draw the graph.
   (a) $y = 3x - 7$ (b) $6x + 4y = 11$ (c) $x - 12y = -6$

René Descartes (1596–1650)

René Descartes was born near Tours, France. He made several important contributions to mathematics, including many of the symbols we use today in algebra.

His major contribution was the development of the coordinate system for graphing points and equations. Today, the coordinate plane is often referred to as the Cartesian plane.

Research Descartes, at the library or on the Internet. For what other accomplishments is he recognized?

Did You Know?

Sir Arthur Conan Doyle was the creator of Sherlock Holmes, perhaps literature's most famous fictional character. One reason for the popularity of this great detective is his use of logic and common sense in solving crimes.

You might enjoy reading the short story *The Musgrave Ritual*, in which Holmes uses ratios and proportions to solve a mysterious disappearance.

2.7 The Roles of *m* and *b* in *y* = *mx* + *b*

There are several ways you can draw a graph. You can sketch one by hand, using a table of values. Or, you can use a graphing calculator. You can also use graphing software such as the *Linear Relations Explorer.*

The Steepness of a Line

1. Graph each equation on the same set of axes.
   (a) $y = 3x$ **(b)** $y = 5x$

2. How are the graphs you created for Question 1 alike? different?

3. Which equation in Question 1 has the graph with the steeper line?

4. Compare the graphs of these lines to those in Question 1.
   (a) $y = 10x$ **(b)** $y = 0.5x$

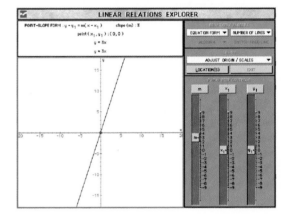

5. Repeat Questions 1 to 3 using these equations.
   (a) $y = 3x + 2$ **(b)** $y = 5x - 3$

6. How do the graphs in Question 5 differ from $y = 3x$ and $y = 5x$?

7. How can you use the equation of a line to predict:
   (a) how steep it is?
   (b) where it crosses the *y*-axis?

8. How is the steepness of a line related to the vertical and horizontal sides of the rate triangle?

The Direction of a Line

1. Graph the line of each equation on the same set of axes.
   (a) $y = 4x$ **(b)** $y = -4x$

2. How are the graphs in Question 1 alike? different?

3. How does a negative number in front of *x* in the equation affect the graph of a line?

The Roles of Slope and 2.8 Intercepts

For an experiment, Marie puts a plastic glass of water in the freezer to find out how quickly it freezes. She measures the temperature of the water every 2 min until it freezes. The water temperature decreases by 1°C every 2 min. The water temperature at the beginning of the experiment was 20°C. Marie created this table of values and graph.

Time (min)	0	2	4	6	8	10	12	14	16	18	20
Temperature (°C)	20	19	18	17	16	15	14	13	12	11	10

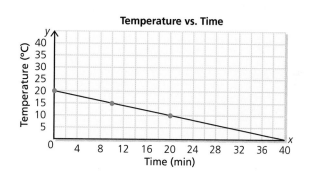

Think, Do, Discuss

1. Write the algebraic equation of the relationship between the variables.

2. What are the coordinates of the point where the line meets the temperature axis? What is the significance of this point?

3. What are the coordinates of the point where the line meets the time axis? What is the significance of this point?

4. What is the rate of change of the temperature? How is this rate related to the tilt of the line?

5. Suppose the water temperature was 25°C at the start of the experiment and the temperature decreased by 1°C every minute.
   (a) How would this affect the table of values? the graph?
   (b) Create the new table of values and draw the new graph.
   (c) What is the new rate of change for temperature?
   (d) What are the coordinates of the points where the line crosses the x-axis and the y-axis?
   (e) Write the new equation of this relationship. Is there a relationship between the rate of change in temperature, the point where the line crosses the y-axis, and the equation of the relationship? If so, explain.

Ideas

The slope of a line, *m*, is a measure of how steep the line is.
- The greater the magnitude of *m*, the steeper the line.
- A line with a positive slope rises to the right. A line with a negative slope falls to the right.
- The value of its slope affects the tilt of a line. The farther the slope is from 0, the steeper the line.
- Slope is the **rate of change** of a linear relation.

- The **intercepts** of a line occur at the points where the line crosses the axes. The intercept is the distance from the origin to this point.
  - The **x-intercept** is the point where the line crosses the *x*-axis. Its *y*-coordinate is 0.
  - The **y-intercept** is the point where the line crosses the *y*-axis. Its *x*-coordinate is 0.

- When the equation of a line is **y = mx + b**, the coordinates of its *y*-intercept are (0, *b*).

Example

Ashi works for the New Music CD company. He earns \$10/h and receives a weekly allowance of \$50 to cover his driving expenses. Find an equation for the relationship between earnings and time. Graph the equation without using a table of values.

Solution

The relationship between Ashi's weekly earnings, *E*, and his hours worked, *h*, can be expressed by $E = 10h + 50$, or $y = 10x + 50$. From the equation, it is clear that the graph of this relationship is linear. The equation is written in the form $y = mx + b$, so the line has a slope of 10 and a *y*-intercept of 50. A graph can be drawn by first plotting the *y*-intercept. A second point can be plotted using the rate triangle or slope.

For every 10 h that Ashi works, his earnings increase by \$100. That is, for every 10 h change in his hours worked, there is a \$100 change in his earnings. To find his rate of earnings for each hour, divide \$100 by 10 h.

$$\$100 \div 10 \text{ h} = \$10/\text{h}$$

This rate is a measure of how a change in hours worked causes a change in earnings. It is called the **rate of change**, or **slope**.

The rate triangle can be drawn between any two points on the graph and will result in the same rate. This is called a **constant rate**. A second point can now be plotted by starting at the **y-intercept** and moving 1 unit to the right, and then 10 units up. Continue this pattern to plot more points. To complete the graph, join the points with a straight line and label the line with its equation.

The line meets the *y*-axis at point (0, 50). The **y-intercept** of the line is 50. This value represents the weekly car expense fee.

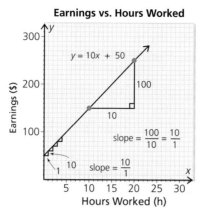

Earnings vs. Hours Worked

$y = 10x + 50$

$$\text{slope} = \frac{100}{10} = \frac{10}{1}$$

$$\text{slope} = \frac{10}{1}$$

Practise, Apply, Solve

A

1. True or False?
   (a) A line with a negative slope is always very steep.
   (b) A line with a positive slope rises to the right.
   (c) The *y*-intercept of a line is the point where *y*-coordinate is 0.
   (d) The *y*-intercept of a line is the point where *x*-coordinate is 0.

2. Arrange the lines in order of increasing steepness.
   (a) $m_1 = \frac{1}{2}$, $m_2 = 6$, $m_3 = 0.75$, $m_4 = 10.5$
   (b) $m_1 = -1$, $m_2 = -5$, $m_3 = -0.25$, $m_4 = -11$

3. Write the equation using the information.
   (a) $m = 6$, $b = 8$ (b) $m = -4$, $b = -6$
   (c) $m = 19$, $b = -4$ (d) $b = 4$, $m = 6$

4. Identify the *y*-intercept and the slope.
   (a) $y = -6x + 14$ (b) $y = 14x + 14$
   (c) $y = 20 + 3x$ (d) $-16x + 10 = y$

5. Match each graph to its equation.
   (a) $y = 4x + 1$ (b) $y = 4x - 1$
   (c) $y = x + 4$ (d) $y = -x + 4$

i.
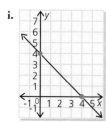

ii.
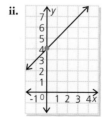

iii.
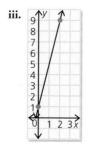

iv.
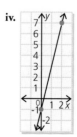

B

6. For each graph, explain what the *y*-intercept, *x*-intercept, and the slope mean in the context of each relationship.

(a)

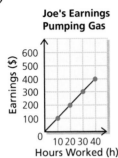

Joe's Earnings Pumping Gas

(b)

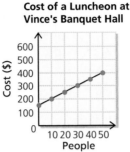

Cost of a Luncheon at Vince's Banquet Hall

(c)

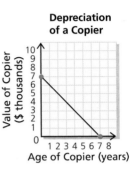

Depreciation of a Copier

7. Write the equation for each line in Question 6. Use *x* and *y* as the variables.

8. A house is expected to increase in value according to $y = 7500x + 125\ 000$, where *y* is the value of the house after *x* years.
  (a) Find the slope of the line and interpret its meaning.
  (b) Find the *y*-intercept and interpret its meaning.
  (c) Find the value of the house after seven years.

9. A car is expected to decrease in value according to $y = -1360x + 17\ 000$, where *y* is the value of the car after *x* years.
  (a) Find the slope of the line and interpret its meaning.
  (b) Find the *y*-intercept and interpret its meaning.

10. Jackie sells cars. Her pay is based on the equation $y = 0.03x + 350$, where *y* is her weekly earnings and *x* is the total value of cars she sells in a week.
  (a) Find the slope of the line and interpret its meaning.
  (b) Find the *y*-intercept and interpret its meaning.
  (c) How much will Jackie earn if she sells $95 000 worth of cars?

11. Mohammed makes bicycle tires and is paid according to $y = 1.25x$, where *y* is his earnings and *x* is the number of tires he makes.
  (a) Find the slope of the line and interpret its meaning.
  (b) Find the *y*-intercept and interpret its meaning.

12. Describe what each graph would look like. Do not use tables of values or technology. Describe where the line crosses the *y*-axis, the direction it slants, and how steep it is.
  (a) $y = 6x$ **(b)** $y = 10x + 5$

  (c) $y = -8x$ **(d)** $y = -3x - 1$

  (e) $y = \frac{3}{4}x$ **(f)** $y = -2.5x - 4$

13. Use the slope and y-intercept to graph each relation.

(a) $y = 3x + 2$ (b) $y = \frac{1}{2}x - 4$ (c) $y = \frac{3}{5}x + 4$

(d) $y = x$ (e) $y = -x$ (f) $y = -2x + 3$

14. A taxi charges a base fee plus $0.75/km. A 10-km trip costs $8.70.

(a) What is the rate of change in this situation?

(b) Write an equation for the cost of hiring a taxi in terms of length of the trip.

(c) Graph the equation.

(d) What does the vertical intercept represent in this situation?

15. A clown will come to children's parties for a base fee plus $5.25 per child. The total fee for a party with ten children is $102.50.

(a) What is the rate of change in this situation?

(b) Write the equation for the cost of hiring the clown, F, in terms of the number of children, c.

(c) Graph the equation.

(d) What does the vertical intercept represent in this situation?

The Chapter Problem — Which Rate Is Better?

Refer back to the Chapter Problem at the beginning of this chapter.

1. Find the y-intercept for each of David's pricing options.

2. (a) What is the slope for each pricing option?

(b) What is the connection between the slope and the rate triangle for each pricing option?

3. Describe the connection between the y-intercept and slope of each line, and the pricing option it represents.

Did You Know?

To describe the location of something on a flat plane, we can use the Cartesian coordinate system. But to describe the location of something that is on the Earth's surface, which is curved, we need another type of coordinate system. Investigate the terms **longitude** and **latitude**. How are they alike and how are they different? Why can't the Cartesian system be used on a curved surface?

The division of a day into 24 h, an hour into 60 min, and a minute into 60 s was probably first practised by the ancient Babylonians. They divided the imaginary circular path of the Sun into 2 equal parts, then they divided the periods of daylight and darkness into 12 parts each. The result is a 24-h day. How does this information relate to the concept of longitude?

Investigate Sandford Fleming (1827–1915) and his role in the creation of time zones. Why did he suggest that there should be 24 time zones? What else did he accomplish?

2.9 Finding the Equation of a Given Line

The building code specifies the pitch, or steepness, that stairs must have. The pitch is the ratio of the **rise** and the **run**. We use these same words when calculating the slope of a line.

$$\text{slope} = \frac{\text{rise}}{\text{run}}$$

Slopes of roofs and stairs have to conform to building codes because of safety considerations. Slopes have to be considered by engineers planning routes for railway tracks and roadways.

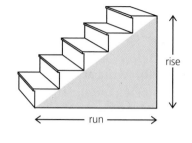

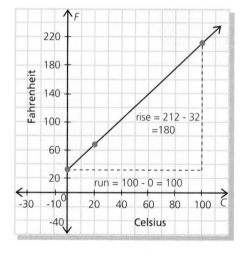

What is the slope of this roof?

Fahrenheit vs. Celsius

Elinor knows that water freezes at 0°C, or 32°F, and that it boils at 100°C, or 212°F. She also knows that room temperature is 20°C, or 68°F. Is there a relationship between the Fahrenheit scale and the Celsius scale? Use a graph to find out.

A linear relationship appears to exist between the two temperature scales. If so, then we can find the rate at which the Fahrenheit value changes as the Celsius value changes. This rate is equivalent to the slope of the line. Drawing the rate triangle helps to find the rise and run.

$$\text{slope} = \frac{\text{rise}}{\text{run}}$$

$$= \frac{180}{100}$$

$$= \frac{9}{5}$$

This means that for each 1° increase in the Celsius scale, the Fahrenheit scale increases by $\frac{9°}{5}$ or 1.8°. The line has a *y*-intercept at 32°F. The equation that represents the relationship is $F = \frac{9}{5}C + 32$ or $F = 1.8C + 32$.

Think, Do, Discuss

1. Copy the graph above. Convert –5°C, –10°C, and –20°C to Fahrenheit and plot these points on the graph.
2. Is there a temperature at which Fahrenheit and Celsius temperatures are equal? Prove it.
3. Find an equation to convert Fahrenheit to Celsius.
4. A rule of thumb for converting Celsius to Fahrenheit is to double and add 30. Over what range of temperatures is this rule reasonable?
5. Write a word equation that shows how to find the rise and run using any two points on the graph.

Finding the Equation

At home, Mei-Ling carries out the water-freezing experiment done in Section 2.8. Unfortunately, she loses her data sheet on the way to school. She does recall this much of the data.

Time (min)	Temperature (°C)
4	19
8	16

She wants to find the temperature of the water 10 min into the experiment.

Think, Do, Discuss

1. Mei-Ling knows the relationship between freezing time and temperature is linear. She plots the data points (4, 19) and (8, 16).

    (a) What is the slope of the line?

    (b) What is the meaning of the slope in this situation?

2. Mei-Ling knows that the equation for the temperature-time relationship must be in the form $y = mx + b$. Use the information about the slope and that (4, 19) is a point on the line to find b.

3. The value of b is 22. This result means that the starting temperature was 22°C and the equation is $y = -\frac{3}{4}x + 22$.

4. Use the equation to find the temperature of the water 10 min into the experiment.

5. Would Mei-Ling have found a different value for b if she had used point (8, 16)?

Focus

Key Ideas

- In equations, the Greek letter Δ (delta) is used to represent the change in a variable. So, the change in y is written Δy and the change in x is written Δx.
- As a result, there are several ways to write the slope:

$$m = \text{slope}$$

$$= \frac{\text{rise}}{\text{run}}$$

$$= \frac{\text{difference of } y\text{-coordinates}}{\text{difference of } x\text{-coordinates}}$$

$$= \frac{\Delta y}{\Delta x}$$

- If $A(x_1, y_1)$ and $B(x_2, y_2)$ are two points on line AB, then the slope of AB is: $m_{AB} = \dfrac{y_2 - y_1}{x_2 - x_1}$
- To find the equation of a line when two points on the line are known:

  1. Find the slope, $m = \dfrac{y_2 - y_1}{x_2 - x_1}$

  2. Find the y-intercept by substituting the coordinates from a point on the line and the slope into $y = mx + b$ and solve for b.

  3. Write the equation, using the values for m and b found above.

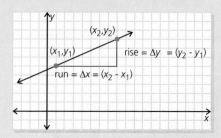

Example

Find the equation of the line that passes through the points $A(-6, -2)$ and $B(4, 3)$.

Solution

Find the slope using the two given points.
In this case, (x_1, y_1) is $(-6, -2)$ and (x_2, y_2) is $(4, 3)$.

$$\text{slope} = \frac{\Delta y}{\Delta x}$$

$$= \frac{y_2 - y_1}{x_2 - x_1}$$

$$= \frac{3 - (-2)}{4 - (-6)}$$

$$= \frac{5}{10}$$

$$= \frac{1}{2}$$

Write the equation in $y = mx + b$ form using $m = \dfrac{1}{2}$.

$$y = \frac{1}{2}x + b$$

Substitute the coordinates for one of the points on the line for x and y in the equation. Solve the resulting equation for b.

Use (4, 3).

$$3 = \frac{1}{2}(4) + b$$
$$3 = 2 + b$$
$$3 = 2 + 1$$
$$\therefore b = 1$$

Use the values you found for m and b to write the equation.

$$y = \frac{1}{2}x + 1$$

Practise, Apply, Solve

1. True or False?
   (a) The run is the horizontal change and the rise is the vertical change.
   (b) The rise is the horizontal change and the run is the vertical change.
   (c) The rise is the vertical change and the run is the vertical change.
   (d) Slope is the ratio $\frac{\text{rise}}{\text{run}}$.

2. The span of a wheelchair ramp is 5 m and the rise is 1 m. Find the slope of the ramp.

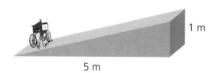

3. There are three uniform steps from the ground to a front porch that is 72 cm above the ground.
   (a) Considering the porch itself as a fourth step, uniform with the others, what is the rise of each step?
   (b) If the run for each step is 25 cm, what is the length of line segment AB?
   (c) What is the slope of the handrail?

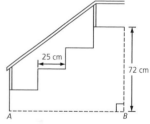

4. A line with equation $y = 2x + b$ passes through the given point. Find the value of b.
   (a) (1, 3)   (b) (2, −3)   (c) (5, 7)
   (d) (−1, 3)   (e) (−5, −7)   (f) (2, −8)

B

5. Each pair of points lies on a straight line. Sketch each line to find its slope.
   (a) (3, 5) and (0, 2)   (b) (3, 3) and (−2, 2)
   (c) (21, −10) and (20, 24) (d) (4, 0) and (6, 18)
   (e) (1, −1) and (2, 2)   (f) (−3, −8) and (−5, −6)
   (g) The x-intercept is 4 and the y-intercept is 3.

6. Use the slope formula to find the slope of each line in Question 5.

7. For each situation, write an equation of the line in the form $y = mx + b$.
   (a) The slope is 3 and the y-intercept is 6.
   (b) The slope is $\frac{3}{2}$ and point (−4, 1) is on the line.
   (c) The slope is $-\frac{3}{2}$ and point (6, −1) is on the line.

(d) The slope is 4 and point $(0, -3)$ is on the line.

(e) The slope is $\frac{5}{6}$ and point $(-12, 3)$ is on the line.

(f) The slope is $-\frac{3}{4}$ and the line passes through the origin.

(g) The x-intercept is 5 and the y-intercept is -2.

8. For each pair of points, find **(i)** the slope of the line passing through them; **(ii)** the y-intercept of the line; and **(iii)** the equation of the line in $y = mx + b$ form.

  (a) $(5, 2)$ and $(-1, 8)$ **(b)** $(-8, 1)$ and $(-9, 2)$

  (c) $(3, 7)$ and $(-5, -9)$ **(d)** $(-4, 0)$ and $(4, 6)$

  (e) $(0, 0)$ and $(-2, 10)$ **(f)** $(-6, 24)$ and $(4, 4)$

9. Find the equation of the line passing through $(3, -1)$ if:

  (a) its slope is $\frac{2}{3}$.   **(b)** its y-intercept is -2.

  (c) its x-intercept is -1.   **(d)** it also passes through $(2, -3)$.

10. The LeBlanc family is driving home. They are using cruise control and their speed is constant. After 3 h, they are 350 km from home. After 5 h, they are 130 km from home.

  (a) What is the independent variable? dependent variable?

  (b) Represent the given information as two points on a graph.

  (c) Write an equation for the line that passes through the two points.

  (d) What do the slope and the y-intercept mean in terms of this situation?

11. This table shows the median family income in Canada in 1984 and 1989.

Year	1984	1989
Family Income ($)	26 433	34 213

  (a) Find the annual rate at which the median income is increasing.

  (b) Model this data by finding an equation of a line that passes through these points.

  (c) Use the equation to predict the median family income in 2010.

12. Autoloaners rent cars based on a fixed daily charge and a cost of $0.55/km. The cost of renting a car for one day and driving it for 250 km is $187.50.

  (a) Which quantity is the dependent variable, distance or cost?

  (b) What is the rate of change in this situation?

  (c) Write an equation for the rental cost in terms of the distance driven.

  (d) Graph the equation.

  (e) What is the cost of renting a car for one day if it is driven 50 km? 130 km? 500 km?

13. A stress test is a method of evaluating the health of a patient's cardiovascular system. A technician monitors the patient's pulse while he or she rides an exercise bike or runs on a treadmill. If the patient's pulse rate exceeds a safe maximum rate, the patient is at risk of a heart attack. The maximum rate is based on the patient's age as shown in this graph.

  (a) What does the y-intercept represent in this situation?

  (b) What does the slope of the graph represent?

  (c) Write an equation for the line.

  (d) Use the equation to find the maximum heart rate in a stress test for a 58-year-old patient.

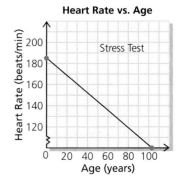

Heart Rate vs. Age

Stress Test

14. The cost of a 30-cm pizza depends on the number of toppings. Each topping costs $0.75. A pizza with three toppings costs $9.
  (a) Write an equation for the cost of the pizza in the form $y = mx + b$.
  (b) Find the cost of a pizza with no toppings.
  (c) Find the cost of a pizza with five toppings.

15. The cost of parking in a downtown parking lot is proportional to the time spent parked. Joel parks for 150 min and the cost is $4.50.
  (a) Write an equation for the cost to park in the form $y = mx + b$.
  (b) Find the cost to park for 25 min.
  (c) Find the cost to park for 3 h and 10 min.
  (d) How long can you park for $6?

16. The cost of having a luncheon catered at the Dew Drop Inn depends on the number of meals served plus a fixed fee to rent the dining room. The cost for 20 meals is $170. The cost for 60 meals is $310.
  (a) Find the cost per meal served.
  (b) Find the cost to rent the dining room.
  (c) Write an equation for the total cost of the luncheon in the form $y = mx + b$.
  (d) Find the cost of a luncheon for 85 people.

C

17. Find the linear *depreciation* equation for this want ad.
  For Sale: 3 year old stereo with matrix surround sound, remote. $1750 new. Asking $800. Call Juan at 874-4329.

18. In 1987, the painting Rising Sunflowers, by Vincent Van Gogh, sold for $36 225 000. An art dealer expects that every 20 years the painting will increase in value by the amount for which it sold in 1987.
  (a) If x represents the time in years after 1987, find the *appreciation* equation.
  (b) Use the equation to predict the value of the painting in 2001.

19. A **median** of a triangle is a line segment joining a vertex to the midpoint of the opposite side. Find the equation of the median from P to the midpoint of QR, in $\triangle PQR$ at the right.

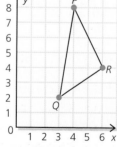

The Chapter Problem — Which Rate Is Better?

Refer back to the Chapter Problem at the beginning of this chapter.
  1. Select any two points on the graph of David's pricing options. Use the coordinates of the points to calculate the slope of each line.
  2. Why are the slopes calculated using these points the same as the slope determined by the rate triangle?
  3. Why doesn't the value of the slope of a line depend on which points are selected?

2.10 Slopes and Equations of Lines: Special Cases

Special Case I

Graph each equation on its own set of axes.

(a) $y = 5x + 2$ **(b)** $y = 5x - 1$

Think, Do, Discuss

1. Describe the relationship between these two lines.

2. How are these lines alike? different?

3. What is the slope of each line?

4. Graph two more lines with this relationship.

5. Write a summary of your findings.

Special Case II

Graph these equations on the same set of axes.

(a) $y = \frac{3}{4}x + 1$ **(b)** $y = -\frac{4}{3}x - 2$

Think, Do, Discuss

1. Estimate the size of the angle formed by these lines. Check your accuracy by measuring the angle with a protractor.

2. What is the relationship between these lines?

3. What is the slope of each line? How are the slopes related to each other?

4. Repeat Steps 1 and 2 for these equations.

(a) $y = 2x$ **(b)** $y = -\frac{1}{2}x$

5. Write a summary of your findings.

Special Case III

Write the coordinates of four points on each line.

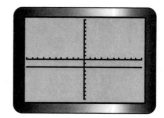

Think, Do, Discuss

1. Is there a pattern in your list of points?
2. How are these lines alike? different?
3. Predict the pattern that would exist in a table of values for a horizontal line.
4. Slope represents rate of change. Predict the value for the slope of a horizontal line.
5. Use two points on each line to find the slope of each line.
6. Which quantity is zero, the rise or the run?
7. Write the equation of the x-axis.
8. Write a conclusion about the graph, equation, and slope of a horizontal line.

Special Case IV

The graphs of two lines are shown. Write the coordinates of four points on each line.

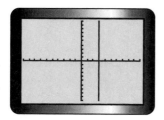

Think, Do, Discuss

1. Is there a pattern in your list of points?
2. How are these lines alike? different?
3. Predict the pattern that would exist in a table of values for a vertical line.
4. Slope represents rate of change. Predict the value for the slope of a vertical line.
5. Use two points on each line to find the slope of each line.
6. Which quantity is zero: the rise or the run?
7. Write the equation of the y-axis.
8. Write a conclusion about the graph, equation, and slope of a vertical line.

Focus

Example

Find the equation of a line that is perpendicular to $y = \frac{3}{5}x - 6$ and passes through point $(9, 6)$.

Solution

The line $y = \frac{3}{5}x - 6$ has a slope of $\frac{3}{5}$. A line that is perpendicular to this one has a slope of $-\frac{5}{3}$. The equation of the new line is of the form $y = -\frac{5}{3}x + b$. To find b, substitute 9 for x and 6 for y and then solve for b.

$$y = -\frac{5}{3}x + b$$

$$6 = -\frac{5}{3}(9) + b$$

$$6 = -\frac{45}{3} + b$$

$$6 = -15 + b$$

$$6 = -15 + 21$$

$$\therefore b = 21$$

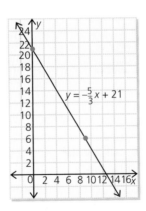

The equation of the line is $y = -\frac{5}{3}x + 21$.

Practise, Apply, Solve

1. Graph.

   (a) $x = 1$ (b) $y = -3$ (c) $x = -5$

   (d) $y = 3$ (e) $x = 0$ (f) $y = \dfrac{1}{2}$

2. Is the vertical change equal to zero for a vertical line or a horizontal line? Explain.

3. Is the horizontal change equal to zero for a horizontal line or a vertical line? Explain.

4. Find the slope of each line and then write its equation.

   (a)
   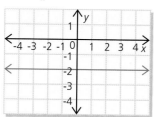

   (b)
   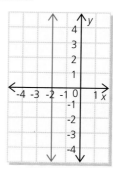

   (c)
   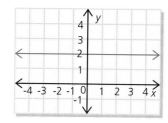

   (d)
   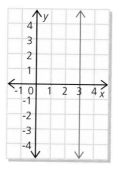

5. True or False?
   (a) The graph of $x = 5$ is parallel to the x-axis.

   (b) The graph of $y = 2$ is parallel to the x-axis.

   (c) The graph of $y = 1.5$ is parallel to the y-axis.

   (d) The graph of $x = -2$ is parallel to the y-axis.

6. Are the lines with the given slopes parallel, perpendicular, or neither?

(a) $m_1 = 3$, $m_2 = -\frac{1}{3}$

(b) $m_1 = \frac{1}{4}$, $m_2 = 4$

(c) $m_1 = \frac{1}{5}$, $m_2 = 0.2$

(d) $m_1 = -5$, $m_2 = \frac{1}{5}$

(e) $m_1 = a$, $m_2 = \frac{1}{a}$

(f) $m_1 = -0.8$, $m_2 = \frac{4}{5}$

B

7. In each of the following, lines k and l pass through the given points. Determine if k and l are parallel, perpendicular, or neither.

(a) k: (2, 3), (4, 4); l: (3, 6), (−7, 1)

(b) k: (2, 5), (4, 11); l: (0, 4), (−9, 7)

(c) k: (4, 3), (6, 7); l: (−2, 1), (0, 0)

(d) k: (−3, −7), (9, −7); l: (3, 5), (−1, 4)

(e) k: (5, 8), (5, −2); l: (−2, 5), (−2, −1)

(f) k: (−5, −1), (−1, 5); l: (3, 4), (7, −2)

8. Write an equation for each line.

(a) Points (3, 6) and (−2, 6) are on the line.

(b) Points (4, −8) and (4, 2) are on the line.

(c) The slope is undefined and point (3, 9) is on the line.

(d) The slope is zero and point (2, 1) is on the line.

(e) The line is vertical and passes through point (−1, −3).

(f) The line is horizontal and passes through point (−4, 5).

9. Write an equation for the line that is:

(a) parallel to $x = 3$ and passes through point (−4, 3).

(b) parallel to $y = 2$ and passes through point (2, 5).

(c) perpendicular to $x = -1$ and passes through (−2, −3).

(d) perpendicular to $y = 4$ and passes through (1, 1).

10. Write an equation for the line that is:

(a) parallel to $y = -2x + 3$ and passes through point (−2, −1).

(b) perpendicular to $\frac{3}{2}x + 2 = y$ and has a y-intercept of −2.

(c) parallel to $y = \frac{5}{3}x - \frac{2}{3}$ and passes through the origin.

(d) parallel to $5x - 3 = y$ and passes through point (2, 4).

(e) perpendicular to $y = 3x + 4$ and has the same y-intercept as the line $y = 2x - 6$.

11. Sarah and Latoya are practising for the 100-m sprint competition. Latoya gives Sarah a 10-m head start. Both sprinters can run at 8 m/s.

(a) Write the equations that model each sprinter's distance in terms of time.

(b) Determine from the equations whether these lines are parallel, perpendicular, or neither.

(c) Graph both equations on the same set of axes to verify your answer to part (b).

(d) Can Latoya catch Sarah before the end of the race? Explain.

12. A triangle has vertices $F(1, -2)$, $G(3, 0)$, and $H(3, -4)$.
  (a) Plot the vertices and draw triangle FGH.
  (b) Use slopes to show that it is a right-angled triangle.

13. Find the equation of a line perpendicular to line AB if:
  (a) $A(-5, 7)$ and $B(-5, -1)$ are the end points of AB.
  (b) $A(4, -3)$ and $B(7, -3)$ are the end points of AB.

C

14. A right triangle has sides defined by the equations $y = kx + 2$, $y = \frac{3}{4}x - \frac{1}{2}$, and $y = \frac{4}{3}x - 1$. What is the value of k?

15. In each case, lines k and l are parallel and contain the given points. Find the unknown values.
  (a) k: $(2, 5)$, $(8, 14)$; l: $(5, 3)$, $(11, y)$
  (b) k: $(-3, 4)$, $(0, -2)$; l: $(2, -2)$, $(0, y)$
  (c) k: $(-4, -7)$, $(-1, 5)$; l: $(2, 8)$, $(x, -4)$

Career: Inventor

Canadian Wendy Murphy is a first-rate problem solver who invented the world's first evacuation stretcher specifically designed to carry infants.

This stretcher is called WEEVAC 6 because it can evacuate six "wee" babies at one time. Her idea came from watching the aftermath of a Mexican earthquake. She asked, "How can I make the evacuation process both safer and quicker?"

To design her product she went through the stages of problem-solving: think about the problem; make a plan; solve the problem; and look back and look ahead.

How do you think the evacuation process could be improved for adults or animals?

Did You Know?

The **aspect** ratio of a screen is the ratio of its width to its height. Measure the width and height of a television screen or computer screen. If it is like most television and computer screens, it will have an aspect ratio of about 4 : 3.

One of the world's largest movie screens is at the Keong Emas Theatre in Jakarta, Indonesia. It measures 28.25 m wide by 21.5 m high. How does the aspect ratio of this screen compare with that of a standard television screen?

Why do you think 4 : 3 is used so frequently for an aspect ratio?

2.11 Conditions for Linear Relationships

Random Data

Make a data table like the one shown. Create a deck of 27 cards consisting of one red suit, one black suit, and a joker.

Shuffle the cards and then draw one. Record its value in the Card Value column. Use joker = 0, ace = 1, jack = 11, queen = 12, and king = 13 for the values of the face cards. Treat a red card as negative and a black card as positive.

Return the card to the deck. Reshuffle the deck and draw another card. Record its value in the next row. Repeat until you have filled ten rows of the table.

Card	Card Value
1	
2	
3	
4	
5	
6	
7	
8	
9	
10	

Think, Do, Discuss

1. Plot the points of the data values.
2. Describe the shape of the graph.

Tiling Pattern Data

Use square tiles, square pieces of paper, or graph paper to copy these tiling patterns.

Extend the pattern until you have completed the tenth picture in the sequence.

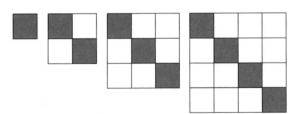

Think, Do, Discuss

1. Copy this table and use the pictures you made to complete it.

Length of Side	Number of Red Tiles	Number of White Tiles	Total Number of Tiles
1			
2			
3			
4			
5			
6			
7			
8			
9			
10			

2. Plot the points showing the relation between Length of Side and Total Number of Tiles.

3. On the same graph, use different colours or shapes to plot the points that show the relationship between Length of Side and Number of Red Tiles. Repeat for Length of Side and Number of White Tiles.

4. Match each graph to one of these descriptions.
   - The relationship is linear.
   - The relationship has a definite pattern but it is not linear.
   - The relationship has no obvious pattern.

5. How does the graph indicate the type of pattern that exists in the data?

6. How can you use the data in a table of values to find what type of pattern exists in the data?

7. Discuss how the description of each activity gave a clue about the existence of a pattern in the data.

Exploring Differences

Make a table that shows the differences between the rows in the data table for the red tiles.

Length of Side	Number of Red Tiles	Difference
1	1	
2	2	$2 - 1 = 1$
3	3	$3 - 2 = 1$
4	4	
5	5	
6	6	
7	7	
8	8	
9	9	
10	10	

Think, Do, Discuss

1. Discuss how the pattern in the difference column relates to the pattern in the data for red tiles.

2. Make a similar table for white tiles. Discuss how the pattern in the difference column relates to the pattern in the data for white tiles.

3. Make a similar table for the total number of tiles. Discuss how the pattern in the difference column relates to the pattern in the data for total number of tiles.

4. Describe how the pattern in the differences relates to the shape of each graph.

5. Discuss whether there is a pattern in differences for the random data.

Focus

Key Ideas

- When the values of the independent variable increase by 1 throughout a table of values, the differences between successive *y*-values form a set of **finite differences**.
- When these differences are used to form a dependent variable column in a table of values, the resulting table is called a **difference table**.
- A table of values represents a **linear relationship** if:
  - when the points are plotted, a single straight line can be drawn through all of them;
  - the finite differences are the same for every row in the difference table; and
  - for all pairs of points in the table, the ratio formed from the differences between the *x*-values and corresponding differences between the *y*-values is the same. (This ratio is the slope of the line.)
- A table of values represents a **nonlinear relationship** if:
  - a single smooth curve can be drawn through every point; and
  - the finite differences are not the same for every row in the difference table.
- A table of values represents a **weak relationship** if the data has no obvious pattern, either in the table of values or on the plot of the data points.

Example

What type of relationship does the data in this table represent?

x	9	6	3	5	8	4	7
y	37	25	13	21	33	17	29

Solution

First, arrange the data in an orderly form. Make a difference table like the one shown below, with the values for the independent variable, *x*, in order from smallest to largest.

Look for a pattern by finding the finite differences. For each change of 1 in the *x*-column, there is a constant change in the *y*-column. The finite differences are the same in each row, so there is a pattern. That is, for all pairs of points, the ratio $\frac{\Delta y}{\Delta x} = \frac{4}{1} = 4$. This relationship is linear.

x	*y*	Δy
3	13	
		$17 - 13 = 4$
4	17	
		$21 - 17 = 4$
5	21	
		$25 - 21 = 4$
6	25	
		$29 - 25 = 4$
7	29	
		$33 - 29 = 4$
8	33	
		$37 - 33 = 4$
9	37	

Practise, Apply, Solve ───────────

A

1. Create the difference table for each table of values. Does the data represent a linear or nonlinear relationship?

(a)
x	y
1	3
2	6
3	9
4	12
5	15

(b)
x	y
1	1
2	4
3	9
4	16
5	25

(c)
x	y
1	5
2	9
3	13
4	17
5	21

(d)
x	y
1	4
2	8
3	13
4	20
5	29

(e)
x	y
2	8
4	64
5	125
3	27
1	1

(f)
x	y
1	2
2	−4
3	7
4	1
5	−5

(g)
x	y
1	−2
4	−8
5	−10
3	−6
2	−4

(h)
x	y
5	0
4	4
3	−6
2	5
1	−3

(i)
x	y
5	32
3	8
1	2
4	16
2	4

(j)
x	y
2	11
4	17
6	23
8	29
10	35

(k)
x	y
5	0
4	2
3	4
2	6
1	8

(l)
x	y
2	0.5
1	1
4	0.25
5	0.2
3	0.33

2. Sketch the graph for each table of values in Question 1. Draw a line or a smooth curve where possible.

3. Find the equation of the line of each linear relationship in Question 1.

B

4. This table gives the monthly payment needed to repay a $10 000 loan over four years at various interest rates.

Interest Rate (%)	8	8.5	9	9.5	10	10.5
Payment ($)	242.51	244.75	247.00	249.26	251.53	253.81

(a) Is this relationship linear or nonlinear?
(b) Graph the data.
(c) Find the monthly payment when the interest rate is 8.25%.
(d) What interest rate would require a monthly payment of $255?

5. A ball is thrown straight up into the air. The table shows the height of the ball at different times.

Time (s)	0	1	2	3	4	5	6
Height (m)	0	25	40	45	40	25	0

(a) Is this relationship linear or nonlinear?
(b) Graph the data.
(c) How high would the ball be after 1.5 s?
(d) When is the ball as high as it can go?
(e) Explain the significance of the *x*-intercepts.

6. This table shows the value of *y*, in dollars, of a car that is *x* years old.

x	0	3	1	2
y	15 000	6 000	12 000	9 000

(a) Is this relationship linear or nonlinear?
(b) Graph the data.
(c) Find the equation of this relationship.
(d) Use the equation to find the value of the car after 1.5 years.
(e) According to the graph, when will the car be worthless? Does this seem realistic? Explain.

7. Air pressure is measured in units called pascals (Pa). The table shows the air pressure at different altitudes.
(a) Graph the data.
(b) Describe the relationship between air pressure and altitude.
(c) Is this relationship linear or nonlinear?
(d) Find the air pressure at 20 km.

Altitude (km)	Air Pressure (Pa)
1	80 000
3	60 000
6	40 000
16	20 000
22	10 000
30	5 000

8. At the beginning of an experiment, a laboratory culture dish contains 500 bacteria. The number of bacteria increases by 50% each hour.
(a) Create a table of values that shows the population after 0, 1, 2, 3, 4, and 5 hours.
(b) Graph the data.
(c) Is this relationship linear or nonlinear?
(d) Find the time it takes for the population to reach 2000 bacteria.

9. The table shows the career goals and assists for some retired NHL players.

Player	Goals	Assists
Jean Beliveau	507	712
John Bucyk	556	813
Alex Delvecchio	456	825
Phil Esposito	717	873
Gordie Howe	801	1049
Stan Mikita	541	926
Jean Ratelle	491	779
Norm Ullman	490	739

(a) Graph the data to find if there is a relationship between goals and assists. Use goals as the dependent variable and assists as the independent variable.

(b) Is this relationship linear or nonlinear?

(c) Can you use your graph to predict the number of assists for a player who scores 500 goals? Explain.

10. In each case, make a table of values of at least eight ordered pairs. Then graph.

(a) $y = x^2$ (b) $y = x^3$ (c) $y = \dfrac{1}{x}$ (d) $y = \sqrt{x}$ (e) $xy = 20$

11. Which relations in Question 10 are linear?

12. Find an equation for each relationship.

(a)

x	y
−2	8
−1	1
0	0
1	1
2	8

(b)

x	y
0	0
1	5
2	10
3	15
4	20

(c)

x	y
−2	−0.5
−1	−1
0	undefined
1	1
2	0.5

Ada King and Babbage's Difference Engine

In the mid-19th century, looms were used to make cloth. The weaving of complicated patterns was controlled by punched cards. Charles Babbage (1792–1871) used this idea to design a calculating machine in which punch cards controlled mathematical operations. He called this machine a difference engine. Because of insufficient interest, Babbage's machine was not built at the time, but a century later, computers were being programmed with punched cards, just as Babbage designed.

Ada Byron King (1815–1852), the Countess of Lovelace, was a brilliant mathematician. She knew Babbage, and documented how his machine would function and solve problems. She was the first person to write what we would call a computer program. The programming language ADA is named for her. Do some research, either at the library or on the Internet, to find out more about how computers were developed and how they are programmed.

2.12 The Equation of the Line of Best Fit

Determining the Equation from a Visual Line of Best Fit

EXPLORATION

This table shows the average salaries of men and women workers in Canada from 1971 to 1996. Colin's assignment is to predict the average earnings for each group in 2010. To do this, he has to create a model that represents the relationship. He graphs the data and places a line of best fit on each set of data.

Year	Average Annual Earnings of Canadians (1976 $)	
	Men	Women
1971	30 013	14 067
1972	31 116	14 348
1973	31 684	14 658
1974	32 415	15 370
1975	33 184	15 956
1976	35 358	16 509
1977	33 547	17 030
1978	33 405	16 971
1979	33 258	17 149
1980	33 299	17 207
1981	32 500	17 431
1982	30 969	17 051
1983	31 160	17 207
1984	30 581	17 596
1985	31 311	17 637
1986	31 746	18 248
1987	32 037	18 523
1988	32 842	18 884
1989	32 913	19 445
1990	32 517	19 459
1991	31 619	19 458
1992	31 516	20 133
1993	30 872	19 865
1994	32 255	20 086
1995	31 527	20 528
1996	32 248	20 902

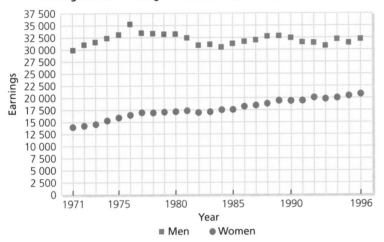

Average Annual Earnings of Canadians (in 1976 $) from 1971 to 1996

■ Men ● Women

Source: Statistics Canada.

Think, Do, Discuss

1. **(a)** Copy this graph. Draw a visual line of best fit for the women's data.
   (b) Find the equation of this line.
   (c) Use the equation to predict the average woman's salary in 2010.

2. Repeat Question 1 for the men's data.

3. Discuss which line will give the more accurate prediction.

Finding the Line of Best Fit 2.13

Using a Graphing Calculator

TECHNOLOGY

Colin uses a graphing calculator to find an exact equation for the data in Section 2.12. He enters the data into the calculator, then uses the calculator's **linear regression** function. (Read your calculator's manual to see how to do this.) The calculator calculates the line of best fit and shows the slope and *y*-intercept for the line. It also shows a value, *r*, called the **correlation coefficient**. This tells how well the line fits the data. These calculator screens show Colin's sequence of steps.

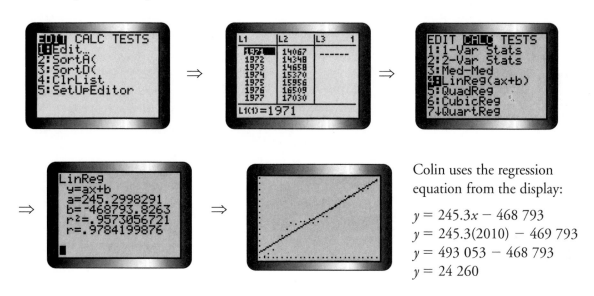

Colin uses the regression equation from the display:

$y = 245.3x - 468\ 793$

$y = 245.3(2010) - 469\ 793$

$y = 493\ 053 - 468\ 793$

$y = 24\ 260$

Colin calculates that in 2010, Canadian women will, on average, earn $24 260 annually.

Think, Do, Discuss

1. Find the equation of the line of best fit for the men's data using graphing technology.
2. Predict the average man's earnings in 2010 using the line from Question 1.
3. (a) Compare the quality of the predictions that were found using the hand-drawn lines to those that were found with graphing technology.
   (b) Discuss the advantages and disadvantages of using graphing technology to find the equation of a line of best fit.
4. For which set of data, men's average earnings or women's average earnings, is the fit of the line to the data better? How do the graph and the correlation coefficient computed by the graphing technology support your conclusion?
5. (a) Make the difference tables for the men's data and the women's data.
   (b) How does the pattern in the differences reflect the fit of the regression line for each set of data?

Focus

Key Ideas

- Graphing technology can be used to compute the equation, called the **linear regression equation**, of a line of best fit.
- When graphing technology is used, it gives the **correlation coefficient**, *r*, for the line. This is a measure of the **goodness of fit** of the line to the data. If the regression line fits the data exactly and has a positive slope, then $r = 1$. If the line fits the data exactly and has a negative slope, then $r = -1$.
- The regression equation can be used to predict values for the relationship represented by the data. Confidence in the quality of the predictions depends on the goodness of fit of the line.
- A table of values represents a relationship for which there is an *approximately linear pattern* if:
  - once the points are plotted, a line of best fit can be drawn through the middle of the cluster of points. Most points will be close to the line of best fit.
  - when a linear regression is carried out using graphing technology, the correlation coefficient is very nearly 1 or -1.
  - the values in the difference column of a difference table made from the data are very close to those expected for an exact linear relation.

Example

Use the linear regression function of a graphing calculator to find the equation of the line of best fit for the data shown in the table. Use the equation to predict the value of *y* when *x* is 55.

x	y
0	7
1	17
2	20
3	25
4	33
5	40
6	50
7	60
8	65
9	72

Solution

Enter the data into the graphing calculator. Use the linear regression function to get the best linear fit to the data.

From the calculator, read the slope and *y*-intercept that the regression function has found. Then write the equation of the line in the form $y = mx + b$. The correlation coefficient tells how close to an exact linear model the representation is. The linear regression function returns this information.

According to the calculator, $a \doteq 7.29$ and $b \doteq 6.09$. So, the equation of the line of best fit is $y = 7.29x + 6.09$. Also, $r = 0.995$, so there is a strong positive correlation.

To predict the value for *y* when $x = 55$, substitute 55 for *x* and evaluate.

$$y = 7.29(55) + 6.09$$
$$y = 400.95 + 6.09$$
$$y = 407.04$$

It can be predicted that when *x* is 55, *y* will be 407.04.

Practise, Apply, Solve

1. Find the equation of the line of best fit using the linear regression function of your spreadsheet or graphing calculator.

(a)
x	y
0	2
1	4
2	3
3	6
4	9
5	11
6	15
7	14
8	12

(b)
x	y
−2	11
−1	5
0	2
1	4
2	11
3	20
4	26
5	30
6	27

(c)
x	y
−9	−10
−8	−8
−7	−6
−6	−4
−5	−2
−4	0
−3	2
−2	4
−1	6

(d)
x	y
1	2
5	8
3	4
6	5
2	0
9	12
4	8
7	10
8	15

2. The following are correlation coefficients produced using linear regression models. Arrange them in order from most confidence to least confidence.

(a) 0.37   (b) 0.89   (c) −0.945   (d) −0.157   (e) 0.985

3. This table gives the winning times in the Olympic men's 400 m freestyle swim, starting with 1960.

Year	Country of Winner	Years after 1960	Time (s)
1960	Australia	0	258.3
1964	United States	4	252.2
1968	United States	8	249.0
1972	United States	12	240.27
1976	United States	16	231.93
1980	Soviet Union	20	231.31
1984	United States	24	231.23
1988	East Germany	28	226.95
1992	Unified Team	32	225.00
1996	New Zealand	36	227.97

(a) Which is the independent variable, years or time?
(b) Find the equation of best fit using the linear regression function on your graphing calculator or software.
(c) Is the line a good representation for this data? Explain.
(d) Use the model to predict the winning time in the 2004 Olympics.

4. This table gives the length of time, in minutes, between eruptions of Old Faithful, a geyser in Yellowstone Park in the United States.

Length of Eruption	3	4.5	4	2.5	3.5	5	2
Time to Next Eruption	68	89	83	62	75	92	57

(a) Graph the data and draw the line of best fit.
(b) Use the linear regression function to find the equation of the line of best fit.
(c) If an eruption lasts 4.75 min, predict the number of minutes until the next eruption.
(d) Will the equation help you to make accurate predictions? Explain.

5. Noreen works for the Ministry of Health. She is measuring the relationship between the amount of physical exercise per week and age. She has collected this data.

Age (years)	20	22	30	30	34	26	26	18	36	36	28	30
Physical Activity (h)	15	11	6	7	6.1	13	8.5	16	3	5.8	11	9

(a) Plot the points on a scatter plot.
(b) Does the data show any correlation between age and the length of time spent exercising per week? If so, what kind of correlation?
(c) Draw the line of best fit.
(d) Use the slope and a point on the line to write an equation for the line of best fit.
(e) Enter the data into a graphing calculator and find the regression line.
(f) Compare your equation with the regression equation. Explain any differences.

6. This table gives the data collected for 19 students. They were surveyed to find out how long they studied for a recent final exam and their score out of 100.
(a) Draw a scatter plot for the data.
(b) Does the scatter plot indicate a positive or negative correlation?
(c) Draw the line of best fit.
(d) Find the slope of the line.
(e) Use the slope and one point on the line to find the equation of the line.
(f) Enter the data on a graphing calculator and find the regression line.
(g) Which equation would be best to make predictions with? Explain.
(h) Predict the score of a student who studied for five hours.

Time Spent Studying (h)	Score (%)
10	100
0	50
1	60
3	70
5	75
4	80
7	95
9	80
9	90

Time Spent Studying (h)	Score (%)
5	85
10	85
4	70
6	85
6	90
9	80
10	95
3	75
2	65
1	45

7. This table shows the mathematics and science marks for 12 students.

Math (%)	38	51	19	53	39	38	66	75	71	35	88	96
Science (%)	50	72	36	64	52	56	80	85	61	40	72	91

   (a) Enter the data into a graphing calculator and find the equation of the regression line.
   (b) How are the marks from the two subjects correlated?
   (c) Predict the science mark of a student who had 85 in math.
   (d) Suppose you know a student's math mark. Could you use the equation you found in (a) to predict the student's English mark? Explain.

8. (a) Think of a survey you could conduct in your class that would show a relationship between two quantities.
   (b) Conduct the survey to collect the data.
   (c) Draw a scatter plot and draw a line of best fit.
   (d) Use a graphing calculator to find the equation of the regression line.
   (e) Use the regression equation to make some predictions. Do the predictions seem reasonable? Explain.

9. The following table gives the height of the women's gold medal high jump at the Olympics since 1976.

Year	1976	1980	1984	1988	1992	1996
Height (m)	1.93	1.97	2.02	2.03	2.02	2.05

Can this data be used to predict the maximum height that female athletes will be able to clear? Explain.

Career: Forensic Medicine

In forensic medicine, doctors can find a person's approximate height from the length of a bone.

For instance, a person's height, H, in centimetres, is related to the length of his or her tibia, t, by one of these formulas.

Female: $H = 2.5t + 74.7$ Male: $H = 2.38t + 78.8$

Work with a partner to test the formulas on yourselves. To find the length of your tibia, sit with both feet flat on the floor and measure the distance between your ankle and the pivot joint of your knee.

Substitute the length into the appropriate formula and calculate the value of H. Compare this value to your actual height.

2.14 Finding the Point of Intersection

Using a Graphing Calculator

Graphing calculators can be used to find the point of intersection of two lines. Both equations must be written in the form $y = mx + b$. To find the point of intersection of $y = x - 3$ and $y = -2x + 3$, enter both equations into the calculator using the Y= key.

```
Y1 = X – 3
Y2 = –2X + 3
```

Draw the graph by pressing the GRAPH key.

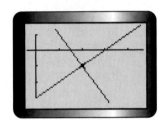

The TRACE feature lets you move along one of the lines to find the point of intersection. To get a more accurate reading, use the ZOOM feature along with the TRACE feature.

The lines intersect. The flashing cursor is very close to $(2, -1)$.

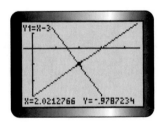

Practise

Use a graphing calculator to find the point of intersection of each pair of lines.

(a) $y = 2x - 7$ and $y = -3x + 3$ **(b)** $y = -x + 7$ and $y = 2x - 5$
(c) $y = -2x + 3$ and $y = 5x + 10$ **(d)** $y = x - 4$ and $y = 2x - 9$

Finding and Interpreting the 2.15 Point of Intersection

Jean is the vice president of the Millennium Wheelchair Co. She needs to know how many wheelchairs the company must sell to earn a profit. This graph shows the revenue and cost relationships for the company.

The **cost** is the amount of money that the company spends to produce its wheelchairs. The **revenue** is the money the company takes in when it sells its wheelchairs.

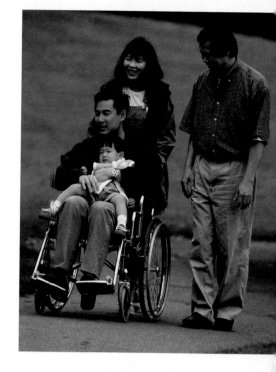

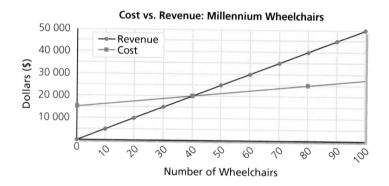

Think, Do, Discuss

1. Find the slope of the cost line and the slope of the revenue line. Explain what the slopes mean in each case.
2. Why do both lines have a positive slope?
3. Explain why the revenue line is steeper than the cost line.
4. Which line is a direct variation and which is a partial variation?
5. Find the y-intercepts of both lines. Explain the meaning of these for each case.
6. Find the equations of each line.
7. Will the company make a profit if it sells

    (a) 200 wheelchairs?   **(b)** 300 wheelchairs?   **(c)** 500 wheelchairs?

8. Find the coordinates of the point where the two lines meet.
9. How many wheelchairs must be sold before the company makes a profit? In business, this point is often called the "break-even point." Explain why.
10. Verify that revenue equals cost at the break-even point. Substitute your answer from Question 8 into the cost and revenue equations, and then compare your answers.

Focus

Key Ideas

- When two lines are graphed on the same set of axes, they may cross each other at some point. This point is called the **point of intersection**.

- This point identifies where the dependent variables are equal in two different relationships.

- If (a, b) is the point of intersection, then when a is substituted for x in the equations, they both produce an answer of b for y. In business, this point is called the **break-even point**.

Example

Find the point of intersection of $y = x - 3$ and $y = -\frac{3}{2}x + 2$.

Solution

Graph both lines on the same set of axes.

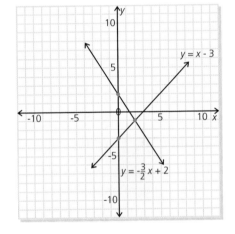

- The y-intercept of $y = x - 3$ is -3. Its slope is 1. Plot the y-intercept, $(0, -3)$. Then move 1 unit to the right and 1 unit up to find a second point, $(1, -2)$. Join these points with a straight line.

- The y-intercept of $y = -\frac{3}{2}x + 2$ is 2. Its slope is $-\frac{3}{2}$. Plot the y-intercept, $(0, 2)$. Then move 2 units to the right and 3 units down to find a second point, $(2, -1)$. Join these points with a straight line.

Carefully examine the graph to find the coordinates of the point of intersection of the two lines. In this case, it is $(2, -1)$.

Check in both equations.

$y = x - 3$			$y = -\frac{3}{2}x + 2$	
left side	right side		left side	right side
-1	$2 - 3$		-1	$-\frac{3}{2}(2) + 2$
-1	-1		-1	-1

Practise, Apply, Solve ─────────

1. Determine the point of intersection of these lines.

(a) $y = \frac{1}{2}x + 1$, $y = -x + 4$

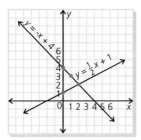

(b) $y = 3$, $y = 2x - 1$

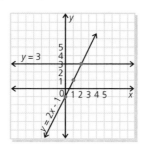

(c) $y = -\frac{3}{4}x + 1$, $y = x$

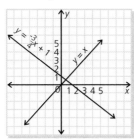

2. (a) How many points of intersection are possible for two different lines?
(b) When will two lines not have a point of intersection?

3. Compare the slopes of each pair of lines. Do they intersect?

(a) $y = 3x - 1$, $y = 2x + 2$ **(b)** $y = 4x + 5$, $y = \frac{1}{4}x - 1$

(c) $y = \frac{1}{2}x - 5$, $y = \frac{1}{2}x + 3$ **(d)** $y = 3x - 7$, $y = 3x + 9$

4. Does each pair of lines intersect at the given point?

(a) (2, 3): $y = x + 1$, $y = 4x - 5$ **(b)** (1, −1): $y = 5x - 4$, $y = 2x - 3$

(c) (0, 2): $y = 3x + 2$, $y = 5x - 1$ **(d)** (6, 2): $y = x - 4$, $y = 2$

(e) (−5, 0): $y = x + 5$, $y = -2x - 10$ **(f)** (−1, −3): $y = 4x + 1$, $y = x - 5$

B

5. Find the point of intersection for each pair of lines.

(a) $y = 4x - 1$, $y = 3x + 4$ **(b)** $y = -x + 8$, $y = 2x - 7$

(c) $y = 3x + 9$, $y = 3x - 1$ **(d)** $y = 3x + 6$, $y = 5x - 4$

(e) $y = x$, $y = -x$ **(f)** $y = 4x + 6$, $y = -x + 1$

(g) $y = 2x - 7$, $y = 6x - 19$ **(h)** $y = 2$, $y = 5$

2.15 FINDING AND INTERPRETING THE POINT OF INTERSECTION **157**

6. Movies To Go rents videos for $2.50 each and has no membership fee. Videorenters rents videos for $2 each but has a $10 membership fee.
  (a) Write an equation for each situation.
  (b) Graph both equations on the same set of axes. Find the point of intersection.
  (c) What does the point of intersection mean in this case?
  (d) What advice would you give to someone who is deciding which video store to use?

7. Ontario Express charges $5 plus $1/kg to send a package out of the province. Day by Day Delivery charges $3.50 plus $1.25/kg.
  (a) Write equations to model this situation.
  (b) Graph both equations on the same set of axes.
  (c) What does the point of intersection mean in this situation?
  (d) When is Ontario Express less expensive than Day by Day Delivery? more expensive?

8. This table shows the winning times for the men's and women's 100 m Olympic sprint.

Year	Men (s)	Women (s)	Year	Men (s)	Women (s)	Year	Men (s)	Women (s)
1896	12.0	———	1928	10.8	12.2	1968	9.95	11.0
1900	11.0	———	1932	10.3	11.9	1972	10.14	11.07
1904	11.0	———	1936	10.3	11.5	1976	10.06	11.08
1906	11.2	———	1948	10.3	11.9	1980	10.25	11.06
1908	10.8	———	1952	10.4	11.5	1984	9.99	10.97
1912	10.8	———	1956	10.5	11.5	1988	9.92	10.54
1920	10.8	———	1960	10.2	11.0	1992	9.96	10.82
1924	10.6	———	1964	10.0	11.4	1996	9.84	10.94

  (a) For each group of data, make a scatter plot using the same set of axes. Use different colours to plot the points for the men's data and the women's data.
  (b) Draw a line of best fit for each situation.
  (c) Find the point of intersection of the two lines. You will have to extend your graph.
  (d) What does the point of intersection mean in this situation?

9. Bill wants to earn extra money selling lemonade in front of his house. It costs $1.20 to start his business and each cup of lemonade costs 6¢ to make. He plans to sell the lemonade for 10¢ a cup.
  (a) Find an equation that represents his costs.
  (b) Find an equation that represents his revenue.
  (c) Graph both equations on the same set of axis.
  (d) What does the point of intersection mean in this case?
  (e) Does Bill make a profit or lose money for
    i. 20 cups sold?   **ii.** 35 cups sold?   **iii.** 50 cups sold?

10. Refer to Question 9. Suppose the cost of making lemonade increases to 10¢ per cup.
  (a) Can Bill still make a profit if he does not increase his selling price? Explain.
  (b) How will this change your original graph?
  (c) What should Bill charge to maintain the same break-even point?

C

11. A car rental agency offers two daily rental plans:
  Plan A: $40 per day with unlimited mileage
  Plan B: $30 per day plus 10¢/km
  (a) What is the break-even point for Plan A and Plan B?
  (b) When is Plan A the better deal?
  (c) When is Plan B the better deal?

12. Find the point of intersection of $3x + 2y = 56$ and $y = x + 6$.

13. Graph $4x + y = -2$ and $8x + 2y = -4$ on the same set of axes.
  (a) What is the slope of each line?
  (b) What is the y-intercept of each line?
  (c) What is the point of intersection of the two lines?

14. Find the point of intersection of each pair of lines.
  (a) $4x - 5y = 9$ and $y = 2x - 2$ **(b)** $y = -3x + 1$ and $x - y = 0$
  (c) $5x + 8y = 12$ and $y = -\frac{5}{8}x + \frac{3}{2}$

The Chapter Problem — Which Rate Is Better?

Refer back to the Chapter Problem at the beginning of this chapter.

1. Determine the point of intersection between the two pricing options.
2. What does the point of intersection mean in this problem?
3. Describe the conditions that must exist that would make one pricing option better than the other.

Career: Traffic Controller

Traffic jams, streets snarled with cars, clogged intersections — city driving is rarely the time-saver it used to be. Surveys show that the average speed of cars in cities is actually slower than the horse-drawn vehicles of a century ago.

To combat modern traffic problems, cities employ traffic controllers who time traffic lights as part of their responsibilities. Maintaining a smooth flow of traffic often presents a complex problem involving logical analysis as well as the help of computers.

To determine the length of time a traffic light should remain green, traffic controllers sometimes use Greenshield's formula: $t = 2.1n + 3.7$

where t is the time in seconds a light should remain green and n is the average number of cars per lane that move through the light. If a light stays green for 31 s, how many cars in one lane should pass through it?

2.16 Collecting Data about Motion

Using Digital Probes

How are speed and direction related to the graph of an object's motion?

The following experiment will use the motion detector and CBL to record data associated with the movement of a person walking. Use the HIKER program to collect and graph the data.

After you complete the investigations that follow, summarize the relationships between the appearance of the graph and the pace and direction of the walker.

Set-Up and Operation of the CBL Unit

1. Make sure that the CBL and calculator are both OFF.

2. Connect the CBL to the calculator using the unit-to-unit connector cable. Connect the cable firmly to the INPUT/OUTPUT (I/O) port on the bottom of the calculator (see diagram).

3. Connect the motion detector to the SONIC port on the CBL. This port is on the left side of the unit.

4. Turn the CBL unit and the calculator ON.

5. Place the motion detector on a desk or chair. Place it so that it can detect the motion of a student walking directly toward or away from the detector.

6. Start the HIKER program on the calculator. The program should pause and display a message "PRESS ENTER TO START GRAPH." When the walker is ready, press ENTER . Have the walker start walking as soon as the motion detector starts making a clicking sound.

Analyzing Collected Data

The unit collects the data and sends it to the calculator, where it is stored as a list in **L1**. The HIKER program plots a distance-time graph. When a reasonable graph has been completed, the coordinates of data points can be read using the TRACE feature of the calculator or any of the calculator's statistical functions.

As well, the LinReg function can be used to find a regression line.

Practise

1. Have the walker walk in such a manner that the graph produced is
   (a) a straight line with a positive slope.
   (b) a straight line with a negative slope.
   (c) a horizontal line.
   (d) a curve that slopes up in a straight line and then down in a straight line.

2. Describe how the walker must have travelled for each of the three segments in this diagram.

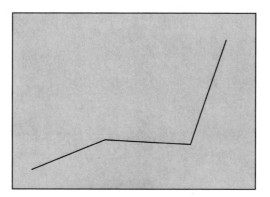

3. Use the TRACE feature to find the coordinates of two points on each graph in parts (a) to (c) above. Use these to find the average speed the walker was walking as the graph was drawn.

4. Use the CBL unit with batteries. Have a student face a wall and hold the calculator and point the CBL straight ahead. Then have the student walk towards the wall or backwards away from it. Try to follow a path that causes the calculator to reproduce the graphs described in Question 1.

Did You Know?

On December 4, 1996, NASA launched the Mars Pathfinder spacecraft. In July 1998, it landed on Mars. In this craft was the first robotic roving vehicle to be sent to another planet. This vehicle, called Sojourner, is about 11 kg and the size of a child's small wagon. Millions of kilometres away, scientists on Earth were able to send signals to Sojourner and drive it over the Martian surface.

Sojourner was designed to perform various experiments, including:
- analyzing soil for density and compactness
- sensing the temperature during the day and the night
- determining the composition of rocks and other surface material
- taking images of the Martian terrain and constructing a map of the landing sight.

Use the Internet or your library to find out more about this probe. What other experiments did it perform? Why are probes like Sojourner useful in space exploration? What other probes have been used to explore outer space?

2.1–2.2 Tables of Values, Patterns, and Graphs ———

- When two quantities are related in some way, they form a **relationship**.
- Values that can change in a relationship are called **variables**.
- In a relationship, the variable that depends on the other variable is the **dependent variable**.
- The variable that does not depend on the other is the **independent variable**.
- In a table of values, the independent variable is placed in the left-hand column and the dependent variable in the right-hand column.
- In a graph, the dependent variable is placed on the vertical axis and the independent variable on the horizontal axis.
- When the graph of a relation is a straight line, the relationship is called **linear**.

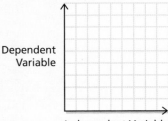

Example

A rental car costs $45/day plus $0.15 for each kilometre it is driven. Create a table of values and draw a graph to see if this relationship is linear.

Solution

The cost of the rental depends on how many kilometres are driven. Cost must be the dependent variable and number of kilometres is the independent variable.

It costs $45 to rent the car. Each kilometre costs an additional $0.15. This amount is added to the $45 rental fee.

Kilometres	Cost ($)
0	45 + 0.15(0) = 45.00
10	45 + 0.15(10) = 46.50
20	45 + 0.15(20) = 48.00
30	45 + 0.15(30) = 49.50
40	45 + 0.15(40) = 51.00
50	45 + 0.15(50) = 52.50

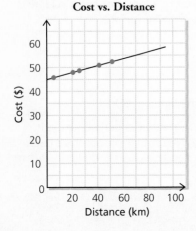

Cost is the dependent variable, so it is plotted on the vertical axis. The number of kilometres is the independent variable, so it is plotted on the horizontal axis. The points that are plotted line up in a straight line. In this case, the relationship between cost and kilometres is linear.

Extra Practice

1. A professional athlete agrees to play for a sports team for $4 million per year and a signing bonus of $6 million.

   (a) Make a table of values of the athlete's earnings. Have one row for each year up to five years.

   (b) Graph the athlete's earnings for playing for five years.

   (c) What patterns do you see in the table and the graph?

2. There is $500 in Lita's bank account. She puts $250 in her account every month.

   (a) Make a table of values of Lita's account. Have one row for each month up to five months.

   (b) Graph Lita's account balance for five months.

   (c) What patterns do you see in the table and the graph?

2.3–2.4 Connecting Equations and Graphs

- A graph can be created by hand from a table of values; with computer spreadsheets or graphing software; or with a graphing calculator.

- To graph a relationship using technology, it must first be written as an algebraic equation. By tradition, x represents the independent variable and y represents the dependent variable.

- On a linear graph a **rate triangle** can be drawn between any two points. The shape of the rate triangle shows how steep the line is.

- A **direct variation** has an equation of the form $y = mx$. The graph of a direct variation crosses the y-axis at $y = 0$.

- A **partial variation** has an equation of the form $y = mx + b$. The graph of a partial variation does not cross the y-axis at $y = 0$, but at some other value, namely b.

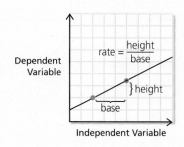

Example

Abdhul sells cars and is paid by commission. He earns a weekly salary of $500 and 2% commission on each car sold. Find the algebraic expression that represents this relationship and graph it using a spreadsheet.

Solution

Abdhul's earnings depend on the value of the cars he sells. His commission is 2% of his weekly sales. The word equation that represents this relationship is:

$$\text{Earnings} = 500 + 2\% \times \text{Weekly Sales}$$

If E represents earnings and W the value of his weekly sales, then an algebraic equation for this relationship is:

$$E = 500 + 0.02W$$

To use the graphing feature of a spreadsheet, first create a table of values.

Spreadsheet with formula entered

	A	B
1	Weekly Sales (W)	Earnings (E)
2	0	=500+0.02*A2
3	20 000	↓
4	30 000	↓
5	40 000	↓
6	50 000	↓
7	60 000	↓

$\Rightarrow$

Spreadsheet with Fill Down command used

	A	B
1	Weekly Sales (W)	Earnings (E)
2	0	500
3	20 000	900
4	30 000	1100
5	40 000	1300
6	50 000	1500
7	60 000	1700

Once the values are entered, the graphing feature of the spreadsheet can be used to draw the graph.

Earnings vs. Weekly Sales

Extra Practice

3. A professional athlete agrees to play for a sports team for $4 million per year and a signing bonus of $6 million.
   (a) Write the word and algebraic equations for this relation.
   (b) Write the equations for graphing this situation with a calculator and with software. Which variable is represented by x? by y? Explain.
   (c) Make the spreadsheet for the first ten rows of a table of values for this relation. Show the cell formulas.
   (d) Is this relation a direct variation or a partial variation? Explain.
   (e) Use a rate triangle to explain how the patterns in the table of values are represented in the graph.

4. There is $500 in Lita's bank account. She puts $250 in her account every month.
   (a) Write the word and algebraic equations for this relation.
   (b) Write the equations for graphing this situation with a calculator and with software. Which variable is represented by x? by y? Explain.
   (c) Make the spreadsheet for the first ten rows of a table of values for this relation. Show the cell formulas.
   (d) Is this relation a direct variation or a partial variation? Explain.
   (e) Use a rate triangle to explain how the patterns in the table of values are represented in the graph.

2.5–2.6 Graphing in Four Quadrants

- The coordinate grid is often called the Cartesian plane.
- The axes divide the plane into four **quadrants.**
- The point where the axes intersect is called the **origin**.
- The horizontal axis is called the x-axis.
- The vertical axis is called the y-axis.
- The ordered pair of numbers that identifies any point is (x, y). The x-value of a point is the x-coordinate and is always written first. The y-value is the y-coordinate and is always written second.
- The coordinates of the origin are $(0, 0)$.
- A dot is used to represent a point on the graph. A capital letter is used to name the points.

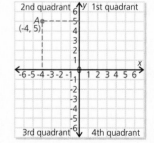

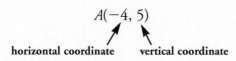

Example

Graph the relationship defined by $y = 5x + 3$.

Solution

Create a table of values. Choose small integers for x.

x	y
−2	
−1	
0	
1	
2	

Substitute each number for x into the equation and evaluate to find y.

x	y
−2	$5(-2) + 3 = -7$
−1	$5(-1) + 3 = -2$
0	3
1	8
2	13

Plot the points.

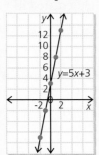

The points are in a straight line, so we join them and label the line with its equation.

Extra Practice

5. The coordinates of three vertices of a square are $A(-6, 3)$, $B(1, 3)$, and $C(1, -4)$. Find the coordinates of the other vertex, D.

6. **(a)** Copy and complete the table of values for the relation $y = 5x - 5$.

x	1	2	3	4	5	6	7
y							

(b) Plot the ordered pairs on the Cartesian plane.

(c) Extend the graph for negative values of *x*.

(d) Name the coordinates of three points in the 3rd quadrant.

(e) Name the coordinates of one point in the 4th quadrant.

(f) Name the coordinates of one point in the 2nd quadrant.

7. For each relationship, construct a table of values and draw the graph. Use $-2, -1, 0, 1$, and 2 for the *x*-coordinates.

(a) $y = 3x + 5$ (b) $y = 2x - 6$ (c) $y = -4x - 3$ (d) $y = 7x + 3$

(e) $y = -x - 2$ (f) $y = -2x + 1$ (g) $y = \frac{1}{2}x - 4$ (h) $y = \frac{1}{4}x + 1$

2.7–2.8 The Roles of Slope and Intercepts

- The slope of a line, **m**, is a measure of how steep the line is.
  - The greater the magnitude of *m*, the steeper the line.
  - A line with a positive slope rises to the right. A line with a negative slope falls to the right.
  - The value of its slope affects the tilt of a line. The farther the slope is from 0, the steeper the line.
  - Slope is the **rate of change** of a linear relation.

- The **intercepts** of a line occur at the points where the line crosses the axes. The intercept is the distance from the origin to this point.
  - The **x-intercept** is the point where the line crosses the *x*-axis. Its *y*-coordinate is 0.
  - The **y-intercept** is the point where the line crosses the *y*-axis. Its *x*-coordinate is 0.

- When the equation of a line is $y = mx + b$, the coordinates of its *y*-intercept are $(0, b)$.

Example

Anthony works for Vision Video. He earns an hourly rate and receives a fixed amount each week to cover his expenses. This table shows his earnings for various hours worked. Find an equation for this relationship.

Hours Worked	20	25	30	40	50
Weekly Earnings ($)	390	450	510	630	750

Solution

A graph can be drawn by first plotting the points.

Earnings vs. Hours Worked

For every 5 h that Anthony works, his earnings increase by $60. That is, for every 5 h change in his hours worked, there is a $60 change in his earnings. To find his rate of earnings for each hour, divide $60 by 5 h.

$$\$60 \div 5 \text{ h} = \$12/\text{h}$$

This is the slope of the line. The line crosses the y-axis at point (0, 150). The **y-intercept** of the line is 150. This represents the weekly expense fee. The graph is linear and the equation must be in the form $y = mx + b$.

The equation of this relation is $y = 12x + 150$, where y is the earnings and x is the hours worked.

Extra Practice

8. Identify the y-intercept and the slope.
  (a) $y = -3x + 13$ **(b)** $y = 11x + 15$
  (c) $y = -20 + 2x$ **(d)** $-18x + 1 = y$

9. A transport truck is expected to decrease in value according to the equation $y = -5500x + 125\ 000$, where y is the value of the truck after x years.
  (a) Find the slope of the line and interpret its meaning.
  (b) Find the y-intercept and interpret its meaning.

10. Graph each relation, using only the slope and y-intercept.
  (a) $y = 2x - 4$ **(b)** $y = -3x + 2$ **(c)** $y = \frac{3}{4}x - 3$ **(d)** $4x - 6 = y$

11. Ethel is a junior programmer for the EDUCAT software company. She earns an hourly rate and receives a weekly amount to cover her expenses. This table shows her earnings for various hours worked.

Hours Worked	20	25	30	35	40
Earnings ($)	700	825	950	1075	1200

  (a) Find an equation for this relationship.
  (b) Find Ethel's earnings if she works 32 h, 45 h, and 53 h.

2.9 Finding the Equation of a Given Line

- In equations, the Greek letter Δ (delta) is used to represent the change in a variable. So, the change in y is written Δy and the change in x is written Δx.

- As a result, there are several ways to write the slope:

$$m = \text{slope}$$

$$= \frac{\text{rise}}{\text{run}}$$

$$= \frac{\text{difference of } y\text{-coordinates}}{\text{difference of } x\text{-coordinates}}$$

$$= \frac{\Delta y}{\Delta x}$$

- If $A(x_1, y_1)$ and $B(x_2, y_2)$ are two points on line AB, then the slope of AB is:

$$m_{AB} = \frac{y_2 - y_1}{x_2 - x_1}$$

- To find the equation of a line when two points on the line are known:

1. Find the slope, $m = \frac{y_2 - y_1}{x_2 - x_1}$.

2. Find the y-intercept by substituting the coordinates from a point on the line and the slope into $y = mx + b$ and solve for b.

3. Write the equation, using the values for m and b found above.

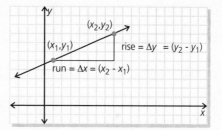

Example

Find the equation of the line that has a slope of 6 and passes through $A(1, 3)$.

Solution

Since we are dealing with a straight line, its equation is of the form $y = mx + b$. In this case the slope is 6, so it is of the form $y = 6x + b$. To find the value of b, substitute the coordinates of point A for x and y.

$$y = 6x + b$$

$$3 = 6(1) + b$$

$$3 = 6 + b \qquad \text{Solve for } b.$$

$$3 = 6 + (-3)$$

$$\therefore b = -3$$

Write the final equation: $y = 6x - 3$.

Extra Practice

12. For each situation, write an equation of the line in the form $y = mx + b$.

   (a) The slope is 5 and the y-intercept is 4.

   (b) The slope is $\frac{3}{2}$ and point $(-2, 1)$ is on the line.

   (c) The slope is $-\frac{1}{2}$ and point $(-6, 5)$ is on the line.

   (d) The slope is -3 and point $(0, 5)$ is on the line.

   (e) The x- and y-intercepts are 4 and 3, respectively.

13. Find the slope of the line that passes through each pair of points. Then find the equation of the line.

   (a) $(1, 4)$ and $(2, 7)$ **(b)** $(0, 1)$ and $(-1, 0)$

   (c) $(-2, 4)$ and $(3, -6)$ **(d)** $(-2, -3)$ and $(1, 9)$

14. Pizzazz Pizza charges a flat amount for a 40-cm pizza with tomato sauce, with an added cost for each topping. A 40-cm pizza with one topping costs $9.25, while a 40-cm pizza with four toppings costs $10.75.

   (a) Find the cost of each additional topping.

   (b) Find the cost of a pizza with no additional toppings.

   (c) Write an equation for the cost of the pizza in the form $y = mx + b$.

   (d) Find the cost of a pizza with five toppings.

2.10 Slopes and Equations of Lines: Special Cases

- Horizontal lines have no x-intercept, are parallel to the x-axis, and have a slope of zero. If $(0, a)$ is the y-intercept of a horizontal line, then the equation of the line is $y = a$.

- Vertical lines have no y-intercept, are parallel to the y-axis, and have an undefined slope. If $(b, 0)$ is the x-intercept of a vertical line, then the equation of the line is $x = b$.

- Parallel lines are lines that are always the same distance apart. Parallel lines have the same slope.

- Perpendicular lines intersect each other at 90° angles. Perpendicular lines have slopes that are **negative reciprocals** of each other. That is, if a line has a slope of $\frac{a}{b}$, then a line perpendicular to it has a slope of $-\frac{b}{a}$.

Example

Find the equation of a line that is parallel to $y = \frac{3}{5}x - 6$ and passes through point $(2, 2)$.

Solution

The line $y = \frac{3}{5}x - 6$ has a slope of $\frac{3}{5}$. A line that is parallel to it also has a

slope of $\frac{3}{5}$. The equation of the new line is of the form $y = \frac{3}{5}x + b$.

To find b, substitute $(2, 2)$ for x and y, and then solve for b.

$$y = \frac{3}{5}x + b$$
$$2 = \frac{3}{5}(2) + b$$
$$2 = \frac{10}{5}$$
$$\frac{10}{5} = \frac{6}{5} + \frac{4}{5}$$
$$\therefore b = \frac{4}{5}$$

The equation of the line is $y = \frac{3}{5}x + \frac{4}{5}$.

Extra Practice

15. Graph, either by hand or with a graphing calculator.
  (a) $x = 2$ **(b)** $y = 5$ **(c)** $x = -3$
  (d) $y = 1$ **(e)** $y = 0$ **(f)** $x = -4$

16. (a) What is the slope of a horizontal line?
  (b) What is the slope of a vertical line?
  (c) What is the relationship between the slopes of two parallel lines?
  (d) What is the relationship between the slopes of two perpendicular lines?

17. Write an equation for a line that is:
  (a) parallel to $y = -5x + 1$ and passes through point $(-2, -1)$.
  (b) perpendicular to $4x + 2 = y$ and has a y-intercept of 5.
  (c) parallel to $y = \frac{3}{4}x - 2$ and passes through point $(8, 4)$.
  (d) parallel to $2x - 3 = y$ and passes through point $(0, -3)$.
  (e) perpendicular to $y = 2x + 1$ and has the same y-intercept as $y = 6x - 2$.

2.11 Conditions for Linear Relationships

- When the values of the independent variable increase by 1 throughout a table of values, the differences between successive y-values form a set of **finite differences**.

- When these differences are used to form the dependent variable column of a table of values, the resulting table is called a **difference table**.

- A table of values represents a **linear relationship** if:
  - a single straight line can be drawn through every data point;
  - the finite differences are the same for every row in the difference table; and
  - for all pairs of points in the table, the ratio formed from the differences between the y-values and corresponding differences between the x-values is the same. (This ratio is the slope of the line.)

- A table of values represents a **nonlinear relationship** if:
  - a single smooth curve can be drawn through every point; and
  - the finite differences are not the same for every row in the difference table.

- A table of values represents a **weak relationship** if the data has no obvious pattern, either in the table of values or on the plot of the data points.

Example

What type of relationship does the data in this table represent?

x	8	3	5	9	7	6	4
y	64	9	25	81	49	36	16

Solution

First, arrange the data in an orderly form. Create the differences table so that the values for the independent variable, x, are in order from smallest to largest.

Look for a pattern by finding the finite differences. For each change of 1 in the x-column, there is a different change in the y-column. The finite differences are not the same in each row, but there is a pattern. This relationship is nonlinear.

x	y	Δx	Δy
3	9		
		4 − 3 = 1	16 − 9 = 7
4	16		
		5 − 4 = 1	25 − 16 = 9
5	25		
		6 − 5 = 1	36 − 25 = 11
6	36		
		7 − 6 = 1	49 − 36 = 13
7	49		
		8 − 7 = 1	64 − 49 = 15
8	64		
		9 − 8 = 1	81 − 64 = 17
9	81		

Extra Practice

18. Create the difference table for each table of values. Does the data represent a linear or nonlinear relationship?

(a)
x	y
1	6
2	10
3	14
4	18
5	22

(b)
x	y
1	3
2	6
3	11
4	18
5	27

(c)
x	y
3	12
4	16
2	8
1	4
5	20

(d)
x	y
1	3
2	9
3	27
4	81
5	243

19. A bacteria culture grows in a laboratory dish. The table shows the number of bacteria in the dish at various time intervals.

Time (h)	0	1	2	3	4	5
Number of Bacteria	4	16	64	256	1024	4096

(a) Is this relationship linear or nonlinear?
(b) Graph the data.
(c) How many bacteria would be in the dish after 90 min?
(d) When does the population reach 10 000?

20. The table shows the value *y*, in dollars, of a rare coin that is *x* years old.

x	0	10	20	30
y	0.25	750.25	1500.25	2250.25

(a) Is this relationship linear or nonlinear?
(b) Graph the data.
(c) Find the equation of this relationship.
(d) Use the equation to find the value of the coin after 15 years.

2.12–2.13 Finding the Line of Best Fit Using a Graphing Calculator

- Graphing technology can be used to compute a line of best fit for data that is called the **linear regression equation**.

- When graphing technology is used, it gives the **correlation coefficient**, *r*, for the line. This is a measure of the **goodness of fit** of the line to the data. If the regression line fits the data exactly and has a positive slope, then $r = 1$. If the line fits the data exactly and has a negative slope, then $r = -1$.

- The regression equation can be used to predict values for the relation represented by the data. Confidence in the quality of the predictions depends on the goodness of fit of the line to the data.

- A table of values represents a relationship for which there is an *approximately linear pattern* if:
  - once the points are plotted, a line of best fit can be drawn through the middle of the cluster of points. Most points will be close to the line of best fit.
  - when a linear regression is carried out using graphing technology, the correlation coefficient is very nearly 1 or -1.
  - the values in the difference column in a difference table made from the data are very close to those expected for an exact linear relation.

Example

Use a graphing calculator and the linear regression function to find the equation of the line of best fit for the data shown.

x	y
0	5
1	12
2	17
3	25
4	33
5	36
6	48
7	51
8	61
9	65

Solution

Enter the data into the graphing calculator. Use the linear regression function to get the best linear fit to the data.

From the calculator, read the slope and y-intercept that the regression function has found. Then write the equation of the line in the form $y = mx + b$. The correlation coefficient tells you how close to an exact linear model your representation is.

In this case, the linear regression function returns this information.

According to the calculator, $a = 6.818$ and $b = 4.618$. So, the equation of the line of best fit is $y = 6.818x + 4.618$. Also, r is very close to 1, so there is a strong positive correlation.

Extra Practice

21. Use the linear regression function of your spreadsheet or graphing calculator to find the equation of the line of best fit.

x	12	10	7	4	0	−3	−5	−6	−9	−12
y	3	5	9	10	15	18	17	21	30	28

22. When students in a chemistry lab mixed acetone and chloroform, the mixture became hot. As time passed, the mixture cooled down. They collected this data.

Time (s)	30	60	90	120	150	180	210	240	270	300
Temperature (°C)	29.6	29.9	29.5	29.2	29.4	29.1	28.7	28.6	28.5	28.3

(a) Plot the points on a scatter plot.
(b) Is there a correlation between temperature and time? If so, what kind of correlation?
(c) Draw the line of best fit.
(d) Use the slope and a point on the line to write an equation for the line of best fit.
(e) Enter the data into a graphing calculator and find the regression line.
(f) Compare your equation with the regression equation. Explain any differences.

2.14–2.15 Finding and Interpreting the Point of Intersection

- When two lines are graphed on the same set of axes, they may cross at some point, which is called the **point of intersection**.
- This point identifies where the dependent variables are equal in two different relationships.
- If (a, b) is the point of intersection, then when a is substituted for x in the equations, they both produce an answer of b for y. In business, this point is called the **break-even point**.

Example

Find the point of intersection of $y = -2x + 3$ and $y = -\frac{3}{2}x + 3$.

Solution

Graph both lines on the same set of axes.

- The y-intercept of $y = -2x + 3$ is 3. Its slope is -2. Plot the y-intercept, $(0, 3)$. Then move 1 unit to the right and 2 units down to find a second point, $(1, 1)$. Join these points with a straight line.
- The y-intercept of $y = -\frac{3}{2}x + 3$ is 3. Its slope is $-\frac{3}{2}$. Plot the y-intercept, $(0, 3)$. Then move 2 units to the right and 3 units down to find a second point, $(2, 0)$. Join these points with a straight line.

Carefully examine the graph to find the coordinates of the point of intersection of the two lines. In this case, it is (0, 3).

Check (0, 3) in both equations.

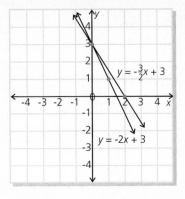

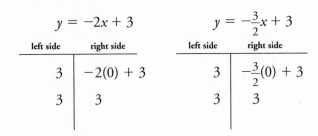

$y = -2x + 3$

left side	right side
3	$-2(0) + 3$
3	3

$y = -\frac{3}{2}x + 3$

left side	right side
3	$-\frac{3}{2}(0) + 3$
3	3

Extra Practice

23. Find the point of intersection for each pair of lines.

(a) $x + y = 4$, $x - 2y = 1$

(b) $x + 2y = 0$, $x - y = 3$

(c) $2x + y = 1$, $x + y = 2$

(d) $6x = 12 - 3y$, $\frac{1}{2}y - x = -5$

(e) $\frac{1}{2}x - y = 8$, $x + \frac{1}{3}y = 2$

(f) $5 + y = 4x$, $x + 2 = \frac{2}{3}y$

24. Faster Fitness has a yearly membership fee of $90, but it costs members only $5 to take an instruction class. At Drop-In Fitness, there is no membership fee, but clients pay $35 per instruction class.

(a) Write an equation for each situation.

(b) Graph both equations on the same set of axes. Find the point of intersection.

(c) What does the point of intersection mean in this case?

(d) What would you advise someone who is trying to choose between the two fitness clubs?

Chapter Summary

In this chapter, you have seen how a linear relationship between two variables can be modelled with a graph or an algebraic equation. You have also seen that the graph or the equation can be used to predict the value of one variable if the value of the other is known. Linear relationships can be graphed by a variety of methods, including by hand, with a graphing calculator, a computer spreadsheet, or other software. Algebraic equations can be represented in different forms, including the slope–y-intercept form ($y = mx + b$) and the standard form ($Ax + By + C = 0$).

Tables of finite differences can be used to determine whether a relationship is linear or not. A line of best fit can be applied to a scatter plot of data to identify trends in the data and make predictions. The equation of a line of best fit or any line can be found if you know: the slope and y-intercept; any two points on the line; or the slope and any point on the line.

1. An experiment showed how much an elastic band stretched when various masses were hung from it. The results are recorded in the table.

Mass (g)	5	10	15	20	25	30
Stretch (cm)	1	2	3	4	5	6

(a) Which quantity is the independent variable and which is the dependent variable?
(b) Plot the ordered pairs on a graph.
(c) Is this relationship linear or nonlinear?
(d) Is this an example of a direct or partial variation?
(e) Estimate how far the elastic will stretch if these masses are attached: 12 g, 40 g, and 45 g.
(f) Estimate the mass attached if the elastic band stretched 3.5 cm, 5.5 cm, and 7.8 cm.
(g) Find the slope and the y-intercept of this line and interpret their meaning in this situation.
(h) Find the equation of this line.

2. A line passes through the points $A(1, -3)$ and $B(3, 5)$. Find:
(a) the slope of the line;
(b) the equation of the line in the form $y = mx + b$;
(c) the slope of a line parallel to AB; and
(d) the slope of a line perpendicular to AB.

3. Manatees are large, gentle sea creatures that live along the Florida coast. The manatee is in danger of extinction. Powerboats have contributed to the demise of the manatee. Environmentalists have collected this data over a 16-year period to see if there is a relationship between the number of registered powerboats and the number of manatees killed each year.

Boats (thousands)	Manatees Killed	Boats (thousands)	Manatees Killed
447	13	585	33
460	21	614	33
481	24	645	39
498	16	675	43
512	24	711	50
513	20	719	47
526	15	727	54
559	34	730	51

(a) Construct a scatter plot and find the line of best fit.
(b) What type of correlation exists in this data? Can the environmentalists claim that powerboats are killing the manatee population?

Chapter Review Test

(c) Find the slope and y-intercept of this line. What do they mean in this situation?

(d) Enter the data into a graphing calculator and find the equation of the linear regression line.

(e) Use the regression equation to predict the number of manatees killed when the number of registered boats reaches 1 000 000.

4. Graph each relation.
   (a) $x = 5$ (b) $y = -2$ (c) $y = \frac{3}{4}x - 2$ (d) $y = -5x - 4$

5. Find the equation of the line that:
   (a) is parallel to the x-axis and passes through point (2, 1).
   (b) has a slope of –2 and passes through point (3, 5).
   (c) has an x-intercept of 2 and a y-intercept of 5.
   (d) has a slope of $\frac{1}{2}$ and the same y-intercept as $y = 2x + 4$.

6. A line passes through $C(4, -5)$ and $D(-2, 2)$. Find:
   (a) the slope of the line.
   (b) the y-intercept of the line.
   (c) the equation of the line in the form $y = mx + b$.
   (d) the x-intercept of the line that is parallel to CD and passes through point (0, 7).
   (e) the y-intercept of the line that is perpendicular to CD and passes through point (7, 6).
   (f) the slope of a line perpendicular to CD.

7. Use the data in the table to answer each question.

Distance (m)	0	4	8	12	16	20	24
Time (s)	0	1	2	3	4	5	6

   (a) Which quantity is the independent variable? the dependent variable?
   (b) Plot the ordered pairs on a graph.
   (c) Is this relationship linear or nonlinear?
   (d) Is this an example of a direct or partial variation?
   (e) Estimate the distance travelled in 2.5 s, 6.25 s, and 8 s.
   (f) Estimate the time taken to travel 3 m, 21 m, and 36 m.
   (g) Find the slope and the y-intercept of this line and interpret their meaning in this situation.
   (h) Find the equation of this line.

8. Find the equation of the line that:
   (a) is perpendicular to the y-axis and has the same y-intercept as $y = -31x - 41$.
   (b) has a slope of $-\frac{2}{3}$ and an x-intercept that is the same as its y-intercept.
   (c) is parallel to $y = 3x + 17$ and has an x-intercept of -2.
   (d) has an x-intercept of -4 and a y-intercept of 3.

Chapter 3

Analyzing and Modelling Nonlinear Situations

In earlier chapters, you saw that some relationships are linear. That is, they can be modelled with straight lines. But not all relationships are linear. Some can be modelled with lines that are curved, rather than straight. Examples of such relationships include the rate at which the world's population is increasing and the rate at which radioactive materials decay. In this chapter, you will learn how to model these and other nonlinear relationships.

In this chapter, you will:

- recognize rational numbers and convert between fractional and decimal form

- perform arithmetic operations with rational numbers, including the use of order of operations

- determine whether a relationship is linear or nonlinear

- explore and graph nonlinear relationships

- apply nonlinear relationships to problems involving movement, measurement, and growth

- understand and apply the principles of operating with exponents, including scientific notation

- understand and apply the exponent laws

- apply the Pythagorean theorem to analyze and solve problems.

179

The Chapter Problem

What Is the Minimum Cost?

The Great Lakes Electric Company needs to run a power line from the shore of a lake to an island that is 500 m away. The closest power line ends 4 km along the shore from the point on the shore that is closest to the island. The company knows from recent jobs that it costs $15/m to lay the power line underwater and $10/m along the shore. Where should the company install the power line to minimize the cost?

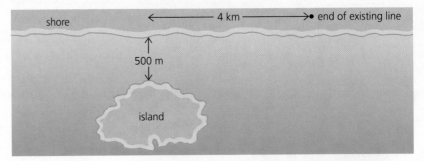

At the end of some lessons in this chapter, questions will refer you back to this problem, and you will be able to use what you have learned to answer them. Keep your notes in a folder, so that at the end of the chapter you can provide a full solution to this problem.

The Challenge

How Does the Population Grow?

Use your research skills to investigate the population changes in your community over the last 25 years. You may find the data at a variety of places, such as the library or the Internet. You might try the Statistics Canada Web site, **www.statcan.com**, for information. Once you have the data, determine if the growth or decline in population is constant, exponential, or neither. Create a graph from your data and try to determine a mathematical expression that models the growth pattern. Use your model to predict the population of the community in 2025. Report on any factors that have influenced the change in population over the last quarter of a century.

Do the same analysis for some other large city, such as Toronto, Kingston, or London. Is the growth rate of your community similar to that of this city? Explain why it is either similar or different. To complete this Challenge, you may need to discuss a research plan with your teacher or with other students. You may also need to research outside the classroom.

Getting Ready

In this chapter, you will be working with powers, fractions, and algebraic expressions. These exercises will help you warm up for the work in this chapter.

1. Simplify.
   (a) $(2)(-3) + (5)(-2)$
   (b) $2^3 + 3^2$
   (c) $\left(\frac{3}{4}\right)\left(\frac{2}{9}\right)$
   (d) $\frac{3}{4} - \frac{2}{9}$
   (e) $(0.01)(1.1)$
   (f) $\frac{15}{-3} - \frac{2}{3}(12 - 9)^2 - 3$

2. Given $c^2 = a^2 + b^2$. Solve for a if $c = 25$ and $b = 24$.

3. Evaluate each of the following when $x = -5$.
   (a) $5x^2 + 3$
   (b) $2x^3 - 3x^2$
   (c) $2x + 10 - x^2$
   (d) $3x + 4x - 7x$

4. Calculate the area of a rectangle with width 5.2 cm and length 6.3 cm.

5. A rectangle has perimeter 40 m and width 8 m. Calculate its length.

6. Evaluate.
   (a) 3^4 (b) 2^5
   (c) 6^2 (d) 8^2
   (e) 3^3 (f) 4^3
   (g) 5^3 (h) $(-4)^2$

7. The volume of a rectangular prism is 79.764 cm³. Calculate the height of the prism if the length is 5.1 cm and the width is 6.8 cm.

8. Calculate the length of the missing side.

   (a)   (b)

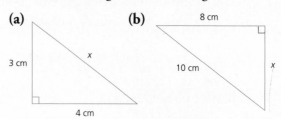

9. Simplify. Remember order of operations.
   (a) $\frac{(5)(-8)(9)}{(-3)(-4)}$ (b) $\frac{(15)(-6)}{(2)(-5)}$
   (c) $5\left(\frac{9 - 15}{3}\right) + 4\left(\frac{18 - 24}{6}\right)$
   (d) $\frac{(9)(-7)}{3} - \frac{(11)(8)}{4}$

10. State the next three numbers in each pattern.
    (a) $3, -1, -5, -9, \ldots$
    (b) $21, 27, 33, 39, \ldots$
    (c) $1, \frac{1}{2}, \frac{1}{4}, \frac{1}{8}, \ldots$
    (d) $0.1, 0.01, 0.001, 0.0001, \ldots$
    (e) $1, 4, 16, 64, \ldots$
    (f) $1, -3, 9, -27, \ldots$
    (g) $2, 10, 50, \ldots$
    (h) $1, 1, 2, 3, 5, 8, \ldots$

11. Write an algebraic expression for the data in the table.

    (a)

x	0	1	2	3	4	5
y	0	2	4	6	8	10

    (b)

x	−1	0	1	2	3	4
y	1	0	−1	−2	−3	−4

    (c)

x	0	1	2	3	4	5
y	3	4	5	6	7	8

    (d)

x	1	2	3	4	5
y	3	5	7	9	11

3.1 Relating Temperature Scales

EXPLORATION

Temperatures are measured using two common scales – Fahrenheit and Celsius. This equation converts Celsius temperatures to Fahrenheit.

$$\text{Fahrenheit temperature} = \frac{9}{5} \times \text{Celsius temperature} + 32$$

Think, Do, Discuss

1. (a) Graph this relationship: $F = \frac{9}{5}C + 32$. Copy this table and use your graph to complete it. Round your answers to one decimal place.

°C	32	212	0	100	40	77
°F						

(b) Use this conversion formula to calculate the exact values. Use fractions if necessary.

2. (a) The conversion formula to express Fahrenheit temperatures in Celsius is Celsius $= \frac{5}{9} \times$ Fahrenheit $- \frac{160}{9}$. Graph this relationship. Use the graph to complete this table. Round your results to one decimal place.

°F	32	212	0	100	40	77
°C						

(b) Use this conversion formula to find the exact values. Use fractions if necessary.

3. Think about the differences between the values expressed as fractions and those written as decimals.
  (a) Which form is more useful, fraction or decimal? Why?
  (b) Which form is more accurate? Why?
  (c) If one of these temperatures were expressed as a fraction, could you find the equivalent decimal version? Explain.
  (d) If one of these temperatures were expressed as a decimal number, could you find the equivalent fraction version? Explain.

4. (a) Why does it make sense to extend the graph to show negative temperatures on both scales?
  (b) Extend the graph and use it to complete this table of values.

°F	−49		−12.5			$33\frac{4}{5}$
°C		−10.5		$2\frac{1}{2}$	$-6\frac{2}{3}$	

5. Find the temperature that has the same numeric value using either scale. Explain how you found it and how you can verify your result.

Introduction to Rational Numbers

The Cartesian Coordinate System

In the Cartesian coordinate system, coordinates can be positive or negative. Values do not have to be whole numbers or integers. They can be decimals or fractions.

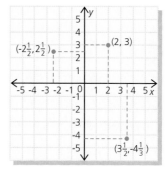

Think, Do, Discuss

1. **(a)** Graph $y = x - 1$.
   (b) Use your graph to estimate the values needed to complete the table.

x	$2\frac{1}{2}$	$\frac{3}{5}$	$2\frac{1}{3}$	$-\frac{5}{8}$	$-2\frac{3}{4}$	$-5\frac{2}{3}$
y						

   (c) On the line, label each point that is listed in the table.

2. **(a)** Convert the x-values in the table to decimals. Use the equation to calculate the corresponding y-values.
   (b) Plot the points with decimal coordinates.
   (c) For which points do decimal coordinates equal their fractional values?
   (d) For which points do the decimal coordinates provide only an approximation of their fractional coordinates? Why?

Fraction-Decimal Conversions

A fraction like $\frac{7}{8}$ represents a **quotient**. It can be treated as a **ratio**, 7 : 8, or as a division problem, $7 \div 8$. The result of the division is 0.875. Some calculators have a decimal-to-fraction conversion feature. It can be used to demonstrate that 0.75 is the same as $\frac{3}{4}$.

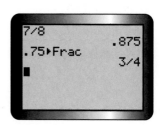

Think, Do, Discuss

1. Use a calculator to convert each number to decimal form. Identify the fractions that represent repeating decimals and those that are terminating decimals.

   (a) $\frac{1}{5}$ **(b)** $\frac{5}{8}$ **(c)** $\frac{1}{6}$ **(d)** $5\frac{1}{3}$ **(e)** $-\frac{3}{5}$ **(f)** $-5\frac{3}{4}$

   (g) $\frac{1}{16}$ **(h)** $\frac{7}{11}$ **(i)** $\frac{6}{13}$ **(j)** $\frac{4}{7}$ **(k)** $2\frac{5}{9}$ **(l)** $4\frac{1}{17}$

2. Find the fraction that corresponds to each decimal number.

   (a) 0.75   **(b)** -3.5 **(c)** 0.62   **(d)** 0.625

   (e) -2.125 **(f)** $2.\overline{3}$ **(g)** $5.\overline{6}$ **(h)** $-3.\overline{63}$

Focus

Key Ideas

- Coordinates in the Cartesian plane can be negative or positive. They can also contain fractions or decimals.

- A positive or negative fraction can be converted to a decimal value by dividing the numerator by the denominator. The resulting decimal either repeats indefinitely or terminates. For example, $\frac{1}{2} = 0.5$ or $\frac{1}{3} = 0.333...$

- When a decimal number repeats, the block of repeating digits is called the **period** of the number and a bar symbol over the repeating digits is used to mark the period. For example, the period of $\frac{1}{11} = 0.\overline{09}$ is 09.

- A **terminating decimal** can be rewritten as a fraction using the place value of the last digit to determine the denominator of the fraction. For example, $0.4 = \frac{4}{10}$ or $\frac{2}{5}$.

- Positive and negative fractions are **quotients** of integers and take the form $\frac{a}{b}$ where a and b are integers, but $b \neq 0$. This set of numbers is called the set of **rational numbers** and is represented by the symbol **Q**.

- Defining properties of sets of numbers:

Set	Examples	Symbol
Natural Numbers	the counting numbers 1, 2, 3, ...	**N**
Whole Numbers	the counting numbers and zero 0, 1, 2, 3, ...	**W**
Integers	positive and negative whole numbers ... −3, −2, −1, 0, 1, 2, 3, ...	**I**
Rational Numbers	numbers of the form $\frac{a}{b}$ where a and b are integers and $b \neq 0$ e.g. $\frac{3}{4}, -\frac{2}{3}, -3\frac{5}{8}, 2.35, -3.921, -8.\overline{234}$	**Q**

Did You Know?

The notes produced by a string instrument change according to the fraction of the string that is being plucked. If the entire length of the string is plucked, you will hear a certain note. If you press the string down at its halfway point, it is shortened to half its length. The sound that it will produce when plucked will now be a full octave higher.

Example 1

Convert $\frac{13}{15}$ and $-2\frac{13}{25}$ to decimals. Discuss the nature of the decimal results.

Solution

Using a calculator leads to these results:

$\frac{13}{15} = 0.8\overline{6}$

This is a repeating decimal with a period of 6. In the calculator display, the final 7 is due to rounding.

You can use the decimal value for $\frac{13}{25}$ from the calculator to find the decimal representation for $-2\frac{13}{25}$.

$$-2\frac{13}{25} = -\left(2 + \frac{13}{25}\right)$$
$$= -(2 + 0.52)$$
$$= -2.52$$

Example 2

Convert −2.625 to its equivalent fraction.

Solution

$$-2.625 = -(2 + 0.625)$$

Change 0.625 to a fraction. 0.625 is a decimal with its last digit having a place value of thousandths.

$$0.625 = \frac{625}{1000}$$

The greatest common factor (GCF) of 625 and 1000 is 125.
The fraction can be expressed in lowest terms:

$$\frac{625 \div 125}{1000 \div 125} = \frac{5}{8}$$

So, $0.625 = \frac{5}{8}$ and $-2.625 = -2\frac{5}{8}$.

Did You Know?

The invention of the thermometer is attributed to Italian astronomer, Galileo Galilei (1564–1642), although the sealed thermometer did not come into existence until about 1650. The modern alcohol and mercury thermometers were invented by the German physicist Gabriel Fahrenheit (1686–1736). He proposed the first widely adopted temperature scale, named after him, in which 32°F is the freezing point of water and 212°F is its boiling point. In the Celsius scale, devised by Swedish astronomer Anders Celsius (1701–44), water freezes at 0°C and boils at 100°C.

Practise, Apply, Solve

1. Plot each point on a Cartesian plane.

(a) $\left(\frac{1}{2}, \frac{1}{3}\right)$ (b) $\left(3\frac{3}{5}, -2\frac{1}{5}\right)$ (c) $\left(-1\frac{3}{4}, 2\frac{1}{2}\right)$ (d) $\left(-4\frac{2}{3}, -2\frac{7}{8}\right)$

(e) $(1.5, 2.25)$ (f) $(4.75, -0.1)$ (g) $(-5.5, 2.9)$ (h) $(-10.3, -9.5)$

2. (a) Write the x-coordinates of the points in Question 1 in order from least to greatest.
   (b) Repeat for the y-coordinates of the points in Question 1.

3. Rewrite each number as a decimal. Indicate whether it terminates or repeats. If it repeats, state the period.

(a) $\frac{1}{8}$ (b) $3\frac{3}{5}$ (c) $7\frac{5}{6}$ (d) $4\frac{7}{11}$

(e) $-\frac{7}{9}$ (f) $-\frac{7}{20}$ (g) $-4\frac{1}{7}$ (h) $-\frac{12}{13}$

4. Convert to the equivalent fraction.
   (a) 0.27 (b) 1.55 (c) -2.975 (d) -3.1875

B

5. Two students converted the mixed number $-2\frac{1}{2}$ to its corresponding improper fraction (sometimes called an *entire* fraction). Who did it correctly, Jasmine or Vito? Identify the error made.

Jasmine $-2\frac{1}{2} = \frac{-2 \times 2 + 1}{2}$

$= \frac{-4 + 1}{2}$

$= \frac{-3}{2}$

Vito $-2\frac{1}{2} = -\left(2\frac{1}{2}\right)$

$= -\left(\frac{2 \times 2 + 1}{2}\right)$

$= -\left(\frac{4 + 1}{2}\right)$

$= -\frac{5}{2}$

6. True or False? Give a reason for your answer. Provide examples to support your answer.
   (a) Every rational number is also an integer.
   (b) Every whole number is also a rational number.
   (c) Every integer is also a rational number.
   (d) Every natural number is also a rational number.
   (e) All decimal numbers are rational numbers.
   (f) All rational numbers can be written as decimal numbers.

7. Suppose circles were used to represent each of the four types of numbers listed in the Key Ideas. Draw a diagram that shows how the sets of numbers are related to one another.

8. (a) Create a table of values for the linear relation $y = 4x + 1$ for $-1 \leq x \leq 1$. Use at least five different values.
   (b) Graph the relation using a graphing tool.

(c) Adjust the display so that $-1 \leq x \leq 1$. You can do this by using the `ZOOM` command or by adjusting the `RANGE` or `WINDOW`.

(d) Use the `TRACE` feature to make sure your values work.

9. True or False? If false, give an example that shows why. If true, explain why.
   (a) The denominator of a rational number can be any integer.
   (b) There are rational numbers that are not integers.
   (c) There are integers that are not rational numbers.
   (d) It is possible to find an integer that fits between any two other integers.
   (e) It is possible to find a rational number that fits between any two other rational numbers.
   (f) Every rational number can be written in fraction form in one unique way.
   (g) Mixed numbers like $2\frac{1}{2}$ are not rational numbers because they cannot be expressed as the ratio of two integers.
   (h) Zero is not a rational number.

10. The list shows the estimated values for π through history.
   (a) Which value is closest to the present day value of π?
   (b) Is π a rational number? Explain.

Approximate Date	Examples	Estimated Value
1700 B.C.E.	Egyptian	$\frac{256}{81}$
220 B.C.E.	Greek (Archimedes)	$3\frac{1}{7}$
150 C.E.	Egyptian (Ptolemy of Alexandria)	$\frac{377}{120}$
470 C.E.	Chinese (Tsu Chung Chi and son)	$\frac{355}{113}$
530 C.E.	Hindu	$\frac{3927}{1250}$
1220 C.E.	European	$\frac{864}{275}$
Present (using Maple software)	3.14159265358979323846264338327950288419716939937510582 09749445922307816406286208998628034825342117068...	

C

11. (a) There are several Internet sites that provide information about π and its history. Find the most recently computed value of π and continue the discussion in Question 10, part (b).
   (b) Computer software like Waterloo Maple or Mathview allows almost unlimited accuracy for computations. If you have access to this kind of software, use it to find the most accurate value of π possible. Discuss any patterns in the decimal portion of the number.

12. Explain why $0.75 = \frac{3}{4}$, but $0.\overline{75} \neq \frac{3}{4}$.

13. Which denominators from the numbers 2 through 10 produce fractions whose decimal equivalents repeat? If a fraction has one of the numbers as its denominator, can you always conclude that it represents a repeating decimal? Explain.

14. Morana used algebra to convert $0.\overline{6}$ to its equivalent fraction. Her reasoning is shown.

Suppose $x = 0.\overline{6}$. Then $x = 0.6666666666666\ldots$
The length of the period is 1. Multiplying by 10 doesn't change the digits after the decimal point.

$$10x = 6.6666666666666\ldots$$
$$\underline{x = 0.6666666666666\ldots}$$

Subtract. $9x = 6$
Then, $x = \frac{6}{9}$ or $\frac{2}{3}$. This result can be verified using a calculator.

Use Morana's process to find the equivalent fractions for each number.

(a) $0.\overline{27}$ **(b)** $0.\overline{123}$ **(c)** $0.0\overline{3}$ **(d)** $-2.0\overline{12}$

15. The decimal equivalent of $\frac{7}{13}$ is shown to 21 decimal places using Maple software.

$$0.076\ 923\ 076\ 923\ 076\ 923\ 077$$

The decimal number can be used to create a "cycle graph". Do this:

  i. Use the first two numbers after the decimal point to form the ordered pair $(0, 7)$.
  ii. Plot the point $(0, 7)$ on a Cartesian plane.
  iii. Use the second and third numbers after the decimal point to form the ordered pair $(7, 6)$.
  iv. Plot the point $(7, 6)$ on a Cartesian plane.
  v. Join the first point to the second.

Repeat the process until you complete the cycle.

(a) Draw cycle graphs for other fractions that have a denominator of 13. How are the graphs the same? How are they different?

(b) Try graphing fractions with different denominators using the procedure above. How do the graphs for repeating decimals differ from those for terminating decimals?

Grace Murray Hopper (1906–1992)

Grace Murray Hopper was one of the pioneers of the computer industry. In 1959, she developed the Bomarc system, which, by 1960, became known as COBOL (COmmon-Business-Oriented-Language). COBOL is based on English phrases and words rather than on numbers and is used mainly for business applications.

She is also credited with coining the term "bug" when she traced an error in the MARK II (an early computer) to a moth trapped in a relay system. The bug was carefully removed and taped into a daily log book. Search the Internet and learn more about this amazing woman. What else did she accomplish?

Combining Rates

Ahmed and Jane each mow lawns to earn summer spending money. They live in a townhouse development and all the lots are the same size. Ahmed found that he can mow 5 lawns in an 8-h working day. Jane can mow 4 lawns in 7 h.

Think, Do, Discuss

1. How long does it take Ahmed to mow one lawn?

2. How long does it take Jane to mow one lawn?

3. Who mows the fastest? Explain.

4. If they each charge $5 a lawn, what do they each earn per hour?

5. After several weeks, Ahmed and Jane decide to work together instead of trying to mow the lawns separately.

  (a) How long will it take to mow one lawn, if Jane and Ahmed work together ?

  (b) If they arrange to mow lawns for 20 customers, how long should it take them to complete the work?

  (c) If they share their earnings equally, what will each earn per hour worked?

  (d) It's summer, and Ahmed and Jane want to work a maximum of 30 h/week each. What is the maximum number of lawns they can mow in a week? What will they each earn?

  (e) Suppose Frank joins Ahmed and Jane. The three teens can mow 25 lawns in 20 h working together. What is Frank's mowing rate?

  (f) If each of the three still wants to work only 30 h/week, what is the maximum number of lawns each can mow?

  (g) How is each person's hourly earnings affected when Frank joins the team?

	Earnings ($/h)
Ahmed	
Jane	
Frank	

6. After working for a while, the teenagers purchase new lawnmowers from their earnings. They hope to increase their mowing speed and so be able to take on additional clients.

  (a) Suppose the new lawnmowers allow the team to increase their mowing speed to $1\frac{1}{2}$ times their previous speed. How does this affect their hourly earnings rate?

  (b) If the new mowers cost the team a total of $600, how many hours must they work to pay off the purchase?

  (c) How many hours must they work before they earn as much as they would have with their old equipment?

  (d) Discuss whether purchasing the new mowers was a good business decision.

Determining the Sign of a Rational Number ——

One key step in working with a rational number is determining whether that number is negative or positive. Every rational number can be written as a ratio of two integers. As a result, the rules for dividing integers tell you the sign of the rational number.

Think, Do, Discuss

1. Is each number negative or positive?

    (a) $-\dfrac{4}{5}$ **(b)** $\dfrac{-2}{3}$ **(c)** $\dfrac{7}{-8}$ **(d)** $\dfrac{-3}{-10}$ **(e)** $\dfrac{-4}{-7}$

2. **(a)** How can you find out by inspection if a rational number in the form $\dfrac{a}{b}$ is positive or negative?
    (b) Explain how you can use a calculator to check the sign of the rational numbers in Question 1.
    (c) Which method is easier to use? Why?

Comparing Rational Number Operations with Integer and Fraction Operations ———

Arithmetic calculations with rational numbers are similar to arithmetic calculations with fractions. The difference with rational numbers is that the numerator or the denominator or both can be negative. Working with rational numbers means simplifying the sign of a number. Then you apply the properties and rules of working with fractions.

Think, Do, Discuss

1. In each question, a fraction calculation is shown in the left column. A similar rational number calculation is shown in the right column.
    (a) How are the calculation steps alike? How are they different?
    (b) At what step in the rational number calculation does the sign become a significant factor?

Fraction Calculation	**Rational Number Calculation**
i. $\dfrac{3}{4} + \dfrac{5}{8} = \dfrac{6}{8} + \dfrac{5}{8}$	$\dfrac{3}{4} + \dfrac{-5}{8} = \dfrac{6}{8} + \dfrac{-5}{8}$
$= \dfrac{6+5}{8}$	$= \dfrac{6+(-5)}{8}$
$= \dfrac{11}{8}$	$= \dfrac{6-5}{8}$
$= 1\dfrac{3}{8}$	$= \dfrac{1}{8}$

	Fraction Calculation	**Rational Number Calculation**

ii.

$$\frac{5}{6} + 2\frac{1}{2} = \frac{5}{6} + \frac{5}{2}$$

$$= \frac{5}{6} + \frac{15}{6}$$

$$= \frac{5 + 15}{6}$$

$$= \frac{20}{6}$$

$$= \frac{10}{3}$$

$$= 3\frac{1}{3}$$

$$\frac{5}{6} - 2\frac{1}{2} = \frac{5}{6} - \frac{5}{2}$$

$$= \frac{5}{6} - \frac{15}{6}$$

$$= \frac{5 - 15}{6}$$

$$= \frac{-10}{6}$$

$$= \frac{-5}{3}$$

$$= -1\frac{2}{3}$$

iii.

$$\frac{3}{4} \times \frac{5}{8} = \frac{3 \times 5}{4 \times 8}$$

$$= \frac{15}{32}$$

$$\frac{-3}{4} \times \frac{-5}{8} = \frac{-3 \times (-5)}{4 \times 8}$$

$$= \frac{15}{32}$$

iv.

$$3\frac{1}{2} \div 2\frac{1}{3} = \frac{7}{2} \div \frac{7}{3}$$

$$= \frac{7}{2} \times \frac{3}{7}$$

$$= \frac{\overset{1}{\cancel{7}}}{2} \times \frac{3}{\underset{1}{\cancel{7}}}$$

$$= \frac{1(3)}{2(1)}$$

$$= \frac{3}{2}$$

$$= 1\frac{1}{2}$$

$$-3\frac{1}{2} \div \left(-2\frac{1}{3}\right) = \frac{-7}{2} \div \frac{-7}{3}$$

$$= \frac{-7}{2} \times \frac{3}{-7}$$

$$= \frac{\overset{1}{\cancel{7}}}{2} \times \frac{3}{\underset{1}{\cancel{7}}}$$

$$= \frac{1(3)}{2(1)}$$

$$= \frac{3}{2}$$

$$= 1\frac{1}{2}$$

2. Find out how to enter a negative number into a computation using your calculator. There should be different keys for a negative sign [+/−] and the subtraction operation [−]. Use your calculator to evaluate the following.

(a) $-3.65 + 4.92$ **(b)** $3.37 - (-2.43)$ **(c)** $-5.04 - (-3.31)$

(d) $(-3.12)(-2.5)$ **(e)** $\frac{2.8153}{0.9}$ **(f)** $\frac{-3.6}{1.2} - \frac{-4.8}{-0.8}$

Focus

Key Ideas

- The overall sign of a rational number expressed in the form $\frac{a}{b}$ is:
  - positive, if the fraction contains an even number of negative signs.
  - negative, if the fraction contains an odd number of negative signs.

- Rational number operations can often be simplified by converting **mixed numbers** to **improper fractions** and writing negative fractions with the negative number in the numerator. To add or subtract, find a common denominator and apply the rules of integer operations to the numerators and denominators. To divide by a rational number, multiply by its reciprocal.

- Negative rational numbers can be entered into a calculator using the negative $(-$ or $+/-)$ key, which is different from the subtraction $(-)$ operation key.

- Sometimes, rational number operations using decimal numbers on a calculator can result in answers that are not accurate as a result of rounding.

Example 1

Evaluate $-2\frac{3}{4} - \left(\frac{-4}{5}\right)$.

Solution

$$-2\frac{3}{4} - \left(\frac{-4}{5}\right) = \frac{-11}{4} - \frac{-4}{5}$$

Convert the mixed number into an improper fraction.

$$= \frac{-11(5)}{4(5)} - \frac{-4(4)}{5(4)}$$

The lowest common denominator (LCD) is 20. Rewrite the fractions with a denominator of 20.

$$= \frac{-55}{20} - \frac{-16}{20}$$

$$= \frac{-55 - (-16)}{20}$$

Now that all of the fractions have the same denominator, subtract the numerators. (Recall that subtracting a negative is like adding a positive.)

$$= \frac{-55 + 16}{20}$$

$$= \frac{-39}{20}$$

The improper fraction is converted to a mixed number.

$$= -1\frac{19}{20}$$

Example 2

Evaluate $-3\frac{3}{8} \times \frac{-2}{3} \div \left(-1\frac{3}{4}\right)$.

Solution

$$-3\frac{3}{8} \times \frac{-2}{3} \div \left(-1\frac{3}{4}\right) = \frac{-27}{8} \times \frac{-2}{3} \div \frac{-7}{4}$$

Convert all mixed numbers to improper fractions with the negative sign in the numerator.

$$= \frac{-27}{8}\left(\frac{-2}{3}\right)\left(\frac{-4}{7}\right)$$

Division by a fraction involves multiplying by its reciprocal.

$$= \frac{\overset{-9}{\cancel{-27}}}{\underset{1}{\cancel{8}}}\left(\frac{\overset{-1}{\cancel{-2}}}{\underset{1}{\cancel{3}}}\right)\left(\frac{\overset{-1}{\cancel{-4}}}{7}\right)$$

Simplify by dividing out any common factors before multiplying.

$$= \frac{-9}{7}$$

Multiply numerators. Multiply denominators.

$$= -1\frac{2}{7}$$

Express the improper fraction as a mixed number.

Practise, Apply, Solve

A

1. Group the numbers so that all members of a group have the same value.

$$\frac{9}{8}, \quad 1\frac{1}{8}, \quad \frac{-9}{8}, \quad \frac{-9}{-8}, \quad -\frac{-9}{-8}$$

2. Order the numbers from least to greatest.

$$-2.87, \quad -3\frac{1}{4}, \quad 0.95, \quad \frac{-16}{3}, \quad 1\frac{5}{8}, \quad -1.\overline{4}$$

3. Calculate.

(a) $\frac{-1}{3} + \frac{-3}{4}$ (b) $\frac{-4}{5} + \frac{2}{3}$ (c) $-\frac{3}{4} - \frac{-2}{3}$ (d) $\frac{2}{-7} - \frac{-3}{7}$

(e) $2 - \left(\frac{-3}{-4}\right)$ (f) $-2\frac{2}{5} - 3\frac{1}{2}$ (g) $-6\frac{1}{4} - \frac{3}{-4}$ (h) $\frac{-3}{4}\left(\frac{-8}{9}\right)$

(i) $-2\frac{4}{5}\left(-2\frac{1}{2}\right)$ (j) $\frac{3}{-5} \div \frac{-2}{3}$ (k) $\frac{-7}{-10} \div \left(-\frac{4}{5}\right)$ (l) $8\frac{1}{3} \div \left(-2\frac{1}{2}\right)$

4. (a) Wah spent $2\frac{1}{4}$ h raking leaves and $\frac{3}{8}$ h washing windows. How much time, in total, did he spend on the two tasks?

(b) One day on the stock market, six stocks declined by these amounts.

$$-8\frac{1}{2}, \quad -10\frac{1}{4}, \quad -12\frac{1}{2}, \quad -6\frac{1}{4}, \quad -9\frac{1}{2}, \quad -21\frac{1}{4}$$

Find the average amount that the stocks declined.

5. Calculate. Verify your answers using a calculator.

(a) $\dfrac{-2}{5} + \dfrac{3}{-4} - 2\dfrac{2}{3}$

(b) $\dfrac{-15}{16} \times 3\dfrac{1}{5} \div \left(-1\dfrac{2}{3}\right)$

(c) $-2\dfrac{1}{3} + \left(\dfrac{3}{-4}\right) \times \left(-1\dfrac{5}{6}\right)$

(d) $-2\dfrac{1}{4} \times \left(1\dfrac{3}{4} - 5\dfrac{1}{2}\right)$

(e) $\left(6\dfrac{3}{4} - \dfrac{-5}{8}\right) \div 2\dfrac{1}{3}$

(f) $\dfrac{2}{5} \times \dfrac{-1}{2} + \left(-1\dfrac{3}{4}\right)$

6. Evaluate each expression using $a = \dfrac{2}{3}$, $b = -\dfrac{1}{8}$, and $c = 1\dfrac{1}{2}$.

(a) $a + bc$

(b) $3a - 4b + 2c$

(c) $ac + ab$

(d) $a(c + b)$

(e) $(a + b)(a - b)$

(f) $-2(a + b - c)$

(g) $\dfrac{a}{b + c}$

(h) $\dfrac{a}{b} + \dfrac{c}{b}$

(i) $\dfrac{a + c}{b}$

7. Evaluate the expressions in Question 6 using $a = -1.3$, $b = 2.6$, and $c = -0.5$.

8. Show that the value provided for x is an exact solution to the equation.

(a) $3x - 7 = -6$; $x = \dfrac{1}{3}$

(b) $\dfrac{3}{4}x - 1 = -7$; $x = -8$

(c) $-\dfrac{3}{4}x + 2 = 3$; $x = -1\dfrac{1}{3}$

9. Explain why using a calculator to check parts (a) and (c) in Question 8 might not result in the left and right sides of the equation being equal. Why shouldn't this be a problem with part (b) of Question 8?

10. (a) Alain can plant one flat of begonias in 0.75 h. If he plants begonias for his entire 7.5 h shift, how many flats does he plant?

(b) A bus uses $\dfrac{1}{10}$ of a tank of fuel to travel a complete route. If the fuel tank is $\dfrac{7}{8}$ full, how many routes can the bus complete without refuelling?

11. Evaluate.

(a) $\dfrac{-0.7 - 2 + 9}{3.1 \times 4 - 6.1}$

(b) $\dfrac{16 - 4.8 \times 2.1}{18 + 6 \div (-6)}$

(c) $\dfrac{15.3 + 2.7 \div 3}{-2 \times 8.1}$

(d) $10^2 - 5 \times 9 + 16^2 \div 12$

12. $1 + \cfrac{1}{1 + \cfrac{1}{1 + \cfrac{1}{2}}}$ is an example of a continued fraction.

(a) Verify that the value of the continued fraction is $1\dfrac{3}{5}$.

(b) Find the continued fraction representation for $1\dfrac{4}{5}$. [Hint: $\dfrac{4}{5} = \dfrac{1}{\frac{5}{4}}$]

(c) Use a calculator to examine the values of the continued fraction at the right as you increase the number of terms in the denominator.

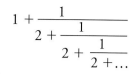

$$1 + \cfrac{1}{2 + \cfrac{1}{2 + \cfrac{1}{2 + \ldots}}}$$

(d) Use a calculator to square each value that you find in part (c). What do you notice?

(e) Based on the pattern you observed, guess the value of this continued fraction.
Check your guess using a calculator.

$$2 + \cfrac{1}{4 + \cfrac{1}{4 + \cfrac{1}{4 + \ldots}}}$$

13. Create a problem based on this circle graph. Give it to a classmate to solve.

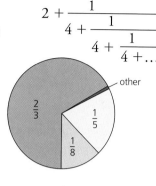

other

$\frac{2}{3}$

$\frac{1}{5}$

$\frac{1}{8}$

14. The perimeter of a rectangle is related to its length and width by the formula $p = 2(l + w)$. Show the steps to obtain each equivalent formula.

l

w

(a) $p = 2l + 2w$

(b) $w = \frac{1}{2}(p - 2l)$

(c) $l = \frac{p - 2w}{2}$

15. The width of a rectangle is $\frac{1}{4}$ of the length. If you increase the width by 12 m and double the length, you obtain a perimeter of 120 m. Find the dimensions of the rectangle.

Career: Cryptographer

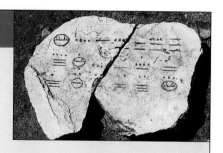

A cryptographer encodes and decodes messages. Cryptography is an essential part of many different areas of work. For instance, in the business of national security, cryptographers are needed to encode important documents.

In archaeology, cryptographers decipher ancient hieroglyphics. For instance, archeologists have decoded the marks on this rock in Mexico. They are numbers that were carved by Maya about 1500 years ago. Do some research about the Maya number system. What numbers are on this rock?

3.5 The Graph and Its Story

Suppose tap water is used to fill these containers. Would the shape of the container affect the relationship between the depth of the water and the different lengths of times the water runs?

Think, Do, Discuss

1. For this exploration, you will need to borrow several differently shaped containers. You could use a beaker, a graduated cylinder, a flask, and a clear 2-L plastic pop bottle. You will also need a watch to keep track of time in seconds and a ruler measured in centimetres.

2. Attach a ruler to the outside of the beaker. Take the beaker and ruler to a tap. Turn the water on so that it runs at a slow, steady rate. Begin to fill the beaker with water and record the length of time it takes for the water level to rise to 3 cm, 6 cm, 9 cm, 12 cm, 15 cm, and so on, until the container is full. Do not change the rate of water flow as you fill the container.

3. Repeat this process for the three other containers you have. Record the data for each container.

4. For each set of data, draw the graph that compares the water level to time. Draw the line or curve that best fits the data. In each case, use time as the independent variable and water level as the dependent variable.

5. Do any of the graphs have similarities? differences?

6. Are any of the graphs linear? nonlinear?

7. Does the shape of the container affect the shape of the graph? Explain.

8. If you performed this exploration again, with the water running at either a faster or slower rate, would the shape of your graphs change? If so, how?

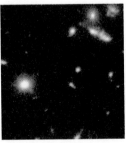

Did You Know?

The number 10^{100} (the digit 1 followed by 100 zeros) is a **googol**. The name googol was invented by the nine-year-old nephew of mathematician Edward Kastner.

Astronomers are used to working with very large numbers like this. This photo was taken by the Hubble space telescope as it orbited the Earth. Our galaxy, the Milky Way, has about 10^{11} stars. This photo shows hundreds of other galaxies outside our own, each with billions of stars. The distance that the telescope can see is considered to be about one tenth of the diameter of the universe. There are estimated to be about 10^{11} galaxies. This means there are about $10^{11} \times 10^{11} = 10^{22}$ stars in the universe.

Billy's mother sends him to the corner store for milk and tells him to be back in 30 min.
Examine the graph and describe Billy's progress.

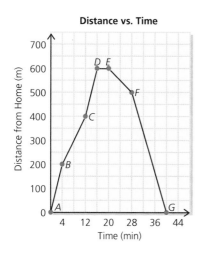

Think, Do, Discuss

1. Why are some line segments on the graph steeper than others?

2. Calculate the slope of the line segments *AB*, *BC*, *DE*, and *FG*. What does this mean in each situation?

3. Over what interval(s) of time is Billy travelling the fastest? slowest?

4. When does Billy reach the store? How do you know?

5. How long did it take Billy to get to the store?

6. How long did Billy stay at the store?

7. When did Billy leave the store to head back home?

8. How long did it take Billy to get home from the store?

9. How is the direction in which Billy is travelling represented on the graph?

10. Did Billy make it home in 30 min?

11. Using the information the graph provides, write a story that describes Billy's trip to the store and back.

Focus

Example

A skydiver jumps from an airplane. The table of values shows her motion for the free-fall part of her jump.

(a) Construct a finite difference table and use the table to determine if the data represents a linear or nonlinear relationship.

(b) Graph the results.

(c) Is the skydiver falling at a constant velocity? Explain.

(d) What do you think causes the results in part (c)?

Time (s)	Distance above Ground (m)
0	6000
4	5920
8	5680
12	5280
16	4720
20	4000
24	3120

Solution

(a)

Time (s)	Distance (m)	Finite Difference (m)
0	6000	
		−80
4	5920	
		−240
8	5680	
		−400
12	5280	
		−560
16	4720	
		−720
20	4000	
		−880
24	3120	

As the time interval increases by 4 s throughout the table, the difference between distances changes by different amounts. When the difference is not constant, the data represents a nonlinear relationship.

(b) Plot the ordered pairs (t, d) and join the points with a smooth curve.

(c) The data represents a nonlinear relationship. As time increases by 4-s intervals in the table, the distance increases by a larger amount over each interval. This means that the velocity of the skydiver is increasing over each 4-s interval. The skydiver is not falling at a constant velocity. In this case, the skydiver is accelerating.

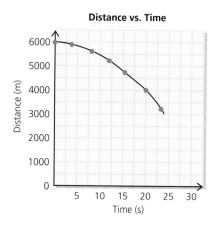

Distance vs. Time

Practise, Apply, Solve

A

1. Match each story to the graph which best describes the story.
   (a) Michael walks to school at a steady pace. He waits once for a stop light and continues to school at a faster pace. After being at school, he returns home without stopping or slowing down.
   (b) A log floating in a slow, steadily moving river goes through two sets of rapids before going over a waterfall into a lake.
   (c) A taxi driver charges a passenger to get in the cab plus a fixed amount for every 100 m.
   (d) A skydiver enters a plane that takes off and climbs at a steady rate. He jumps out and free-falls until the parachute opens. He descends the rest of the way at a constant speed.

i.
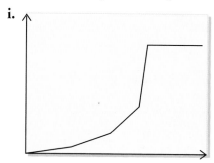

ii.
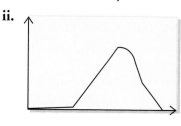

iii.
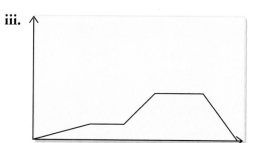

iv.
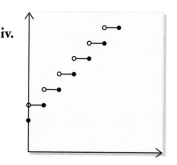

2. This graph shows how a car travels over time.

(a) Over what interval of time is the object travelling the slowest? fastest?

(b) When does the object start to return to its starting point? When does it get there?

(c) Determine the slope of the graph between 20 s and 26 s.

(d) What does a zero slope mean in the context of this graph?

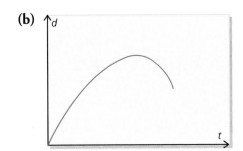

Distance vs. Time

3. Write a story to match each graph.

(a)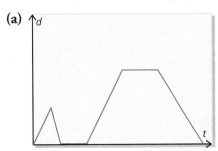

(b)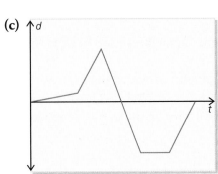

(c)

(d)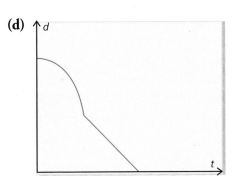

4. Water is poured into this container at a constant rate. Draw a graph that represents this situation where d is depth and t is time.

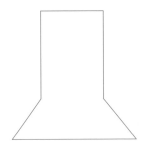

5. A drag racer begins from a stopped position and drives the length of a race track. The table of values shows the distance from his starting position after each second of his run.

Time (s)	Distance (m)
0	0
1	9.3
2	37.2
3	83.7
4	148.8
5	232.5
6	334.8
7	455.7

(a) Create a finite difference table. Does the data represent a linear or nonlinear relationship?

(b) Graph the relationship.

(c) Is the driver accelerating, decelerating, or travelling at a constant velocity? Explain.

6. (a) In each set of data, determine if it represents a linear or nonlinear relationship.

(b) In each set of data, determine if the object is accelerating, decelerating, moving at constant velocity, or a combination of all three.

i.

Time (s)	Distance (m)
7	19
8	22
9	25
10	28
11	31

ii.

Time (s)	Distance (m)
10	35
11	37
12	38
13	38.5
14	38.75

iii.

Time (s)	Distance (m)
0	0
1	7
2	16
3	29
4	49
5	89

iv.

Time (s)	Distance (km)
0	5
1	10
2	15
3	20
4	25
5	30
6	36
7	48
8	72
9	74
10	75

7. A driver leaves at 8:00 a.m. and drives 120 km by 9:30 a.m. From then until 10:30 a.m., she travels another 50 km. She drives an additional 200 km by 12:30 p.m. She travels at a constant speed during each period of time.
   (a) Draw the distance-time graph that represents the trip.
   (b) When is the car travelling the fastest? slowest?
   (c) What type of relationship is this?
   (d) What is the average speed for the entire trip?

8. A baseball is hit straight up into the air. The table shows the height of the ball after various time intervals.
   (a) Does the data represent a linear or nonlinear relationship?
   (b) Graph the data.
   (c) What is the height of the ball after 1.5 s?
   (d) When will the baseball be at 44 m?
   (e) When is the ball accelerating?
   (f) When is the ball decelerating?
   (g) When is the ball stopped?
   (h) What is the maximum height the ball reaches?
   (i) What effect does gravity have on the velocity of the ball?

Time (s)	Height (m)
0	1
1	26
2	41
3	46
4	41
5	26
6	1

9. The table shows the length of time needed to drive 100 km at various speeds.
   (a) Copy and complete the table by determining the missing times. (time = distance/speed)
   (b) Graph the data. What is the dependent variable? the independent variable?
   (c) Select three points on the graph that are separated by equal intervals of speed. Calculate the rate triangles between the first and second points and between the second and third points. Are the values the same or different?
   (d) Is the relationship linear or nonlinear?

Speed (km/h)	Time (h)
100	1
75	
50	
25	
12.5	
10	
1	

10. A race car travels around a race track. The graph of speed vs. time for the car is shown.

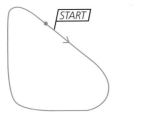

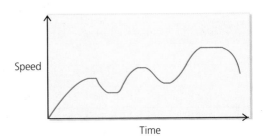

(a) What do the positive slopes represent?

(b) What do the negative slopes represent?

(c) What do the horizontal parts of the graph represent?

(d) Follow the graph and tell a story about the car as it makes one lap around the track.

11. Draw a graph of speed vs. time as a car makes one circuit of each track. The arrow shows the direction the car is moving.

(a)

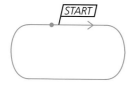

(b)

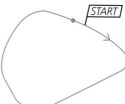

(c)

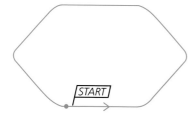

(d)

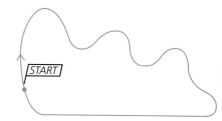

 C

12. Sheila takes a driver education course before applying for her driver's licence. One of the topics studied is the relationship between speed and stopping distance. The instructor gives Sheila this table:

Speed (km/h)	10	20	30	40	50	60	70	80	90	100	110	120	130	140
Stopping Distance (m)	3.7	7.6	12.0	17.1	22.9	29.8	37.9	47.5	58.6	71.6	86.5	103.5	122.8	144.7

(a) Graph the data using stopping distance as the dependent variable.

(b) Determine the rate triangle from 60 km/h to 70 km/h and from 70 km/h to 80 km/h.

(c) What do you notice about the rate of change in stopping distance as the speed increases by 10 km/h in part (b)?

(d) Sheila says, "If I drive twice as fast, I just need to leave twice as much distance between my car and the car in front of me." Explain whether this is accurate.

The Chapter Problem — What Is the Minimum Cost?

Refer back to the Chapter Problem at the beginning of the chapter.

1. Does this problem deal with velocity in any way?
2. What are the factors that affect the overall cost of laying the power line?

3.7 Creating Difference Tables

Using a Graphing Calculator/Spreadsheet

In Chapter 2 you were introduced to the difference table. Below is some data that a group of students collected. They were investigating the relationship between the height of a right triangle and the size of one of the acute angles in the triangle.

Using a large protractor and three metre sticks, they created right triangles that always had a base of 10 cm. They started with an angle of 5° and increased the angle by 5° each time. They recorded the height of each triangle.

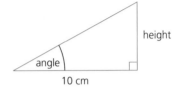

Angle (°)	5	10	15	20	25	30	35	40	45	50	55	60
Height (cm)	0.9	1.8	2.7	3.6	4.8	5.8	7.0	8.4	10	11.9	14.3	17.3

To decide if the relationship between the angle and the height of the triangle is linear, a difference table must be created.

Creating a Difference Table on a Spreadsheet

All of the data must be entered into the spreadsheet. In this case, the angles are entered into column A and the heights in column B.

Here, the data in column A has been entered in increasing order. This is important when creating a difference table.

	A	B	C
1	Angle	Height	Difference
2	5	0.9	
3	10	1.8	
4	15	2.7	
5	20	3.6	
6	25	4.8	
7	30	5.8	
8	35	7.0	
9	40	8.4	
10	45	10	
11	50	11.9	
12	55	14.3	
13	60	17.3	

To calculate the differences, the formula "=B3-B2" is entered in cell C3. The **Fill Down** command is then used to calculate the remaining differences.

The resulting table is on the right. ➡

	A	B	C
1	Angle	Height	Difference
2	5	0.9	
3	10	1.8	0.9
4	15	2.7	0.9
5	20	3.6	0.9
6	25	4.8	1.2
7	30	5.8	1.0
8	35	7.0	1.2
9	40	8.4	1.4
10	45	10	1.6
11	50	11.9	1.9
12	55	14.3	2.4
13	60	17.3	3.0

Examining the differences leads to the conclusion that the relationship between angle and height in a right triangle is nonlinear. The graph can be drawn using a smooth curve.

Creating a Difference Table on a Graphing Calculator

These instructions are for one type of calculator. You may need to check your calculator's instruction manual. First, enter the data into the calculator. To do this, press STAT , then move the cursor to **EDIT** and select **1:EDIT** from the menu.

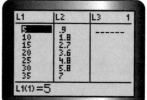

Data entered in L1 and L2

- Move the cursor to the cell below **L1**. Enter all the angle values into the list **L1**. Enter each value and press ENTER until all the angles have been entered.

- To make sure the data in **L1** is in increasing order, use the sorting capabilities of the calculator. Press STAT and move the cursor down to **EDIT**, then **SORTA(**. Enter **L1)** and press ENTER . The data in **L1** will now be arranged in ascending order.

- Move the cursor to the cell below **L2**. Enter all the corresponding heights into the list **L2**. Press ENTER after each height is entered.

- To create the difference table, first exit the STAT **EDIT** by pressing 2nd QUIT .

- Press 2nd [LIST] . Move the cursor to the **Ops** menu. Move the cursor to ΔList (and enter **L2**). Press ENTER .

- A list of differences between each consecutive element of **L2** will be shown. This list is created by subtracting the first element of **L2** from the second element of **L2** and so on down the list.

- To store this list in **L3**, press STO▶ and then **L3**.

The graphing calculator also brings us to the same conclusion. The relationship between the acute angle and the height of a right triangle is nonlinear.

Practise

Use a spreadsheet or a graphing calculator to create a difference table for each set of data.

(a)
x	2	4	6	8	10	12	14
y	12	24	36	48	60	72	84

(b)
x	12	6	8	4	10	2	14
y	53	22	27	14	38	8	44

(c)
x	12	11	10	9	8	7	6
y	35	38	41	44	47	50	53

(d)
x	1	4	7	2	3	5	6
y	3	5	8	9	12	11	13

3.8 Relationships in Geometric Figures

Antonio wants to determine if a relationship exists between the area of a right triangle and the length of the triangle's hypotenuse. He remembers the relationship that exists in right triangles called the Pythagorean theorem:

The square of the hypotenuse (the longest side) is equal to the sum of the squares of the other two sides ($H^2 = h^2 + b^2$).

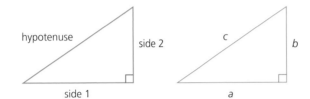

where c is the hypotenuse.

Or in other words:

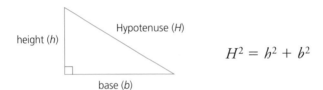

$$H^2 = h^2 + b^2$$

Using dynamic geometry software, Antonio creates a right triangle with a fixed base of 30 cm. His first triangle has a hypotenuse of 35 cm. He creates several other triangles, increasing the length of the hypotenuse by 5 cm each time. He records the length of the hypotenuse and the height of each triangle he creates in this table.

Base (cm)	Hypotenuse (cm)	Height (cm)	Area (cm²)
30	35		
30	40		
30	45		
30	50		
30	55		
30	60		
30	65		

Think, Do, Discuss

1. Using dynamic geometry software or three metre sticks, follow Antonio's procedure and measure the heights of the seven triangles. Copy the table on the opposite page and record your measurements.

2. Calculate the heights using the Pythagorean theorem to check the accuracy of your measurements. Round your answers to one decimal place.

3. Calculate the area of each triangle to one decimal place. Use the base of 30 cm each time, along with the calculated heights of the triangles.

4. Create a difference table for hypotenuse and area. Does a linear or nonlinear relationship exist? Explain.

5. Graph your data.

6. Write an algebraic equation to model this relationship.

Antonio wonders if all relationships between sides of this triangle have the same type of graph.

Think, Do, Discuss

1. Graph the relation area vs. height.

2. Is the relationship linear or nonlinear?

3. Write an algebraic equation to model this relation.

Alan Turing (1912–1954)

In World War II, the Germans used a machine called Enigma to send coded messages. The English mathematician Alan Turing developed early versions of computers that were able to break these codes. In doing so, he helped to shorten the war in Europe by about two years.

Can you decipher this message?

AQWJ CXGD TQMG PVJG EQFG

Hints: C = A. You may need to regroup the letters.

Turing was also a pioneer in the fields of computer science and artificial intelligence. He developed the Turing test, a method for deciding whether computers could "think."

Focus

Key Idea

- Measurements associated with geometric figures involve relationships that can be either linear or nonlinear.

Example

Several students collected this data for 12 triangles. Use it to determine what type of relationship exists between the hypotenuse of a right triangle and the size of one of the acute angles, when the base is fixed at 10 cm.

Angle (°)	5	10	15	20	25	30	35	40	45	50	55	60
Height (cm)	0.9	1.8	2.7	3.6	4.8	5.8	7.0	8.4	10	11.9	14.3	17.3

Solution

First, calculate the hypotenuse, c, using the Pythagorean theorem.
Round to two decimal places.

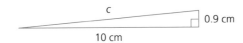

In the first case:

$$c^2 = (0.9)^2 + (10)^2$$
$$= 0.81 + 100$$
$$= 100.81$$
$$c = \sqrt{100.81}$$
$$\doteq 10.04$$

Calculating the length of the hypotenuse for each of the given heights produces this data.

Angle (°)	5	10	15	20	25	30	35	40	45	50	55	60
Height (cm)	0.9	1.8	2.7	3.6	4.8	5.8	7.0	8.4	10	11.9	14.3	17.3
Hypotenuse (cm)	10.04	10.16	10.36	10.63	11.09	11.56	12.21	13.06	14.14	15.54	17.45	19.98

Using a spreadsheet gives this differences table.

	A	B	C
1	Angle	Hypotenuse	Difference
2	5	10.04	
3	10	10.16	0.12
4	15	10.36	0.20
5	20	10.63	0.27
6	25	11.09	0.46
7	30	11.56	0.47
8	35	12.21	0.65
9	40	13.06	0.85
10	45	14.14	1.08
11	50	15.54	1.40
12	55	17.45	1.91
13	60	19.98	2.53

The differences show that the relationship between angle and the length of the hypotenuse in a right triangle is nonlinear. The graph can be drawn using a smooth curve.

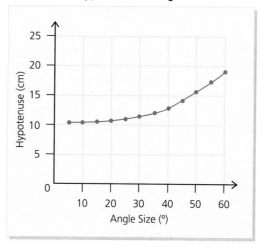

Hypotenuse vs. Angle Size

Practise, Apply, Solve

A

1. For this question, use cubes to construct several 3-D shapes. If cubes are unavailable, then draw an accurate diagram.
(a) Make these shapes.

  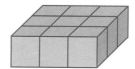

(b) Make three more shapes by following the pattern above. Each time a shape is made, determine the following information and record it in the table of values:

    i. the length of the top

    ii. the width of the top

    iii. the perimeter of the top

    iv. the area of the top

    Sketch a diagram of the shape.

	Shape	Length of Top	Width of Top	Perimeter of Top	Area of Top
1	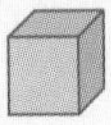	1	1	4	1
2	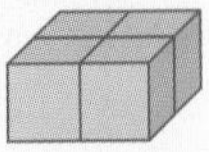				
3	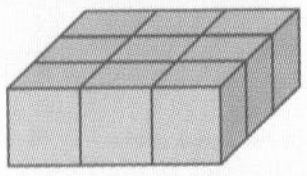				
4					
5					
6					

(c) For each of these shapes, construct a differences table using the data you collected. Is each relationship linear or nonlinear?

   i. length vs. width

   ii. length vs. perimeter

   iii. length vs. area

   iv. perimeter vs. area

(d) Sketch the graph for each relationship in part (c).

2. (a) Copy and complete the table of values.

   (b) Is the relation between the number of cubes and the number of exposed faces linear or nonlinear?

   (c) Write an algebraic expression that models the relation.

Shape	Number of Cubes	Number of Exposed Faces	Finite Differences
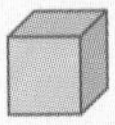	1	5	
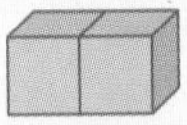	2	8	
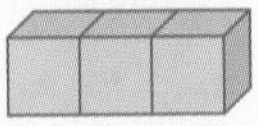	3		
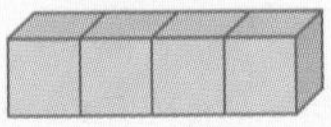	4		
Model	n		

3. (a) Complete the table of values.
(b) Determine whether the relation between the width of the top and the area of the top is linear or nonlinear.
(c) Write an algebraic expression which models the relation.

Shape	Length of Top	Width of Top	Area of Top	Finite Differences
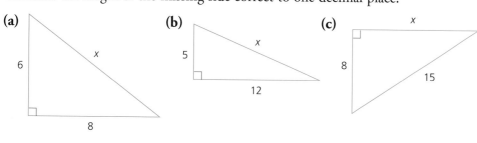	2	1	2	
Model		n		

4. Calculate the length of the missing side correct to one decimal place.

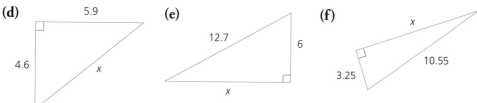

(a) 6, x, 8

(b) 5, x, 12

(c) x, 8, 15

(d) 5.9, 4.6, x

(e) 12.7, 6, x

(f) x, 3.25, 10.55

B

5. (a) Refer to the table on the next page. Examine and extend the pattern of rectangles and complete the table of values.
(b) Identify the relationship between length and area as linear or nonlinear.
(c) Write the formula for area in terms of length and width.
(d) Graph the relation area vs. length.

Diagram	Length	Width	Area	Finite Differences
	1	9	9	

6. The formula for calculating the circumference of a circle is $C = \pi d$, where d is the diameter.
   (a) Use a spreadsheet to construct a table of values by choosing different diameters and calculating the circumference.
   (b) Is the relationship between circumference and diameter linear or nonlinear?
   (c) Graph the relationship.

7. Melissa has 16 m of fencing to make a rectangular enclosure for her dog.
   (a) Draw all possible rectangular enclosures using whole numbers from 1 to 7 for the dimensions.
   (b) Organize the data in a table of values with the headings Length, Width, and Area.
   (c) Is the relationship between length and area linear or nonlinear?
   (d) Graph the relation area vs. length. Let the length of the rectangle include all whole numbers from 1 to 7.
   (e) What dimensions give the maximum area for a perimeter of 16 m? How is this shown on the graph?
   (f) Write an algebraic model that links the width of the enclosure to the perimeter and length.
   (g) Write an algebraic model that links area to the independent variable, length.

8. Repeat Question 7 for a perimeter of 24 m, using whole numbers from 1 to 11 for the dimensions.

9. Set up a spreadsheet to determine the maximum area of a rectangle with perimeter 64 m.

10. Marsha leans a 6.0 m ladder against a wall. The base of the ladder is 1.5 m from the wall. How far up the wall will the ladder reach?

11. On his way to school, Abdul cuts across a vacant lot that measures 110 m by 55 m. He walks diagonally from corner to corner. One day, a fence is built around the lot and he has to walk around. How much farther does he have to walk?

12. A tugboat and a cruiser leave the harbour at the same time. The tugboat travels due north at 12.0 km/h. The cruiser travels due east at 22.0 km/h. How far apart are the boats after 4 h?

C

13. Write an expression for the width, *w*, of a rectangle for each perimeter given.
   (a) 10 m   **(b)** 16 m   **(c)** 25 m   **(d)** 35 m

14. (a) Solve $2l + 2w = 50$ for *w*.
   (b) Solve $2l + 2w = 75$ for *l*.
   (c) Solve $2l + 2w = p$ for *l*.

15. Find the length of the missing side accurate to one decimal place.

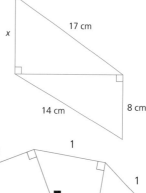

16. (a) Find the missing lengths.
   (b) How would you use the diagram to make a side $\sqrt{7}$ in length?

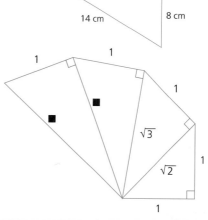

The Chapter Problem — What Is the Minimum Cost?

Refer to the Chapter Problem at the beginning of the chapter.

1. Calculate the cost of laying the power line straight from the island to the nearest point on the shore, and then down the shore to the existing line.

2. Calculate the length of power line required to go from the island directly underwater to the existing line. You will need to use the Pythagorean theorem, with all measurements in metres.

3. Create a table of values for the total cost for different land-water combinations. Start with 0 km on land and total distance underwater. Next, determine the cost for 500 m on land, the rest underwater. Continue this pattern until you have the last option calculated for 4 km on land. Use a table like this to record your data.

Distance on Land (m)	Distance Under Water (m)	Cost on Land ($)	Cost Under Water ($)	Total Cost ($)
0				
500				
1000				
4000	500			

3.9 Models of Growth

Powers of Two

A scientist places one bacterium in a petri dish and watches it multiply. The bacteria grow by the process of cell division. Each bacterium duplicates itself, then divides, creating two bacteria from one. Under a microscope, the scientist counts the number of bacteria every hour and records the data in this chart.

Time (h)	Number of Bacteria
0	1
1	2
2	4
3	8
4	16
5	
6	
7	

Think, Do, Discuss

1. Use the pattern in the chart to determine the number of bacteria after 5 h, 6 h, and 7 h.
2. In the Number of Bacteria column, how is the next row in the table related to the previous row?
3. Does this data represent a linear or nonlinear relationship?
4. Graph the data.
5. Copy the table into your notebook and add a third column titled Powers of Two. Express each of the values in the Number of Bacteria column as a power of two and record it in the table. What is the significance of the base? of the exponent?
6. How can you write one as a power of two? Explain.
7. Using N for the number of bacteria and t as the time (in hours), explain why $N = 2^t$ models this relationship.
8. Use your calculator to predict the number of bacteria in the dish after 10 h, 20 h, 30 h, 40 h, and 50 h. The calculator shows some of the numbers in a different format. What does this format mean?
9. **(a)** Assume the scientist starts with 10 bacteria and each bacterium doubles every hour. Create a new table from 0 to 7 h.
   (b) In the Number of Bacteria column, how is each row related to the previous row?
   (c) Express each value in the Number of Bacteria column as a product of 10 and a number. What do you notice?

(d) Using N for the number of bacteria and t as the time (in hours), explain why $N = 10(2^t)$ models this relationship.

(e) Using the equation you created and your calculator, predict the size of the population after 10 h, 30 h, and 50 h.

Negative Exponents

This table represents the number of bacteria in a petri dish at various times. In this table, 0 means now and 1 means 1 day from now. The population is measured in millions of bacteria.

Time (days)	Population (millions)
0	1
1	2
2	4
3	8
4	16

Think, Do, Discuss

1. Graph this relationship.
2. In this table 0 represents now. How could you represent 1 day ago in this table? 2 days ago? 3 days ago?
3. Draw the table shown above in your notebook. In the three blank rows, enter in the data that would correspond to the population 3, 2, and 1 days ago.
4. In your table, make sure that all values are expressed as fractions in lowest terms. Add a third column to your table and express all of the population values as powers of two. It may be easier to start with the largest value and work backwards.
5. When a power has a negative exponent, what type of number does it represent?
6. Create a rule that would represent the expression x^{-n}.
7. Add the new points to the graph you created. Determine the population four and five days ago, then add these to your graph. Express these numbers as powers of two.
8. As the negative exponents get smaller, what happens to the population of bacteria?
9. Add a fourth column to your table. In this column, using the y^x key on your calculator, express all the powers of two as decimals.
10. Using your calculator, predict the size of the population 10, 20, 30, 40, and 50 days ago. Explain the calculator display. Why does your calculator do this?
11. Are all of your predictions for the size of the population from Question 10 reasonable answers? Explain.

Focus

Key Ideas

- A relationship where population increases by a **constant** multiplier with each time interval is nonlinear.

- If the constant multiplier is greater than 1, the relationship is called **exponential growth**. The constant multiplier is called the growth factor.

- The equation that describes exponential growth is $y = ca^x$. c is the initial population, a is the growth factor, and x is time.

- The graph of $y = a^x$, $a > 1$, is an increasing curve that always passes through $(0, 1)$.

- When an exponent is zero, it gives a value of 1. $x^0 = 1$ (for example: $5^0 = 1$).

- When a power with a base greater than 1 has a negative exponent, it gives a fractional value. $x^{-n} = \dfrac{1}{x^n}$ $\left(\text{for example: } 5^{-2} = \dfrac{1}{5^2} = \dfrac{1}{25}\right).$

- Scientific notation is a way of writing very large and very small numbers in a convenient form. To express a number in scientific notation, write it as the product of a decimal between 1 and 10 and a power of 10.

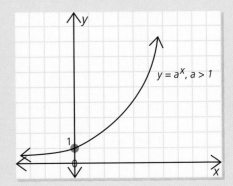

Standard Form	Scientific Notation
123 000 000	1.23×10^8
0.003 45	3.45×10^{-3}

Example

The population of a colony of cells is growing so that it will triple every hour. If the current population is 200 cells, determine the number of cells in the colony:

(a) 7 h from now   **(b)** 15 h from now   **(c)** 2 h ago

Solution

The population triples in size every hour. Creating a table of values clearly shows that this is a relationship of exponential growth.

Time (h)	0	1	2	3	4	5
Population	200	600	1800	5400	16 200	48 600

In this case, the initial population is 200 and the growth factor is 3. An equation that models this relationship is $y = 200(3)^x$, where y is the population and x is time.

(a) In 7 h from now:

$$y = 200(3)^7$$
$$= 200(2187)$$
$$= 437\ 400$$

(b) In 15 h from now:

$$y = 200(3)^{15}$$
$$= 200(14\ 348\ 907)$$
$$= 2.8697814 \times 10^9$$

(c) 2 h ago:

$$y = 200(3)^{-2}$$
$$= 200\left(\frac{1}{3^2}\right)$$
$$= 200\left(\frac{1}{9}\right)$$
$$= \frac{200}{9}$$
$$\doteq 22.2$$

Practise, Apply, Solve

(A)

1. Examine each table of values. Is the relationship in the data linear, exponential, or neither?

(a)

x	y
0	1
1	3
2	9
3	27

(b)

x	y
0	−1
1	2
2	5
3	8

(c)

x	y
0	1
1	6
2	11
3	16

(d)

x	y
0	1
1	5
2	25
3	125
4	625
5	3125
6	15 625

(e)

x	y
0	12
1	10
2	8
3	6
4	4
5	2
6	0

(f)

x	y
4	135
1	5
5	405
3	45
2	15
7	3645
6	1215

2. Write each expression as a power.
   (a) $10 \times 10 \times 10$ **(b)** $2 \times 2 \times 2$ **(c)** $(5)(5)(5)(5)$
   (d) $(3)(3)(3)(3)(3)$ **(e)** $(-2)(-2)$ **(f)** $(-4)(-4)(-4)(-4)$

3. Identify the base of each power and write the power in expanded form.
   (a) 7^3 **(b)** $(-7)^3$ **(c)** -7^3 **(d)** 6^{-3} **(e)** $(-6)^{-3}$
   (f) -6^{-3} **(g)** a^2 **(h)** $(-a)^2$ **(i)** $-a^2$

4. Write as a power with a positive exponent.
   (a) 2^{-1} **(b)** 3^{-2} **(c)** 5^{-2} **(d)** 4^{-3} **(e)** a^{-2} **(f)** b^{-3}

5. Expand each power and evaluate.

(a) 3^7 (b) 2^4 (c) 10^6 (d) 8^3 (e) $(8)^3$
(f) $(4)^3$ (g) 5^0 (h) $(-7)^0$ (i) -4^0 (j) 3^{-2}
(k) 2^{-3} (l) 4^{-2} (m) $(-3)^{-2}$ (n) $(-1)^4$ (o) $(-1)^5$
(p) $(-1)^{100}$ (q) $(-1)^{101}$ (r) $(-2)^{-5}$ (s) 6^{-2} (t) -6^{-2}

6. Use the y^x key on a calculator to evaluate each power.

(a) 3^8 (b) 2^9 (c) 5^0 (d) 10^0 (e) $(-2)^5$
(f) $(-5)^2$ (g) $(-1)^{10}$ (h) $(-1)^{11}$ (i) $(2)^{-5}$ (j) $(3)^{-2}$
(k) $(-2)^{-4}$ (l) $(5)^{-3}$ (m) $(-4)^{-3}$ (n) $(-1)^{-100}$

7. Express in scientific notation.

(a) 2300   (b) 135 000   (c) 0.085   (d) 0.002 37
(e) 12 000 000   (f) 125   (g) 0.000 00854   (h) 765 234
(i) 1 234 000   (j) 23 004   (k) 0.000 000 04   (l) 222 002
(m) 23.5×10^2 (n) 0.004×10^{-3} (o) 1283×10^5 (p) 12.67×10^{-3}

8. Express in standard form.

(a) 1.2×10^2 (b) 2.567×10^5 (c) 1.345×10^{-2}
(d) 2.49×10^7 (e) -3.678×10^{-5} (f) 1.25×10^0
(g) 6.712×10^{-1} (h) 2.85×10^{-4} (i) -2.456×10^6
(j) 2.3004×10^{-3} (k) 5.0×10^5 (l) -6.0×10^{-6}

9. Identify as greater than one or less than one.
(a) The area of Canada is about 9.98×10^6 km^2.
(b) A computer takes about 4.4×10^{-6} s to do an addition operation.
(c) The diameter of the universe is about 8.0×10^{23} km.
(d) A carbon atom has a radius of about 8.0×10^{-11} m.

10. Very small and very large numbers are entered and displayed on a calculator using scientific notation. To evaluate 0.000 000 000 23 × 0.000 000 000 061, the numbers must be entered using scientific notation and the EE or EXP key.

First rewrite the numbers in scientific notation: $(2.3 \times 10^{-10}) \times (6.1 \times 10^{-11})$.

Enter them this way: 2.3 EE +/− 10 × 6.1 EE +/− 11 =

The display shows 1.403 – 20 .

This means the answer is 1.403×10^{-20} or 0.000 000 000 000 000 000 014 03.

Write the number from each calculator display as a decimal.

(a) 4.35 9   (b) 6.053 −5   (c) 1.63 10   (d) 4.521 −12

11. Calculate.
(a) $(6.9 \times 10^{-13}) \times (5.2 \times 10^{14})$ (b) 0.000 000 000 72 × 4 370 000 000

12. Evaluate as a fraction in lowest terms.

(a) $5^{-1} + \left(\dfrac{2}{3}\right)^2$ (b) $(2^{-2} \times 3^2) \times (2 \times 3)$ (c) $\dfrac{3}{4} - 4^{-2}$

(d) $(2^7 \times 2^2 \times 3^5) \times (2^6 \times 3^2)$ (e) $3^{-1} + 2^{-1}$ (f) $(-5)^2 + (-12)^2$

13. A colony of 6 million bacteria is growing in a petri dish. The population, P, after t hours is given by $P = (6 \times 10^6)(2)^t$.

(a) What is the initial population of the bacteria colony?

(b) How long will it take for the population to double?

(c) What is the population after 4 h?

(d) Graph this relationship over a time interval of 5 h.

14. If $x = -2$, $y = -3$, $a = 2$, and $b = 1$, find each value.

(a) a^2 (b) $x^{-1} + y^{-1}$ (c) $(ab)^2$ (d) x^y (e) $x^2 + y^{-1}$ (f) $\left(\dfrac{a}{b}\right)^x$

15. Someone offers to pay you $1000/d or 1¢ on day one, 2¢ on day two, 4¢ on day three, 8¢ on day four, and so on, doubling the previous day's payment each time. Which payment plan is better for 10 d? 20 d? 30 d?

16. A piece of paper is folded in half, then folded in half again and again. Suppose this folding could be continued 50 times.

(a) Predict from these choices the height of the layers of paper after 50 folds.
- as high as a desk
- as high as a person
- to the ceiling of a room
- to the top of the CN Tower
- from the Earth to the moon
- from the Earth to the sun

(b) Check your answer to part (a) by expressing the number of layers as a power written in scientific notation. Use this information as reference points.
- 500 sheets of paper are about 5 cm thick.
- The CN Tower is about 550 m high.
- It is about 3.8×10^8 km from the Earth to the moon.
- It is about 1.5×10^{11} km from the Earth to the sun.

17. The population of a colony of cells is growing so that it will triple every hour. Suppose the current population is 200 cells. How many hours ago was there only one cell?

The Chapter Problem — What Is the Minimum Cost?

Refer to the Chapter Problem at the beginning of the chapter.

1. Create a difference table using the distance on land and the total cost.
2. Is the data linear or nonlinear? Explain.
3. Create a graph of total cost vs. length on land.
4. Use the graph to determine the combination that minimizes the total cost.

3.10 Powers with Rational Bases

Half-Life

Uranium is a naturally occurring substance that is found in some minerals. It is used in nuclear reactors to create electricity.

Uranium is radioactive, so it undergoes a process called radioactive decay. As time goes on, the radioactive uranium releases energy and changes into another element, such as lead. The rate of decay for different radioactive materials is called **half-life**. If a radioactive material has a half-life of one day, and a sample contains 10 g of the material today, then tomorrow it will contain only half the amount, or 5 g.

Pickering Nuclear Reactor

This table represents the amount of uranium left at different points in time. In this case, 0 means now and 1 is 1 day from now.

Time (d)	0	1	2	3	4	5	6	7	8
Radioactive Material (g)	80	40	20	10					

Think, Do, Discuss

1. Use the pattern in the table to determine the mass of radioactive material that will be left on days four to eight.
2. In the Radioactive Material row, how is the next value in the table related to the previous value?
3. Does this data represent a linear or nonlinear relationship?
4. Graph the data.
5. Copy the table into your notebook and add a third row titled Powers of Two. In this row, express each value in the Radioactive Material row as a product of eighty and a fraction.
6. Write each fraction as a power of two. What is the significance of the base? What is the significance of the exponent?
7. Using M for the initial mass of radioactive material and t as the time (in days), write an equation that models this relationship.
8. Using your calculator, predict the mass of radioactive material remaining after 10 days, 20 days, and 30 days.

Interest Earned

On the day she was born, Nora's family invested $5000 for her college education. The investment earns 8% per year and, at the end of each year, the interest is added to the balance in her account. Nora plans to go to college when she is 18. She wants to know what this investment will grow to by the time she reaches her 18th birthday.

Nora creates a spreadsheet and uses it to determine the value of the investment.

	A	B	C	D
1	Year	Amount at Beginning of Year ($)	Interest at End of Year ($)	Amount at End of Year ($)
2	1	5000		
3	2			
18	17			

Think, Do, Discuss

1. Calculate the interest Nora will earn at the end of the first year. What will her balance be after the first year?
2. What will Nora's balance be at the start of the second year?
3. Determine the interest she earns in the second year and find her balance at the end of the second year.
4. Nora realizes that she could save a lot of time and effort if she uses the power of the spreadsheet. What formula should she use to find the cell entry for B2? C2? A3?
5. Here is part of the spreadsheet that Nora created.

	A	B	C	D
1	Year	Amount at Beginning of Year ($)	Interest at End of Year ($)	Amount at End of Year ($)
2	1	5000	400	5400
3	2	5400	432	5832
4	3	5832	466.56	6298.56
5	4	6298.56	503.88	6802.44
6	5	6802.44	544.20	7346.64
7	6	7346.64	587.73	7934.37
8	7	7934.37	634.75	8569.12
9	8	8569.12	685.53	9254.65
10	9	9254.65	740.37	9995.02
18	17	17129.71	1370.38	18500.09

6. How much money will Nora have on her eighteenth birthday?
7. Take the values in C3 and C2 and divide them (C3/C2). Repeat for C4 and C3, C5 and C4, and C10 and C9. What do you notice? What is the significance of this number?
8. If A is the amount of the investment and n is the number of years the money has been invested, write an equation that models this relationship.
9. What type of relationship does this represent?
10. Recreate Nora's spreadsheet and use it to graph this relationship.
11. If Nora let this money continue to earn interest, how much will she have when she turns 70?

Focus

Key Ideas

- Exponential growth relationships can have constant multipliers that are rational numbers.

- If the constant multiplier has a value between 0 and 1, then the relationship is called **exponential decay**. The constant multiplier is called the **decay factor**.

- The graph of $y = a^x$, $0 < a < 1$, is a decreasing curve that always passes through $(0, 1)$.

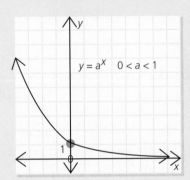

- A special type of exponential decay is **half-life**. The expression that models half-life is $M = c\left(\dfrac{1}{2}\right)^{\frac{t}{h}}$.

  c is the mass of the original mass of radiaoctive material.

  $\dfrac{1}{2}$ is the decay factor.

  t is time.

  h is the half-life of the substance.

- **Compound interest** occurs when interest earned is added to the principal (the original amount invested) and this sum becomes the new principal. It is the type of interest earned in most savings accounts and registered retirement savings plans.

- Compound interest is an example of exponential growth. It has a growth factor of $(1 + I)$, where I is the interest rate per investment period.

- $A = P(1 + I)^n$ is the equation that models compound interest.

  A is the amount that the investment is worth.

  P is the principal (the amount of money invested).

  I is the interest rate per period.

  n is the number of times interest is calculated over the length of the investment.

Did You Know?

Music and mathematics are closely connected. For instance, the notes that composers use to indicate how long a note should be held are like fractions.

Do some research. How much longer is one whole note than one eighth note? than one thirty-second note? What other connections between music and mathematics can you find?

Example

Latoya has $1000 to invest in a new bank account. The bank offers four types of accounts. Each one pays 6% interest, but over different schedules. Here are her options:

A: 6%/a compounded annually ("/a" means "per annum" or "per year")

B: 6%/a compounded semi-annually

C: 6%/a compounded quarterly

D: 6%/a compounded monthly

If she holds this investment for five years, which option will give her the greatest return?

Solution

Latoya knows that annually means that interest is paid once a year, semi-annually is twice a year, quarterly is four times a year, and monthly is 12 times a year. She creates this table to compare the four options.

Option	Principal (P)	Number of Times Interest is Paid per Year	Interest Rate per Period (I)	Number of Times Interest is Paid Over 5 Years (n)	Calculation = $P(1 + I)^n$	Amount (A)
A	$1000	1	$0.06 \div 1 = 0.06$	$1 \times 5 = 5$	$1000(1.06)^5$	$1338.23
B	$1000	2	$0.06 \div 2 = 0.03$	$2 \times 5 = 10$	$1000(1.03)^{10}$	$1343.92
C	$1000	4	$0.06 \div 4 = 0.015$	$4 \times 5 = 20$	$1000(1.015)^{20}$	$1346.86
D	$1000	12	$0.06 \div 12 = 0.005$	$12 \times 5 = 60$	$1000(1.005)^{60}$	$1348.85

Even though the interest rate is the smallest for option D, it generates the largest return because the interest is calculated more often. Option D is Latoya's best choice.

Practise, Apply, Solve

1. Evaluate.
   (a) 3.5^2 to the nearest tenth
   (b) -6.7^3 to the nearest hundredth
   (c) 13.9^4 to the nearest thousandth
   (d) 6.7^{-4} to the nearest ten thousandth
   (e) $(-5.1)^{-5}$ to the nearest hundred thousandth

2. Write with a positive exponent and whole number or decimal base.
   (a) $\left(\frac{1}{5}\right)^{-1}$
   (b) $\left(\frac{1}{7}\right)^{-1}$
   (c) $\left(\frac{1}{10}\right)^{-2}$
   (d) $\left(\frac{1}{8}\right)^{-2}$

3. Evaluate. Answer as a fraction.
   (a) $\left(\frac{2}{5}\right)^3$
   (b) $\left(-\frac{3}{4}\right)^2$
   (c) $\left(\frac{2}{3}\right)^{-1}$
   (d) $\left(\frac{3}{8}\right)^0$

   (e) $\left(\frac{4}{7}\right)^{-2}$
   (f) $\left(\frac{8}{9}\right)^2$
   (g) $\left(-\frac{4}{7}\right)^3$
   (h) $-\left(-\frac{1}{2}\right)^{-3}$

4. A sample of radioactive material decays according to the expression $M = 500\left(\frac{1}{2}\right)^{t}$, where M is the mass of the sample at time t. Mass is measured in grams and time is measured in years.
   (a) What is the initial mass of the material?
   (b) What is the half-life of this material?
   (c) How much of the material will remain after 2 years? 8 years? 20 years?
   (d) How much of the material was there at this time last year? 4 years ago?

5. Joshua has made an investment where the interest is compounded quarterly. The amount of his investment today is represented by $A = 4500(1.02)^{40}$. Determine:
   (a) his original principal.
   (b) the number of times the interest is calculated per year.
   (c) the length of his investment.
   (d) the annual interest rate the bank is giving him.
   (e) the amount his investment is worth.

B

6. A certain radioactive material has a half-life of 35 years. If 100 g of material is present now, how many grams will be present in 350 years?
   (a) Use a table of values to determine the answer.
   (b) Use the half-life formula to determine the answer.

7. Radon, a radioactive substance, has a half-life of 25 days. If 200 g of radon are present now:
   (a) how many grams will be present in 200 days?
   (b) how many grams will be present in 1000 days?
   (c) how many days will it take for the sample to decay to 25 g?

8. Five years ago, Lakeisha's parents invested $10 000 in a savings plan for her. The table shows the value of her investment at the end of each year for the past 5 years.

Year	0	1	2	3	4	5
Balance ($)	10 000	10 700	11 449	12 250	13 108	14 026

   (a) Graph Balance vs. Year.
   (b) Identify from the graph whether the relation is linear or nonlinear.
   (c) Use the table of values to identify the relation as linear or exponential.
   (d) Write an equation that represents this relation.
   (e) How much will the investment be worth in another three years if the rate of growth is the same?

9. A certain radioactive material loses its mass every 50 years as shown by the table of values.

Mass (mg)	64	32	16	8	4	2	1	$\frac{1}{2}$	$\frac{1}{4}$
Number of 50-year Intervals	(Start) 0	1	2	3	4	5	6	7	8

(a) Examine the change in mass to determine if this data is linear or nonlinear.

(b) What type of model does this data represent?

(c) Graph the data.

(d) Write an algebraic equation to represent this data.

(e) How many years from now will it have a mass of 4 mg? 0.5 mg? 0.125 mg?

10. Lee saves $1000 and can invest in either simple interest or compound interest. Examine the table of values.

Time (years)	Simple Interest	Compound Interest
0	1000	1000
1	1100	1100
2	1200	1210
3	1300	1331
4	1400	1464
5	1500	1611

(a) Which set of data is linear and which is exponential?

(b) Graph both sets of data on the same axes. Extrapolate the data for up to 10 years.

(c) Write an equation to represent each set of data.

11. Determine the amount that each investment is worth.

(a) $500 is invested at 5%/a compounded annually for 4 years.

(b) $1000 is invested at 8%/a compounded semi-annually for 10 years.

(c) $5000 is invested at 8%/a compounded quarterly for 3 years.

(d) $2000 is invested at 3%/a compounded monthly for 3 years.

(e) $550 is invested at 2%/a compounded quarterly for 7 years.

(f) $900 is invested at 7%/a compounded semi-annually for 40 months.

(g) $800 is invested at 6%/a compounded monthly for 50 months.

12. Beth inherits $25 000. She decides to invest it and leave the money invested until she becomes a millionaire. The rate of interest is 12%/a. At the end of each year, any interest earned is added to the investment. Complete the spreadsheet to determine the number of years it will take for the inheritance to grow to $1 000 000. When using the computer, you will have to determine formulas for C2, D2, A3, and B3.

	A	B	C	D
1	Year	Opening Amount	Interest	Closing Amount
2	1	$25 000		
3				

13. The charge remaining in a battery decreases as the battery is used. The charge C, in coulombs, after t days is given by $C = (3 \times 10^{-4})(0.7)^t$. Find the charge after 5 days.

14. The population of a small town is decreasing exponentially according to $P = 3750(0.93)^t$, where t is measured in years from the present date.
  (a) Find the population of the town in 6 years.
  (b) By what percentage of the original population is the town decreasing?

 C

15. Which financial institution provides the better investment?

Smartmoney Trust Co.: Earn 5.25%/a compounded monthly

Investors Savings & Loan: Money market account paying 5.35%/a compounded annually

16. A small office buys a computer for $4575. Each year, its value is expected to be 65% of its value the previous year. Find the value of the computer after 5 years.

Career: Genetic Engineer

All cells of living organisms contain huge DNA molecules (called chromosomes) that can contain thousands of genes. Genes are parts of DNA molecules that encode information on what an organism looks like, how it behaves, and many other characteristics.

When a cell divides, each of the two resulting cells contains all the genetic information of the original. All the cells of an organism have a common set of genes that determine the organism's nature.

Genetic engineers can alter the genes of an organism. One technique they use is gene splicing, in which chemicals are used to snip off certain genes and replace them with others. For example, in 1987 some genetic engineers used a gene from a bacteria cell to make some tomato plants resistant to caterpillars.

One of the major successes of genetic engineering was the development of bacteria that produce insulin, a drug needed by diabetics. Because cell growth involves repeated doubling, large numbers, and very small organisms, exponents are frequently used by genetic engineers.

Did You Know?

Radiocarbon, or carbon-14, is a radioactive form of carbon. It has an atomic weight of 14 and is heavier than ordinary carbon, which has an atomic weight of 12.011.

Radiocarbon is used to determine the age of fossils and other ancient objects. Radiocarbon dating is the process of dating an object by measuring the amount of radiocarbon it contains. This dating technique was developed by the American chemist Willard F. Libby (1908–1980) in 1947.

Exponent Laws

Remember the bacteria investigation from Section 3.9. A single bacterium in a petri dish multiplies exponentially. A technician counted the number of bacteria every hour and recorded the data.

Time (h)	Number of Bacteria	Powers of Two
0	1	
1	2	
2	4	
3	8	
4	16	
5	32	
6	64	
7	128	
8	256	

Think, Do, Discuss

1. Express each of the values in the Number of Bacteria column as a power of two.
2. Anjay, a lab assistant, noticed some relationships in the data that was collected. He noticed that entries in the Number of Bacteria column were related to each other through multiplication. For example, $2 \times 4 = 8$ and $4 \times 16 = 64$. Write any multiplication relationships that exist in the data for this column in your notebook.
3. Anjay also noticed that this relationship worked with the powers of two.

   $2 \times 4 = 8$ ($2^1 \times 2^2 = 2^3$), also $4 \times 16 = 64$, ($2^2 \times 2^4 = 2^6$).

   Using the other relationships you discovered, check to see if this pattern works as well.
4. Write a rule that you could follow to help you multiply powers of two together.
5. Could this rule be used for all powers? Explain.
6. Look at the data in the Number of Bacteria column again. Are there any entries that are related to each other through division? If so, write several of them down.
7. Do these division relationships also work for powers of two?
8. Write a rule that other students could use to divide powers of two.
9. Could this rule be used for all powers? Explain.
10. Anjay also noticed that if he took some of the values from the Number of Bacteria column and squared them or cubed them, the values showed up as entries further down the table.

    $8^2 = 64$ and $4^3 = 64$. Also, $16^2 = 256$ and $4^4 = 256$.

    If these values are changed to powers of two, does the relationship still hold? Explain.
11. Write a rule that students could use to simplify a power of a power of 2.
12. Could this rule be used for all powers? Explain.

Focus

Example

Simplify.

    (a) $(x^2y^3)(x^4y^2)$ **(b)** $\dfrac{x^5y^4}{x^2y^2}$ **(c)** $(x^2y^3)^3$

Solution

(a)

$$(x^2y^3)(x^4y^2) = x \cdot x \cdot x \cdot x \cdot x \cdot x \cdot y \cdot y \cdot y \cdot y \cdot y$$
$$= x^6y^5$$

or

$$(x^2y^3)(x^4y^2) = x^{(2 + 4)}y^{(3 + 2)}$$
$$= x^6y^5$$

(b)

$$\frac{x^5y^4}{x^2y^2} = \frac{x \cdot x \cdot x \cdot x \cdot x \cdot y \cdot y \cdot y \cdot y}{x \cdot x \cdot y \cdot y}$$
$$= x^3y^2$$

or

$$\frac{x^5y^4}{x^2y^2} = x^{(5 - 2)}y^{(4 - 2)}$$
$$= x^3y^2$$

(c)

$$(x^2y^3)^3 = (x \cdot x \cdot y \cdot y \cdot y)(x \cdot x \cdot y \cdot y \cdot y)(x \cdot x \cdot y \cdot y \cdot y)$$
$$= x \cdot x \cdot x \cdot x \cdot x \cdot x \cdot y \cdot y \cdot y \cdot y \cdot y \cdot y \cdot y \cdot y \cdot y$$
$$= x^6y^9$$

or

$$(x^2y^3)^3 = x^{2 \times 3}y^{3 \times 3}$$
$$= x^6y^9$$

Did You Know?

On April 1, 1999, the new territory of Nunavut was created from the eastern half of the Northwest Territories. This photograph shows the ceremonies marking the event. This marks the first time that the map of Canada has changed since Newfoundland joined in 1949. Before Nunavut was created, the Northwest Territories covered about $\dfrac{7}{20}$ of the total area of Canada. About what fraction of Canada's area does Nunavut cover?

Practise, Apply, Solve

A

1. Use a numerical example to illustrate each law.
   (a) $x^m \times x^n = x^{m+n}$
   (b) $x^m \div x^n = x^{m-n}$
   (c) $(x^m)^n = x^{mn}$

2. Simplify.
   (a) $(2^2)(2^3)$ (b) $(3^2)(3^4)$
   (c) $(5^3)(5)$ (d) $(4^3)(4^7)(4^2)$

3. Simplify.
   (a) $2^5 \div 2^2$ (b) $4^6 \div 4^3$
   (c) $7^6 \div 7$ (d) $10^{10} \div 10^8$

4. Simplify.
   (a) $(3^4)^2$ (b) $(9^4)^3$
   (c) $(2^5)^3$ (d) $(10^6)^6$

5. Express as a single power, then evaluate.
   (a) $(2^2)(2^5)$ (b) $(4^{-3})(4^4)$ (c) $(5^{-3})(5^5)$
   (d) $(3^{-1})(3^4)$ (e) $(2^{-2})(2^{-3})$ (f) $(10^2)(10^3)(10^{-4})$
   (g) $(-2)^2(-2)^3$ (h) $(3^5)(3^{-7})(3^4)$

6. Express as a single power, then evaluate.
   (a) $\frac{2^5}{2^2}$ (b) $\frac{4^6}{4^3}$ (c) $\frac{10^{10}}{10^5}$
   (d) $\frac{2^{-5}}{2^2}$ (e) $\frac{3^{-3}}{3^{-2}}$ (f) $\frac{3^2}{3^{-2}}$
   (g) $10^6 \div 10^{-3}$ (h) $5^{-2} \div 5^{-3}$

7. Express as a single power, then evaluate.
   (a) $(2^3)^2$ (b) $(3^2)^3$ (c) $(4^{-1})^2$
   (d) $(5^{-1})^{-2}$ (e) $(10^3)^{-2}$ (f) $(10^{-2})^{-3}$
   (g) $(6^{-1})^{-1}$ (h) $(28^{13})^0$

8. Simplify.
   (a) $(m^4)(m^2)$ (b) $(n^5)(n^{-3})$ (c) $(x^{-4})(x^{-2})$
   (d) $(r^8)(r^{-2})$ (e) $(w^{-6})(w^{-7})$ (f) $(m^3)(m^{-4})(m^2)$
   (g) $(p^{-3})(p^{-2})(p^8)$ (h) $(b^5)(b^{-3})(b^{-7})$ (i) $(x^4)^2$
   (j) $(y^3)^{-4}$ (k) $(m^{-2})^{-3}$ (l) $(p^{-4})^2$
   (m) $\frac{m^6}{m^2}$ (n) $\frac{y^{15}}{y^5}$ (o) $\frac{x^7}{x^{10}}$
   (p) $s^{12} \div s^3$ (q) $t^{12} \div t^{-4}$ (r) $\frac{h^{-8}}{h^{-9}}$

9. Simplify.

(a) $(2y^3)^4$ (b) $(3x^5)^2$ (c) $(5y^6)^{-1}$

(d) $(4y^{-7})^3$ (e) $(10b^8)^3$ (f) $(10c^3)^{-2}$

(g) $(-2y^{-3})^{-3}$ (h) $(-2m^2)^4$

10. Evaluate.

(a) $(2^2)^4 - (3^3)^2$ (b) $(9^{-1})^{-2} - (7^{-2})^{-1}$

(c) $(10^2)^5 - (10^3)^3$ (d) $-(10^{-2})^{-1} - (10^3)^{-1}$

11. Evaluate.

(a) $\dfrac{(8^6)(8^{-3})}{8^4}$ (b) $\dfrac{(7^{-2})(7^{-5})}{7^9}$

(c) $\dfrac{(3^2)(4^3)(3^5)(4^2)}{(3^7)(4^5)}$ (d) $\dfrac{(2.0 \times 10^8)(4.0 \times 10^7)}{3.0 \times 10^{12}}$

(e) $\dfrac{(5^2)^3(7^3)^4}{(7^{11})(5^5)}$ (f) $\dfrac{(5^{-2})(6^{-5})}{(5^4)^{-1}(6^{-2})^3}$

12. Convert to scientific notation and evaluate. Leave the simplified answer in scientific form.

(a) $0.000\ 000\ 000\ 000\ 9 \times 0.000\ 000\ 000\ 08$

(b) $200\ 000\ 000\ 000 \times 0.000\ 000\ 000\ 7$

(c) $\dfrac{800\ 000\ 000}{0.000\ 000\ 2 \times 0.0004}$

13. Evaluate.

(a) $2^4 + 2^{-2} - 2^0 \times 2^{-1}$ (b) $5^2 + 5^{-2} \times 5^{-1}$

(c) $\dfrac{3^0 + 1}{3^{-5}} \div 3^6 - 3^{-1}$ (d) $10^{-3} \times \dfrac{1}{10^{-5}} + (10^3)^0 - 10^{-1}$

14. (a) Evaluate $(x^5)^2(x^7)^3(x^2)^{-6}$ when $x = 2$.

(b) Evaluate $\dfrac{(m^5)^2}{m^{11}} + \dfrac{(n^2)^3}{n^7}$ when $m = 3$ and $n = 4$.

15. Find the value of the exponent that makes each equation true.

(a) $4^3 = 2^\blacksquare$ (b) $6^9 = 216^\blacksquare$ (c) $625^2 = 25^\blacksquare$ (d) $27^4 = 3^\blacksquare$

16. Write each power in simplified form.

(a) 4^5 as a base 2 power   (b) 9^6 as a base 3 power

(c) 27^4 as a base 3 power   (d) $(-125)^7$ as a base -5 power

17. Write all powers using a common base, then simplify.

(a) $\dfrac{16^3}{2^4}$ (b) $\dfrac{25^4}{5^5}$

(c) $\dfrac{3^5}{81^2}$ (d) $\dfrac{(128^3)(64^2)}{32^5}$

18. Simplify.

(a) $(x^3y^5)(x^4y^3)$ (b) $(x^{-2}y^4)(x^4y^{-1})$ (c) $\dfrac{x^3y^6}{x^2y^3}$

(d) $\dfrac{x^{-3}y^{-4}}{x^2y^{-2}}$ **(e)** $(x^3y^4)^4$ **(f)** $(x^{-2}y^5)^{-2}$

(g) $\dfrac{(xy^3)(x^{-3}y^4)}{x^2y^{-1}}$ **(h)** $\dfrac{(x^4y^5)}{(x^2y^2)^2}$

19. Use $a = -2$, $b = -1$, and $c = 4$. Find the value of each.

(a) $\dfrac{a^5}{a^2}$ **(b)** $(b^3)^2$ **(c)** $\dfrac{(c^2)^3}{c^5}$ **(d)** $\dfrac{a^3b^3}{ab}$ **(e)** $\dfrac{(ab)^3}{a^2b}$

20. (a) Construct a chart or matrix to show the relationship between millimetres, centimetres, metres, and kilometres. Show all combinations and express each number as a power with base 10.
(b) Use the chart to determine the number of centimetres in 5 km.
(c) How many centimetres are in 6 mm?
(d) A piece of steel plate is used to make a railway car. The plate is 2.5 m wide, 3.2 m long, and 5 mm thick. Determine the volume of steel in cubic centimetres.

The Chapter Problem — What Is the Minimum Cost?

Refer to the Chapter Problem at the beginning of the chapter.

1. In the previous section, you estimated the combination that would minimize the cost.
To find the exact combination, you should use a graphing calculator. Graph the equation
Cost $= 10x + 15\sqrt{500^2 + (4000 - x)^2}$. Use the trace function to determine a more accurate combination.

2. If x represents the length of line on land, explain how the equation above represents the total cost to lay the line to the island.

Sophie Germain (1776–1831)

Sophie Germain was born in Paris. At an early age, she developed a keen interest in mathematics. Despite being barred from the École Polytechnique because she was female, she continued to study mathematics through the lecture notes of male professors. Under the pseudonym of M. Leblanc, she would write comments on various studies or theories. So great was her intellect that she won high praise from the mathematician Lagrange.

In 1816, she won an award for her paper on elasticity. In the 1820s, she proved that for each odd prime $p < 100$, the Fermat equation, $x^p + y^p = z^p$, can have a solution only if integers x, y, and z are divisible by p.

Do research on the Internet or the library on Sophie Germain or Lagrange.

3.12 Investigating Relationships

TECHNOLOGY

Using Digital Probes

In our attempt to understand the world around us, we collect data and try to find patterns or relationships. In this book, you have seen many examples of relationships that are linear and nonlinear.

Digital probe technology allows us to collect large amounts of data and analyze it quickly.

Conduct the following experiments and use the technology to help you find the most appropriate mathematical model.

As a project, design your own experiment to explore the relationships involved in a phenomenon of your choice.

Experiment 1: Dropping an Object

You will need the BALLDROP and SELECT programs.

Set-Up and Operation of the CBL Unit

1. Make sure that the CBL and calculator are both OFF.
2. Connect the CBL to the calculator using the unit-to-unit connector cable. Connect the cable firmly to the input/output port on the bottom of the calculator (see diagram below).
3. Connect the motion detector to the SONIC port on the CBL. This port is on the left side of the unit.
4. Turn the CBL unit and the calculator ON.
5. Place the motion detector on the floor (facing up) in an open spot in the classroom.
6. Three students are needed for this experiment: the catcher catches the dropped objects before they hit the motion detector. The dropper holds and drops the objects. The CBL operator controls the CBL.
7. Select a light object, such as a notebook, to drop over the motion detector.
8. Turn on the CBL and the calculator.
9. Start the program BALLDROP on the calculator. The motion detector will start clicking. Pressing the TRIGGER button on the CBL will start the data collection process. Do not press this button until instructed to do so by the operator.

10. The catcher should move into position to catch the falling object, keeping his or her hands clear of the motion detector's beam.

11. The dropper should hold the object about 1.5 m above the motion detector. When the CBL displays Ready, the operator should press TRIGGER and instruct the dropper to drop the object. The catcher catches the object above the motion detector.

Think, Do, Discuss

1. Analyze the graph of the collected data. Explain why the graph has the shape it does. Try the experiment again using a different object. Does the graph change? Explain.

2. Have the dropper throw a ball into the air above the motion detector. The catcher should allow the ball to rise then fall over the motion detector before it is caught.

3. Use the TRACE feature to find the coordinates of the highest point reached by the ball. What shape is the graph? Write an explanation for its shape.

4. What type of relationship is this?

Experiment 2: A Graph of Sound

You will need the BEATS and SOUND programs. You will also need a microphone/amplifier with CBL DIN adapter, tuning forks, and a rubber tuning fork hammer.

Set-Up and Operation of the CBL Unit

1. Connect the CBL unit to the calculator with the unit-to-unit link cable using the I/O ports located on the bottom edge of each unit. Press the cable ends in firmly.

2. Connect the microphone to Channel 1 (CH1) on the top edge of the CBL unit.

3. Turn on the CBL unit and the calculator. The CBL system is now ready to receive commands from the calculator.

4. Start the SOUND program on the calculator. The program will pause execution and wait for you to press `ENTER`.

5. Select a tuning fork whose frequency is between 200 and 300 Hz.

6. Strike the tuning fork with the rubber hammer and place the vibrating fork as close as possible to the microphone. (Do not let the fork actually touch the microphone.)

7. As soon as the tuning fork is close to the microphone, press `ENTER`.

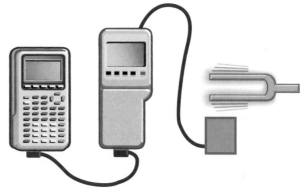

Think, Do, Discuss

1. When you are satisfied with the graph, make a copy for your notes.
   Pressure is stored in **L1** and time (in seconds) is stored in **L2**. Explain why the graph appears as it does.

2. Repeat this procedure at least two more times using different tuning forks. Does this have an affect on the graphs? Explain why.
3. What type of relationship is this?

Experiment 3: Newton's Law of Cooling

You will need the COOL TEMP program. You will also need a temperature probe, a hot plate, a medium beaker, a laboratory thermometer, water, and ice.

Set-Up and Operation of the CBL Unit

1. Connect the CBL unit to the calculator with the unit-to-unit link cable using the I/O ports located on the bottom edge of each unit. Press the cable ends in firmly.
2. Connect the temperature probe to CH2 on the top edge of the CBL.
3. Turn on the CBL unit and the calculator. The CBL is now ready to receive commands from the calculator.
4. Read the laboratory thermometer to determine the room temperature in degrees Celsius and record this value as C in your lab notebook. Store this value in variable C on the calculator.

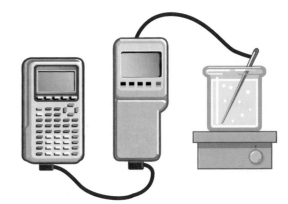

5. Fill a medium beaker with water and place the beaker on the hot plate. When the water begins to boil, place the temperature probe in the beaker for several seconds.
6. Make sure the CBL is turned on. Start the COOL TEMP program on the calculator. Remove the temperature probe from the boiling water and press ENTER on the calculator to start collecting data.
7. The probe should remain exposed to the air while the CBL and calculator collect the temperature data. To avoid conduction and evaporation effects on the temperature probe, do not place the probe directly on the tabletop or expose it to any drafts.

Think, Do, Discuss

1. Put a copy of the graph in your notes. Be sure to include appropriate scales and axis labels on the printout. Observe and analyze the data collected. What does the graph tell you about the way an object cools? Create a differences table from the collected data.
2. Repeat this experiment two more times. For one of the trials, start with the temperature probe in an ice bath and allow it to warm up when removed. Determine if this is an exponential relationship.
3. What type of relationship is this?

Chapter Review

3.1–3.2 Positive and Negative Fractions and Decimals

- Coordinates in the Cartesian plane can be negative or positive. They can also contain fractional or decimal values.

- A positive or negative fractional value can be converted to a decimal value by dividing the numerator by the denominator. The resulting decimal either repeats indefinitely or terminates. For example, $\frac{1}{2} = 0.5$ or $\frac{1}{3} = 0.333...$

- When decimal values repeat, the block of repeating digits is called the **period** of the number and a bar symbol is used to mark the period. For example, the period of $\frac{1}{11} = 0.\overline{09}$ is 09.

- Terminating decimals can be converted by rewriting them in their fractional form using the place value of the last digit to determine the denominator of the fraction. For example, $0.4 = \frac{4}{10}$ or $\frac{2}{5}$.

- Positive and negative fractions are **quotients** of integers and take the form $\frac{a}{b}$, where a and b are integers, but $b \neq 0$. This set of numbers is called the set of **rational numbers** and is represented by the symbol **Q**.

- These are the properties of each set of numbers.

Set	Examples	Symbol
Natural Numbers	the counting numbers 1, 2, 3, …	N
Whole Numbers	the counting numbers and zero 0, 1, 2, 3, …	W
Integers	positive and negative whole numbers … −3, −2, −1, 0, 1, 2, 3, …	I
Rational Numbers	numbers of the form $\frac{a}{b}$ where a and b are integers and $b \neq 0$	Q

Extra Practice

1. True or False? Use examples to explain your reasoning.
   (a) The set of integers consists only of the set of natural numbers and the set of whole numbers.
   (b) All rational numbers can be written as fractions or decimals.
   (c) All decimal numbers are either integers or rational numbers.
   (d) 0 is the only number that is a natural number, a whole number, an integer, and a rational number.
   (e) The addition of all the integers and all the whole numbers results in the set of natural numbers.

2. **(a)** Set up a table of values for the relation $y = -\frac{1}{2}x + 3$ for $-1 \leq x \leq 1$. Use at least five different values.

(b) Graph the relation by hand.

(c) Use a graphing tool to check your graph. Adjust the display so that $-1 \leq x \leq 1$ using either the ZOOM command or by adjusting the RANGE .

3.3–3.4 Rational Number Operations

- The overall sign of a rational number expressed in the form $\frac{a}{b}$ is:
  - positive, if the fraction contains an even number of negative signs.
  - negative, if the fraction contains an odd number of negative signs.
- Rational number operations can often be simplified by converting mixed numbers to improper fractions and writing negative fractions with the negative number in the numerator. To add or subtract, find a common denominator and apply the rules of integer operations to the numerators and denominators. To divide by a rational number, multiply by its reciprocal.
- Negative rational numbers can be entered into a calculator using the negative ($-$ or $+/-$) key, which is different from the subtraction ($-$) operation key.
- Sometimes, rational number operations using decimal numbers on a calculator can result in answers that are not accurate as a result of rounding.

Example

Evaluate $-3\frac{1}{2} - \left(\frac{-2}{3}\right)$.

Solution

$$-3\frac{1}{2} - \left(\frac{-2}{3}\right) = \frac{-7}{2} - \frac{-2}{3}$$
$$= \frac{-7(3)}{2(3)} - \frac{-2(2)}{3(2)}$$
$$= \frac{-21}{6} - \frac{-4}{6}$$
$$= \frac{-21 - (-4)}{6}$$
$$= \frac{-21 + 4}{6}$$
$$= \frac{-17}{6}$$
$$= -2\frac{5}{6}$$

Extra Practice

3. Simplify. Express your answers in simplest terms.

(a) $-\frac{14}{10}$

(b) $-\frac{3}{5} + \left(\frac{-3}{4}\right) - \frac{7}{10}$

(c) $\left(-4\frac{1}{6}\right)\left(-7\frac{3}{4}\right)$

(d) $\left(-2\frac{1}{3}\right) - \left(-3\frac{1}{2}\right)$

(e) $-\frac{1}{3} - \frac{1}{8}$

(f) $6 - \left(-\frac{1}{5}\right) - \left(-\frac{1}{2}\right)$

3.5–3.6 Models of Movement

- In a problem involving movement, the graph shows displacement (distance, height, or depth) versus time. Distance, height, or depth is the dependent variable and time is the independent variable.

  The rate of change in this relationship is speed or **velocity**:

  $$v = \frac{\Delta d}{\Delta t} = \frac{\text{the change in distance}}{\text{the change in time}}$$

- Before drawing the graph, finite differences should be used to determine the nature of the relationship (linear or nonlinear, line segment or smooth curve).

- In a linear relationship, the velocity is constant.

- In a nonlinear relationship, the velocity changes with time. This change means there is non-zero acceleration or deceleration.

Example

Julio ran to the corner store and back home as shown on the graph.

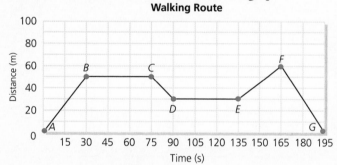

Walking Route

(a) What line segment represents the fastest speed? Explain.
(b) What line segment indicates the slowest speed (but still moving)?
(c) What line segments indicate he was stopped? Explain.

Solution

(a) Line segment *FG* is the steepest line. This means the change in distance over time is the greatest. The line represents the fastest speed.
(b) Line segment *EF* is the line with the most gradual slope. This means that Julio is travelling at the slowest speed.
(c) Line segments *BC* and *DE* have a slope of zero. This means the change in distance with respect to time is zero. He was stopped.

Extra Practice

4. A hotel courtesy bus takes David from the airport to his hotel. Use the Distance vs. Time graph to create a story that traces the route of the bus.

Courtesy Bus Trip

5. Calculate the finite differences. Does the data represent a linear or nonlinear relationship?

(a)

x	y
10	23
20	43
30	63
40	83

(b)

x	y
1	1
2	7
3	17
4	31

(c)

x	y
1	−2
3	−8
7	−20
13	−38

6. A rock falls over a cliff. The speed of the rock at various times is shown in the table of values.

Time (s)	Speed (m/s)
0	0
1	5
2	20
3	45
4	80
5	125

(a) Graph the data. What is the dependent variable? the independent variable?

(b) Does the data represent a linear or nonlinear relationship? Explain.

(c) Explain what is happening to the rock as it falls to the ground.

3.7–3.8 Investigating Relationships in Geometric Figures

- Measurements associated with geometric figures involve relationships that can be either linear or nonlienar.

Example

These diagrams show points joined by the line segments.

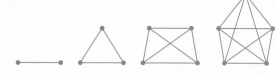

(a) Extend the pattern to include figures with up to six points.

(b) Create the graph of number of line segments vs. number of points.

(c) Identify the graph as linear or nonlinear.

(d) Explain in words how to determine the number of line segments formed in terms of the number of points.

(e) Write a relationship for the number of line segments formed in terms of the number of points used.

Solution

(a)

Number of Points	Number of Line Segments
2	1
3	3
4	6
5	10
6	15

(b)

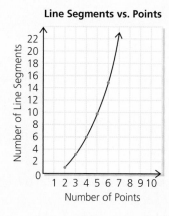

(c) The graph represents a nonlinear relationship.

(d) To determine the number of line segments formed in terms of the number of points, it is helpful to look at the table and examine the pattern.

Points (p)	Line Segments (n)	Pattern
2	1	$\frac{(2)(1)}{2} \rightarrow 1$
3	3	$\frac{(3)(2)}{2} \rightarrow 3$
4	6	$\frac{(4)(3)}{2} \rightarrow 6$
5	10	$\frac{(5)(4)}{2} \rightarrow 10$

Here, multiplying the number of points by one less than the number of points and dividing by two gives the number of line segments.

(e) The relationship is $n = \dfrac{p(p-1)}{2}$, where n is the number of line segments and p is the number of points.

Extra Practice

7. **(a)** Draw these polygons: triangle, quadrilateral, pentagon, hexagon.

(b) Copy and complete the chart.

Polygon	triangle	quadrilateral	pentagon	hexagon
Number of Diagonals				

(c) Predict the number of diagonals in polygons with seven and eight sides.

(d) By calculating finite differences, determine whether the data is linear or nonlinear.

(e) Graph the data.

(f) Write an expression for the number of diagonals in terms of the number of sides in the polygon.

8. Frieda walks to school. She travels along a straight sidewalk for 1.3 km and then turns a right angle corner and walks another 0.8 km along a straight sidewalk. How much distance would she save if she could walk diagonally from her house to school?

9. Two planes leave Sudbury airport at about the same time. One flies due east at 180 km/h. The other flies due south at 210 km/h. How far apart are the planes after 4 h?

3.9 Investigating Models of Growth

- A relationship where population increases with time by a **constant** multiplier is nonlinear.

- If the constant multiplier is greater than 1, the relationship is called **exponential growth**. The constant multiplier is called the growth factor.

- The equation that describes exponential growth is $y = c(a)^x$. c is the initial population, a is the growth factor, and x is time.

- The graph of $y = a^x$, $a > 1$, is an increasing curve that always passes through $(0, 1)$.

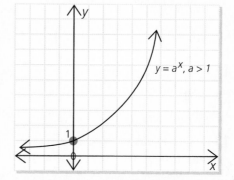

- When an exponent is zero, it gives a value of 1. $x^0 = 1$ (for example: $5^0 = 1$).

- When a power with a base greater than 1 has a negative exponent, it gives a fractional value.

$$x^{-n} = \frac{1}{x^n} \quad \left(\text{for example: } 5^{-2} = \frac{1}{5^2} = \frac{1}{25} \right).$$

- Scientific notation is a way of writing very large and very small numbers in a convenient form. To express a number in scientific notation, write it as the product of a decimal between 1 and 10 and a power of 10.

Standard Form	Scientific Notation
123 000 000	1.23×10^8
0.003 45	3.45×10^{-3}

Example

Given the power 5^{-3}.

(a) Identify the base.
(b) Identify the exponent.
(c) Is the value of the power positive or negative?
(d) Write the power with a positive exponent.
(e) Write it in expanded form.
(f) Evaluate it.

Solution

(a) The base is 5.
(b) The exponent is -3.
(c) Since the base is greater than zero, then the value of the power is greater than zero. It is positive.

(d) $5^{-3} = \frac{1}{5^3}$ **(e)** $5^{-3} = \frac{1}{(5)(5)(5)}$ **(f)** $5^{-3} = \frac{1}{125}$

Extra Practice

10. Expand and evaluate.

(a) 3^4 (b) $(-2)^5$ (c) -3^4 (d) $\left(\dfrac{2}{3}\right)^3$ (e) 4^{-2}

(f) 10^{-3} (g) $(6n)^2$ (h) $(-2y)^7$ (i) $(3m)^3$ (j) $\left(-\dfrac{2}{3}k\right)^3$

11. Evaluate and express as a fraction in lowest terms.

(a) $5^{-1} + 7^{-1}$ (b) $4^{-2} - 15^0 + 3^4$

(c) $\left(\dfrac{3}{4}\right)^{-1} - \left(\dfrac{3}{5}\right)^{-1} + \left(\dfrac{3}{7}\right)^{-1}$ (d) $-3^4 + (-3)^3 - (-3)^2$

12. Express each pair of numbers in scientific notation.

(a) 630 000 000, 0.000 000 063

(b) 72 100 000 000, 0.000 000 000 721

13. Use a calculator to evaluate.

(a) $(7.3 \times 10^{-14}) \times (6.8 \times 10^{20})$

(b) $\dfrac{0.000\ 000\ 000\ 000\ 13 \times 0.000\ 000\ 000\ 121}{11\ 000\ 000\ 000}$

3.10 Powers with Rational Number Bases

- Exponential growth relationships can have constant multipliers that are rational numbers.
- If the constant multiplier has a value between 0 and 1, the relationship is called **exponential decay**. The constant multiplier is called the **decay factor**.
- The graph of $y = a^x$, $0 < a < 1$, is a decreasing curve that always passes through $(0, 1)$.

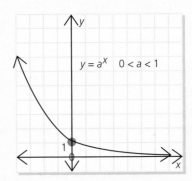

- A special type of exponential decay is **half-life**. The expression that models half-life is $M = c\left(\dfrac{1}{2}\right)^{\frac{t}{h}}$.

  c is the mass of the original mass of radioactive material.

  $\dfrac{1}{2}$ is the decay factor.

  t is time.

  h is the half-life of the substance.

- **Compound interest** occurs when interest earned is added to the principal (the original amount invested) and this sum becomes the new principal. It is the type of interest earned in most savings accounts and registered retirement savings plans.
- Compound interest is an example of exponential growth. It has a growth factor of $(1 + I)$, where I is the interest rate per investment period.

- $A = P(1 + I)^n$ is the equation that models compound interest where:
  A is the amount that the investment is worth;
  P is the principal (the amount of money invested);
  I is the interest rate per period; and
  n is the number of times interest is calculated over the length of the investment.

Example

Shanti inherits $10 000 when she is 16 years old. She invests it at 8% compounded annually.
On her 25th birthday, she cashes in the investment.
The table of values shows how her savings grow over the years.

Time (years)	Amount ($)
0	10 000
1	10 800
2	11 664
3	12 597
4	13 605
5	14 693
6	15 869
7	17 138

(a) Identify the data as linear or nonlinear.
(b) Graph the results.
(c) Determine the growth factor and use the value to determine the amount of money she had on her 25th birthday.
(d) Write an equation to represent this relationship.
(e) What will the amount be on Shanti's 40th birthday if she chooses not cash in her inheritance?

Solution

(a) Make a column of differences. The differences are not the same, so the data is nonlinear.

Time (years)	Amount ($)	Differences (d)
0	10 000	
		800
1	10 800	
		864
2	11 664	
		933
3	12 597	
		1008
4	13 605	
		1088
5	14 693	
		1176
6	15 869	
		1269
7	17 138	

(b)

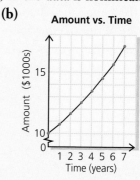

Amount vs. Time

(c) The growth factor is calculated by dividing the amount she had each year by the previous year's amount.

$$\frac{\text{Year 3 Amount}}{\text{Year 2 Amount}} = \frac{12\ 597}{11\ 664} \doteq 1.08 \qquad \frac{\text{Year 5 Amount}}{\text{Year 4 Amount}} = \frac{14\ 693}{13\ 605} \doteq 1.08$$

The growth factor is 1.08.

Shanti turns 25 in year 9, or two more interest calculations. The amount is 17 138(1.08)(1.08) or 19 990. On her 25th birthday she will have $19 990.

(d) The data is represented by the exponential equation $y = ca^x$.

Here c is 10 000 and a is 1.08.

The equation is $y = 10\ 000(1.08)^x$.

(e) On Shanti's 40th birthday:

$$x = 40 - 16$$
$$= 24$$

$$y = 10\ 000(1.08)^{24}$$
$$\doteq 63\ 411.807$$

The amount will be $63 411.81.

Extra Practice

14. Use the y^x key on a calculator to evaluate each power.
    (a) $(1.08)^9$ (b) $10\ 000(1.08)^9$ (c) 6^5
    (d) 3^8 (e) $(1.1)^{11}$ (f) $(-5)^5$

15. A certain radioactive material has a half-life of 100 years, as shown in the table of values.

Mass (mg)	32 768	16 384	8192	4096
Number of 100-year Intervals	0	1	2	3

    (a) Is the data linear or nonlinear?
    (b) Graph the data for six 100-year intervals.
    (c) Write an equation to represent the data.
    (d) What mass of material remains after 1000 years?

16. Identify the relationship of the data in each table as linear or nonlinear.

(a)

x	y
0	1
1	1.1
2	1.21
3	1.331
4	1.4641

(b)

x	y
0	1
1	6
2	11
3	16
4	21

(c)

x	y
0	1
1	1
2	5
3	19
4	49

(d)

x	y
0	1
3	−11
4	−15
7	−27
8	−31

17. Determine the amount that each investment is worth.

(a) $1500 invested at 12%/a compounded annually for 4 years.

(b) $1200 invested at 10%/a compounded semi-annually for 10 years.

(c) $500 invested at 4%/a compounded quarterly for 3 years.

(d) $25 000 invested at 12%/a compounded monthly for 3 years.

(e) $5500 invested at 12%/a compounded quarterly for 5 years.

(f) $1900 invested at 6%/a compounded semi-annually for 36 months.

3.11 Investigating the Exponent Laws

- To multiply powers with the same base, keep the base the same and add the exponents.
$a^m \times a^n = a^{(m + n)}$ (for example: $(3^4)(3^6) = 3^{(4 + 6)} = 3^{10}$)

- To divide powers with the same base, keep the base the same and subtract the exponents.
$\frac{a^m}{a^n} = a^{(m - n)}$ (for example: $(4^6) \div (4^3) = 4^{(6 - 3)} = 4^3$)

- To simplify a power of a power, keep the base the same and multiply the exponents.
$(a^m)^n = a^{m \times n}$ (for example: $(2^5)^3 = 2^{5 \times 3} = 2^{15}$)

Example

Evaluate $\left(\frac{(3^{12})(3^5)}{3^{15}} \right) + (4^9)(4^{-8}) - (2^3)^2$.

Solution

$$\left(\frac{(3^{12})(3^5)}{3^{15}} \right) + (4^9)(4^{-8}) - (2^3)^2 = 3^{(12 + 5 - 15)} + 4^{(9 + (-8))} - 2^{3(2)}$$
$$= 3^2 + 4^1 - 2^6$$
$$= 9 + 4 - 64$$
$$= -51$$

Extra Practice

18. Express as a single power, then evaluate.

(a) $(2^3)(2^5)$ (b) $(5^{-6})(5^8)$ (c) $(3^{-2})(3^{-1})$

(d) $\dfrac{8^{10}}{8^{12}}$ (e) $\dfrac{7^{-5}}{7^{-7}}$ (f) $5^{-2} \div 5^{-3}$

(g) $\dfrac{10^{10}}{10}$ (h) $(2^2)^3$ (i) $(6^{-2})^{-1}$

(j) $(35^{12})^0$ (k) $(5^{-1})^3$ (l) $10^5 \div 10^{-3}$

19. Simplify.

(a) $(m^5)(m^3)$ (b) $(x^7)(x^{-3})$ (c) $\dfrac{p^8}{p^4}$

(d) $(b^3)(b^{-5})(b^2)$ (e) $(y^4)^3$ (f) $(w^{-3})(w^{-3})$

(g) $(x^{-2})^{-4}$ (h) $\dfrac{t^6}{t^{-7}}$ (i) $(m^{-2})(m^{-3})(m^{-4})$

(j) $\dfrac{(x^2)(x^{-3})^4}{x^5}$

20. Simplify.

(a) $(4t^3)^2$ (b) $(-5x^5)^3$ (c) $(-10y^5)^4$ (d) $(-x^{-1})^{100}$

21. Simplify by writing both powers as powers with a common base, then evaluate.

(a) $\dfrac{16^4}{2^9}$ (b) $\dfrac{27^3}{9^4}$ (c) $\dfrac{64^2}{32^5}$

Chapter Summary

In an earlier chapter, you saw how to model, graph, and analyze linear relationships. In this chapter, you learned how to do the same for nonlinear relationships, and used nonlinear relationships to solve problems involving movement, measurement, and growth. The different ways to determine whether a relationship is linear include graphing the data and calculating finite differences. If the differences in each row are not the same, then the relationship is nonlinear.

1. Evaluate. Verify your answers using a calculator.

   (a) $\frac{-8}{3} + \frac{-2}{5} + 6\frac{1}{3}$

   (b) $-\left(-\frac{7}{5}\right) + \frac{1}{8} - 2$

   (c) $\left(\frac{3}{2}\right)\left(-7\frac{1}{2}\right) - \left(\frac{-2}{-3}\right)$

   (d) $\left(\frac{2}{3} - \frac{-1}{3}\right) \div \left(\frac{-3}{4} - \frac{-2}{3}\right)$

   (e) $\dfrac{1\frac{3}{5} - \frac{-2}{3}}{\frac{1}{-8} - \frac{-3}{4}}$

2. List the defining properties and symbols for the set of natural numbers, whole numbers, integers, and rational numbers.

3. Evaluate.

   (a) 3^5

   (b) 4^0

   (c) $(-2)^7$

   (d) 3^{-3}

   (e) $(5^2)^3$

   (f) $(3^4)(3^5) \div (3^3)^2$

   (g) -7^2

   (h) $(-6)^{-2}$

4. Express each number in scientific notation.

   (a) 437 000 000 000

   (b) 0. 000 000 000 135

5. The solar system is about 12 000 000 000 000 km in diameter. Light travels about 300 000 km/s. How many seconds does it take for light to travel across the solar system?

6. Shasta runs one kilometre each day as part of her daily exercise. The graph shows her distance from home as she runs her route.
   (a) Between what two points does Shasta run the fastest?
   (b) Describe what is happening between points C and D.
   (c) When does Shasta begin to travel towards home?
   (d) How long does it take her to get home?
   (e) How fast was she running back home?

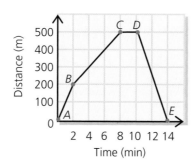

Distance vs. Time

Chapter Review Test

7. The diagonal of a square cornfield is 20 m. Determine the perimeter of the field correct to one decimal place.

8. A large hailstone falls from a cloud 5000 m above the ground. The data shows its approximate distance above the ground at various times.

Time (s)	0	5	10	15	20
Distance (m)	5000	4875	4500	3875	3000

(a) Does the data represent a linear or nonlinear relationship? Explain.
(b) Plot the data and draw the graph.
(c) At approximately what time does the hailstone hit the ground?

9. A bacteria colony starts with 20 bacteria and triples in size every hour.
(a) Write an expression that models this relationship.
(b) How many bacteria will there be in the colony after 24 h?

10. Ming invests $25 000 in an account that earns interest at 10%/a compounded quarterly. How much money will he have in 10 years?

11. Simplify $\dfrac{(x^6y^{-5})(x^{-2}y^{-2})^3}{(xy^2)^{-1}}$.

Cumulative Review Test I

1. Evaluate.
   (a) $\dfrac{5}{-7} - \dfrac{-2}{3}$

   (b) $-2\dfrac{3}{11} - 4\dfrac{2}{9}$

   (c) $2\dfrac{2}{5} \times \left(1\dfrac{3}{4} - 3\dfrac{1}{2}\right)$

   (d) $\left(-\dfrac{3}{4}\right)\left(\dfrac{4}{-5}\right) \div \dfrac{3}{8}$

2. Given the line with equation $y = -\dfrac{3}{4}x - 3$.
   (a) State the x-intercept.
   (b) State the y-intercept.
   (c) Graph the line.
   (d) What is the slope of the line?
   (e) Name three other points on this line.

3. State the equation of the line through point $(0, -2)$ that is parallel to the line with equation $y = -4x + 7$.

4. Find the equation of the line through $A(-2, 4)$ and $B(5, -3)$. Put the equation into the form $y = mx + b$.

5. A puppy's mass is measured each week and the data is recorded.

Age (weeks)	1	2	3	4	5	6	7
Mass (kg)	1.8	2.1	2.2	2.4	2.5	2.5	2.7

   (a) Draw the scatter plot of the data.
   (b) Draw the line of best fit.
   (c) Select from the correlations, -0.9, -0.3, 0.3, and 0.9, the value that best describes the data.
   (d) Use the graph of the line to find the slope. What does this represent?
   (e) Find the y-intercept. What does this represent?
   (f) Determine the equation of either the line of best fit or the linear regression line.
   (g) Use the equation to predict the mass of the puppy after 10 weeks.
   (h) Would this equation give a reasonable estimate of the puppy's mass after 50 weeks? Explain.

6. Sarah is responsible for selecting the disc jockey for the school dance. She asks the students in her grade 9 math class to choose from a list of five DJs. She selects the DJ based on the class's preference.
   (a) What type of sampling is this?
   (b) Explain why this type of sampling could lead to conclusions that are not valid.
   (c) Sarah needs to redesign her sampling procedure to reduce bias. She does not want to ask every student in the school for his or her opinion. Describe what she could do.

7. High Energy Gas Company charges its customers $12 per month plus ten cents per cubic metre of gas used. The New Gas Company charges $20 a month plus nine cents per cubic metre.

   (a) Write an equation to represent the total cost per month for each company.

   (b) Identify the independent and dependent variables.

   (c) Graph both equations on the same axes.

   (d) How many cubic metres of gas are consumed at the point where the cost for either company is the same?

   (e) What is the cost at the point of intersection of the two lines?

8. Swapan inherits $10 000 and invests it. The table shows how the money grows each year.

   (a) Calculate the finite differences. Is the data linear or nonlinear?

   (b) Graph the data.

Time	Dollars
0	10 000
1	11 500
2	13 225
3	15 209
4	17 490
5	20 114

9. A tree is 5 m high. At various times during the day the length of the tree's shadow is measured. The measurements are 2 m, 4 m, 6 m, 8 m, and 10 m.

   (a) Determine the distance from the tip of the tree to the tip of its shadow correct to one decimal.

   (b) Enter the data from part (a) into the table and calculate the finite differences. Is the data linear or nonlinear? Explain.

Length of Shadow (m)	2	4	6	8	10
Distance from Tip to Tip					
Finite Differences					

   (c) Graph "Distance from Tip to Tip" vs. "Shadow Length."

10. Alexandria invests $500 at 6%/a compounded annually for 7 years. What is the amount of the investment at the end of the seventh year?

Chapter 4

Extending Algebraic Skills

Algebra is the branch of mathematics that uses symbols to represent information in a convenient, compact form. For instance, in algebra, the concept:

three times a number plus six
can be expressed
as $3n + 6$.

In today's world, it is important to be skillful in the use of algebra. For example, NASA engineers track the shuttle as it orbits the Earth. Computer programs use algebraic models to project its orbit.

In this chapter, you will:

recognize that a linear model can be expressed as a polynomial

identify polynomials and describe their parts

use polynomials to describe relationships

add and subtract polynomials

multiply and factor polynomials.

Connections

The Chapter Problem

How Long Can They Ski?

The student Peer Tutors at Saltfleet District High School are planning a ski trip to Green Mountain Ski Resort. The Peer Tutors have raised $5000 for the ski trip and know that 24 students and three adults will be going on the trip. How many days can the group stay based on the following costs?

- The resort charges its guests $25 a day for an adult lift ticket and $15 a day for a student lift ticket.

- Accommodation costs are $20 per person per day, and meals are $14 per person per day.

- Everyone going on the trip must rent skis at a flat rate of $21 for each adult and $14 for each student.

- Travel expenses are $180 for a bus, plus $94 a day for the driver.

At the end of some lessons in this chapter, questions will refer back to this problem, and you will be able to use what you have learned to answer them. Keep your notes in a folder because, at the end of the chapter, you should be able to provide a full solution to the problem.

The Challenge

How Many Are Left?

A speaker was so boring that one-half of the audience left after a few minutes. Five minutes later, one-third of the remaining audience left. Ten minutes later, one-fourth of those remaining left, leaving only nine people in the audience. How many people were in the audience at the beginning of the lecture?

Mathematics Teacher, March 1996, p. 216.

As you work through the chapter, you will develop skills that will help you solve this Challenge. You might find it helpful to work with other students so that you can share ideas. You also may need to consult with your teacher or do research outside the classroom. Keep notes as you work. This will help you to organize your ideas, remember different strategies you've tried, and help you to present how you solved the Challenge to other students.

Getting Ready

In this chapter, you will be working with algebraic expressions and polynomials. These exercises will help you warm up for the work you will be doing in this chapter.

1. Simplify.
- (a) $3 - 6$
- (b) $-5 - 7$
- (c) $-8 \div 2$
- (d) $5(-3)$
- (e) $-4(5 - 7)$
- (f) $-4(8) + 7(6) - 3$
- (g) $-2 + 7$
- (h) $6(-4)$
- (i) $-2(-4)$
- (j) $12 + 7 - 9$
- (k) $\dfrac{16}{(-2)} + \dfrac{8}{(-4)} - \dfrac{(-9)}{(-3)}$
- (l) $-3(-7) + \dfrac{(-12)}{3} - 2(8)$

2. Simplify.
- (a) $4.25 + 8.3$
- (b) $0.5 - 1.5$
- (c) $-2.3 - 3.8$
- (d) $-6.25 - 0.3$
- (e) $1.2(4.1 - 6.1)$
- (f) $6.21 + 9.21$
- (g) $-7.4 - 4.8$
- (h) $-0.4 + 1.2$
- (i) $4.1 - 3.6$
- (j) $-3.6 + 4.1$
- (k) $16.6 - 8.12$
- (l) $-0.3(0.2) + 0.4(-0.1)$
- (m) $\dfrac{4.5}{(-9)} + \dfrac{(-3.5)}{7} - \dfrac{0.25}{0.5}$
- (n) $-2.1(0.1) + \dfrac{(-1.6)}{0.4} + 3.5(0.2)$

3. Simplify.
- (a) $\dfrac{1}{2} + \dfrac{3}{4}$
- (b) $\dfrac{1}{2} + \left(-\dfrac{3}{4}\right)$
- (c) $-\dfrac{5}{8} - \dfrac{2}{3}$
- (d) $-\dfrac{5}{8} + \dfrac{2}{3}$
- (e) $2\dfrac{1}{2} + 3\dfrac{5}{8}$
- (f) $2\dfrac{1}{2} - 3\dfrac{5}{8}$
- (g) $-5\dfrac{2}{3} + 6\dfrac{1}{2} - 4\dfrac{5}{6}$
- (h) $\left(-\dfrac{3}{5} + 2\dfrac{7}{10}\right) - \left(2\dfrac{1}{8} - 3\dfrac{1}{4}\right)$

4. Simplify.
- (a) $\left(-\dfrac{1}{4}\right)(20) + \left(\dfrac{1}{5}\right)(-30) - \left(\dfrac{1}{6}\right)(42)$
- (b) $\dfrac{2}{3}\left(3\dfrac{2}{5} + 4\dfrac{1}{4}\right)$
- (c) $0.7(-8.2 - 2.1) - 1.4(3.7 + 5.2)$
- (d) $\left(-\dfrac{1}{3}\right)6 + \left(\dfrac{1}{4}\right)24 - \left(\dfrac{1}{7}\right)28$
- (e) $\left(9\dfrac{1}{2}\right)(14) + \left(-\dfrac{1}{6}\right)(42) + \left(\dfrac{2}{3}\right)(9)$
- (f) $\dfrac{1}{5}(20) - \left(-\dfrac{1}{5}\right)(10) + \left(\dfrac{1}{4}\right)(20)$

5. Evaluate.
- (a) $2x + 5$ when $x = -6$
- (b) $14 - 7x$ when $x = -5$
- (c) $\left(-\dfrac{3}{4}\right)\left(m - \dfrac{1}{2}\right)$ when $m = \dfrac{2}{3}$
- (d) $4a - 5b$ when $a = 2\dfrac{1}{4}$ and $b = -3\dfrac{2}{5}$
- (e) $-0.3m + 1.3n$ when $m = 0.1$ and $n = 0.01$
- (f) $21 - 2x$ when $x = 6$
- (g) $5 + 3x$ when $x = -5$
- (h) $\left(\dfrac{3}{5}\right)(2x + 1)$ when $x = 7$
- (i) $\left(-\dfrac{1}{4}\right)(x + 8)$ when $x = 8$

6. Find the value of the variable that makes each of the following true.
- (a) $x + 7 = -10$
- (b) $3x - 5 = 19$
- (c) $4 + \dfrac{1}{2}m = 3$
- (d) $-5 = 9r - 7$
- (e) $0.4y - 1.3 = 2.7$
- (f) $2x + 5 = 9$
- (g) $3x + 4 = 7$
- (h) $0.3y + 2.1 = 3.2$
- (i) $4.5x - 9 = 0$

7. Solve for the remaining variable.
- (a) for w if $A = lw$ and $A = 100$ m², $l = 20$ m
- (b) for P if $P = 2(l + w)$ and $l = 15$ cm, $w = 8$ cm
- (c) for t if $I = Prt$ and $I = \$19.20$, $P = \$120$, $r = 8\%$

8. Simplify.
- (a) $(x^3)(x^5)$
- (b) $x^8 \div x^3$
- (c) $(x^{-2})^{-3}$
- (d) $(x^2y^3)(x^{-5}y^4)$
- (e) $(x^{-4}y^{-3}) \div (x^3y^{-1})$
- (f) $(x^{-2}y^4)^{-5}$

4.1 Adding and Subtracting Simple Polynomials

Like Terms

Todd recently graduated from high school and has started his own landscaping business. To run his business effectively, he must keep track of the weekly payroll for his employees. His crew works the same number of hours each week, except in bad weather.

This table shows how each employee is paid:

Todd	Salary of $600 each week
Truck Driver	$10 per hour plus $150 for expenses
Experienced Assistant	$14 per hour
Student Labourer	$8 per hour

Think, Do, Discuss

1. Create a spreadsheet to help Todd keep track of the weekly payroll.

	A	B	C	D	E	F
1	Hours Worked	Todd	Truck Driver	Assistant	Labourer	Weekly Payroll
2						
3						

   Write a spreadsheet formula for each employee that will calculate their weekly earnings. All formulas should be in terms of A2 where possible.

2. Write a spreadsheet formula that will determine the weekly payroll for the company by adding together the cells representing each employee.

3. If x is used to represent the number of hours worked each week, write an algebraic expression to represent the weekly earnings for each employee. Do all your expressions contain x? Why or why not?

4. Write an algebraic expression that can be used to determine the weekly payroll. How many expressions are added together? Can this expression be written in a simpler way? Explain.

5. Write a spreadsheet formula that calculates the weekly payroll all in terms of cell A2.

6. Occasionally, the crew must work over 40 h in a week. When this happens, they are paid time-and-a-half for all hours above 40. Todd does not pay himself overtime. Calculate the hourly overtime rate for the other three employees.

7. If x represents the regular hours worked (up to 40) and y represents overtime hours (above 40), write an algebraic expression that represents the weekly earnings for each employee. Can the x and y expressions be added together? Explain.

8. Write an algebraic expression that represents the total weekly payroll including all overtime. Can this expression be simplified in any way? Explain.

Unlike Terms

A pool table is always twice as long as it is wide. The Cue Ball Company makes pool tables according to this relationship but in many different sizes. Each table top must have rubber bumpers around the outside edge and a felt top. The rubber bumpers cost $2.25/m and the felt material for the top costs $28/m^2.

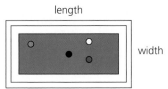

length

width

Think, Do, Discuss

1. If x is used to represent the width of the table, write an algebraic expression for the length.

2. What quantity is needed to find the amount of felt needed for each table? What quantity is needed to find the amount of rubber needed for each table?

3. Write an algebraic expression to represent:

(a) the amount of felt needed to cover the surface of the table; and

(b) the amount of rubber needed for each table.

4. Write an algebraic expression that represents the total cost for felt and rubber for the table top. Can this expression be simplified? Explain.

5. Your cost formula should contain an x^2 expression and an x expression. Can these two terms be added together? Why or why not?

6. Use the cost expression to determine the cost of the materials for the top of a table that has a width of 1.5 m.

Did You Know?

Snooker is a game of pocket billiards played with 15 red balls, 6 balls of other colours, and, of course, the white cue ball. Balls are worth different points.

red – 1 point	yellow – 2 points	green – 3 points	brown – 4 points
blue – 5 points	pink – 6 points	black – 7 points	

A player must sink a red ball before sinking any coloured ball. If a coloured ball is sunk and there are still any red balls on the table, then the coloured ball is put back on the table. Once all of the red balls are off the table, the coloured balls must be sunk in order from lowest value to highest value.

What is the maximum number of points a player could get in one turn, if she or he sunk all the balls without missing a shot?

Focus

Key Ideas

- In an algebraic expression such as $3x + 2$,
  $3x$ and 2 are called **terms** of the expression.
  $3x$ is a **variable term** and 2 is a **constant**.

- In the term $3x$, 3 is called the **coefficient**
  and x is called the **variable**.

- **Like terms** have the same variables *and* exponents. They can be combined by addition or subtraction.
  $2y$ and $8y$ are like terms. $(2y + 8y = 10y)$
  $3x^2$ and $5x^2$ are like terms. $(3x^2 - 5x^2 = -2x^2)$

- **Unlike terms** have different variables or different exponents and cannot be combined by addition or subtraction.
  $3x$ and $7y$ are unlike terms.
  $2x^2$ and $6x$ are unlike terms.

- Algebraic expressions are also called polynomials. **Polynomials** are expressions in which terms are added or subtracted.

- Simple polynomials have special names based on the number of terms found in the polynomial.

Name	Number of Terms	Example
monomial	1	$3x^4$
binomial	2	$3x^4 + 5y$
trinomial	3	$2x^2 - 6x + 7$

- Polynomials can be added or subtracted. This is done by adding or subtracting the like terms of the polynomials. Combining like terms is called **simplifying**.

Example

Simplify $(2x^2 + 3x + 1) - (x^2 - 2x - 3)$.

Solution

Algebra tiles can be used to represent polynomials.

$x^2 =$ ▉ $x =$ ▉ $1 =$ ▪ $-x^2 =$ ▇ $-x =$ ▌ $-1 =$ ▪

Algebra Tile Model

Algebraic Solution

These are two trinomials.
$(2x^2 + 3x + 1) - (x^2 - 2x - 3)$.

Group like terms together.

$$= (2x^2 - x^2) + (3x - (-2x)) + (1 - (-3))$$
$$= (2x^2 - x^2) + (3x + 2x) + (1 + 3)$$

Subtracting x^2 is the same as adding $-x^2$.

Subtracting $-2x$ is the same as adding $2x$.

Subtracting -3 is the same as adding 3.

Collect like terms. Simplify by adding or subtracting the coefficients of the like terms.

$$= x^2 + 5x + 4$$

Practise, Apply, Solve

A

1. What is the coefficient of each term?

(a) $5w$ (b) $-3x$ (c) $-7y$ (d) m (e) $-4.3m$ (f) -6 (g) $-m$ (h) $\frac{3}{4}r$

2. Which of the following polynomials are monomials, binomials, or trinomials?

(a) $3x - 2y$ (b) $-5xy$ (c) $4x^2 - 3x + 7$

(d) $21xy^3$ (e) $3x^2 - 9xy$ (f) $6y - 5x - 12$

3. Identify like terms.

(a) $3x, 4y, -2x$ (b) $-2g, 3f, -5g$

(c) $6m, -1.5m, 4n, 3m^2$ (d) $-\frac{1}{2}y, -4x, 2\frac{1}{2}y, 6x^2$

(e) $0.5x, -2.1y^3, -0.8y^3, 2y$ (f) $-3.75rs, 3.2m, -5.1n, 4.25rs$

4. Simplify.

(a) $2l + 3l$ (b) $-5m + 2m$ (c) $-3x - 5x$

(d) $4r - r$ (e) $-y - y - y$ (f) $-6p - 3p + 5p$

(g) $2y^2 + 7y^2$ (h) $12x^2 - 6x^2$ (i) $3m^3 - 2m^3 + 4m^3$

(j) $5s^2 + 2s^2 - 3s^2$ (k) $\frac{3}{4}w^2 - \frac{2}{3}w^2 + \frac{1}{2}w^2 - \frac{4}{3}w^2$

5. Simplify.

(a) $3m - 2n + 4m$ (b) $5s + 2s - 3t$ (c) $3x - 4y - 6x$

(d) $7y - 3y - x^2 + 4x^2$ (e) $3h + 1 + 2h + 5$ (f) $2n - 3 - 5n + 7$

(g) $-5x + 2 - 8 - 7x$ (h) $\frac{3}{4}a - \frac{1}{2}b - \frac{1}{5}a + \frac{2}{5}b$ (i) $3m - 2n + 4 + 7 - 5n - 4m$

(j) $0.4x - 0.3x + 0.2y - x$ (k) $-x^3 - 2x^2 + 3x^2 + 6x^3$

(l) $2xy - 4x^3 + 7xy - 3 - 5x^3$

6. Simplify.

(a) $(5h + 3) + (2h - 8)$ (b) $(5x + 6) + (2x - 8)$

(c) $(2x - 3y) + (3x + y)$ (d) $(2m + 3n) + (5m - 4n)$

(e) $(2y^2 - 3y + 4) + (-5y^2 + 5y - 3)$ (f) $(3x^2 - 4xy + 6y^2) + (6x^2 - 8xy - 3y^2)$

7. Simplify.
(a) $(5h + 3) - (2h - 8)$
(b) $(5x + 6) - (2x - 8)$
(c) $(5x - 4y) - (3x + 2y)$
(d) $(12m + 13n) - (6m + 4n)$
(e) $(3y^2 - 2y + 1) - (-5y^2 + 2y - 3)$
(f) $(3x^2 - 4xy + 6y^2) - (6x^2 - 8xy - 3y^2)$

B

8. Simplify.
(a) $(4h + 2) + (2h - 8) - (2h - 3)$
(b) $(15h + 6) - (2h - 18) - (5 + 7h)$
(c) $(3x - 4y) - (2x + 5y) + (6x - 7y)$
(d) $(4m + 3n) - (6m - 4n) + (5m - 3n)$
(e) $(4x^2 - 2xy + 7y^2) + (6x^2 - 8xy - 3y^2) - (5x^2 - xy + y^2) + (x^2 - 3xy - 7y^2)$

9. Joan and Fred both work for Acme Condominium Maintenance. Joan is a plumber who charges \$35 to visit the job site. Her hourly rate is \$43.50. Fred repairs furnaces. He charges \$41 for a service call plus \$38.75/h. Let x represent the number of hours they work.
(a) Represent Joan's bill as a polynomial.
(b) Represent Fred's bill as a polynomial.
(c) Write a new polynomial that represents Joan and Fred's combined charge, assuming that they both work x hours at a site.
(d) Calculate their combined charge if they both work 8 h at the same complex.

10. Michelle and David work in the dining room of a cruise ship. They are saving money for a house. Michelle is a waitress and David is a busboy. Their entire earnings are based on tips. Michelle's weekly tips average \$160/table. David's weekly tips average \$40/table. Michelle spends \$100/week for room and board. David spends \$25/week for room and board.

(a) Write a polynomial to represent Michelle's weekly earnings after she pays for room and board.
(b) Write a polynomial to represent David's weekly earnings after he pays for room and board.
(c) David and Michelle work the same number of tables. Write a single polynomial that combines David's and Michelle's earnings.
(d) Evaluate the earnings for five tables.
(e) Suppose David works seven tables and Michelle works five tables. Can the single polynomial in part (c) be used to calculate their joint earnings? Explain.

11. In a certain card game, players earn points for each card they play. They lose points for cards they still have in their hands at the end of the game. The cards have these values.
• f points: kings, queens, jacks • g points: 10, 9, 8, 7, 6 • h points: 5, 4, 3, 2, ace
(a) Write a polynomial to represent the score if these cards are played:
K K Q J 8 8 7 6 6 4 3 2 A A A
(b) Write a polynomial to represent the points earned if these cards are left in the player's hand: Q Q J J J 10 5 5 3
(c) Write a polynomial combining the points lost for cards played and not played.
(d) Evaluate the total score if $f = 5$, $g = 3$, and $h = 1$.

12. Simplify.
(a) $(8.25h + 10.25) + (9.8h + 11.40)$
(b) $(0.35x + 1.7) - (0.82x + 3.4)$
(c) $(2.6m + 3.5n) - (4.5n - 2.8m)$
(d) $(5.03y - 4.212) + (9.21y + 8.352)$

(e) $\left(\dfrac{2}{5}m - \dfrac{3}{8}n\right) - \left(\dfrac{3}{5}m + \dfrac{5}{8}n\right)$ **(f)** $\left(-\dfrac{3}{4}s + \dfrac{1}{2}t\right) + \left(\dfrac{4}{5}s - \dfrac{2}{7}t\right)$

C

13. Grade 9 students at Highland Secondary School raise money for charity with a competition between boys and girls. Each group has a jar to collect pennies. The group with the greater number of pennies at the end of the week wins.

To increase the amount of money raised and to make the contest more interesting, there is one special rule. Any coin that is not a penny reduces the total value of pennies by the value of that coin. That means opposing teams put these coins in the other team's jar to act as a negative value. A loonie subtracts 100 pennies from the jar; a quarter subtracts 25 pennies, and so on. (At the end of the week, all money in the jars goes to charity.)

This is what the jars looked like at the end of each day.

Day	Boys' Coins						Girls' Coins					
	P	N	D	Q	L	T	P	N	D	Q	L	T
Monday	250						306					
Tuesday	410	3	2				455	2		1		
Wednesday	613	11	6	5			715	10	2	3		2
Thursday	851	15	20	11	4	2	938	25	11	8	5	3

(P = pennies, N = nickels, D = dimes, Q = quarters, L = loonies, and T = toonies)

(a) Write polynomials to represent the score from day to day for both boys and girls.
(b) On Thursday afternoon, an announcement is read over the PA system. The purpose is to inspire students to contribute more money and win the game. Write the announcement.
(c) This is how the jars looked on Friday. Who won?

Boys	1287P	27N	38D	21Q	7L	4T
Girls	1526P	38N	22D	15Q	8L	5T

(d) How much money was donated to charity?

The Chapter Problem — How Long Can They Ski?

Refer back to the Chapter Problem at the beginning of this chapter.

1. If d is used to represent the number of days, write expressions to represent the cost of:
    (a) skiing for each adult   **(b)** skiing for each student
    (c) the bus and its driver   **(d)** accommodation for each person
    (e) food for each person.

4.2 The Distributive Property

Distributing

Recall Todd's landscaping business from the previous section. He had a crew of three people working for him. The pay structure for his crew is shown below.

Todd	Salary of $800 each week
Truck Driver	$10 per hour plus $150 for expenses
Experienced Assistant	$14 per hour
Student Labourer	$8 per hour

Todd's business has been very successful and has expanded. His company is now called the Evergreen Landscaping Company, and the number of employees has increased dramatically. He now has four truck drivers, three assistants, and fifteen student labourers. He has also given himself a raise. He now earns a salary of $800/week.

Think, Do, Discuss

1. Suppose x is the number of hours each person works and each person works the same number of hours. Write an algebraic expression to represent:
    (a) the weekly earnings of the truck drivers
    (b) the weekly earnings of the assistants
    (c) the weekly earnings of the labourers.

2. Can any of the above expressions be simplified? Explain.

3. Write an algebraic expression to represent the total weekly payroll for all 22 employees including Todd. Can this expression be simplified? Explain.

4. Use the expression you created to determine the weekly payroll expense for a 40-hour work week.

5. Occasionally, the crew must work more than 40 h in a week. When this happens, they are paid time-and-a-half for all hours above 40. Todd does not pay himself overtime. Calculate the hourly rate for the other three positions for overtime hours.

6. Let x represent the regular hours worked (up to 40) and y represent overtime hours (above 40). Write an algebraic expression to represent the weekly payroll for the entire company. Can this expression be simplified? Write an explanation of how you developed the algebraic expression.

7. Use the expression you created to determine the company's payroll for a 45-h work week.

Expanding

What does $2(3x - 1)$ actually mean?

$2(3x - 1)$ means two groups of $3x - 1$.

Think, Do, Discuss

1. How many x-tiles are there in total?

2. How many negative unit tiles are there in total?

3. Write an equivalent algebraic expression for $2(3x - 1)$.

4. How can you arrive at this expression directly from the multiplication question? Explain.

5. Write a rule you could use to multiply a polynomial by a constant.

6. Use the rule you created to write an equivalent expression for $5(6x^2 - 2x + 4)$.

Factoring

What is another multiplication expression that means the same as $4x - 8$?

Here is $4x - 8$ modelled using algebra tiles.

Think, Do, Discuss

1. Rearrange the tiles into several groups, with equal numbers of grey tiles and red tiles in each group.

2. Now arrange the tiles into two groups. How many grey tiles and how many red tiles are in each group? Write the multiplication expression that represents this new arrangement.

3. Can an arrangement of tiles be made to produce three equal groups? Explain.

4. Arrange the tiles into 4 groups. How many grey tiles and red tiles are in each group? Write the multiplication expression that represents this arrangement.

5. What is the maximum number of groups containing the same number of tiles that you could form from the expression? Explain.

6. Write the multiplication expression for $5x + 15$.

7. Show that if $5x + 15$ is divided by one of its factors, the answer is the other factor.

Focus

Key Ideas

- A polynomial can be multiplied or divided by a constant. The result is called the expanded form of the polynomial.
- When a polynomial is expanded, each term of the polynomial is multiplied or divided by the constant. This is called the **distributive property**.

$$a(b + c) = ab + ac \qquad 2(3x + 5) = 2(3x) + 2(5) \qquad \frac{6x + 14}{2} = \frac{6x}{2} + \frac{14}{2}$$
$$= 6x + 10 \qquad\qquad = 3x + 7$$

constant   expanded form

- To multiply (or divide) a polynomial by a constant, multiply (or divide) the coefficient of each term by the constant, and then write the new terms.
- **Factoring** is the opposite of expanding. If every term of a polynomial is divisible by the same constant, the constant is called a common factor.

Here are examples of factoring:

$$ab + ac = a(b + c) \qquad 8x - 16 = 8(x - 2)$$

                  common factor   common factor

- A polynomial is not considered to be completely factored until the greatest common factor has been factored out.

  For example, $8x - 16 = 2(4x - 8)$ is not completely factored.
  But, $8x - 16 = 8(x - 2)$ is completely factored.

Example

(a) Expand and simplify $-5(3x - 4y + 6) - \frac{1}{2}(-6x + 4y + 8)$.

(b) Factor $16x^2 - 4x + 20$.

Solution

(a)

$-5(3x - 4y + 6) - \frac{1}{2}(-6x + 4y + 8)$ Distribute the constant to each term of the polynomial.

$= -5(3x) - 5(-4y) - 5(6) - \frac{1}{2}(-6x) - \frac{1}{2}(4y) - \frac{1}{2}(8)$ Simplify each term by multiplying.

$= -15x + 20y - 30 + 3x - 2y - 4$ Collect like terms.
$= -15x + 3x + 20y - 2y - 30 - 4$
$= -12x + 18y - 34$

(b)

$16x^2 - 4x + 20$ All are terms divisible by 4.   Look for the greatest common factor — the largest number that will divide evenly into all the terms of the polynomial.
$= 4(4x^2 - 1x + 5)$

Remove the common factor and divide it into all the terms of the polynomial.

Practise, Apply, Solve

1. The cost of a pizza is given by the equation $C = 8.00 + 0.50t$. C is the cost in dollars and t represents the number of toppings.

(a) Copy and complete the table.

t	$C = 8.00 + 0.50t$	$2C$	$3C$
0			
1			
2			
3			

(b) What does column $2C$ represent?

(c) Expand $3(8.00 + 0.50t)$. What does this represent? Find the cost for this order if all pizzas have 2 toppings.

2. (a) How many terms are in $6(2 \times b)$? in $6(2 + b)$?

(b) Write a sentence explaining how you would answer each question.

3. Simplify.

(a) $2(3h)$ (b) $4(-3x) + 5(2x)$ (c) $5(3x) - 2(4x)$

(d) $-2(5m) + 4(m)$ (e) $-1(3r) + 2(-r) - 5(3r)$ (f) $9(-8q)$

(g) $(-4c)(-2d)$ (h) $-6(2b)$ (i) $(2a)(3b)(-4c)$

4. Simplify.

(a) $\dfrac{-12m}{3}$ (b) $\dfrac{16n}{-4}$ (c) $\dfrac{-30a}{-6}$

(d) $\dfrac{28r}{-7}$ (e) $\left(\dfrac{15m}{-3}\right) - \left(-\dfrac{18m}{6}\right)$ (f) $\left(\dfrac{3r}{-3}\right) + \left(\dfrac{12r}{-3}\right) - \left(\dfrac{18r}{-3}\right)$

5. Find the missing factor.

(a) $8xy = (\blacksquare)(2xy)$ (b) $-6x^2 = (3x^2)(\blacksquare)$

(c) $15x^2y = (5x^2)(\blacksquare)$ (d) $-49a^2b^3 = (\blacksquare)(7b^3)$

(e) $-12x^3y^3 = (3y^3)(\blacksquare)$ (f) $30m^2n^3 = (-5m^2)(\blacksquare)$

6. Expand.

(a) $5(3h + 2)$ (b) $-6(4h - 3)$ (c) $4(3x - 2y)$

(d) $-5(-2a + 3b - 8)$ (e) $3(-2n + 3m - 4s)$ (f) $-(2x + 5)$

(g) $-(x^2 - 3x + 7)$ (h) $4(3x^2 + 5x - 9)$ (i) $-2(-y^2 - y - 1)$

7. Simplify.

(a) $\dfrac{16h + 12}{4}$ (b) $\dfrac{30m - 6}{-6}$

(c) $\dfrac{-18n + 12p}{-3}$ (d) $\dfrac{24x - 18y - 6}{6}$

(e) $\dfrac{35a + 28b - 14c}{7}$ (f) $\dfrac{25l - 30m + 15n}{5}$

8. Find the missing factor.

(a) $3x - 3y = \blacksquare(x - y)$ (b) $mx - my = m(\blacksquare)$

(c) $2a + 8b = \blacksquare(a + 4b)$ (d) $28x^2 - 21y^3 = 7(\blacksquare)$

(e) $-20x^2 - 5y = \blacksquare(4x^2 + y)$ (f) $35a^4 - 36a^3 = -(\blacksquare)$

(g) $8x^3 - 4x^2 + 10x = \blacksquare(4x^2 - 2x + 5)$ (h) $x^2y - y = \blacksquare(x^2 - 1)$

9. Factor, where possible.

(a) $5x - 15$ (b) $6x - 3y$ (c) $10x - 15y - 30$

(d) $-4x + 8y$ (e) $18x^2 - 24x + 12$ (f) $21y - 28x - 14z$

(g) $45a - 30b + 60c$ (h) $45x^3 - 50x^2 + 15y$ (i) $7x - 5y + 3$

10. Simplify.

(a) $\frac{1}{4}(12 + 4x)$ (b) $-\frac{1}{3}(15x - 9)$

(c) $\frac{5}{8}\left(\frac{2}{3}m - \frac{3}{4}n + \frac{3}{8}\right)$ (d) $-3.2(4.1a + 1.3b - 2.7)$

(e) $-1\frac{1}{2}\left(2\frac{1}{3}r - 3\frac{5}{6}s\right)$ (f) $-2\frac{1}{2}\left(-1\frac{2}{5}t + 3\frac{1}{5}u\right)$

11. Expand and simplify.

(a) $6(8 + 3c) + 4(10 + 2c)$

(b) $5(2x - 3y) - 4(3x + 6y)$

(c) $5(3x + 4y) - 2(2x - 5y) + \frac{1}{2}(2x + 4y)$

(d) $3(2a - 3b + 4c) + 5(3a + 4b - c)$

(e) $-4(2m - 3n + 1) + 6(-m + 5n - 1) - 3(4m - n)$

(f) $2(x^2 - 3x + 6) - 3(2x^2 - 4x - 1)$

(g) $3(2x^2 - 1) + 6(2x - 3) - (2x^2 - 5x)$

(h) $6(x + 5) - 2x$

(i) $8(2p + 2) + 2(p - 6)$

(j) $3x^2 + 6(x^2 - 2x) + 10x$

(k) $3p - (2k + 4p) + k$

12. Expand and simplify.

(a) $\frac{3}{5}\left(2\frac{1}{3}a - 2\frac{1}{2}b\right) - \frac{1}{2}\left(2\frac{1}{5}a + 3\frac{2}{3}b\right)$

(b) $\frac{1}{6}\left(3\frac{1}{5}a + \frac{2}{3}b\right) + \frac{1}{3}\left(\frac{1}{2}a - \frac{1}{2}b\right)$

(c) $-2\frac{3}{4}\left(1\frac{3}{8}a - 3\frac{1}{2}b\right) + \frac{1}{2}\left(1\frac{3}{8}a + 2\frac{1}{2}b\right)$

(d) $-\frac{2}{5}\left(3\frac{1}{3}a + 2\frac{1}{2}b\right) + \frac{2}{7}\left(\frac{1}{2}a - \frac{3}{4}b\right)$

(e) $-1.25(3.1m + 2.2n) - 2.15(1.2m - 3.2n)$

(f) $\frac{2}{13}\left(3\frac{1}{4}a - 3\frac{1}{4}b\right) + \frac{5}{13}\left(3\frac{1}{4}a - 3\frac{1}{4}b\right)$

13. Paula has entered the following formulas into a spreadsheet.

	A	B	C	D	E	F	G	H
1	3	=3*A1+5	=2*A1+2	=B1+C1	=B1−C1	=C1−B1	=5*B1−4*C1	=(3*E1)/2
2	4							
3	5							

(a) Suppose that the value in cell A1 was a variable, h. Write the simplified polynomial, in terms of h, for cells D1, E1, F1, G1, and H1.

(b) Evaluate each polynomial you found in part (a) for $h = 3$, 4, and 5.

(c) Enter the formulas that Paula has used into a spreadsheet of your own. Evaluate them for $h = 3$, 4, and 5.

(d) Compare your answers to parts (b) and (c).

14. Simplify each expression, then evaluate for $a = 3$.

(a) $6(2a + 4) - 3a$

(b) $15 - 2(a - 5)$

(c) $-10a - 2(a^2 + 7)$

(d) $-(2a - a^3) - a^2$

15. (a) Find an expression for the area of the rectangle.

(b) Find an expression for the perimeter of the rectangle.

(c) Find the area when $x = 2$.

(d) Find the perimeter when $x = \frac{1}{2}$.

2x + 5
10

16. A company purchased two kinds of cars for their sales force. The following expressions give the value of each vehicle after it has depreciated for x years.

sedans: $V = -2400x + 19\,600$

sports utility vehicle: $V = -3100x + 24\,500$

(a) The company has 12 sales representatives that drive sedans and 3 executives that drive SUVs. Write an expression that represents the combined value of the company's sales fleet after x years.

(b) Create a spreadsheet that will determine the cost of each vehicle type and the combined value of all the cars for 0 to 6 years.

(c) What did the company pay for the SUVs? the sedans?

(d) Which vehicle type is depreciating at a faster rate?

17. A real estate company has analyzed the value of two kinds of properties. They use the following formulas to predict the value of the property after t years.

rental home: $V = 1200t + 145\,000$

rental condo: $V = 1350t + 165\,000$

(a) What part of each formula determines whether the property increases or decreases in value?

(b) Determine an expression that represents the total value of the properties if the real estate company owns 25 homes and 53 condos.

(c) Determine the total value of their properties in 5 years.

C

18. Find the missing values.

   (a) $(3x^2 + 2xy - 2) + (3x^2 + 4xy + 8) = \blacksquare(x^2 + xy + 1)$

   (b) $2(5a^3 - b^3) + 6(a^3 + b^3) = \blacksquare(4a^3 + b^3)$

   (c) $(4x^2 - 3x + 2) - (x^2 - 6x - 1) = \blacksquare(x^2 + x + 1)$

   (d) $(10x^2 - 12x + 8) + (-2x^2 - 12x + 8) = \blacksquare(x^2 - 3x + 2)$

   (e) $(-x^2 + 20x - 7) + (-5x^2 - 11x + 4) = \blacksquare(2x^2 - 3x + 1)$

The Chapter Problem — How Long Can They Ski?

Refer back to the Chapter Problem at the beginning of this chapter.

The students at Saltfleet District High School now know how to determine all of their costs for the ski trip to Green Mountain Ski Resort.

1. Write a polynomial for the cost, for *d* days, of:
   (a) skiing for all adults including lift ticket and ski rental
   (b) skiing for all students including lift ticket and ski rental
   (c) accommodation for all skiers
   (d) food for all skiers
   (e) transportation for all participants.

2. Write a single polynomial in terms of *d* that represents the total cost of the ski trip.

Did You Know?

Suppose aliens took you on a short trip to outer space. You tell your story to people, but they do not believe you. To prove your claims, some scientists recommend that the next time you ask the aliens to give you some verifiable piece of information.

One suggestion is to ask for an accurate value for the universal constant of gravitation. This constant, *G*, is thought to be the same throughout the universe. Its generally accepted value is:

$$G = 6.670 \times 10^{11}$$

The final digit, zero, is not likely accurate. As scientists keep developing more accurate methods of measurement, they will be able to give a more precise value for the constant.

If the aliens gave you a very precise value for *G*, and as the years passed this value is found to be correct, then people would be more likely to believe your story.

Factoring Polynomials **4.3**

Using the *Binomial Grid Explorer*

Algebra tiles can be used to represent the factors of a polynomial. For instance, here is a model of the polynomial $2x + 4$.

The area of the model represents the polynomial $2x + 4$. Since area = length × width, the length and width of the rectangle represent the factors of $2x + 4$. In this case, the length is $x + 2$ and the width is 2.

$2x + 4 = 2(x + 2)$

How to Use the *Binomial Grid Explorer*

1. Start the *Binomial Grid Explorer*.

2. With this *Explorer*, you can factor expressions of the type $ax^2 + bx + c$.

In this case, you are going to factor $5x + 10$.

In the ENTER EXPRESSION area in the top right corner, select STANDARD .

Then, enter $a = 0$, $b = 5$, and $c = 10$. Select OK . Be sure that the + button is selected in the TILES REGION.

3. To begin, place 10 unit tiles in the bottom right quadrant of the grid. Place the first tile in the top left corner of this quadrant.

Place the tiles one at a time, by moving the arrow to the location where a tile is to go and clicking the mouse.

To place groups of tiles, click and hold the mouse button and drag the arrow across a region of the grid.

Let go of the button to place the tiles.

4. Now do the same for the $5x$ term. Place five x-tiles in the top right quadrant of the grid. Place the first x-tile in the bottom left corner of this quadrant. If the tiles are arranged correctly, a check mark will appear. Tiles are placed correctly when a rectangular arrangement of tiles models the expression. The length and width of the rectangle represent the factors of the polynomial.

If you do not get a check mark, select CLEAR to clear the screen and try again. Once you obtain the check mark, select SHOW to see how this model represents the factors of $5x + 10$.

5x + 10 modelled

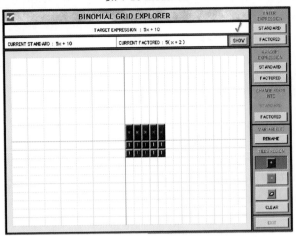

The factors of 5x + 10 shown

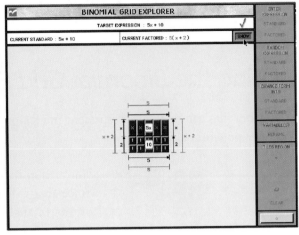

5. Click on << to return to the grid.

6. Factor $4x - 16$. Be sure to use negative (red) tiles to represent -16.

7. Factor $x^2 + x$. Enter $a = 1$, $b = 1$, and $c = 0$.

Practise

Use the *Binomial Grid Explorer* to factor:

(a) $8x + 2$ **(b)** $3x - 15$ **(c)** $4x + 12$ **(d)** $6 - 2x$

(e) $5x - 25$ **(f)** $2x^2 + 4x$ **(g)** $9x^2 - 3$ **(h)** $x^2 + 4x$

(i) $6x - 24$ **(j)** $4x^2 + 4x$ **(k)** $7x + 14$ **(l)** $8 - 16x$

Career: Data Researcher

The world is full of interesting facts. Some of these facts are found in the wild. For instance, the data researchers in the photograph are collecting facts about walruses.

Some facts are found in the library. For instance, did you know that on average there are 1.5×10^5 hairs on a human head? The world population is approximately 5×10^9. This means there are about 7.5×10^{14} hairs!

Interesting facts like these are often gathered by data researchers. A researcher may work for a client to gather information of a specific nature or obtain data from a variety of areas. Why do you think a client would hire a researcher?

Extending Algebraic Skills with Polynomials

Expanding

In the previous section, you saw that expressions like $2(3x + 4)$ could be expanded using the distributive property:

$$2(3x + 4) = 2(3x) + 2(4)$$
$$= 6x + 8$$

How would you expand $3x^2(4x^2 - 5x + 2y)$?

Think, Do, Discuss

1. Does it seem reasonable to use the distributive property in this situation? Explain.
2. How does the fact that you are multiplying by a monomial term instead of a constant affect the multiplication?
3. What rule do you need to remember in order to multiply $3x^2$ by the first two terms of the polynomial?
4. Can you multiply $3x^2$ and $2y$ together? Write an explanation of how this can be done.
5. Expand $3x^2(4x^2 - 5x + 2y)$. Can you collect any like terms in this situation?
6. Use what you have learned to expand $2xy(3x - 5y + 4xy)$.

Factoring

You have also seen the distributive property used to factor polynomials.

$$25x - 15y + 30 = 5(5x - 3y + 6)$$

In fact, multiplying the factors together is a simple way to check if your factors are correct. Can an expression like $6x^2 - 3x$ be factored in a similar manner?

Think, Do, Discuss

1. Determine the largest number that can be factored from $6x^2 - 3x$.
2. Are the two terms divisible by anything else besides a number? If so, what?
3. What is the monomial that can be factored out of $6x^2 - 3x$? What is the other factor?
4. Determine the greatest common factor of $4x^4 + 2x^3 - 6x^2$.
5. Determine the greatest common factor of $4x^2y + 24xy^2 - 8xy$.
6. Factor $x^4y^3 + x^3y^3 - x^5y^2$.
7. Write a rule for finding the greatest common factor in a polynomial.

Focus

Key Ideas

- Monomials can be multiplied or divided whether the variables are the same or different.

  $(2x)(3y) = 6xy$ $\frac{6xy}{2x} = 3y$

  $(2x^3)(5x^2) = 10x^5$ $\frac{10x^5}{5x^2} = 2x^3$

- The distributive property is used to multiply or divide a polynomial by a monomial.
- When multiplying by a monomial, each term of the polynomial must be multiplied by the monomial.

$$2x^2(3x^2 + 5x - 4) = 2x^2(3x^2) + 2x^2(5x) + 2x^2(-4)$$
$$= 6x^4 + 10x^3 - 8x^2$$

- When dividing by a monomial, each term of the polynomial must be divided by the monomial.

$$\frac{6x^3 + 10x^2y - 8x^2}{2x^2} = \frac{6x^3}{2x^2} + \frac{10x^2y}{2x^2} - \frac{8x^2}{2x^2}$$
$$= 3x + 5y - 4$$

- A monomial can be used to factor an expression. It must divide evenly into all of the terms of the polynomial you are factoring.

$$\Rightarrow \underline{6x^2y^3 - 9x^4y^5} = 3x^2y^3(2 - 3x^2y^2)$$

All are terms divisible by $3x^2y^3$.

- To simplify polynomial expressions, expand using the distributive property, then collect all like terms by adding or subtracting.

Example

Factor $10ax^3 + 15abx^2 - 30ax$.

Solution

Look for the greatest common factor for each term in the trinomial.

$10ax^3 = (2)(5)ax^3$	5 is the common factor for the coefficients.
$15abx^2 = (3)(5)abx^2$	ax is the common factor for the variables.
$30ax = (6)(5)ax$	The greatest common factor is $5ax$.

Divide each term by the common factor $5ax$.

$$10ax^3 + 15abx^2 - 30ax = 5ax(2x^2 + 3bx - 6)$$

The original polynomial can now be written as the product of the common factor and another polynomial.

Practise, Apply, Solve

1. Write a simplified expression for the area of each rectangle.

(a)

$5x$ $2y$

(b)

$5r$

r^2

(c)

$2n^2$

$3m$

(d)

$3c^2$

$2ab$

(e)

$3n^3$

$2m^2$

(f)

$7mn^2$

$8pq^2$

2. Simplify.

(a) $(2a)(4b)$ **(b)** $(-6x)(5y)$ **(c)** $\dfrac{12mn}{4n}$ **(d)** $\dfrac{-15abc}{5ac}$

(e) $(-9m)(3n)$ **(f)** $\dfrac{9xy}{-3x}$ **(g)** $(4x)(3y)(-2z)$ **(h)** $(-5ab)(-7c)$

(i) $\dfrac{-27pqr}{-3pqr}$ **(j)** $\dfrac{15x^2y}{-3y}$ **(k)** $\dfrac{28m^3n}{14n}$ **(l)** $(15ab^2)(-3c^2d)$

(m) $(-5c^2)(2bd^2)(-3a^2)$ **(n)** $\dfrac{27a^2bc^2d}{9a^2d}$

3. Expand.

(a) $n(5 + 3n)$ **(b)** $2R(R - 5)$ **(c)** $-3k(2k - 1)$ **(d)** $-y(4y + 7)$

(e) $5d(2d^2 - d - 3)$ **(f)** $-3c(4 - 5c + c^2)$ **(g)** $-s(3s^2 - 5s + 2)$ **(h)** $2t^2(7 - 4t + t^2)$

4. Divide.

(a) $\dfrac{4xy - 8}{4}$ **(b)** $\dfrac{3m^2n - 6n}{3n}$

(c) $\dfrac{10a^2b + 15bc^2}{-5b}$ **(d)** $\dfrac{30x^2y^3 - 20x^2z^2 + 50x^2}{10x^2}$

(e) $\dfrac{16mnp - 24mnr + 32kmn}{8mn}$ **(f)** $\dfrac{(lw - lwy)}{lw}$

5. Each rectangle shows the area and some other information. Find the missing side.

(a) $A = 12x$

$3x$

(b) $A = 36abc$

$9ab$

(c) $A = 16x^2y$

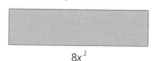

$8x^2$

(d) $A = 9x^4$

6. Simplify.

(a) $(5np)(8np)$ (b) $(-3j)(4k)(2jk)$ (c) $3x^2(4x^3y)$

(d) $-5mn^3(2m^7)$ (e) $(3x^2y^3)(4ax^2y)$ (f) $(-8g^2h)(-7fg^3h^2)$

(g) $(10rst)(-3r^2t)$ (h) $(-2a^2b)(4ab^2)(-7ab^3)$

7. Simplify.

(a) $\dfrac{15ab^4}{3b^3}$ (b) $\dfrac{21x^5y^2z}{-7x^2y}$ (c) $\dfrac{-45m^3n^5p^7}{9m^2n^2}$

(d) $\dfrac{20r^{15}s^{10}}{5r^5s^5}$ (e) $\dfrac{9a^2b^3c^4}{-3abc}$ (f) $\dfrac{28e^5fg^4}{14fg}$

8. Simplify.

(a) $3x^2(6x^3 + 2x^2)$ (b) $5y^3(2y^4 + 3y^2 + 1)$

(c) $6ab^3(2a^2b - 3ab^2)$ (d) $7m^2n^3(2m^2n^3 + 5mn^4 - 3m^3np)$

(e) $\dfrac{12x^3 - 8x}{4x}$ (f) $\dfrac{9p^2q - 3pq^2}{3pq}$

(g) $\dfrac{30m^3n^4 - 12m^5n^3}{6m^2n}$ (h) $\dfrac{15x^2y^3 - 20x^5y^2 + 25x^3y^4}{5xy^2}$

9. Simplify.

(a) $k(5 - k) - 3(2k - k^2)$

(b) $2t(t + 3) + 4t(t - 2)$

(c) $-a(2a - 1) - 2a(3a - 5)$

(d) $3p(4 - 2p) - 5p(2 - 3p)$

(e) $4s(s^2 + 4s + 2) - 2s(3s^2 - 6s + 9)$

(f) $3b(4 - 2b + 7b^2) + 5b(b^2 + 4b - 5)$

10. Expand and simplify.

(a) $3y(x - 2) + 2y(x + 5)$ (b) $5x(3 - x) + 4x(2x - 5)$

(c) $2x(5x + 3y) - 7y(2x + 2y)$ (d) $4x(3x + 2y - 2) + 3y(x - 5y + 3)$

(e) $a^2(3a + 5b - 2) + a(4a^2 - 2ab + 3a)$

(f) $2x(3x + 5y) - 2(x^2 + 3xy) - 5y(3x^2 - 2x)$

(g) $-(3a^2 - 2ab + b) + b(3a - 5b) - 2a(3a - b)$

(h) $5(3a - 2b) - [5a - (2a + b)]$

(i) $3x(2x + y) - 2x[3 - (2x + 4)]$

(j) $4a(3a^2 - 2a + 4) - 3a^2(2a - 5) + a^2[3a^2 - (a + 4)]$

11. Identify the greatest common factor.

(a) $xy,\ yz$ (b) $6abc,\ 9acd,\ 15abc$

(c) $4x^3,\ 6x^2$ (d) $x^3y^5,\ x^6y^4$

(e) $10x^5y^3,\ 45x^4y^7,\ 30x^6y^4$ (f) $2x^6y^4,\ 6x^4y^2,\ 8x^5y^3$

12. (a) Determine the quotient when $4x + 2$ is divided by 2. Check by multiplying 2 by the quotient.

(b) Divide $15m^2n^3 - 3m^3n^2$ by $3m^2n^2$. Check by multiplying the factors.

13. Factor.

(a) $8x + 4$ (b) $15abc - 5b$

(c) $16mnp + 24mpq$ (d) $4x^3 + 6x^2 - 8x$

(e) $14y^4 - 21y^3 + 28y^2$ (f) $12x^3y^4 - 4x^2y^2 + 8x^3y^5$

(g) $25a^5b^3 + 35a^3b^4 - 20a^4b^5$ (h) $3g^4k^4 - 9g^5k^4 + 18g^4k^5$

14. A rectangle has area $8x^6y^7 - 6x^5y^5$ units. If one of the dimensions is $2x^3y^4$ units, what is the other dimension?

15. The perimeter of a square is $16x^2y - 12xy$ units. Determine:

(a) the dimensions of each side.   (b) the area if $x = 2$ cm and $y = 3$ cm.

16. Expand and simplify.

(a) $(x + 2)(x + 5)$ (b) $(x + 6)(x - 6)$ (c) $(x + 5)(x - 3)$

(d) $(2x + 3)(3x - 2)$ (e) $(x + y)(2x + 3y)$ (f) $(2x - 5)^2$

17. Find a formula for the perimeter, then simplify by factoring.

(a) 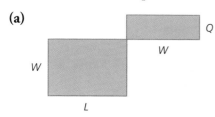   (b)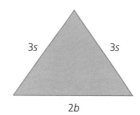

18. Simplify.

(a) $\dfrac{1}{x} + \dfrac{2}{y}$ (b) $\dfrac{2}{x} - \dfrac{3}{6x^2}$ (c) $\dfrac{1}{x + 1} + \dfrac{1}{x - 1}$

The Chapter Problem — How Long Can They Ski?

Refer back to the Chapter Problem at the beginning of this chapter.

1. Write an equation that represents the total cost of the ski trip. Simplify the equation so that the total cost, C, is on the left side of the equation and all the other terms are on the right side of the equation.

2. Draw a graph that represents the relationship between the total cost of the trip and the number of days the trip lasts.

3. Use the graph to determine the number of days the trip can last, based on the amount of money the group raised.

4. How much money must each person contribute to stay an extra day?

4.1 Adding and Subtracting Simple Polynomials

- In an algebraic expression such as $3x + 2$, $3x$ and 2 are called **terms** of the expression. $3x$ is a **variable term** and 2 is a **constant**.
- In the term $3x$, 3 is called the **coefficient** and x is called the **variable**.

$3x$

coefficient   variable

- **Like terms** have the same variables *and* exponents. They can be combined by addition or subtraction.
  $2y$ and $8y$ are like terms. $(2y + 8y = 10y)$
  $3x^2$ and $5x^2$ are like terms. $(3x^2 - 5x^2 = -2x^2)$
- **Unlike terms** have different variables or different exponents and cannot be combined by addition or subtraction.
  $3x$ and $7y$ are unlike terms. $\Rightarrow$ $2x^2$ and $6x$ are unlike terms.
- Algebraic expressions are also called polynomials. **Polynomials** are expressions in which terms are added or subtracted.
- Simple polynomials have special names based on the number of terms found in the polynomial.

Name	Number of Terms	Example
monomial	1	$3x^4$
binomial	2	$3x^4 + 5y$
trinomial	3	$2x^2 - 6x + 7$

- Polynomials can be added or subtracted. This is done by adding or subtracting the like terms of the polynomials. Combining like terms is called **simplifying**.

Example

Simplify $(4x^2 + 5x + 2) - (2x^2 - 2x - 7) + (-3x^2 + x - 3)$.

Solution

$(4x^2 + 5x + 2) - (2x^2 - 2x - 7) + (-3x^2 + x - 3)$
$= (4x^2 - 2x^2 + (-3x^2)) + (5x - (-2x) + x) + (2 - (-7) + (-3))$ Group the like terms and
$= 4x^2 - 2x^2 - 3x^2 + 5x + 2x + x + 2 + 7 - 3$ simplify.
$= -x^2 + 8x + 6$ This is the result of adding and subtracting like terms.

Extra Practice

1. Simplify.

(a) $3x + 2x$ (b) $6y - 4y$ (c) $-6m - 3n$

(d) $5r - 8r$ (e) $8a - (-6a)$ (f) $-3b - (-7b)$

(g) $\frac{1}{4}m - \frac{2}{3}m$ (h) $-\frac{8}{5}p - \frac{3}{2}p$

2. Simplify by collecting like terms.

(a) $3a + 2a + 3b - 2b$ (b) $4x + x - y + 3y$

(c) $-x + 2y + 4y - 3y$ (d) $6a - 4b + 7a - b$

(e) $3m - n + m - 2m$ (f) $-\frac{1}{2}x + \frac{3}{4}y + \frac{1}{3}x - \frac{1}{2}y$

(g) $1\frac{1}{8}m - 2\frac{3}{5}n - 2\frac{1}{4}m + 2\frac{3}{10}n$ (h) $-4.5r + 3.2s + 3.1r - 2.2t + 4.3s - 5.1t$

3. Simplify.

(a) $(3m - 2n) - (5m + 5n)$ (b) $(3x - 2y + z) - (2x + y - z)$

(c) $(10m - 3) - (7m - 3)$ (d) $(4k + 2n - 3m) + (5k - 4n - 2m)$

(e) $(5k + 7) - (11 - 2k) + (3k - 9)$ (f) $(4x + 2y) - (5x - 3y) - (4x - 2y)$

(g) $(0.3x - 7.5) - (-0.2x + 6.35)$ (h) $\left(-\frac{3}{5}a + \frac{1}{7}b\right) - \left(-\frac{2}{7}a + \frac{4}{5}b\right)$

4. The length, in metres, of a rectangular field is $8m + 5$ and the width is $6m - 2$. Write an expression for the number of metres of fencing needed to enclose the field.

4.2 The Distributive Property

- A polynomial can be multiplied or divided by a constant. The result is called the expanded form of the polynomial.

- When a polynomial is expanded, each term of the polynomial is multiplied or divided by the constant. This is called the **distributive property**.

$$a(b + c) = ab + ac \qquad 2(3x + 5) = 2(3x) + 2(5) \qquad \frac{6x + 14}{2} = \frac{6x}{2} + \frac{14}{2}$$
$$= 6x + 10 \qquad\qquad\qquad = 3x + 7$$

    constant   expanded form

- To multiply (or divide) a polynomial by a constant, multiply (or divide) the coefficient of each term by the constant, and then write the new terms.

- **Factoring** is the opposite of expanding. If every term of a polynomial is divisible by the same constant, the constant is called a common factor.

Here are examples of factoring:

$$ab + ac = a(b + c) \qquad 8x - 16 = 8(x - 2)$$

common factor   common factor

- A polynomial is not considered to be completely factored until the greatest common factor has been factored out.

For example, $8x - 16 = 2(4x - 8)$ is not completely factored.
But, $8x - 16 = 8(x - 2)$ is completely factored.

Example

Ranjan and Indira share expenses for their home. Ranjan earns \$18 an hour; he drives to work and pays \$5 a day for gas and parking. Indira earns \$21 an hour; she takes the train, which costs \$7.50 a day. After paying his transportation costs, Ranjan spends 35% of the remainder of his earnings to pay the mortgage. Similarly, Indira pays 30% of her net earnings for food and utilities. Assuming that they both work the same number of hours and days, write an expression for their combined household expenses.

Solution

Let h represent the number of hours worked, and d the number of days.

After paying transportation costs, Ranjan's earnings are $18h - 5d$.
His mortgage expenses are $0.35(18h - 5d)$.

After she pays her transportation costs, Indira's earnings are $21h - 7.50d$.
Her household expenses are $0.30(21h - 7.50d)$.

$$\text{Total expenses} = 0.35(18h - 5d) + 0.30(21h - 7.50d) \qquad \text{Add the polynomials.}$$
$$= 6.30h - 1.75d + 6.30h - 2.25d \qquad \text{Multiply the constants by the numerical coefficients of each term.}$$

$$= 6.30h + 6.30h - 1.75d - 2.25d \qquad \text{Collect like terms.}$$
$$= 12.60h - 4.00d \qquad \text{Simplify.}$$

Extra Practice

5. Simplify.

(a) $6(8b)$ (b) $-3(-8a)$ (c) $\dfrac{24x}{-2}$ (d) $-\dfrac{36b}{9}$

(e) $\dfrac{-42m}{7}$ (f) $\dfrac{1.5n}{0.3}$ (g) $-5(3m) - \left(\dfrac{8m}{-2}\right)$ (h) $6(-3n) + \left(\dfrac{-18n}{-6}\right)$

6. Expand.

(a) $3(x + 2)$ (b) $7(-25 + 4w)$ (c) $-8(2m - 2)$
(d) $\dfrac{-18r - 12s}{-6}$ (e) $-5(2a - 3b - 4c)$ (f) $\dfrac{3}{4}(8m - 12n + 20p)$
(g) $0.6(0.5C - 0.2f + 1.2g)$ (h) $-\dfrac{2}{3}\left(\dfrac{3}{4}x - \dfrac{3}{8}y + 9z\right)$

4.3–4.4 Extending Algebraic Skills with Polynomials —

- Monomials can be multiplied or divided whether the variables are the same or different.

$(2x)(3y) = 6xy$ $\qquad \dfrac{6xy}{2x} = 3y$

$(2x^3)(5x^2) = 10x^5$ $\qquad \dfrac{10x^5}{5x^2} = 2x^3$

- The distributive property is used to multiply a polynomial by a monomial.
- When multiplying by a monomial, each term of the polynomial must be multiplied by the monomial.

$$2x^2(3x + 5y - 4) = 2x^2(3x) + 2x^2(5y) + 2x^2(-4)$$
$$= 6x^3 + 10x^2y - 8x^2$$

- When dividing by a monomial, each term of the polynomial must be divided by the monomial.

$$\frac{6x^3 + 10x^2y - 8x^2}{2x^2} = \frac{6x^3}{2x^2} + \frac{10x^2y}{2x^2} - \frac{8x^2}{2x^2}$$

$$= 3x + 5y - 4$$

- A monomial can be used to factor an expression. It must divide evenly into all of the terms of the polynomial you are factoring.

$$\underbrace{6x^2y^3 - 9x^4y^5}_{} = 3x^2y^3(2 - 3x^2y^2)$$

All terms are divisible by $3x^2y^3$.

- To simplify polynomial expressions, expand using the distributive property, then collect all like terms by adding or subtracting.

Example

Expand and simplify $2x^2y(3x - 5y) + 3x(2x^2y + xy^2) - 4x^2y^2$.

Solution

$2x^2y(3x - 5y) + 3x(2x^2y + xy^2) - 4x^2y^2$ Expand using the distributive property.

$= 6x^3y - 10x^2y^2 + 6x^3y + 3x^2y^2 - 4x^2y^2$ Group together like terms.

$= 6x^3y + 6x^3y - 10x^2y^2 + 3x^2y^2 - 4x^2y^2$ Collect like terms.

$= 12x^3y - 11x^2y^2$

Extra Practice

7. Expand and simplify.

    (a) $4(x - 3) + 5(x + 6)$ **(b)** $-2(4 - 3x) + 4(2x - 5)$

    (c) $4(5x - 3) - 7(3x + 1)$ **(d)** $5x(3x + 2y - 2) - 2x(x - 5y + 3)$

    (e) $a^2(2a + 6b - 7) + a(2a^2 - 6ab + a)$

    (f) $-4x(3x + 5y) - 5(x^2 + 3xy) - 2y(6x^2 - 2x)$

    (g) $\frac{4a^3b^4 - 8a^2b^2}{4a^2b^2} - \frac{3a^2b^2 - 6a^3b^4}{3a^2b^2}$

8. Factor.

    (a) $10x + 5$ **(b)** $7abc - 21bc$

    (c) $24mnp + 12mpq$ **(d)** $3x^3 + 6x^2 - 9x$

    (e) $21y^4 - 14y^3 + 28y^2$ **(f)** $2x^3y^4 - 6x^2y^2 + 10x^3y^5$

    (g) $72a^5b^3 + 36a^3b^4 - 48a^4b^5$ **(h)** $28g^4k^4 - 52g^5k^4 + 44g^4k^5$

Chapter Summary

In this chapter, you have seen how to add and subtract polynomials, and how to use the distributive property when multiplying or dividing them.

Chapter Review Test

1. Simplify.
   (a) $5h - 3k - 2 - 2h + 6k - 7$
   (b) $0.3x + 4.1y - 3.6 - 0.7x - 3.2y + 0.7$
   (c) $(3m + 5) - (6m - 7) + (4m - 3)$
   (d) $\frac{2}{3}n + \frac{1}{3}p - \frac{1}{4}n + \frac{3}{4}p$
   (e) $4(6x - 2) - 3(5x - 2)$
   (f) $2x(3x - 7y + 1) - 4y(3 - 2x - y)$

2. Factor.
   (a) $15x^2 - 5x + 10$
   (b) $a^2b^2 + a^2b - a^2$
   (c) $15x^2y - 10xy^2 + 30y^3$
   (d) $21m^3n^2 + 14m^2n^3 - 35m^2n^2$

3. Find the missing polynomial.
   (a) $(3x^2 + 2xy - 1) + (x^2 + xy + 5) + (\blacksquare) = 5x^2 - 3xy + 3$
   (b) $(5a^3 - 3a^2b + ab^2 + b^3) + (a^3 + a^2b + 4ab^2 + b^3) + (\blacksquare) = 3a^3 - 2a^2b + ab^2 - 2b^3$
   (c) $(4x^2 - 3x + 2) - (x^2 + x + 2) + (\blacksquare) = 5x^2 + 3x - 2$
   (d) $(3a^2 - 2ab + b^2) - (a^2 + 3ab - b^2) - (2a^2 + ab + 2b^2) + (\blacksquare) = 3a^2 - 2ab + b^2$

4. Simplify.
   (a) $\dfrac{-18r - (-12s)}{6} + \dfrac{15s - 9r}{3}$
   (b) $5(3m - 2n) + 6(-2n + 3m)$
   (c) $4(3a - 2b + 5) - 3(5a + 3b - 2)$
   (d) $-\dfrac{2}{3}\left(\dfrac{1}{4}x - 6\right) + \dfrac{3}{4}\left(\dfrac{2}{3}x + 8\right)$
   (e) $0.25(4r + 3t - 6) - 0.75(3r - 4t + 5)$
   (f) $\dfrac{-30x + 24y - 12}{2} - \left(\dfrac{25x - 30y - 15}{5}\right)$

5. Joya has change in her pocket consisting of nickels, dimes, and quarters. The number of quarters is twice the number of dimes and the number of dimes is twice the number of nickels.
   (a) Write an algebraic expression that represents the number of coins she has, using only one variable.
   (b) Write an algebraic expression that represents the value of these coins.
   (c) How much money does she have in her pocket, if she has four nickels?

Chapter 5

Modelling: Using Equations to Ask and Answer Questions

People often use equations to model real situations so they can analyze the situations in more detail and make predictions about them. For instance, economists use equations to answer questions about the stock market or the economy of a country. Equations are used to solve many other real-world problems.

In this chapter, you will:

- make a table of values and graph a relationship that shows how to combine the values of two variables

- use the table of values and the graph to answer questions about the relationship

- write a word equation and an algebraic equation to represent the relationship

- use both informal and formal algebraic methods to solve for the value of one variable in a two-variable relationship

- apply rational number operations to solve linear equations in a single variable

- solve first-degree equations involving more complex polynomials

- rearrange the equation of a linear relationship to either slope–y-intercept form or standard form

- solve real-world problems that can be modelled using linear relationships in two variables.

Connections

The Chapter Problem

How Much Exercise?

Carol enjoys high-impact aerobics and mountain biking. Her friend, Steve, swims and jogs. Each tries to schedule a 90-min workout a minimum of three times a week. They found this table on the Internet. The rate at which an individual burns calories depends on the person's mass and the intensity of his or her exercise.

Activity (1 hour)	Calories Burned	
	Carol (64 kg)	Steve (86 kg)
High-Impact Aerobics	445	620
Jogging (7 min/km)	636	885
Mountain Biking	540	753
Swimming	508	708

Carol tries to burn 780 calories during her exercise sessions while Steve's target is 1100 calories. They want to know if there is a way for each of them to do the same two types of activities of the four listed and still meet their individual calorie consumption goals in 90 min of exercise.

At the end of some lessons in this chapter, questions will refer back to this Chapter Problem, and you will be able to use what you have just learned to answer them. Keep your notes in a folder, so that at the end of the chapter, you can provide a full solution to the Chapter Problem.

The Challenge

What Are the Average Earnings?

This table shows the average weekly salaries people earned in some Canadian industries from 1993 to 1997. Suppose you were considering a career in one of these industries. Which would likely provide the best weekly salary in 2010? To complete this Challenge, you may need to discuss a research plan with your teacher or with other students. You may also need to research outside the classroom.

Industry	1993	1994	1995	1996	1997
Accounting and Bookkeeping	534.45	567.39	579.34	609.77	631.81
Finance, Insurance, and Real Estate	633.17	644.23	658.48	704.59	742.17
Computer and Related Services	727.74	795.61	800.95	829.90	888.17
Educational and Related Services	675.22	671.84	669.68	671.64	668.38
Management Consulting Services	655.70	645.83	678.08	691.92	705.97

Getting Ready

In this chapter, you will be working with equations and variables. These exercises will help you warm up for the work you will be doing in the chapter.

1. Evaluate.
   (a) $1\frac{2}{3} + 2\frac{3}{4}$
   (b) $2\frac{1}{2} - 1\frac{5}{8}$
   (c) $1\frac{1}{4} + \left(-1\frac{2}{5}\right)$
   (d) $2\frac{3}{4} - \left(-2\frac{5}{8}\right)$
   (e) $5\frac{1}{4} \times 2\frac{2}{3}$
   (f) $5\frac{1}{4} \div 2\frac{2}{3}$
   (g) $-3\frac{4}{5} \times 1\frac{2}{3}$
   (h) $2\frac{5}{6} \div \left(-2\frac{2}{3}\right)$

2. Evaluate.
   (a) $-8 + 6$
   (b) $-4 - (-6)$
   (c) $4 - (-9)$
   (d) $7 + (-6) - (-1)$
   (e) $-(3 - 7)$
   (f) $(-6 + 2)(-8 - 2)$
   (g) $-2 - (-3 + 5)$
   (h) $(-9 + 2)(-5 - 2)$
   (i) $\frac{-5 + (-15)}{-3 - 2}$
   (j) $\frac{-9 + (-3)}{-4 - (+8)}$
   (k) $-2(-3 + 4) - 6(-3 - 2)$
   (l) $3(-5 - 3) - 6(-8 - (-4))$

3. Evaluate each expression using the given values for the variables.
   (a) $3x - 7y; x = 2, y = -2$
   (b) $-4a + 2b; a = -10, b = 5$
   (c) $-9r - 7s; r = -3, s = 4$
   (d) $3\frac{1}{3}m - (-\frac{5}{2})n; m = -3, n = 2$
   (e) $3pq + \frac{1}{4}; p = \frac{2}{3}, q = \frac{5}{8}$
   (f) $1.25r - 0.25t; r = 2.1, t = 10$
   (g) $\frac{1}{3}x - 2xy; x = \frac{3}{4}, y = \frac{5}{6}$
   (h) $6.75a - a(-2.5b); a = 2.5, b = -1.1$

4. Find the value of the variable that makes each equation true.
   (a) $-x = 5$
   (b) $y + 7 = -2$
   (c) $5w + 1 = 11$
   (d) $-2 - x = -6$
   (e) $-2x - 3 = 9$
   (f) $3t + 4 = -8$
   (g) $2z - 8 = -4$
   (h) $\frac{a + 5}{2} = 3$
   (i) $5 - 2b = 7$
   (j) $-3y + 2 = -5$
   (k) $\frac{2x - 1}{5} = -3$
   (l) $\frac{6 - 2w}{7} = 2$

5. Each inequality describes conditions on a variable. Give two sample values for the variable that meet each condition. Explain what each condition means. Each variable is rational.
   (a) $x \leq 2$
   (b) $y > 2$
   (c) $-1 < a < 1$
   (d) $b \leq -3$
   (e) $w \geq -5$
   (f) $-1 \leq x \leq 2$
   (g) $-5 < y \leq -3$
   (h) $0 \leq z < 10$

6. Graph each equation for $0 \leq x \leq 10$, $x \in Q$.
   (a) $y = 2x - 3$
   (b) $y = -2x + 3$
   (c) $y = \frac{2}{3}x + 1$
   (d) $y = -\frac{3}{2}x + 1$
   (e) $y = -0.5x + 3$
   (f) $y = -\frac{3}{4}x - 3$
   (g) $2y = 4x - 4$
   (h) $-2y = 4x + 6$

7. Write each word equation as an algebraic equation.
   (a) Three times a number increased by five is ten.
   (b) The product of five and three more than a number equals twelve.
   (c) One third of a number increased by twice the number is the same as two.
   (d) A number doubled is equal to seven.
   (e) One quarter of a number is the same as five squared.
   (f) Four less than three times a number is thirteen.
   (g) Twice a number divided by seven gives a quotient of five.
   (h) A number tripled is five more than the number.

Mary is trying to plan how to invest her money. She wants to place part of her money in safe investments like bonds or guaranteed investment certificates (GICs) that she knows will return 4%.

She also wants to put some of her money into slightly riskier stocks. An investment advisor has told her to expect about a 10% return on these.

Mary wants to use a graph to determine how she can combine her investments to produce a yearly return of $500.

She begins by writing this word equation to describe the situation.

Total return = return from safe investments + return from risky investments

Since Mary knows her expected rate of return for each type of investment, she writes:

$500 = 4\%$ return from safe investments + 10% return from risky investments

Then she shortens the equation by writing it algebraically. She uses S to represent the amount in safe investments and R to represent the amount in more risky investments.

$$500 = 0.04S + 0.10R$$
or
$$0.04S + 0.10R = 500$$

Think, Do, Discuss

1. **(a)** Which of the variables in the relationship should be the independent variable and which should be the dependent variable?
   (b) Why is it difficult to decide?
   (c) How does your answer to part (a) affect how you will set up the table of values?
   (d) How does your answer to part (a) affect how you will draw the graph of the relationship?

2. **(a)** The ordered pair (0, 0) cannot satisfy the equation. Why?
   (b) None of the values can be negative. Why?
   (c) What are the greatest possible amounts Mary can put in either type of investment? Explain.
   (d) Describe the special meaning of the ordered pairs that have a 0 as one of the coordinates.

3. (a) Suppose Mary invested these amounts in safe investments. For each one, find the amount she should put into more risky investments to still earn $500.

Safe Investment Amount (S)	$1000	$2000	$3000	$4000	$5000	$6000
Interest on S (4% of S)	0.04 × 1000 = 40					
Interest left for R (500 − Interest on S)	460					
Higher Risk Amount (R) (0.10R = Interest left for R)						

(b) Describe any pattern you noticed in your completed table.
(c) What information does the pattern in the table give you about the relation?
(d) What strategy can you use to find acceptable pairs of values for S and R?

4. (a) Graph the relationship between S and R.
(b) What type of relation does it appear to be?
(c) What additional information would you need to be more certain of your conclusion? Explain.

5. (a) Suppose Mary invested these amounts in risky investments. For each one, find the amount she should put into safer investments to still earn $500.

Higher Risk Amount (R)	$1000	$1250	$2250	$3510	$3655	$4375.27
Safe Investment Amount (S)						

(b) Is it more accurate to use the table of values or the graph to interpolate or extrapolate values?
(c) What strategy can you use for checking the accuracy of your results?

6. In all cases, safe investments earn 4% and riskier investments earn 10%. Find the combination of safe and risky investments that meets each of these conditions and still earns $500 annually.
(a) Mary wants the value of the safe investments to be double the value of the risky ones.
(b) Mary wants the value of the risky investments to be double the value of the safe ones.
(c) Mary wants the amounts invested in each type to be equal.

7. What are the limitations of using the table of values for making predictions or answering questions? What are the limitations of using the graph?

Focus

Example

Graph $2t + 5g = 500$.

Solution

Set up a table of values showing several data points for this equation. The easiest substitution is to replace one of the variables with 0.

Substitute $t = 0$ into $2t + 5g = 500$.

$$2(0) + 5g = 500$$
$$5g = 500$$

g must be 100.

The point $(0, 100)$ is the g-intercept of the graph, since it falls on the g-axis.

Now, substitute $g = 0$ into the equation.

$$2t + 5(0) = 500$$
$$2t = 500$$

t must be 250.

The point $(250, 0)$ is the t-intercept of the graph since it falls on the t-axis.

t	g
0	100
250	0

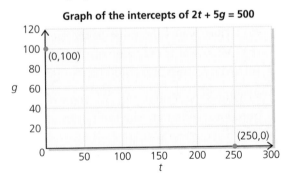

Graph of the intercepts of $2t + 5g = 500$

The column label in the table and the axis label on the graph show t is treated as if it were the independent variable and g were the dependent variable. This could have been reversed.

Find additional points by selecting convenient values of t or g.

Substitute a convenient value for one of the variables into the equation. Find a value for the other value that makes the equation true.

Substitute $t = 100$ into $2t + 5g = 500$.

$$2(100) + 5g = 500$$
$$200 + 5g = 500$$
$5g$ must be 300, then
g must be 60.

The point (100, 60) is on the graph.

Now, substitute $g = 20$ into the equation.

$$2t + 5(20) = 500$$
$$2t + 100 = 500$$
$2t$ must be 400, then
t must be 200.

The point (200, 20) is on the graph.

Add these points to the table of values and plot them on the graph.

t	g
0	100
250	0
100	60
200	20

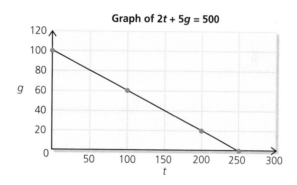

The data points fall along the line shown in the graph.

Practise, Apply, Solve

1. David has to make orange juice from water and concentrated juice. He has to fill a 10-L container.
   (a) Write a word equation that describes this situation.
   (b) If David used 9 L of water, how much concentrate did he use?
   (c) If David used 9.8 L of water, how much concentrate did he use?
   (d) What are values of the intercepts for the graph of this relation?

2. A candy store is making up a mixture of chocolate-coated almonds and chocolate-coated raisins. The almonds cost $30/kg and the raisins cost $8/kg. The final value of the mixture is to be $150.
   (a) Write a word equation that describes this situation.
   (b) Write an algebraic equation to describe this situation.
   (c) Find the mass of chocolate-coated raisins if the mass of the almonds is 1 kg.
   (d) Find the mass of the almonds if the mass of the raisins is 15 kg.
   (e) What are the values of the intercepts for the graph of this relation?

3. Jamie builds chairs and tables in her shop. It takes her 3 h to make a chair and 7 h to make a table. Jamie works 60 h a week.

    (a) Create a table of values that shows all possible combinations of chairs and tables Jamie can make in one week.

    (b) Find the maximum number of chairs Jamie can make in a week.

    (c) Find the maximum number of tables Jamie can make in a week.

    (d) What restrictions are there on the values you can choose for the variables in this situation? Why?

    (e) Graph the relation that represents this situation.

    (f) What are the values of the intercepts for the graph of this relation?

4. Henri sharpens skates at a local arena. He charges $3 to sharpen a pair of figure skates and $2.50 for a pair of hockey skates. Last Saturday he earned a total of $240.

    (a) Create a table of values with at least five possible combinations of figure and hockey skates Henri can sharpen to earn $240.

    (b) Find the largest number of pairs of hockey skates he can sharpen to earn $240.

    (c) Find the largest number of pairs of figure skates he can sharpen to earn $240.

    (d) What restrictions are there on the values you can choose for the variables in this situation? Why?

    (e) Graph the relation that represents this situation.

    (f) What are the values of the intercepts for the graph of this relation?

5. **(a)** Create a table of values and graph of the relation described by $3x + 5y = 60$.

    (b) State the coordinates of the x- and y-intercepts.

    (c) If the values of x and y must be non-negative, describe any other restrictions on x and y.

B

6. Christine has two jobs in sales. She earns a commission of 3% on sales at a clothing store. Her commission at the hardware store is 5%.

    (a) How much must she sell at just the hardware store to earn $500 in commission?

    (b) How much must she sell at just the clothing store to earn $500 in commission?

    (c) Create a table of values with at least three more data points that shows possible combinations of sales at the two stores that will earn Christine a total of $500 in commission.

    (d) Use the table of values to graph this relation.

    (e) Why are the additional points in part (c) not necessary for the completion of the graph?

    (f) State the values of the intercepts for the graph of this relation. What does each intercept mean in this situation?

7. Gregor is planning a driving trip. He knows that part of his trip will be along major highways and part will be along country roads or city streets. The speed limit is 100 km/h on highways and 60 km/h on other roads. The total time he wants to spend driving is 12 h.

    (a) If all his driving was on highways, how far would he travel?

    (b) If all his driving was on country roads, how far would he travel?

(c) Construct a table of values that shows three more combinations of times Gregor could spend driving on highways and on country roads. The total time of the trip is 12 h.

(d) Graph the relation that represents this situation.

(e) State the values of the intercepts for the graph of this relation. What does each intercept mean in this situation?

(f) Use the graph to find the distance he travels if he spends twice as much time on the highway as on country roads.

8. Freda has $24 to purchase nickels and quarters from the bank for change for a craft fair.

(a) What is the maximum number of quarters she can purchase?

(b) What is the maximum number of nickels she can purchase?

(c) Graph this situation and use it to find the number of each type of coin she must purchase under these conditions:

    i. The number of nickels and the number of quarters must be equal.

    ii. The number of nickels must be 5 times the number of quarters.

9. Create a table of values to graph each equation. State the maximum value for each variable if all values must be non-negative. Find the value indicated.

(a) $10d + 100l = 1250$; the value of d when $l = 11$

(b) $110h + 55c = 550$; the value of c when $h = 1.5$

(c) $0.04x + 0.02y = 375.50$; the value of x when $y = 1000$

10. Brittany has $200 to spend on stamps for mailing brochures. Research the cost to mail a letter within Canada and the cost to mail one to the United States. Find the combination of stamps Brittany can purchase that uses as much of the $200 as possible.

11. Part A of a math exam is scored out of 20 marks. Part B is out of 15. To find a student's final exam score as a percentage, the teacher multiplies the Part A score by 2 and the Part B score by 4. Marks on either part can be fractional or decimal values.

(a) Find at least five combinations of Part A and Part B scores that could produce a final mark of exactly 50% on the exam.

(b) What is the minimum Part B score needed to get a passing mark of 50%?

(c) Why it is not possible to pass the exam using only a Part A score?

(d) Graph the possible Part A and Part B scores needed to achieve 50%.

(e) Compare your graph in part (d) to one that shows the Part A and Part B scores needed to get a final mark of 60%, 70%, or 80%.

The Chapter Problem — How Much Exercise?

Refer back to the Chapter Problem at the beginning of the chapter.

1. Create a table of values for Carol that shows the combination of times she can spend on mountain biking and high-impact aerobics in order to burn 780 calories.

2. Create a table of values for Steve that shows the combination of times he can spend swimming and jogging in order to burn 1100 calories.

5.2 Solving Simple Equations

Using the *Algebra Tiles Explorer*

The *Algebra Tiles Explorer* uses coloured
tiles to represent the terms of an
equation. There are lettered tiles to
represent values of a variable. Unit tiles,
or 1-tiles, are used to represent
numbers. Dark grey tiles represent
positive values and red tiles represent
negative values.

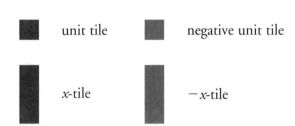

unit tile   negative unit tile

x-tile $-x$-tile

You can also do this Exploration with real algebra tiles.

Example 1

Solve $2x + 1 = 9$.

Solution

Tile Representation	Explanation
	There are two x-tiles and one unit tile on the left and nine unit tiles on the right. $$2x + 1 = 9$$
	Eliminate the unit tile on the left. Do this by adding a negative unit tile to each side of the equation, since $1 + (-1) = 0$. $$2x + 1 + (-1) = 9 + (-1)$$
	Simplify. $$2x = 8$$
	Regroup the tiles to find the value of the variable x. $$\frac{2x}{2} = \frac{8}{2}$$
	Solve for x. $$x = 4$$

Example 2

Solve $2x - 3 = -5$.

Solution

	$2x - 3 = -5$
	Eliminate 3 negative unit tiles on the left. Do this by adding 3 positive unit tiles to each side of the equation, since $-3 + 3 = 0$. $2x - 3 + 3 = -5 + 3$
	Simplify. $2x = -2$
	Regroup the tiles to find the value of the variable x. Simplify. $\dfrac{2x}{2} = \dfrac{-2}{2}$ $x = -1$

Example 3

Solve $-3x + 2 = -4$.

Solution

	$-3x + 2 = -4$
	Simplify. $-3x + 2 + (-2) = -4 + (-2)$ $-3x = -6$
	Regroup the tiles into three equal groups. There are now three $-x$-tiles on the left side and three groups of two -1-tiles on the right side. $\dfrac{-3x}{3} = \dfrac{-6}{3}$
	Simplify. $-x = -2$
	Determine the value of x. Reverse the sign on each side of the equation by multiplying each side of the equation by -1. $-1(-x) = -1(-2)$ $x = 2$

Practise

Solve each equation using algebra tiles or the *Algebra Tiles Explorer*.

(a) $3x + 2 = -4$ (b) $3c + 1 = 4$ (c) $3z - 7 = 8$ (d) $-4x = 12$

(e) $3x + 2 = -8$ (f) $3a - 4 = -5$ (g) $-5y + 8 = -4$ (h) $-6w + 10 = 16$

5.3 Finding Values That Satisfy a Linear Relation

Part I

Ralph works part-time for a bike repair shop. Ralph earns $2 for each tire he installs and $5 for each gear mechanism he assembles. Tire installations take less time than gear assemblies.

His boss can afford to pay Ralph a maximum of $100 each week. What combinations of tire and gear installations will allow Ralph to earn $100?

Ralph represents the situation using the equation $2t + 5g = 100$, where t is the number of tire installations and g is the number of gear assemblies. At first, Ralph tried substituting values for t and g by trial-and-error. Then he decided to use a more organized approach to find values for t and g.

He started by finding the intercepts of the graph of the relation.

Substitute $t = 0$ into $2t + 5g = 100$. Solve for g.	Substitute $g = 0$ into $2t + 5g = 100$. Solve for t.

$$2(0) + 5g = 100$$
$$0 + 5g = 100$$
$$5g = 100$$
$$\frac{5g}{5} = \frac{100}{5}$$
$$g = 20$$

$$2t + 5(0) = 100$$
$$2t + 0 = 100$$
$$2t = 100$$
$$\frac{2t}{2} = \frac{100}{2}$$
$$t = 50$$

One combination is 0 tire installations and 20 gear assemblies.

One combination is 50 tire installations and 0 gear assemblies.

Think, Do, Discuss

1. The two solutions to the equation provide valid combinations of tire and gear installations that will earn Ralph $100. Explain what each solution means.

2. Explain how algebra tiles could have been used to get $g = 20$ from $5g = 100$.

3. Suppose Ralph plotted these combinations as points on the graph of the relation.
   (a) Where would each of these points be placed?
   (b) What information does each point provide about the graph?

Part II

Next, Ralph picks a value for one of the variables and tries to find the value of the other variable that makes the equation true.

Try $t = 10$ in $2t + 5g = 100$.
$$2(10) + 5g = 100$$
$$20 + 5g = 100$$

Ralph reasons to isolate the $5g$ term on the left, he needs to subtract 20 from both sides of the equation.

$$20 + 5g - 20 = 100 - 20$$
$$5g = 80$$
$$\frac{5g}{5} = \frac{80}{5}$$
$$g = 16$$

Ralph checks his solutions $t = 10$, $g = 16$ by substituting these values into the equation.

$$2t + 5g = 2(10) + 5(16)$$
$$= 20 + 80$$
$$= 100$$

Since the result is 100, Ralph is now sure that $t = 10$ and $g = 16$ is a valid combination.

Try $g = 6$ in $2t + 5g = 100$.
$$2t + 5(6) = 100$$
$$2t + 30 = 100$$

$$2t + 30 - 30 = 100 - 30$$
$$2t = 70$$
$$\frac{2t}{2} = \frac{70}{2}$$
$$t = 35$$

Check: $t = 35$ and $g = 6$

$$2t + 5g = 2(35) + 5(6)$$
$$= 70 + 30$$
$$= 100$$

$t = 35$ and $g = 6$ is a valid solution for the equation.

Think, Do, Discuss

1. **(a)** Substitute $t = 6$ into the equation. Find the value of g.
   (b) Check that the values are correct by substituting them into the equation.
   (c) Explain why this value for g does not solve Ralph's problem.
   (d) Discuss why it is possible to find a combination of t and g values that makes the equation true, but does not solve Ralph's problem.

2. **(a)** Use the method illustrated in the example to find five more combinations of values for t and g that solve the equation.
   (b) Graph the values.
   (c) Use the graph to find at least two more combinations that make the equation true.
   (d) Check that each pair of values from part (c) actually satisfies the equation and is a possible solution to the problem.
   (e) Complete the table of values by finding all possible combinations that will earn Ralph $100. Use the graph to help you locate possible solutions.

3. Suppose business is good and Ralph's boss decides he can afford to pay Ralph $240 each week.
   (a) Find several combinations of tire and gear installations that would earn Ralph the new amount each week.
   (b) Compare the graph of this new situation with the original one.
   (c) Are there more solutions for this new problem than for the original? Why?

Focus

Key Ideas

- When a relationship is described by an equation of the form $ax + by = c$, a table of values can be constructed by first substituting a value for one of the variables and then solving the resulting equation for the other variable.

- A pair of values that satisfies the **equation** is called a **solution** to the equation.

- When solving an equation, isolate the terms containing the variable on one side of the equation.

- Every step in the equation-solving process requires that the same operation be performed on both sides of the equation to maintain the equality.

- Each solution pair should be checked by substituting the values into the equation to make sure that no errors were made during the solution process.

- Pairs of values for the variables can be found that satisfy the equation, but some may not be acceptable solutions due to physical limitations in the problem.

- A complete graph of the equation shows all possible solution pairs for the equation.

- The values found using a graph may only be approximate solutions for the equation. This results from our inability to read and draw the graph precisely.

Example 1

Solve for x.

$$5x - 20 = 10$$

Solution

Check the solution.

$$5x - 20 = 10$$
$$5x - 20 + 20 = 10 + 20$$
$$5x = 30$$
$$\frac{5x}{5} = \frac{30}{5}$$
$$x = 6$$

left side	right side
$5x - 20$	10
$= 5(6) - 20$	
$= 30 - 20$	
$= 10$	

Example 2

Solve for x.

$$\frac{3}{4}x - \frac{1}{2} = 2$$

Solution

Using Decimals

$$\frac{3}{4}x - \frac{1}{2} = 2$$

$$0.75x - 0.5 = 2$$

$$0.75x - 0.5 + 0.5 = 2 + 0.5$$

$$0.75x = 2.5$$

$$\frac{0.75x}{0.75} = \frac{2.5}{0.75}$$

The calculated value of the right side of the equation is shown on a graphing calculator.

The solution expressed as a repeating decimal is $x = 3.\overline{3}$. Check the solution using a calculator.

Using Fractions

$$\frac{3}{4}x - \frac{1}{2} = 2$$

$$\frac{3}{4}x - \frac{1}{2} + \frac{1}{2} = 2 + \frac{1}{2}$$

$$\frac{3}{4}x = 2\frac{1}{2}$$

$$\frac{\frac{3}{4}x}{\frac{3}{4}} = \frac{2\frac{1}{2}}{\frac{3}{4}}$$

$$x = \frac{5}{2} \times \frac{4}{3}$$

$$x = \frac{10}{3}$$

$$x = 3\frac{1}{3}$$

Check the solution.

left side	right side
$\frac{3}{4}x - \frac{1}{2}$	2
$= \frac{3}{4}\left(3\frac{1}{3}\right) - \frac{1}{2}$	
$= \frac{3}{4}\left(\frac{10}{3}\right) - \frac{1}{2}$	
$= \frac{5}{2} - \frac{1}{2}$	
$= \frac{4}{2}$ or 2	

Practise, Apply, Solve

1. Solve each equation by isolating the variable.

(a) $x - 8 = 12$ (b) $3 + m = 15$ (c) $20 + p = -5$

(d) $18 = 2 + s$ (e) $m + 2 = -12$ (f) $8 + r = 9$

(g) $16 = 4 + x$ (h) $-3 + x = 10$ (i) $16 = m - 13$

(j) $p - 4 = 19$ (k) $15 = x - 3$ (l) $7 + k = -1$

2. Solve.

(a) $2m = 8$ (b) $4y = 12$ (c) $6p = -12$

(d) $5k = -15$ (e) $2n = 12$ (f) $3x = 36$

(g) $4k = 16$ (h) $8m = -64$ (i) $5h = -35$

(j) $-2y = -34$ (k) $5x = 12$ (l) $-3x = 27$

3. Solve.

(a) $\frac{x}{3} = 8$ (b) $\frac{a}{4} = 2$ (c) $\frac{b}{3} = -5$

(d) $\frac{w}{2} = -8$ (e) $\frac{c}{3} = 4$ (f) $\frac{k}{6} = 8$

(g) $\frac{x}{2} = -7$ (h) $-6 = \frac{b}{4}$ (i) $-2 = \frac{x}{5}$

(j) $x \div 2 = 5$ (k) $a \div 3 = -4$ (l) $y \div 5 = 6$

4. Solve.

(a) $2m + 1 = 9$ (b) $3p - 3 = 6$ (c) $2q + 2 = 6$

(d) $3t - 2 = 7$ (e) $3k + 4 = 13$ (f) $5p - 9 = 36$

(g) $4a + 1 = 9$ (h) $5c - 8 = 17$ (i) $5n - 14 = 31$

(j) $3x + 5 = 11$ (k) $4x - 3 = -11$ (l) $17 = 4y - 3$

5. Solve.

(a) $\frac{k}{3} + 1 = 4$ (b) $\frac{x}{2} - 3 = 11$ (c) $\frac{b}{3} - 1 = 9$

(d) $\frac{n}{2} + 6 = 8$ (e) $\frac{x}{4} - 2 = 6$ (f) $\frac{k}{3} - 2 = 7$

(g) $\frac{x}{5} - 1 = 1$ (h) $\frac{y}{3} + 2 = 6$ (i) $8 = \frac{d}{5} - 1$

(j) $\frac{1}{2}x + 8 = 16$ (k) $3 = \frac{3}{2}x - 3$ (l) $\frac{1}{4}x - 3 = 4$

6. Solve.

(a) $2.5x + 6 = 13.5$ (b) $1.5y - 8 = 3$ (c) $3.5 = 2 + 1.5p$

(d) $13 = 6 - 3.5k$ (e) $0.3x + 0.8 = 0.5$ (f) $11 = 4.5 - 7.5y$

(g) $11 = 2 - 4.5c$ (h) $4.4m - 0.3 = 0.8$ (i) $16 = 7.3 + 2.4k$

(j) $2m + 6.1 = 16.5$ (k) $4x - 2.8 = 4.8$ (l) $15.8 - 6m = 5$

B

7. A candy store is making up a mixture of chocolate-coated almonds and chocolate-coated raisins. The almonds cost $30/kg and the raisins cost $10/kg. The final value of the mixture is to be $150. The mix contains 7.5 kg of raisins.
(a) Write an equation that describes this situation.
(b) Solve the equation for the required mass of almonds. Show all steps in the solution and explain the reasoning for each step.

8. Jamie builds chairs and tables in her shop. It takes her 3 h to make a chair and 7 h to make a table. Jamie works 60 h a week. She made three tables last week.
(a) Write an equation that describes this situation.
(b) Solve the equation to find the number of chairs she made last week. Show all the steps in the solution and explain what is happening in each step.

9. Christine has two jobs in sales. She earns a commission of 3% on sales at a clothing store. Her commission at the hardware store is 5%. Last week she earned $800. Her sales at the clothing store totalled $2500.
(a) Write an equation that describes this situation.
(b) Find her total sales at the hardware store by solving your equation. Show all the steps in the solution and explain your reasoning for each step.

10. Nathan's boss sent him to the bank to get quarters and nickels. He has $250 to spend on the coins. Quarters are sold in rolls of 40. Nickels are sold in rolls of 40. Nathan bought 17 rolls of quarters.
(a) Write an equation that describes this situation.
(b) Find the number of rolls of nickels Nathan bought by solving your equation. Show all your steps. Explain your reasoning for each step.

11. Refer to Question 8.
(a) Last week, Jamie made 10.25 chairs. Write the equation that describes this situation and solve it to find the number of tables she made that week.
(b) If she made $2\frac{1}{3}$ tables, solve the equation to find the number of chairs she made.
(c) Jamie's company bought new equipment that reduces the manufacturing time to 2.5 h per chair and 5.5 h per table. If she worked 40 h last week and made 6.5 tables, how many chairs did she complete?

12. Refer to Question 9.

    (a) Suppose Christine's clothing sales were $2135.50. Solve the appropriate equation to find the required sales at the hardware store.

    (b) What if her sales at the hardware store were $4275.20? Solve the equation to find the required sales at the clothing store.

    (c) Imagine that Christine gets a raise and now earns 4% commission at the clothing store. How much must she sell at the clothing store to earn $1000 when her sales at the hardware store are $11 000?

13. Refer to Question 10.

    (a) Suppose Nathan purchased 22 rolls of quarters. Solve the appropriate equation to find the number of rolls of nickels he purchased.

    (b) If Nathan purchased 40 rolls of nickels, solve the necessary equation to find the number of rolls of quarters he bought.

    (c) Suppose Nathan needed to buy dimes as well as quarters and nickels. A roll of dimes contains 50 coins. If he had $320 to spend and bought 16 rolls of nickels and 9 rolls of quarters, how many rolls of dimes did he buy?

14. Solve each equation. Show and describe each step of your solution. Check your answers.

    (a) $5a = -20$ **(b)** $-3b = -15$ **(c)** $c - 8 = -14$

    (d) $d + 20 = -10$ **(e)** $-e - 7 = 0$ **(f)** $\frac{1}{2}t = 6$

    (g) $2g = \frac{2}{3}$ **(h)** $\frac{1}{3}h = 5$ **(i)** $\frac{i}{3} = 5$

    (j) $0.25j = 3$ **(k)** $0.75k = 0.8$ **(l)** $5n = 2.75$

    (m) $\frac{m}{0.6} = 3$ **(n)** $w - 0.37 = 2.8$ **(o)** $0.5y + 2.25 = 0.75$

15. Solve each equation. Show all steps and then check your solutions.

    (a) $3a + 8 = 17$ **(b)** $4b - 7 = 13$ **(c)** $-3c + 4 = 19$

    (d) $-5d - 2 = -10$ **(e)** $6e + 12 = 0$ **(f)** $6 - 5f = 16$

    (g) $\frac{1}{3}g + 7 = 18$ **(h)** $\frac{2}{3}h + \frac{1}{4} = \frac{1}{2}$ **(i)** $\frac{5}{6}i - \frac{3}{4} = \frac{1}{4}$

    (j) $\frac{1}{5} + \frac{3}{10}j = \frac{3}{5}$ **(k)** $\frac{5}{9} - \frac{3}{4}k = \frac{1}{3}$ **(l)** $\frac{7}{10} - \frac{3}{5}l = \frac{3}{10}$

    (m) $0.4m + 3.5 = 5.1$ **(n)** $1.5n + 2.6 = 3.05$ **(o)** $2.9 - 2p = 0.5$

16. Abimael has two part-time jobs. He earns $7.50/h working at the local hardware store and $10/h tutoring a neighbour in math. He is paid only for complete hours of work.

    (a) Find at least five combinations of time at each job that will earn Abimael $180.

    (b) Graph this relation.

    (c) What are the intercepts for the graph? What does each represent in terms of the situation? Why do the intercepts represent the limits for the values of the variables for this situation?

(d) Suppose Abimael's employers will pay him for work completed to the nearest minute. How many hours must he tutor to earn $200 if he has already worked 11.5 h at the hardware store?

    i. Use the graph to find a possible solution.
    ii. Solve the appropriate equation to find the exact solution.
    iii. Compare the accuracy of the two methods.

17. Substitute the indicated value into the equation then solve accordingly.

(a) $3x + 2y = 12$; find x when $y = 1.5$

(b) $0.25a - b = 10$; find a when $b = 8$

(c) $90p + 45q = 3600$; find q when $p = 25$

(d) $10d - 100l = 1250$; find d when $l = 11.5$

(e) $110h + 55c = 550$; find c when $h = 3.5$

(f) $0.04x + 0.02y = 380$; find x when $y = 9500$

(g) $\frac{2}{5}a + \frac{3}{4}b = \frac{7}{8}$; find a when $b = \frac{1}{2}$

(h) $6\frac{1}{3}m - \frac{1}{4}n = 6$; find m when $n = 1\frac{1}{3}$

18. Solve each equation by isolating the variable.

(a) $3y = 12 + 2y$ **(b)** $6y - 3 = 9y$ **(c)** $9m = 4m - 10$

(d) $8y + 4 = 7y$ **(e)** $6k = 4k - 4$ **(f)** $6 - 3x = 3x$

(g) $6y = 36 - 3y$ **(h)** $8y = 36 + 7y$ **(i)** $2m = 6m - 20$

(j) $7p = 6 + 5p$ **(k)** $2y + 1 = y + 4$ **(l)** $28 - y = 5y - 2$

19. Solve each equation by isolating the variable.

(a) $5m - 2 = 2m + 4$ **(b)** $6t + 10 = -12 - 5t$

(c) $-7r - 1 = 2r + 26$ **(d)** $6 - 8y = 2y - 44$

(e) $4m - 3m = 5m - 28$ **(f)** $3y + y - 7 = 2 - 2y$

(g) $2x + 8 = x - 12$ **(h)** $18 + 3x - 5 = 65 - x$

(i) $3 + 3x - 10 = 5x + 31$ **(j)** $5k - 4 = 3k + 12$

20. The perimeter of the triangle is 37 m. Find the length of each side.

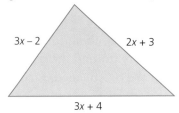

$3x - 2$

$2x + 3$

$3x + 4$

C

21. Leah is training to be a pilot. She has to pay \$125/h for flying lessons in an aircraft. Flight simulator time costs \$70/h. She can spend a maximum of \$7000 on her training.

(a) Suppose Leah has to pay a full entire hour even if she only uses part of it. Graph the relation that shows the combinations of simulator and aircraft flight times that will cost her a total of \$7000.

(b) Suppose Leah can negotiate to pay by the half-hour instead of by the full hour. Modify your graph accordingly.

(c) Modify the graph to show what happens if Leah can pay by the quarter-hour.

(d) How would the graph change if Leah could pay by the minute?

(e) Leah wants to spend twice as much time in the aircraft as in the simulator. How close can she get to this goal under each of the situations described above, without exceeding her \$7000 limit?

The Chapter Problem — How Much Exercise?

Refer back to the Chapter Problem at the beginning of the chapter.

1. Find the amount of time Carol will have to spend biking if she wants to do aerobics for only 20 min, but still plans to burn 780 calories.

2. Find the amount of time Steve will have to jog if he wants to burn a total of 1100 calories, but swims for only 30 min.

Mary Fairfax Somerville (1780–1872)

Mary Fairfax Somerville was born on December 20, in Jedburgh, Scotland. At 13, Mary studied simple arithmetic and algebra.

In 1825, she carried out a series of experiments on magnetism. She presented a paper, "The Magnetic Properties of the Violet Rays of the Solar Spectrum," to the Royal Society. It received favourable reviews for its attention to detail. Further distinction was awarded to Mary Somerville when she became the first woman elected to the Royal Astronomical Society in 1835.

Another female scholar was elected to this society in 1835. Who was she?

Exploring the Regression 5.4 Equation

Using a Graphing Calculator

In Section 5.3, Ralph created a table of values to represent possible combinations of tire and gear installations. He wanted all possible combinations that would allow him to earn $100. He earns $2 for each tire he installs and $5 for each gear mechanism he assembles. His values are shown.

Tires	Gears
0	20
50	0
10	16
35	6

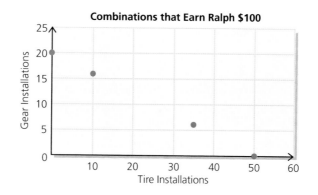

Combinations that Earn Ralph $100

Think, Do, Discuss

1. The data has a very strong linear pattern. Use graphing technology to plot the data and do a linear regression on it.
   (a) Write the regression equation.
   (b) State the r-value from the linear regression. What does the r-value tell you about the quality of fit of the linear equation to the data?
   (c) Plot the regression equation.
   (d) Use the **TRACE** feature of the calculator to find new combinations of tire and gear installations that will earn Ralph $100. Why don't all the points on the line actually solve the problem?
   (e) Why are pairs found using the **TRACE** feature good approximations to solutions of the equation?
   (f) Describe how to make the approximate solutions found using the **TRACE** feature more accurate.
   (g) Explain the meaning of the slope of the regression line in the context of Ralph's situation.

2. Suppose Ralph wanted to work more hours and his boss could pay him $500 per week.
   (a) Create a table of values with at least five points. Graph this new relation.
   (b) Compare the slopes and intercepts of the new graph to the previous one. What stays the same and what changes? Why?

5.5 Rearranging the Equation of a Line

Finding a Formula

Ralph reviewed his work.

Substitute $t = 10$ into $2t + 5g = 100$. Solve for g.	**Step**	Substitute $t = 30$ into $2t + 5g = 100$. Solve for g.
$2(10) + 5g = 100$		$2(30) + 5g = 100$
$20 + 5g - 20 = 100 - 20$	**A**	$60 + 5g - 60 = 100 - 60$
$5g = 80$		$5g = 40$
$\dfrac{5g}{5} = \dfrac{80}{5}$	**B**	$\dfrac{5g}{5} = \dfrac{40}{5}$
$g = 16$		$g = 8$

After selecting a number for t, he performed the same sequence of steps every time.

Step A: Isolate the variable term by subtracting $2t$ from both sides of the equation.
Step B: Divide both sides of the equation by the numerical coefficient of the g term.

Think, Do, Discuss

1. Why are there exactly two steps needed to solve each equation?
2. Why are the same steps used each time?
3. **(a)** Substitute two different values for g. Solve each equation to find the value for t.
   (b) How are the steps used to solve these equations similar to those used in the example above? How are they different?

Ralph noticed that no matter what value of t was substituted, the same sequence of steps was used to solve for g. So, he reasoned that there should be a formula for finding g. This formula could be used to find g-values more easily. He could also enter the formula and graph it using a graphing tool.

He found the formula using the same steps as above:

$2t + 5g = 100$		**Step**
$2t + 5g - 2t = 100 - 2t$	**A**	Isolate the variable term by subtracting $2t$ from both sides of the equation.
$5g = 100 - 2t$		
$\dfrac{5g}{5} = \dfrac{100 - 2t}{5}$	**B**	Divide both sides of the equation by the coefficient of the g term.
$g = \dfrac{100 - 2t}{5}$		

Think, Do, Discuss

1. (a) Simplify the formula for *g* by dividing both terms in the equation by 5. Express the formula in a form that allows you to create a graph using graphing technology.
    (b) Use a graphing calculator to draw the graph.

The Equation and Its Graph

Think, Do, Discuss

1. How could Ralph use the [TRACE] feature to find potential solutions to the equation? How could he use the [ZOOM] feature to make the approximations more accurate?

2. Ralph developed the equation $g = \frac{100 - 2t}{5}$ by solving for *g* in terms of *t*. The linear regression function of the calculator has produced the equation $g = -0.4t + 20$. Describe how to find the slope and *y*-intercept (or *g*-intercept) of the regression line from the equation $g = \frac{100 - 2t}{5}$.

3. What do the intercepts of the line represent?

4. What can you now conclude about the type of graph a relation of the form $ax + by = c$ will have? Why?

5. What shortcuts can you now use to graph relations of the form $ax + by = c$? Why?

6. (a) Find and then graph the formula for *t* in terms of *g*.
    (b) How is it like the graph of the equation for *g*? How is it different?
    (c) Compare the intercept values for this graph to those of the graph for *g* shown above. How are they the same? How are they different?
    (d) What is the meaning of the slope of this graph in Ralph's problem? How does that compare to the meaning of the slope of the graph for *g*?

Focus

> ## Key Ideas
>
> - Solving $ax + by = c$ for y in terms of x produces the new equation $y = \dfrac{c - ax}{b}$.
> - The table of values for an equation of the form $ax + by = c$ can supply the data needed to draw a graph.
> - The slope and y-intercept of the line can be found from the equation $y = \dfrac{c - ax}{b}$.
> - Since an equation in $ax + by = c$ form can be written in $y = mx + b$ form, its graph must be a straight line. That means the intercepts and the slope can be used in sketching the graph.

Example

Recall that Mary used the equation $0.04S + 0.10R = 500$ to represent her investment situation. She wants to invest in safe investments that earn 4% and more risky stocks that return 10%. She hopes to earn $500 a year. Use a graph of Mary's equation to find additional possible investment combinations.

Graphing Tool Solution (Graphing Calculator or Graphing Software)

First, solve the equation for one of the variables in terms of the other. This will produce a formula that can be entered into a graphing tool. Choose to solve for R, although S could also have been selected.

$$0.04S + 0.10R = 500$$

$$0.04S + 0.10R - 0.04S = 500 - 0.04S$$

$$0.04S - 0.04S + 0.10R = 500 - 0.04S$$

$$0.10R = 500 - 0.04S$$

$$\frac{0.10R}{0.10} = \frac{500 - 0.04S}{0.10}$$

$$R = \frac{500 - 0.04S}{0.10}$$

Next, enter this equation into a graphing tool.
Use it to TRACE for additional solutions.

The TRACE shows (6475, 2410) as a solution. This corresponds to $R = \$2410$ and $S = \$6475$. R is treated as the independent variable since the equation was solved for S in terms of R.

The calculation verifies that this possible solution works.

Since money amounts have to be rounded to the nearest cent, the next pair to check is (8557.45, 1577.02). This solution also works.

The pair (3559.57, 3576.17) has been rounded to the nearest cent. The calculated result is off due to rounding. It is unlikely that you could get closer to $500 by adjusting the S and R values any further.

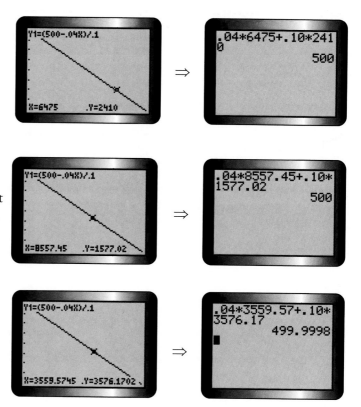

Graphing by Hand Solution

Since the graph of the relation $0.04S + 0.10R = 500$ is a straight line, first find and then plot the intercepts.

<table>
<tr><td>S-intercept</td><td>R-intercept</td></tr>
<tr><td>Substitute $R = 0$.</td><td>Substitute $S = 0$.</td></tr>
<tr><td>$0.04S + 0.10(0) = 500$</td><td>$0.04(0) + 0.10R = 500$</td></tr>
<tr><td>$0.04S = 500$</td><td>$0.10R = 500$</td></tr>
<tr><td>$\dfrac{0.04S}{0.04} = \dfrac{500}{0.04}$</td><td>$\dfrac{0.10R}{0.10} = \dfrac{500}{0.10}$</td></tr>
<tr><td>$S = 12\ 500$</td><td>$R = 5000$</td></tr>
</table>

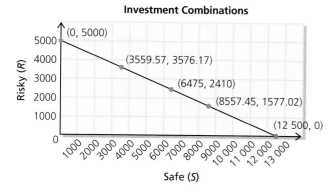

Investment Combinations

Three other possible solutions are marked on the graph. These need to be checked by substituting them into the original equation. The values might need to be adjusted to make them work exactly.

Did You Know?

Many Arab scholars have contributed to the study of mathematics. One of these was Al-Khwarizmi (780–850 CE), who wrote a famous text called *Al-kitab al-muhtasar fi hisab al-jabr wa-l-muqabala*. The word *algebra* comes from the words *al-jabr* in this title. They mean reduction, which is what you do when you reduce or simplify an equation.

Al-Khwarizimi was famous for his mathematical genius. Once, he was asked how long a powerful caliph (ruler) would live. "Fifty years!" said the mathematician, but the caliph died ten days later. Maybe Al-Khwarizimi was protecting himself by keeping the bad news from the caliph.

Another famous scholar was Omar Khayyam. Khayyam was a Persian writer who lived from about 1050 to 1123 CE. Today, he is mostly known as the author of the *Rubaiyait*, a collection of verses about the joys and regrets of life. But he also wrote several important books on algebra. In addition, he was the royal astronomer and constructed a calendar that may have been more accurate than the one commonly used now.

Practise, Apply, Solve

1. David has to make orange juice from water and concentrated juice. He has to fill a 10-L container.
    (a) Write an equation to express the amount of concentrate used in terms of the amount of water.
    (b) Write an equation to express the amount of water used in terms of the amount of concentrate.

2. A candy store is making a mixture of chocolate-coated almonds and chocolate-coated raisins. The almonds cost $30/kg and the raisins cost $8/kg. The total cost of the mixture is to be $150.
    (a) Write an equation to express the mass of almonds in terms of the mass of raisins.
    (b) Write an equation to express the mass of raisins in terms of the mass of almonds.

3. Henri sharpens skates at a local arena. He charges $3.00 to sharpen a pair of figure skates and $2.50 for a pair of hockey skates. Last Saturday he earned a total of $240.
    (a) Write an equation to express the number of hockey skates sharpened in terms of the number of figure skates.
    (b) Write an equation to express the number of figure skates sharpened in terms of the number of hockey skates.

4. Solve each equation for y in terms of x. State the x-intercept, the y-intercept, and the slope of the graph for each.
    (a) $3x + y = 5$ (b) $2x + 5y = -10$ (c) $3y - 4x = -12$
    (d) $x + y = 0.75$ (e) $0.25x + 0.5y = 1$ (f) $0.4x - 0.2y = 3.5$
    (g) $\frac{1}{2}x + \frac{3}{4}y = 6$ (h) $\frac{2}{3}x + \frac{5}{6}y = 10$ (i) $\frac{4}{5}y - 2\frac{1}{2}x = 20$

5. Start with the equation $3x + 5y = 60$.
  (a) Solve for y in terms of x.
  (b) State the slope and the intercepts of the graph of the relationship without referring to the graph.
  (c) Use a graph to verify that the slope and intercept values in part (b) are correct.

6. Start with the equation $2a - 5b = 20$.
  (a) Solve for a in terms of b.
  (b) Graph this relation using b as the independent variable.
  (c) State the slope and the intercepts of the graph.
  (d) Solve for b in terms of a.
  (e) Graph the relation using a as the independent variable.
  (f) State the slope and intercepts of this graph.
  (g) Compare the slope of the two graphs.

B

7. **(a)** Solve $0.3a + 0.6b = 10.5$ for a.
  (b) What are the intercepts and the slope of the graph?
  (c) Graph the equation.

8. **(a)** Solve $1.4c + 2.8d = 3.2$ for d.
  (b) State the intercepts of the graph. State the slope of the graph.
  (c) Draw the graph.

9. **(a)** Solve $2.25w + 3.15z = 0.02$ for z.
  (b) State the intercepts of the graph. State the slope of the graph.
  (c) Draw the graph.

10. Eve operates an apple farm. She spreads a mixture of a fertilizer called All Grow and a weed suppressant, No Weed, around her trees each autumn. She plans to spend $800 in total. All Grow costs $2.50/kg and No Weed costs $5/kg.
  (a) Use a graphing tool to draw the graph of the relation that represents this situation.
  (b) Use the graph to find the combination when the ratio of All Grow to No Weed is 2 : 1.
  (c) Is there a combination where the amounts of the two ingredients are equal? Show your reasoning algebraically and graphically.

11. Gregor is planning a driving trip. He knows that part of his trip will be along major highways and part will be along country roads or in the city. The speed limit on the highways is 100 km/h while the limit on the other roads is 60 km/h. The total time he wants to spend driving is 12 h.
  (a) Use a graphing tool to draw the graph of the relation that represents this situation.
  (b) Use the graph to find the distance he travels if he spends twice as much time on the highway as on country roads.
  (c) Is there a combination where the distances he travels on the highway and country roads are equal? Show your reasoning algebraically and graphically.

12. Identify each relation as linear or nonlinear. For those that are linear, state the intercepts and the slope, and use them to sketch the graph.

(a) $3x - 5y = 15$ **(b)** $y = 7 - 4x$ **(c)** $2x^2 + y = 5$

(d) $y = -3x - 4$ **(e)** $\frac{5}{8}y = -\frac{3}{4}x - 5$ **(f)** $3x - y^2 = 2$

13. For each of the following relations, create a table of values that contains six ordered pairs. Use a difference table to determine if each relation is linear or nonlinear.

(a) $y = 2x + 5$ **(b)** $y = x^2 - 3$ **(c)** $2x + 3y = 6$

(d) $y = 2^{x+1}$ **(e)** $\frac{y}{x} = 1$ **(f)** $x^2 + y^2 = 25$

(g) $2y = 4x$ **(h)** $y = x^3$

14. You can represent two-variable equations and expressions using algebra tiles. These tiles model the equation $2x + 5y = 10$.

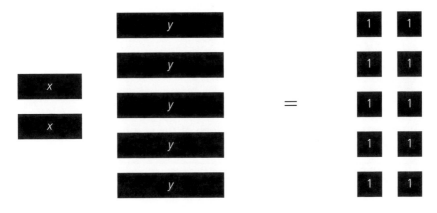

(a) Draw algebra tile diagrams to show the process of solving the equation for y in terms of x.

(b) Why are the tiles difficult to use at a certain step in the process?

(c) Suggest a way to draw a diagram that gets past that difficulty.

(d) Repeat the process for solving the equation for x in terms of y.

15. The Alltime watch company makes two kinds of watches and cannot keep up with the demand for them. The profit on digital watches is $15 per watch. The profit on dial watches is $20 per watch. The company wants to make at least $20 000 profit per week. However, the production ratio of digital to dial watches has to be 3 : 2 due to limitations on the manufacturing equipment. Under these conditions, how many watches of each type must be produced to meet the company's profit target?

16. Chiaki is organizing a neighbourhood candy hunt for the children who live nearby. She spent $102 to buy 500 large candies and 400 small candies. The ratio of the price of a large candy to the price of a small candy is 7 : 4. Find the prices of one large and one small candy.

17. A company that specializes in baseball equipment produces left-handed gloves and right-handed gloves in the ratio 8 : 1. The cost of making a left-handed glove is $9, while the cost of making a right-handed glove is $12. The company wishes to keep its costs below $15 000 per week. What is the greatest number of gloves of each type that can be made this week without exceeding the $15 000 cost mark?

18. Create an equation in slope–y-intercept form and then create a problem based on your equation. Exchange problems with a classmate.

The Chapter Problem — How Much Exercise?

Refer to the Chapter Problem at the beginning of this chapter.

1. Use technology to draw a graph of the exercise times for Carol that will allow her to burn a total of 780 calories. Use the graph to find a combination of times in which she burns an equal number of calories by mountain biking and by aerobics.
2. Use a graph to find the exercise times for Steve that will allow him to burn an equal number of calories by swimming and by jogging, if the total number of calories burned is 1100.

Amalie Emmy Noether (1882–1935)

Amalie Emmy Noether was one of the most outstanding mathematicians in the area of abstract algebra. After graduating from the University of Erlangen in Germany, she obtained a teaching position at the University of Göttingen. Despite opposition from her male colleagues, she proved to be an extraordinary professor. She left Germany to accept a professorship at Bryn Mawr College in Pennsylvania.

Other notable women mathematicians are: Hypatia, Maria Gaetana Agnesi, Sonja Kovalevsky, and Grace Chisholm Young.

Do some research on these mathematicians. What were their accomplishments?

5.6 Solving Polynomial Equations

Using the *Algebra Tiles Explorer*

Use the *Algebra Tiles Explorer* to model equations involving brackets. Click on $()$, then ENTER EQUATION . Enter the values to model $2(x + 5) = 2(2x - 4)$, then click OK .

Left Side	Right Side

Solution

1. Rewrite the expression without brackets by counting the number of different types of tiles. On the *Explorer* this is done with the DISTRIBUTE button.

$$2x + 10 = 4x - 8$$

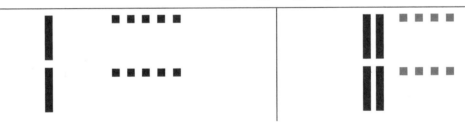

2. Isolate the variables on the left side.
$$2x + 10 - 4x = 4x - 8 - 4x$$

3. Simplify.
$$-2x + 10 = -8$$

4. Isolate the variable by eliminating 10 from the left side.

$$-2x + 10 - 10 = -8 - 10$$

5. Simplify.

$$-2x = -18$$

6. Group.

$$\frac{-2x}{-2} = \frac{-18}{-2}$$

7. Simplify.

$$x = 9$$

You can use the *Algebra Tiles Explorer* to solve and verify equations with and without brackets. To learn more about the *Algebra Tiles Explorer*, work through the computerized lesson. Once you know how to use the *Explorer*, solve the following equations.

Practise

Solve and verify using the *Algebra Tiles Explorer*.

(a) $3y - 24 = 6y$ **(b)** $10x = 5x + 25$ **(c)** $4t + 2 = 3t + 12$

(d) $3(x - 5) = 6$ **(e)** $12 = 6(n + 7)$ **(f)** $2(x + 6) = 4x$

(g) $2(4p - 5) = 3(6 - 2p)$ **(h)** $6(q - 1) = 3(q + 2)$ **(i)** $5(m - 3) = 3(m + 1)$

(j) Solve and verify five more equations using the **RANDOM EQUATION** button.

Expanding and Simplifying

The Johnson Machining Company has four large milling machines and three smaller ones. Each large machine costs $65/h to operate, with a $20 start-up labour cost. Each small machine costs $40/h to operate, with a $12 start-up labour cost. The company operates all seven machines at a daily charge of $4676.

If the cost of operating one large machine is L dollars and the cost of operating one small machine is S dollars, then the equation for the total cost is $4L + 3S = 4676$.

For how many hours do the machines run each day?

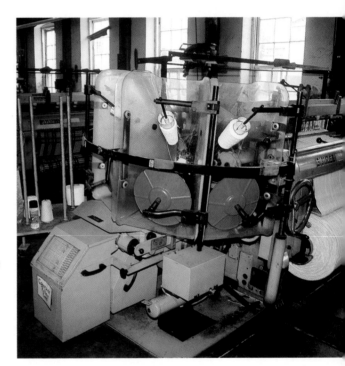

Think, Do, Discuss

1. If h represents the number of hours the machines run, write an expression for the cost of running a large machine for one day.

2. Write an expression for the cost of running a small machine for one day.

3. Write an equation that represents the total cost of running all seven machines.

4. What can you do to eliminate the brackets in the equation?

5. Expand the equation. Can you simplify the resulting equation? How?

6. Explain what must be done to solve the equation for h.

7. Solve the equation for h. How can you check to make sure your answer is correct?

8. What is the first thing that must be done to solve an equation involving brackets?

Eliminating Fractions

You've used this formula to convert Fahrenheit temperatures to Celsius.

$$C = \frac{5}{9}(F - 32)$$

Can you use this formula to convert Celsius into Fahrenheit?

Think, Do, Discuss

1. Substitute 20°C into the formula. What is the resulting equation?

2. Is there a number you could multiply all of the terms of the equation by to eliminate the fractions?

3. Multiply all terms of the equation by this number. What happens on the right side of the equation? Why?

4. Solve the equation. What does the answer mean in this situation?

5. Suppose you had to solve $\frac{2x}{4} + \frac{x}{3} = 5$. Is there a number you could multiply all of the terms of the equation by to eliminate the fractions?

John Fields (1863–1932)

John Charles Fields was probably the first significant research mathematician at the University of Toronto. He was born in Hamilton, Ontario and graduated from the University of Toronto in 1884. After getting his Ph.D. at Johns Hopkins University in 1887, he continued his studies in Europe with noted mathematicians like Max Planck. He returned to Canada to teach at the University of Toronto, where he remained until his death.

Fields was particularly interested in algebraic functions. His papers are currently held by the Thomas Fisher Rare Books Collection at the University of Toronto. In his will, he established the Fields Medal, which is mentioned in the film *Good Will Hunting*. It was first awarded in 1936 and is looked upon as the Nobel Prize of Mathematics. Consistent with Fields's wish that the award recognize both existing work and the promise of future achievement, it was agreed to restrict the medals to mathematicians under the age of 40.

The Fields Institute for Research in Mathematical Sciences, on College Street in Toronto, is also named in his honour.

Focus

Example 1

Solve for x.

$$3(x - 1) + 2(3x + 1) = 0$$

Solution

$3(x - 1) + 2(3x + 1) = 0$	Expand using the distributive property to eliminate the brackets.
$3x - 3 + 6x + 2 = 0$	Combine like terms on both sides of the equation.
$3x + 6x - 3 + 2 = 0$	
$9x - 1 = 0$	Add or subtract terms on both sides of the equation to isolate variable terms.
$9x = 0 + 1$	
$9x = 1$	Simplify both sides of the equation.
$\dfrac{9x}{9} = \dfrac{1}{9}$	Divide both sides of the equation by the coefficient of the variable.
$x = \dfrac{1}{9}$	Simplify the answer.

Example 2

Solve for x.

$$\frac{4x-1}{4} + \frac{2x-1}{5} = 2$$

Solution

$$20\left(\frac{4x-1}{4}\right) + 20\left(\frac{2x-1}{5}\right) = 20(2)$$

Multiply each term by the lowest common denominator and simplify to eliminate the fractions.

$$5(4x-1) + 4(2x-1) = 40$$

Expand using the distributive property to eliminate the brackets.

$$20x - 5 + 8x - 4 = 40$$

Combine like terms and simplify.

$$28x - 9 = 40$$

Isolate the variable term and continue to simplify.

$$28x = 40 + 9$$

$$28x = 49$$

$$\frac{28x}{28} = \frac{49}{28}$$

Divide both sides of the equation by the coefficient of the variable.

$$x = \frac{49}{28}$$

Simplify the answer.

$$x = \frac{7}{4}$$

$$x = 1\frac{3}{4} \text{ or } 1.75$$

Practise, Apply, Solve

1. Solve.

(a) $2x - 5 = 7$

(b) $3x + 4 = 10$

(c) $-5x + 1 = -4$

(d) $6 = 3 - 3x$

(e) $12 - 2x = 4x$

(f) $3x - 5 = 2x + 4$

(g) $3x - 4 - 5x = -3x - 2$

(h) $3 - 6x + 5x = 4 + x$

2. Solve.

(a) $\frac{x}{3} = 2$

(b) $\frac{c}{5} = -2$

(c) $\frac{-d}{4} = 2$

(d) $\frac{2x}{7} = 2$

(e) $\frac{-3x}{4} = -3$

(f) $\frac{6x}{8} = 3$

3. Solve.

(a) $3(x - 5) = 6$

(b) $6(n + 7) = 12$

(c) $4(t - 3) = 0$

(d) $5(3 + 2d) = -5$

(e) $-2(k + 5) = 20$

(f) $7(4 - y) = 42$

(g) $-4(2z + 3) = 12$

(h) $9(u - 5) = 0$

(i) $2(-5 + 3b) = 8$

(j) $-3(5 - 6a) = 39$

(k) $-7(-3 - 2j) = -35$

(l) $10(3k - 13) = -100$

(m) $18 = 3(4 + p)$

(n) $-24 = 8(2s + 5)$

4. Solve.

(a) $\frac{x+1}{2} = 3$ (b) $\frac{x-1}{5} = -3$ (c) $\frac{2x+1}{3} = 5$

(d) $\frac{x}{2} - \frac{x}{3} = 3$ (e) $\frac{2x}{5} + 2 = \frac{1}{2}$ (f) $\frac{3s}{4} - \frac{2s}{3} = 6$

(g) $\frac{3k}{5} - 6 = \frac{k}{3}$ (h) $-4r = r + \frac{5}{2}$ (i) $\frac{2y+3}{3} = y + 2$

5. Solve.

(a) $3(y + 4) = 15y$ (b) $p - 6 = 2(p - 6)$

(c) $7(d + 1) - (1 + 5d) = 0$ (d) $5(n + 3) = 9n + 3$

(e) $-3(x + 2) = 27x + 24$ (f) $4(h + 13) = 19h + 22$

(g) $7z - 4 = 3(z + 4)$ (h) $v + 23 = -3(v + 3)$

B

6. Solve.

(a) $3(q - 1) = 2(q - 2)$ (b) $3(n + 1) = 5(n - 3)$

(c) $2(4p - 5) = 3(6 - 2p)$ (d) $7(4 - 3z) = -8(2z - 1)$

(e) $4(c - 1) = 3(-2c + 2)$ (f) $5(3 + 4v) = -13(1 - v)$

7. Solve.

(a) $3(2h - 5) + 4(3h + 2) = 11$ (b) $-5(7 - 2m) + 3(8 - 4m) = 21$

(c) $8(3n + 5) = 72 - 4(5n - 3)$ (d) $2(3p - 4) - 10 = 5(6 - 2p)$

(e) $\frac{1}{2}(6u - 2) - \frac{3}{4}(8u + 12) = 5$ (f) $8 - \frac{2}{5}(25 - 10a) = \frac{3}{7}(14a - 21)$

(g) $2.3(4.2q - 3.8) = 5.8(6.2 - 3.1q) + 10.36$

(h) $\frac{3}{5}(10 + 15y) + 7 = -\frac{2}{3}(12 - 24y)$

(i) $7(3r + 11) + 4r + \frac{5}{2} = \frac{21}{2}$

(j) $-6(2z + 3) - 13 = 4(5 - 7z) + 3$

(k) $7 + \frac{1}{3}(4w - 5) = \frac{4}{7}(4w + 1)$

8. Given $3x + y = 15$:

(a) solve for y if $x = -2$ (b) solve for x if $y = 4$ (c) solve for x if $y = 2x - 1$

9. Given $2x - 3y = 9$:

(a) solve for x if $y = 1\frac{2}{3}$ (b) solve for y if $x = -2\frac{1}{2}$ (c) solve for x if $y = 5y - 4$

10. Given $\frac{3}{2}x + \frac{5}{3}y = 10$:

(a) solve for x if $y = 2\frac{2}{5}$ (b) solve for y if $x = 6$ (c) solve for y if $x = \frac{7}{3}y$

11. Solve.

(a) $\frac{x+3}{4} = \frac{x+5}{6}$ (b) $\frac{y+2}{3} = \frac{2y+3}{5}$ (c) $\frac{2c+4}{5} - \frac{7c-6}{15} = 2$

12. Solve.

(a) $\dfrac{4d+7}{3} - 5d - \dfrac{5}{7} = 6$ (b) $4h + \dfrac{9-4h}{5} = \dfrac{13}{2} + \dfrac{7}{3}$ (c) $\dfrac{-11j}{3} + 4j - \dfrac{7}{4} = \dfrac{11}{12}$

C

13. Ameet joins a book club. The first six books are free, but after that he pays $8.98 per book.
(a) Write an equation for the cost of b books.
(b) How much would he pay for eight books?
(c) Ameet receives his first shipment of books with a bill for $53.88. How many books did he order?

14. A square has sides of length $2k - 1$ units. A triangle has sides of length $k + 2$ units. The square and the triangle have the same perimeter. What is the value of k?

15. Solve.

$$\dfrac{2}{3}\left(\dfrac{1}{4}x - 2\right) - \dfrac{8}{15}\left(\dfrac{3}{16}x + \dfrac{1}{4}\right) = 5\dfrac{1}{2} - \dfrac{1}{3}(2x + 5)$$

16. Solve.

$$-\dfrac{3}{5}\left(\dfrac{25}{9} - \dfrac{1}{3}x\right) + \dfrac{7}{4}\left(\dfrac{8}{21}x - 13\right) = \dfrac{11}{2}x + \dfrac{5}{7}\left(14x + \dfrac{42}{25}\right)$$

17. A wholesale outlet has two grades of coffee, one selling for $8/kg and the other selling for $10/kg. The manager wants to mix the two grades to get 200 kg of coffee to sell for $8.75/kg. How much of each grade of coffee should be mixed?

18. A broker invested $10 000. Part of the money was invested at 8% per annum, and the remainder at 10% per annum. If the investments earned $872 in one year, how much was invested at 10%?

19. A chemist has 100 mL of a 40% acid solution. She wants to reduce the strength of the solution to 25% acid by adding distilled water. How much water should she add?

The Chapter Problem — How Much Exercise?

Refer to the Chapter Problem at the beginning of the chapter.

1. Explain what the significance of using times like 1.5 h or $\dfrac{3}{4}$ hour has when making tables of values and graphs for the combinations of times used by Steve and Carol.
2. If you could not use rational numbers for the times, how would that affect the appearance of the graphs?
3. Rational numbers can be negative. Is it possible to use negative values in the equations that represent Carol and Steve's problem? Explain.

5.8 Standard Form of a Linear Equation

You have seen the equation of a straight line written in the forms $ax + by = c$ and $y = mx + b$. The graph of a line is the same, regardless of the form of its equation.

Slope–y-Intercept Form

When there is a linear relationship that shows how one variable depends on the other, that relationship is expressed in the form $y = mx + b$. The form $y = mx + b$ is called the **slope–y-intercept** form because the value of m is the slope of the line and the value of b is its y-intercept.

Standard Form

When a quantity is written as the sum of two variable terms, the equation $ax + by = c$ is used. For convenience, equations in this form are usually rearranged so that all the quantities appear on the left side of the equation with 0 on the right side.

An equation of the form $Ax + By + C = 0$ is said to be in **standard form**. The equation is transformed using the rules of algebra so that the numerical coefficients represented by A, B, and C are all integers and A is positive. Any of A, B, or C can be 0, but not both A and B at the same time.

Think, Do, Discuss

1. Which equations are not in standard form? Explain why they are not.
   (a) $-2x + y = 6$ (b) $y = 3x - 7$ (c) $3x - 4y + 5 = 0$
   (d) $y + 4x - 1 = 0$ (e) $5x - 4 = 0$ (f) $0 = 3x - y$
   (g) $x = 2$ (h) $3x = 5$ (i) $y = 0$

2. Rearrange each equation so it is in standard form.
   (a) $2x + y = 6$ (b) $y = 3x - 7$ (c) $-3x + 4y + 5 = 0$
   (d) $y - 4x - 1 = 0$ (e) $5x - 4 = 2y$ (f) $2 = 3x - y$
   (g) $x = 2$ (h) $-3x = 5$ (i) $y - 6 = 0$

3. When equations are in slope–y-intercept form, they often have rational numbers for the slope or the intercept.

   This example shows how the equation is transformed to standard form.

$$y = \tfrac{2}{3}x + 5$$
$$3y = 3\left(\tfrac{2}{3}\right)x + 3(5) \qquad \text{Step A}$$
$$3y = 2x + 15 \qquad \text{Step B}$$
$$2x + 15 = 3y \qquad \text{Step C}$$
$$2x + 15 - 3y = 3y - 3y \qquad \text{Step D}$$
$$2x - 3y + 15 = 0 \qquad \text{Step E}$$

(a) Why is the equation in Step A true based on the original equation?

(b) Why should Step B be a logical result of step A?

(c) What operation was performed to reach Step C from Step B?

(d) Why is subtracting $3y$ from both sides of the equation in Step D a valid operation?

4. (a) Describe a shortcut that would let you go directly from the original equation to Step C in a single operation.

(b) Use the shortcut to transform the equation $y = \frac{5}{6}x - 4$ to standard form.

(c) How would you modify the shortcut to transform $y = \frac{3}{5}x + \frac{2}{3}$ to standard form?

5. Suppose you were asked to graph $3x + 5y - 15 = 0$.

(a) Find the slope, the y-intercept, and the x-intercept of the line.

(b) Which of these were difficult to find? Which were easy to find? Why?

6. Suppose you were asked to graph $y = \frac{-3}{5}x + 3$.

(a) Find the slope, the y-intercept, and the x-intercept of the line.

(b) Which of these were difficult to find? Which were easy to find? Why?

7. (a) How can you tell if the equations in Questions 5 and 6 represent the same line?

(b) What information is easier to find using the standard form of the equation of the line?

(c) What information is easier to find using the slope–y-intercept form?

(d) Which form of the equation of a line is easier to use when graphing by hand? Why?

(e) Which form is easier to use with a graphing tool? Why?

8. Sometimes, it is more useful to have the equation in slope–y-intercept form than in standard form. This example shows how this transformation can be done.

$$3x + 5y - 7 = 0$$

$$3x + 5y - 7 - 3x + 7 = 0 - 3x + 7 \qquad \text{Step } \mathbf{A}$$

$$5y = -3x + 7 \qquad \text{Step } \mathbf{B}$$

$$\frac{5y}{5} = \frac{-3x + 7}{5} \qquad \text{Step } \mathbf{C}$$

$$y = \frac{-3}{5}x + \frac{7}{5} \qquad \text{Step } \mathbf{D}$$

(a) Why was $3x$ subtracted and 7 added to each side in step A? Why are these operations valid?

(b) Why is the operation in Step C valid ?

9. Follow the steps in Question 8 and transform $Ax + By + C = 0$ to slope–y-intercept form.

(a) What is the value of m?

(b) What is the value of b?

Did You Know?

In how many ways can a necktie be tied? People tend to use one of four knots to tie their neckties. But in 1999, Thomas Fink and Yong Mao used mathematical models to find 85 different knots that could be used.

Focus

Key Ideas

- When a linear relation is represented by an equation in the form $y = mx + b$, it is said to be in **slope–y-intercept form**. The value of m is the slope of the line and the value of b is the y-intercept of the line.

- When a linear relation is represented by an equation of the form $Ax + By + C = 0$ in which A, B, and C are integers and A is positive, it is said to be in **standard form**.

- The two forms of the equation of a line are interchangeable. Either form can be transformed to the other using simple algebraic manipulation.

- $m = \dfrac{-A}{B}$ and $b = \dfrac{-C}{B}$ can be derived from the equation $Ax + By + C = 0$, when $B \neq 0$.

Example

A line has the equation $3x - 2y + 4 = 0$.
Find the slope and y-intercept and use these to sketch the graph.

Solution

Method 1:

$$m = \frac{-A}{B} = \frac{-(3)}{-2} = \frac{3}{2} \qquad b = \frac{-C}{B} = \frac{-(4)}{(-2)} = 2$$

The graph can be sketched using a y-intercept of $(0, 2)$ and a slope of $\dfrac{3}{2}$.

Method 2:
Rewrite the equation in slope–y-intercept form.

$$3x - 2y + 4 = 0$$
$$3x - 2y + 4 - 3x - 4 = 0 - 3x - 4$$
$$\frac{-2y}{-2} = \frac{-3x - 4}{-2}$$
$$y = \frac{-3x}{-2} - \frac{4}{-2}$$
$$y = \frac{3}{2}x + 2$$

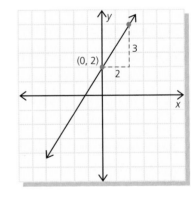

The graph can be sketched using a y-intercept of $(0, 2)$ and a slope of $\dfrac{3}{2}$.

Practise, Apply, Solve

1. Which equations are in standard form, which are in slope–y-intercept form, and which are in neither form?

- **(a)** $-3x + 2y = 6$
- **(b)** $5y = 3x - 7$
- **(c)** $-3x - 4y - 5 = 0$
- **(d)** $y + 4x - 1 = 0$
- **(e)** $5x + 4 = 0$
- **(f)** $0 = 3x - y$
- **(g)** $x = 2$
- **(h)** $3x = 5$
- **(i)** $y = 0$
- **(j)** $x + y = 0$
- **(k)** $0.5x - y + 1 = 0$
- **(l)** $\frac{1}{3}x + \frac{2}{3}y = 1$
- **(m)** $y = 0.2x - 4$
- **(n)** $-y = 3x + 2$
- **(o)** $y = \frac{-2}{5}x - 1$

2. Find the equation of the linear relation being described. Use the form of the equation that is most directly related to the description.

- **(a)** The line has a slope of -0.3 and a y-intercept of -2.
- **(b)** The line has x-intercept 3 and y-intercept -4.
- **(c)** Mary works at two jobs. The total number of hours she works is 38 h per week.
- **(d)** Carl works as a car salesman. He earns a base salary of $150 a week plus 6% commission on his total sales for the week.
- **(e)** A box contains a mixture of 46¢ stamps and 53¢ stamps. The total value of the stamps in the box is $76.
- **(f)** The line is parallel to the line with equation $y = 2x + 5$ and has a y-intercept of 1.5.
- **(g)** The line is perpendicular to the line with equation $y = \frac{-3}{4}x + \frac{7}{8}$ and has a y-intercept of -10.

3. State the x- and y-intercepts of the following equations. Use the intercepts to draw a graph.

- **(a)** $2x - 5y = 10$
- **(b)** $4x + 5y = 20$
- **(c)** $x = 5$
- **(d)** $y = -2$
- **(e)** $x + y = 0$
- **(f)** $x - y - 9 = 0$
- **(g)** $2x + 3y = 0$
- **(h)** $4x + 5y - 20 = 0$
- **(i)** $5x - 4y - 20 = 0$

4. Express each equation in Question 3 in the form $y = mx + b$. State the slope of each line.

5. Express each equation in standard form.

- **(a)** $y = 3x + 5$
- **(b)** $y = -2x - 11$
- **(c)** $2x - 3y = 12$
- **(d)** $\frac{1}{3}x = 2y - 5$
- **(e)** $\frac{x + 5}{3} = 2y$
- **(f)** $0.5x + 1.2y = 3.5$
- **(g)** $-x + 2y = 7$
- **(h)** $\frac{5}{2}x - \frac{3}{4}y = \frac{1}{3}$
- **(i)** $-0.2y - 0.1x - 0.5 = 0$

6. Write each equation in standard form, then state the x- and y-intercepts of the graphs of each equation.

- **(a)** $4x + 6y = -8y - 7$
- **(b)** $y = 2y - 7x + 3$
- **(c)** $\frac{2}{5}y - \frac{3}{5}x + \frac{7}{10} = 0$
- **(d)** $\frac{2}{3} + 3x = \frac{1}{3}y + 3x$
- **(e)** $4x + 3y = \frac{6}{17}$
- **(f)** $\frac{13}{31}x - \frac{21}{31}y = -\frac{18}{31}$

⬤ **B**

7. Determine the equation of the linear relation being described. Explain the significance of the slope and the intercepts in each case.

(a) Tiffany lends Rob $50, and Rob pays her back by giving her $5 every day until the debt is repaid.

(b) Andrew works as a computer administrator. He earns a base salary of $200/week plus $20 for every computer problem he fixes.

(c) The line is perpendicular to the line with equation $4x - 5y + 13 = 0$ and has a y-intercept of -3.

(d) Fillipe collects hockey cards. One brand costs $1.20 per pack while another brand costs $2.10 per pack. Fillipe can spend up to $33.60.

(e) Peggy takes driving lessons and dance lessons. She attends lessons for a total of 12 h a week.

(f) A house is purchased for $210 000, then depreciates by 2% of the purchase price every year.

8. Two airplanes are tracked on the same coordinate system on a radar screen. One plane follows a path described by the equation $y = \frac{2}{5}x - 2$ and the other follows a path described by the equation $2x - 5y - 7 = 0$. Determine whether the planes collide.

9. Aline has written a multiple-choice test. She receives one point for each correct answer, but loses $\frac{1}{4}$ point for each incorrect answer. No marks are deducted for a question not answered. She answered 41 questions and received a score of 34.75.

(a) Write an equation that expresses her score in terms of correct and incorrect answers.

(b) Graph this equation.

(c) Write an equation that represents her total questions answered.

(d) Graph this equation on the same grid as the graph in (b).

(e) Locate the point of intersection and record its coordinates.

(f) Describe the meaning of these coordinates in this situation.

(g) Express both equations in standard form.

10. Ralph works part-time for a bike repair shop. He earns $2 for each tire he installs and $5 for each gear mechanism he assembles. Last week he completed 40 jobs and earned $110.

(a) Write an equation that represents the total number of jobs Ralph completed last week.

(b) Write an equation that represents his week's earnings.

(c) Graph the two equations on the same coordinate grid.

(d) Describe the significance of the point at which the lines intersect. What do the coordinates tell you about the situation?

(e) Express both equations in standard form.

11. A candy store is making up a mixture of chocolate-coated almonds and chocolate-coated raisins. The almonds cost $10.50/kg and the raisins cost $5/kg. The total cost of the mixture is to be $150. The store made up 19 kg of the mixture.

(a) Write an equation that represents the total mass of the mixture.

(b) Write an equation that represents the total value of the mixture.

320 Chapter 5 **Modelling: Using Equations to Ask and Answer Questions**

(c) Graph the two equations on the same coordinate grid.

(d) Describe the significance of the point of intersection of the two lines. What do the coordinates of this point tell you about the situation?

(e) Express both equations in standard form.

12. A shoe company specializes in dress shoes and running shoes. Each pair of running shoes costs $20 to make, while each pair of dress shoes costs $32 to make. This month the company plans to make 4800 pairs of shoes altogether. The company also has $116 400 available for production costs this month.
   (a) Write an equation that represents the total number of pairs of shoes.
   (b) Write an equation that represents the total production costs for this month.
   (c) Graph the two equations on the same coordinate grid.
   (d) Describe the significance of the point at which the lines intersect. What do the coordinates of this point tell you about the situation?
   (e) Express both equations in standard form.

13. Raymond is a hockey fan. He roots for one team in particular.
   (a) Raymond's team had 83 points at the end of the season. Write an equation that expresses the point total in terms of wins and ties, and graph the relation.
   (b) Raymond's team lost 32 games and played 80 games in all. Write an equation that represents the total number of games played in terms of wins and ties, and graph the relation on the same grid as the graph in (a).
   (c) Locate the point of intersection and record its coordinates. What do the coordinates of this point tell you about the situation?

C

14. Christine has two sales jobs. She earns $100 a week, plus a commission of 3% on sales at a clothing store. Her commission at the hardware store is 5%. Last week she earned $750 on total sales of $15 000 from the two stores. Find her sales at each store.

15. Hard candy is $2/kg and soft candy is $4/kg. How many kilograms of each candy must be mixed to obtain 60 kg of candy that would be worth $3/kg?

16. Cathy is a stockbroker. One group of her clients purchases low-risk stocks, while the other group of her clients purchases high-risk stocks. Cathy earns a commission of 4% on the total value of low-risk stocks that she sells, and a commission of 11% on the total value of high-risk stocks that she sells. She also earns a base salary of $300 a week. Last week Cathy sold stocks worth a total of $14 250 and earned a total of five times her base salary. Find out the value of each type of stock that she sold.

Did You Know?

To identify a specific tooth in a person's mouth, the mouth is divided into four quadrants, and the teeth in each quadrant are numbered from 1 to 8. Each tooth can then be described using two numbers. The first number describes the quadrant of the tooth. The second number describes its position in that quadrant. For example, the top front teeth (central incisors) are (1, 1) and (2, 1), while the bottom wisdom teeth (third molars) are (3, 8) and (4, 8).

5.9 Problem Solving and Linear Equations

Investment Options

Recall Mary's investment problem. She wants to put money into two kinds of investments. Risky investments pay a higher return, but there is a chance she will lose money. Safer investments like bonds or investment certificates pay lower returns, but the original money is guaranteed. The risky investment she is considering pays a 10% return, while the safer investment pays 4%. She wants a return of $500 on her investments this year.

Earlier, you saw that this situation could be represented by this equation, where S represents the amount of money in safe investments and R is the amount in risky investments.

$$0.04S + 0.10R = 500$$

Suppose Mary has $7000 to invest. This statement can be represented by this equation.

$$S + R = 7000$$

The graphs of the two equations are shown and the point at which they intersect is marked.

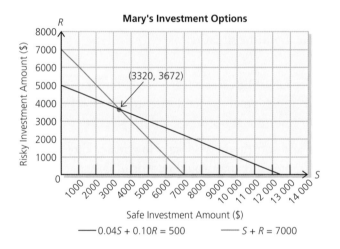

Mary's Investment Options

Think, Do, Discuss

1. **(a)** How could equations for Mary's problem be entered into a graphing tool like a graphing calculator or a spreadsheet to create the corresponding graphs? Why is the slope–y-intercept form more useful than standard form in this situation?
    (b) How could the coordinates of the intersection point be found once the graphs have been made?

2. **(a)** How accurately do the coordinates (3320, 3672) represent the point of intersection of the two lines? How can you test the accuracy of the values?
    (b) Find a better estimate of the coordinates of the point of intersection.
    (c) What does each of the coordinates represent? What do the coordinates mean in Mary's problem?

3. **(a)** Show how the investment return equation $0.04S + 0.10R = 500$ can be transformed into $R = -0.4S + 5000$.

(b) Show how the available funds equation $R + S = 7000$ can be transformed into $R = -S + 7000$.

4. **(a)** There is a point (R, S) that is on both graphs. Locate that point. Substitute the values of the coordinates of that point, R and S, into both equations. Explain what you observe.

(b) What must be true of the two equations when the coordinates of that point are substituted? Are there any other points for which this happens? Explain.

5. Mary carried out these steps to solve her investment problem.

$$-0.4S + 5000 = -S + 7000$$
$$-0.4S + 5000 - 5000 = -S + 7000 - 5000 \qquad \text{Step } \mathbf{A}$$
$$-0.4S = -S + 2000 \qquad \text{Step } \mathbf{B}$$
$$-0.4S + S = -S + 2000 + S$$
$$0.6S = 2000 \qquad \text{Step } \mathbf{C}$$
$$\frac{0.6S}{0.6} = \frac{2000}{0.6} \qquad \text{Step } \mathbf{D}$$
$$S \doteq 3333.33 \qquad \text{Step } \mathbf{E}$$

(a) When is the equation that Mary wrote in Step A true?

(b) In Steps B, C, and D, Mary simplified and then solved the equation. Describe what she did in each step and explain why it was justified.

(c) What does the value of S represent?

(d) Mary substituted $S = 3333.33$ into the equation $R = -S + 7000$ and found the corresponding value of R to be 3666.67. What does this R-value mean?

(e) What conclusions can be drawn about Mary's investment problem?

(f) What happens when you substitute the value of S into both the left side and the right side of the equation in Step A? Why should this happen?

Did You Know?

Chess probably originated in India about 1400 years ago. Today, chess is played around the world, for pleasure and in competition. It is a fun, challenging game that develops the ability to think logically.

To develop computers that can calculate faster and better, mathematicians write chess programs. Twenty years ago, serious computer chess games were thought to be impossible. Today they are common, with the computer often winning.

Find out how the knight moves in chess. Start at one corner of the chess board and move the knight so that it lands once on every square. This is called the Knight's Tour.

Focus

Key Ideas

- When a problem can be described by two linear relationships between two variables, there is usually a single point that satisfies both equations simultaneously. This point is the point of intersection of the two graphs that represent the relations.

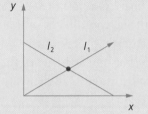

- The coordinates of the point of intersection represent the **solution** of the system of the two equations for the relations.
- Estimates of the point's coordinates can be found by graphing. If the equations are graphed simultaneously using graphing technology, the TRACE and ZOOM features can be used to improve the estimate of the coordinate values.
- The solution estimates can be improved by substituting the values into the original equations and adjusting them until the equations indicate that the result has been improved.
- The slope–y-intercept forms of the two equations can be set equal to each other to represent the situation that exists only at the point of intersection. At that point the values of the dependent and independent variables satisfy both equations at the same time. This equation can then be solved to find the value of the independent variable. This value can then be substituted into one of the equations to find the value of the dependent variable.
- Substitute into the left and right sides of the equation to check the solution. If the solution is correct, both sides of the equation will produce the same result.

Example

The members of a math club held a car wash for charity. They washed 49 vehicles. They charged \$4 per car and \$6 per truck and earned a total of \$230. How many of each type of vehicle did they wash?

Solution 1: Using a graphing calculator

Let c represent the number of cars washed and t represent the number of trucks washed.

The equation that represents the total number of vehicles washed is $c + t = 49$.
In slope–y-intercept form, the equation is $t = 49 - c$.
The equation that represents the total revenue earned is $4c + 6t = 230$.
Use these steps to put the equation in slope–y-intercept form.

$$4c + 6t = 230$$
$$4c + 6t - 4c = 230 - 4c$$
$$6t = -4c + 230$$
$$\frac{6t}{6} = -\frac{4c}{6} + \frac{230}{6}$$
$$t = -\frac{2c}{3} + 38\frac{1}{3}$$

The equations $t = 49 - c$ and $t = -\frac{2c}{3} + 38\frac{1}{3}$ were entered into a graphing calculator and graphed. The TRACE shows approximate coordinates for the point of intersection (31, 18).

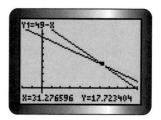

Substituting these values into the revenue equation yields $4(31) + 6(18) = 232$.

These values do not satisfy the equation.

After zooming in and tracing, the improved estimate is (32, 17). These values satisfy the equation.

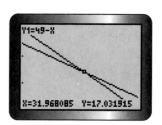

Solution 2: Solving a pair of algebraic equations

The graphs of two relations have a point in common where their lines intersect. The two equations of the graphs must produce the same value of t for the same value of c, when the coordinates of the intersection point, (c, t), are substituted.

At the point of intersection, the two equations $t = 49 - c$ and $t = \frac{-2}{3}c + \frac{115}{3}$ must have equal values of t. The two equations can be combined for $49 - c = \frac{-2}{3}c + \frac{115}{3}$.

The new equation can be solved.

$$49 - c = \frac{-2}{3}c + \frac{115}{3}$$

$$3(49 - c) = 3\left(\frac{-2c}{3} + \frac{115}{3}\right)$$

Eliminate the fractions by multiplying both sides by 3.

$$147 - 3c = -2c + 115$$

$$147 - 3c - 147 + 2c = -2c + 115 + 2c - 147$$

Isolate the variables.

$$-c = -32$$

Divide by -1.

$$c = 32$$

Substitute $c = 32$ into the vehicle equation, $t = 49 - c$.

$$t = 49 - 32$$
$$= 17$$

These values satisfy the revenue equation.

Practise, Apply, Solve

1. Graph each pair of equations. Find the point of intersection by using the graphs and then by solving an equation. Check your solution.

(a) $y = 3x + 5$, $y = 2x + 4$
(b) $y = -3x - 10$, $y = 2x + 5$
(c) $y = -\frac{1}{2}x + 2$, $y = \frac{1}{2}x - 3$
(d) $x + 2y - 5 = 0$, $x + y + 5 = 0$
(e) $2x + 3y - 6 = 0$, $2x + 4y + 1 = 0$
(f) $y = 0.3x - 4$, $y = 0.4x + 5$

2. Solve each pair of equations graphically and algebraically. Check your solution.

(a) $y = x + 2$, $y = 2x + 6$
(b) $y = 7x - 9$, $y = 9x + 1$
(c) $b = 3a + 4$, $b = 5a + 2$
(d) $x = 10 - 3y$, $x = 8 - y$
(e) $y = 0.5x + 2.3$, $y = 0.25x + 4$
(f) $x = 8 - 1.5y$, $x = 2 - 3.25y$
(g) $y = 8x - 12$, $y = -7x + 3$
(h) $y = 12x$, $y = 36$
(i) $y = x - 7$, $y = 2x + 3$
(j) $y = 1.8x - 3.2$, $y = -3.2x + 1.8$
(k) $y = 5x + 1$, $y = x + 6$
(l) $5 + 7x + y = 0$, $5 + 100x + y = 0$
(m) $y + 8 = 3x$, $3y - 6 = 3x$
(n) $r = s + 6$, $r = 2s - 8$
(o) $t = 5x - 3$, $t = 3x + 1$
(p) $y = 13x + 26$, $y = 12x + 23$
(q) $7x + 5y = 9$, $7x + 4y = 4$
(r) $y = 2.7x + 0.9$, $y = 6.2x + 2.4$

B

3. Solve each equation algebraically. Check by graphing and then by substitution.

(a) $\frac{2}{3}x - 3 = \frac{1}{2}x + 1$
(b) $1\frac{2}{5} - \frac{1}{2}x = 3 - \frac{3}{4}x$
(c) $1.5x - 2.45 = -2.25 + 0.5x$
(d) $\frac{-4}{5}x - \frac{1}{2} = \frac{7}{10}x + \frac{1}{5}$
(e) $\frac{1}{8}x - \frac{5}{6} = \frac{3}{4}x + \frac{1}{4}$
(f) $5\frac{1}{2} - r = 3\frac{1}{4}r + \frac{2}{3}$
(g) $0.3r + 1.73 = 3.3r - 0.91$
(h) $\frac{-2}{3}y + \frac{3}{5} = 2\frac{1}{5}y + \frac{2}{3}$
(i) $1.35g + 2.65 = 0.45g + 4.45$
(j) $-s + \frac{3}{10} = \frac{2}{7}s - \frac{2}{5}$

4. Ralph works part–time for a bike repair shop. He earns $2 for each tire he installs and $5 for each gear mechanism he assembles. Last week he did a total of 40 installations and assemblies, and earned $110. How many of each type of installation did he complete?

5. A candy store is making a mixture of chocolate-coated almonds and chocolate-coated raisins. The almonds cost $10.50/kg and the raisins cost $5/kg. The final cost of the mixture is to be $150. The store made 19 kg of the mixture. What was the mass of each ingredient in the mixture?

6. Henri sharpens skates at a local arena. He charges $3.00 to sharpen a pair of figure skates and $2.50 for a pair of hockey skates. Last Saturday he earned a total of $240 while sharpening 94 pairs of skates. How many pairs of each type of skate did he sharpen?

7. Gregor is planning a driving trip. Part of his trip will be along major highways and part will be along country roads or on city streets. The speed limit on the highways is 100 km/h while the limit on the other roads is 60 km/h. The total time he wants to spend driving is 12 h and he has to travel 850 km. How much time should he plan to spend on each type of road?

8. Eve operates an apple farm. She spreads a mixture of a fertilizer called All Grow and a weed suppressant, No Weed, around her trees each autumn. She spent $800 this autumn to fill the spreader. All Grow costs $2.50/kg and No Weed costs $5.00/kg. Her spreader holds 200 kg of mixture. How much of each did she use?

9. Brittany has $500 to spend on stamps. Research the cost to mail a letter within Canada and to mail one to the United States. Find the combination of stamps Brittany can purchase that uses as much of the $500 as possible if she must buy 10 times as many stamps for letters to be mailed in Canada as stamps for letters to the U.S.

10. An investment club invested part of $8000 at 10% and the rest at 12%. If the annual income from these investments is $900, how much was invested at each rate?

11. A delivery truck travels 80 km in the same time that a cargo plane travels 288 km. The speed of the plane is 228.8 km/h faster than the speed of the truck. What is the speed of the delivery truck?

12. A sales clerk can choose from two salary plans: straight 7% commission or $150 + 2% commission. How much would the clerk have to sell for each plan to produce the same monthly paycheque?

13. How much of a 40% antifreeze solution must a mechanic mix with an 80% antifreeze solution if 20 L of a 50% antifreeze solution are needed?

14. Gretchen has two part-time jobs. She earns $8/h at her first job, and $7/h at the second. Last week she worked a total of 19 h and earned a total of $145. How many hours did she work at each job?

The Chapter Problem — How Much Exercise?

Refer back to the Chapter Problem at the beginning of the chapter.

1. Show how Carol can combine her two preferred activities into a 90-min workout that burns 780 calories.
2. Show how Steve can combine his two preferred activities into a 90-min workout and still burn 1100 calories.
3. Examine the various pairs of activities. Is there a way that Carol and Steve both can do the same two exercise activities for 90 min and both meet their personal calorie targets?

Chapter Review

5.1–5.2 Exploring Relationships with Two Variables

- Relationships that describe how to combine two quantities can usually be represented by an equation of the form $ax + by = c$.

- In real-world situations of this type, usually x is greater than 0 and y is greater than 0.

- In some situations, it does not matter which variable should be treated as the independent variable and which should be the dependent variable.

- The first column of a table of values and the horizontal axis of the graph should correspond to the variable whose value is most likely to be chosen first. The other variable will then be used for the other column and axis.

- Graphing a relationship is possible using a table of values. The values for the table can be found using a **trial-and-error** or **guess-and-check** process.

- The intercepts for the graph of the relation correspond to the values found after substituting 0 for one of the variables and solving for the other.

Extra Practice

1. Drena has a business making holiday decorations. She spent 70 min after school last week making decorations. She needs 3.5 min to make a paper wreath and 2.0 min to make a paper candle.
   (a) What is the maximum number of wreaths she could make?
   (b) What is the maximum number of candles?
   (c) Construct a table of values with three more combinations.
   (d) Graph this relation.
   (e) Use the graph to find the number of wreaths when the number of candles is 28.

2. Kent spent $18 on chips and popsicles over a period of time. The chips cost $0.75 per bag and the popsicles cost $0.25.
   (a) How many bags of chips could he buy for $18?
   (b) How many popsicles could he buy for $18?
   (c) Graph this relation using the information in parts (a) and (b).
   (d) Use the graph to find the combination in which the number of popsicles is equal to three times the number of bags of chips.

5.3 Finding Values That Satisfy a Linear Relation

- When a relationship is described by an equation of the form $ax + by = c$, a table of values can be constructed by first substituting a value for one of the variables and then solving the resulting equation for the other.

- A pair of values that satisfies the **equation** is called a **solution** to the equation.

- When solving an equation, isolate the terms containing the variable on one side of the equation.

- Every step in the equation-solving process requires that the same operation be performed on both sides of the equation to maintain the equality.

- Each solution pair should be checked using the original equation to make sure that no errors were made during the solution process.

- Pairs of values for the variables can be found that satisfy the equation, but some may not be acceptable solutions due to physical limitations in the problem.

- A complete graph of the equation displays all possible solution pairs for the equation.

- The values found using a graph may be approximate solutions to the equation. This results from our inability to read and draw the graph precisely.

Example

Pat has some money to invest. There are two types of investments she is prepared to use: guaranteed investment certificates (GICs) that pay an annual return of 4.25%, and a mutual fund that has paid an average of 9.625% annually over the last three years. Pat's goal is to earn at least $400 on her investments each year. The GICs are a safe investment because they are guaranteed not to lose money, but the mutual fund could lose money.

Find some possible investment combinations that allow Pat to achieve the return on investment she wants and use the values to graph the relationship. Assume that the mutual fund continues to pay 9.625%.

Solution

The word equation and algebraic equation for this situation are:

$$\$400 = 4.25\% \text{ return from GICs} + 9.625\% \text{ from mutual fund}$$
$$400 = 0.0425G + 0.096\,25M$$

Substitute a value for one variable and solve for the other.

The easiest values to find correspond to the intercepts of the graph and result from using a value of 0 for one of the variables.

Substitute $G = 0$ and solve for M.

$$400 = 0.096\,25M$$
$$M = \frac{400}{0.096\,25}$$
$$\doteq 4155.8441$$

To the nearest cent, M would be $4155.84.

Substitute $M = 0$ and solve for G.

$$400 = 0.0425G$$
$$G = \frac{400}{0.0425}$$
$$\doteq 9411.764\ldots$$

To the nearest cent, G would be $9411.76.

To find additional points, choose a value for one variable and solve for the other.

Substitute $G = 1000$ and solve for M.

$$400 = 0.0425G + 0.096\,25M$$
$$= 0.0425(1000) + 0.096\,25M$$
$$= 42.5 + 0.096\,25M$$
$$M = \frac{400 - 42.5}{0.096\,25}$$
$$\doteq 3714.285$$

To the nearest cent, M would be $3714.29.

Substitute $M = 1000$ and solve for G.

$$400 = 0.0425G + 0.096\,25M$$
$$= 0.0425G + 0.096\,25(1000)$$
$$= 0.0425G + 96.25$$
$$G = \frac{400 - 96.25}{0.0425}$$
$$\doteq 7147.058$$

To the nearest cent, G would be $7147.06.

Graph these points. They appear to represent a linear relationship.

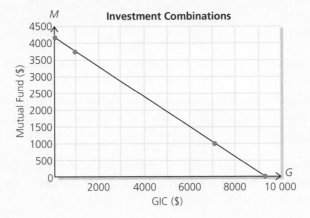

Extra Practice

3. It takes Jefferson $1\frac{1}{2}$ h to travel to work by bus. It takes 1.2 h by car. One month, his total time for travelling to work was 26.4 h. He travelled 12 times on the bus.

   (a) Write the equation for this situation and solve it to find how many times he travelled by car. Show all the steps in your solution.

   (b) What if Jefferson had travelled 12 times by car? Solve the necessary equation to find the number of times he travelled by bus. Show all your steps.

(c) Jefferson moves closer to work and now requires 1.2 h to travel by bus and 0.8 h by car. How many times did he travel by bus if his travelling time was 20 h and he travelled by car 10 times?

4. Tickets to a dance cost $6.50 in advance. Tickets at the door cost $8.
   (a) A group spent $177.50 on tickets. They bought ten tickets at the door. Write an equation to describe this situation and solve it to find the number of tickets bought in advance by the group.

   (b) Another group spent $249, but they bought ten tickets in advance. Solve the appropriate equation to find the number of tickets that this group bought at the door.

   (c) A senior citizens' group received a discount of $\frac{1}{5}$ off the advance ticket price. They spent $98 and bought five tickets in advance. How many tickets did they buy at the door?

5. A candy store is making a grab bag of candy with gum and chocolate pieces. Each piece of gum costs $0.12 and each piece of chocolate costs $0.78. The final value of one bag should be $2.04. The store wants to make 100 grab bags. How many pieces of chocolate and gum will be in all the bags that the store makes?

5.4–5.5 Rearranging the Equation of a Line

- Solving $ax + by = c$ for y in terms of x produces the new equation $y = \frac{c - ax}{b}$.
- The table of values for an equation of the form $ax + by = c$ can supply the data needed to draw a graph.
- The slope and y-intercept of the line can be found from the equation $y = \frac{c - ax}{b}$.
- Since an equation in $ax + by = c$ form can be written in $y = mx + b$ form, its graph must be a straight line. That means that the intercepts and the slope can be used in sketching the graph.

Example

Rearrange the equation for Pat's investment options (see page 329) into the form $y = mx + b$.

Solution

$$400 = 0.0425G + 0.096\,25M$$
$$400 - 0.0425G = 0.0425G + 0.096\,25M - 0.0425G$$
$$\frac{400 - 0.0425G}{0.096\,25} = M$$
$$M = \frac{-0.0425}{0.096\,25}G + \frac{400}{0.096\,25}$$

This equation can be graphed using a graphing tool. Adjust the WINDOW to make it all fit.

Extra Practice

6. Solve each equation for y in terms of x. State the x-intercept, the y-intercept, and the slope of the graph for each. Draw each graph.

(a) $-0.3x - 0.55y = 1$ **(b)** $\frac{2}{5}x - (-\frac{1}{8}y) = \frac{1}{4}$ **(c)** $3x + y = 100$

(d) $0.28x + 3.1y = 0.5$ **(e)** $\frac{3}{2}x + 2\frac{5}{8}y = 6$ **(f)** $0.99x - 0.11y = 0$

7. Solve each of the equations in Question 6 for x in terms of y. State the intercepts and the slope of each graph and use them to draw each graph with x as the dependent variable.

5.6–5.7 Solving Polynomial Equations

- Solving a polynomial equation means determining the value for the variable that makes the equation true.

- Polynomial equations can be solved by methods such as:
  - expanding using the distributive property to eliminate fractions or to eliminate brackets

  - collecting like terms

  - simplifying, so that the unknown variable is isolated on one side of the equation

  - multiplying or dividing both sides of the equation so that the coefficient of the variable is 1.

Example

A sports store pays minimum wage plus commission on sales. The employees can choose between a monthly commission of 5% on sales over $500, or 3% on sales over $200. Find the value of merchandise that must be sold that makes the two commissions the same.

Solution

Let S represent the number of dollars in sales.

No commission on the first $500 can be represented by $S - 500$.

No commission on the first $200 can be represented by $S - 200$.

At 5%, the amount of commission is $0.05(S - 500)$.

At 3%, the amount of commission is $0.03(S - 200)$.

The commissions are equal when $0.05(S - 500) = 0.03(S - 200)$.

$$0.05(S - 500) = 0.03(S - 200)$$

$0.05S - 25 = 0.03S - 6$ Multiply each term by the constant.

$0.05S - 0.03S = -6 + 25$ Isolate the variable term.

$0.02S = 19$ Simplify like terms.

$\dfrac{0.02S}{0.02} = \dfrac{19}{0.02}$ Divide by the coefficient of S.

$S = 950$

The commissions are the same for sales of $950.

Extra Practice

8. Solve.

(a) $2(n + 11) = 5(n - 2)$

(b) $7(4 - 3r) = -8(2r + 1)$

(c) $\frac{1}{3}(q - 3) = \frac{1}{5}(q + 1)$

(d) $4.5(2n - 1) = 3.1(5n + 4)$

(e) $\dfrac{2x - 3}{3} = \dfrac{4 - 5x}{4}$

(f) $5(3p + 12) - 4 = -3(2p - 6)$

(g) $5(2y - 1) - 3(4y - 6) = 7$

(h) $-\frac{5}{8}(4b - 16) = \frac{2}{3}\left(9 - \frac{15b}{8}\right)$

9. Solve $5x - 3y = 7$ for the value of x when:

(a) $y = \frac{3}{4}$

(b) $y = 4x - 2$

10. Dance tickets are $5 for students and $6 for guests. How many guests are at the dance if $1300 is collected and 250 people are present?

5.8 Standard Form of a Linear Equation

- When a linear relation is represented by an equation in the form $y = mx + b$, it is said to be in **slope–y-intercept form**. The value of m is the slope of the line and the value of b is the y-intercept of the line.

- When a linear relation is represented by an equation of the form $Ax + By + C = 0$ in which A, B, and C are integers, and A is positive, it is said to be in **standard form**.

- The two forms of the equation of a line are interchangeable. Either form can be transformed to the other using simple algebraic manipulation.

- $m = \frac{-A}{B}$ and $b = \frac{-C}{B}$ can be derived from the equation $Ax + By + C = 0$, when $B \neq 0$.

Example

For the equation $3x - 2 = 5y$:

(a) Write the equation in standard form.
(b) Determine the slope and y-intercept using the values of the coefficients A, B, and C.
(c) Sketch the graph.

Solution

(a) Rearrange $3x - 2 = 5y$ in the form $Ax + By + C = 0$.
   This gives $3x - 5y - 2 = 0$.

(b) The slope is:

$$m = -\frac{A}{B}$$

$$= -\frac{3}{-5}$$

$$= \frac{3}{5}$$

The y-intercept is:

$$b = -\frac{C}{B}$$

$$= -\frac{(-2)}{-5}$$

$$= -\frac{2}{5}$$

(c) Sketch the graph.

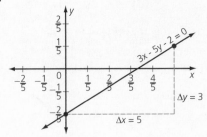

Extra Practice

11. Write in standard form.

    (a) $-5x + 3y = 6$ (b) $4y = -3x + 2$ (c) $y = \frac{2}{3}x - 4$ (d) $\frac{3}{4}x = \frac{2}{3}y + \frac{1}{2}$

12. State the slope and y-intercept.

    (a) $3x + 4y = 5$ (b) $3y + 7x + 1 = 0$ (c) $5y - 3x = 2$

13. Denise is a freelance artist. She earns $315 for each illustration and $105 for each piece of technical art. In the past month, Denise has finished 15 pictures and earned $3675.

    (a) Write an equation that represents the total number of pictures that Denise completed last month.

    (b) Write the equation in standard form that represents her total earnings in the past month.

    (c) Graph the two equations on the same coordinate grid.

    (d) Describe the significance of the point at which the lines intersect. What do the coordinates tell you about this situation?

5.9 Problem Solving and Linear Equations

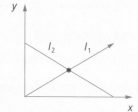

- When a problem can be described by two linear relationships between two variables, there is usually a single point that satisfies both equations simultaneously. This point is the point of intersection of the two graphs that represent the relationships.

- The coordinates of the point of intersection represent the **solution** of the system of the two equations for the relationships.

- Estimates of the point's coordinates can be found by graphing. If the equations are graphed simultaneously using graphing technology, the TRACE and ZOOM features can be used to improve the estimate of the coordinate values.

- The solution estimates can be improved by substituting the values into the original equations and adjusting them until the equations indicate the result has been improved.

- The slope–y-intercept forms of the two equations can be set equal to each other to represent the situation that exists only at the point of intersection. At that point the values of the dependent and independent variables satisfy both equations at the same time. This equation can then be solved to find the value of the independent variable. This value can then be substituted into one of the equations to find the value of the dependent variable.

- Substituting into the left and right sides of the equation can check the solution to the equation. If the solution is correct, both sides of the equation will produce the same result.

Example

Use algebra to find the exact solution to Pat's investment problem on page 329. Assume Pat has $6000 to invest.

Solution

Rewrite $G + M = 6000$ and $400 = 0.0425G + 0.096\ 25M$ in slope–y-intercept form.

$$G + M = 6000 \qquad\qquad\qquad 400 = 0.0425G + 0.096\ 25M$$
$$M = 6000 - G \qquad\qquad -0.0425G + 400 = 0.096\ 25M$$
$$\frac{-0.0425G}{0.096\ 25} + \frac{400}{0.096\ 25} = \frac{0.096\ 25M}{0.096\ 25}$$
$$M = -0.441\ 558\ 4G + 4155.844\ 16$$

At the point of intersection, these equations must be equal. Set them equal and solve for G.

$$-0.441\ 558\ 4G + 4155.844\ 16 = 6000 - G$$
$$-0.441\ 558\ 4G + G = 6000 - 4155.844\ 16$$
$$0.558\ 441\ 6G = 1844.155\ 84$$
$$G = \frac{1844.155\ 84}{0.558\ 441\ 6}$$
$$\doteq 3302.325$$

Pat should invest \$3302.33 in GICs and \$6000 − \$3302.33 = \$2697.67 in mutual funds. Check these values with the investment equation.

$$0.0425G + 0.096\ 25M = 0.0425(3302.33) + 0.096\ 25(2697.67)$$
$$= 140.35 + 259.65$$
$$= 400$$

This means the amounts invested add to \$6000, as required, and produce a return of \$400.

Extra Practice

14. Solve each pair of equations graphically and algebraically.

(a) $x + y = 1$
$3x + 5y + 2 = 0$

(b) $3x - 4y = 2$
$5x + 4y = 6$

(c) $-\frac{1}{3}x + 5 = \frac{1}{2}y - 2$
$2\frac{2}{5}y - 4x = 0$

(d) $-0.5x - 0.2y = -2.9$
$10.5x - 0.1y = 9.3$

Chapter Summary

In this chapter, you showed that relationships of the form $ax + by = c$ are linear and that the dependent variable can be x or y. One way to graph these relationships is to find and plot the x- and y-intercepts. Additional points can be found by replacing x or y with a number, and solving for the remaining variable. To solve a linear equation, isolate the variable on one side of the equation. Relationships of the form $ax + by = c$ can be written in different ways, including slope–y-intercept form ($y = mx + b$) and standard form ($Ax + By + C = 0$).

Chapter Review Test

1. Solve each equation.

   (a) $3y - 24 = 6y$

   (b) $10x = 5x + 25$

   (c) $4y = 2y - 8$

   (d) $30 - 6x = 4x$

   (e) $4 - 5n = -9 + 8n$

   (f) $7n - 4 = 3n - 8$

   (g) $\frac{x}{4} - 1 = \frac{x}{5}$

   (h) $\frac{x}{6} - \frac{2}{3} = 2$

   (i) $\frac{1}{2}a + \frac{5}{3} = \frac{3}{4}a - \frac{7}{3}$

2. Given $-1.7x + 0.8y = 7.1$:

   (a) State the intercepts and slope for the graph.

   (b) Draw the graph.

3. Determine the points of intersection using algebra. Check using graphing and substitution.

   (a) $3x + y - 1 = 0, 2x = y - 6$

   (b) $0.25x + 0.75y = -0.75, 0.15x + 0.25y = -0.05$

   (c) $\frac{1}{2}x - y = -3, x - \frac{2}{3}y = -2$

4. Rearrange each equation by solving for the indicated variable.

   (a) $\frac{3}{2}m - 24 = \frac{6}{5}n$ Solve for n.

   (b) $3(7m - 4) = 2(5n - 1)$ Solve for m.

5. For the equation $\frac{3}{2}y + \frac{2}{3}x = 5$:

   (a) Write the equation in standard form.

   (b) State the slope and y-intercept.

6. David has two part–time jobs. He earns \$14/h at one and \$11/h at the other. David wants to know how many hours it will take him to earn \$1000.

   (a) Find five combinations of the number of hours David could work at each job to earn \$1000.

   (b) Graph the relation.

7. Trudy is starting a cake-catering business. To start, she will have to invest \$378 in her business. It costs her \$5 for the ingredients of each cake. She sells her cakes for \$26 each.

   (a) Find the equations that represent her costs and revenue.

   (b) Graph both equations on the same axes.

   (c) Find the minimum number of cakes that Trudy has to sell to make a profit.

8. Solve.

(a) $\dfrac{5x - 3}{4} = \dfrac{5 - 4x}{5}$

(b) $5(7r - 3) - \dfrac{3}{4}(12r - 8) = 4$

(c) $\dfrac{a + 3}{3} + \dfrac{a - 2}{2} = 1$

(d) $\dfrac{1}{3}(x + 2) + \dfrac{1}{6}(x - 5) = \dfrac{-4}{3}$

9. Solve $5x - 3y + 7 = 0$ for the value of x when:

(a) $y = 15$ (b) $y = 3x + 2$

10. Katerina starts a skate-sharpening business. She paid $600 for a skate-sharpening machine and pays an employee $2 for every pair of skates sharpened. She charges $5 to sharpen skates. How many pairs of skates must be sharpened for her to make back the money she paid for the skate-sharpening machine?

11. The local hydroelectric commission charges its customers $0.1190/kW•h for the first 500 kW•h. It charges $0.0719 for each additional kilowatt-hour of power used. Bjarni's bill is $159.23. How many kilowatt-hours of electricity did he use?

12. A bicycle manufacturer builds racing bikes and mountain bikes, with the per-unit manufacturing costs as shown. The company has budgeted $15 900 for labour and $13 075 for materials. How many of each type of bicycle can be built?

Model	Cost of Material	Cost of Labour
racing	$55	$60
mountain	$70	$90

13. The graphs of $5x - 3y = 35$, $7x - 3y = 43$, and $4x - ay = 61$ all intersect at the same point. Find the value of a.

Cumulative Review Test 2

1. Evaluate.

   (a) -5^2

   (b) 2^{-5}

   (c) $\dfrac{(4^{-3})(4^5)}{4^2}$

   (d) $\dfrac{(10^3)^{-2}}{(10^{-2})^4}$

   (e) $\dfrac{(3.0 \times 10^6)(4.0 \times 10^7)}{2.0 \times 10^{12}}$

   (f) $\dfrac{(128^4)(64^3)}{32^8}$

   (g) $5^0 + \left(\dfrac{1}{3}\right)^3 - \left(\dfrac{1}{3}\right)^{-3}$

   (h) $x^a + y^a$ when $x = \dfrac{2}{3}$, $y = \dfrac{3}{4}$, $a = -1$

2. Simplify.

   (a) $(m^5)(m^{-3})$

   (b) $\dfrac{y^{16}}{y^4}$

   (c) $(10x^2)^{-3}$

   (d) $(x^4 y^5)(x^3 y^4)$

   (e) $\dfrac{-30ab}{-6}$

   (f) $\dfrac{-35a + 7b - 14c}{7}$

   (g) $5(3x^2 + 5x - 7) - 2(4x^2 - 3x + 5)$

   (h) $3x^2(4x^2 - 7x) - 5x^2(3x^2 - 2x)$

   (i) $(-5m^2 n^3)(4m^3 n^2)$

   (j) $\dfrac{20 r^{20} s^{15}}{5 r^5 s^3}$

   (k) $\dfrac{20x^2 y^4 - 15x^5 y^2 + 30x^3 y^4}{10x^2 y^2}$

3. Factor.

   (a) $16xyz + 24xzw$

   (b) $8g^4 h^5 - 12g^2 h^3$

4. Solve.

   (a) $5x + 3 = 13$

   (b) $2 - 4x = 6x + 12$

   (c) $8(4s - 2) = 48$

   (d) $2(3p - 6) = 5(4 - p)$

   (e) $\dfrac{2a + 3}{4} = \dfrac{a + 5}{6}$

   (f) $\dfrac{1}{2}(6x - 2) - \dfrac{3}{4}(8x + 12) = 5$

5. Ayesha is on the school cross country running team. This graph shows her training routine starting from the school.

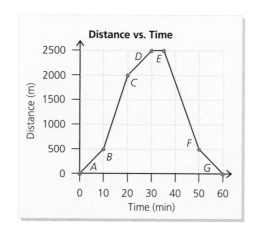

Cumulative Review Test 2

(a) Which line segment shows her fastest speed? Explain.

(b) Which line segment shows she is not moving? Explain.

(c) Which line segment shows she is sprinting towards the school? How do you know she is moving towards the school?

(d) Identify the line segments where she is running at 50 m/min.

6. (a) Two Internet service providers advertise in the local paper. Information Technology Co. charges \$20/month plus \$2/h. The World Around Us Co. charges \$10/month plus \$2.50/h. Write equations to represent the cost per month for each company's services. Define all variables used.

(b) Both companies offer a special discount for a one-year subscription. Information Technology Co. gives a 10% discount and The World Around Us Co. gives a 15% discount. Write equations to represent the new cost per month for each company once the discount is applied.

(c) What is the discounted cost for each company if 35 h of Internet time are used? 60 h?

(d) How many hours must be used each month for the providers to charge the same discounted price?

7. Jurgen has two sales jobs. He earns 10% commission on all sales at a jeans store. He also works at a tire store and earns 9% on those sales. He expects to make \$900.

(a) Write an equation that describes his total earnings at both stores.

(b) During one pay period he sold \$6000 worth of tires. What were his sales at the jeans store if he made \$900 in total?

8. Determine the point of intersection of $y = 3x + 5$ and $y = -4x - 2$ using algebra. Use graphing technology to verify your solution.

9. Find all three possible values of x for which the following equation is true.

$$x^{3x + 5} = 1$$

Review of Essential Skills and Knowledge – Part II

Measurement: Area and Perimeter

The following formulas are used to find areas and perimeters.

Square: $A = s^2$, $P = 4s$

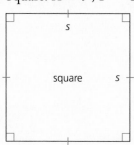

Rectangle: $A = lw$, $P = 2(l + w)$

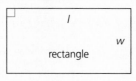

Triangle: $A = \frac{1}{2}bh$, $P = a + b + c$

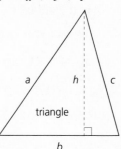

Trapezoid: $A = \frac{1}{2}(a + b)h$, $P = a + b + c + d$

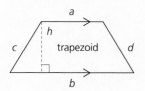

Parallelogram: $A = bh$, $P = a + b + c + d$

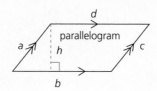

Area: the number of square units needed to cover the surface

area = 16 square units

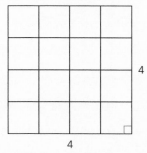

Perimeter: the distance around the outside of a closed figure

perimeter = 5 + 6 + 7 = 18 units

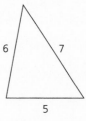

Practise

Round your answers to one decimal place.

1. Find the area of each of the following.

   (a) rectangle: $l = 15$ m, $w = 7$ m
   (b) square: $s = 27$ cm
   (c) triangle: $b = 17$ cm, $h = 12$ cm
   (d) trapezoid: $a = 28$ cm, $b = 17$ cm, $h = 8$ cm
   (e) circle: $r = 8.7$ cm
   (f) parallelogram: $b = 46$ cm, $h = 18$ cm

2. (a) A rectangle has an area of 44.16 cm². If its length is 9.2 cm, find the width.
   (b) A triangle has an area of 10.26 cm². If its base is 9.5 cm, find its height.

3. How much paper, without overlapping, is required to cover a box with length 18.3 cm, width 13.1 cm, and height 6 cm?

4. Calculate the perimeter of each figure.

(a)

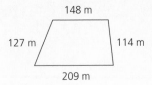

148 m
127 m
114 m
209 m

(b)

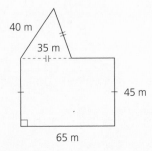

40 m
35 m
45 m
65 m

5. Calculate the area of each figure.

(a)

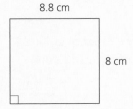

8.8 cm
8 cm

(b)

25.34 cm

(c)

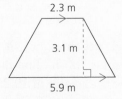

2.3 m
3.1 m
5.9 m

(d)

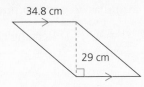

34.8 cm
29 cm

(e)

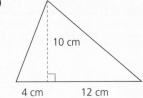

10 cm
4 cm   12 cm

6. Calculate the area of each figure.

(a)

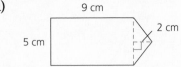

9 cm
5 cm   2 cm

(b)

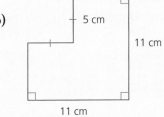

5 cm
11 cm
11 cm

(c)

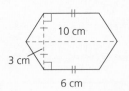

10 cm
3 cm
6 cm

Measurement: Working with Circles

The ratio of the circumference of a circular object to its diameter is a constant (π).

$\frac{C}{d} \doteq 3.14$ (to 2 decimal places) ◄——— Use $\pi \doteq 3.14$.

approximately equal to

Example 1

Find the circumference of a circle with radius 5.2 cm.

Solution

$C = 2\pi r$ Always write the formula.
$ \doteq 2(3.14)(5.2)$
$ \doteq 32.656$ Round to one decimal place.

The circumference is 32.7 cm.

Example 2

Find the area of a circle with diameter 4.8 cm.

Solution

$A = \pi r^2$ Always write the formula.
$ \doteq (3.14)(2.4)^2$
$ \doteq 18.0864$ Round to one decimal place.

The area is 18.1 cm².

Circle: $A = \pi r^2$
$ C = 2\pi r$
$ C = \pi d$

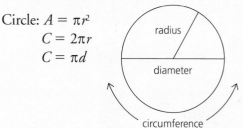

Practise

Round your answers to one decimal place.

1. Copy and complete the table for circles.

	Radius	Diameter	Circumference	Area
(a)	16.1 cm			
(b)		9.4 m		
(c)			25.1 cm	
(d)				78.5 m²
(e)			20.4 cm	
(f)				124.6 cm²

2. The radius of a circle is 16.3 cm. Calculate:

   (a) the circumference.

   (b) the area.

3. The diameter of a circle is 9.8 m. Calculate:

   (a) the circumference.

   (b) the area.

4. The circumference of a circle is 51.496 cm. Calculate:

   (a) the radius.   **(b)** the area.

5. A circular rug has a radius of 43 cm. Find its area.

6. A forest ranger can see a forest fire as far as 21.5 km away from the tower. Find the circumference of the region seen from the tower.

7. A rotating lawn sprinkler can reach a point 11.5 m from its position. Find the area of the circular region that can be watered from a fixed position.

8. The diameter of a dime is 1.7 cm, a nickel 2.1 cm, and a quarter 2.3 cm.

  (a) Find the circumference of each coin.
  (b) Find the area of one side of each coin.
  (c) How much greater is the circumference of a quarter than the circumference of a dime?
  (d) How much more is the area of one side of a quarter than the area of one side of a nickel?

9. Find the area of each shaded region.

(a)

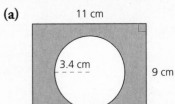

11 cm

3.4 cm

9 cm

(b)

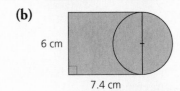

6 cm

7.4 cm

(c)

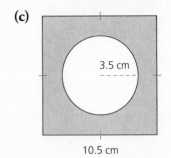

3.5 cm

10.5 cm

(d)

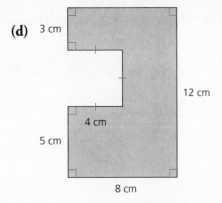

3 cm

12 cm

4 cm

5 cm

8 cm

(e)

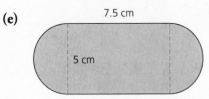

7.5 cm

5 cm

(f)

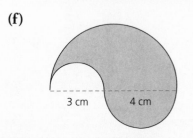

3 cm   4 cm

(g)

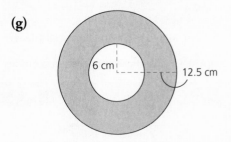

6 cm

12.5 cm

Measurement: Volume and Surface Area

To solve problems, we need to calculate volume, V, and surface area, SA.

Volume: the amount of space occupied by a three-dimensional object

Surface Area: the sum of the area of the faces of a three-dimensional object

Rectangular prism:

$V =$ (area of base)(height), $V = lwh$

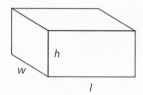

$SA =$ sum of the areas of all sides

$SA = 2(wl) + 2(wh) + 2(hl)$

Triangular prism:

$V =$ (area of base)(height), $V = \frac{1}{2}bhH$

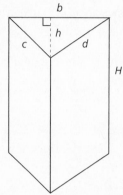

$SA =$ sum of the areas of all sides

$SA = 2(\frac{1}{2}bh) + (bH) + (dH) + (cH)$

Practise

Round your answers to one decimal place as needed.

1. Find the volume.

(a)

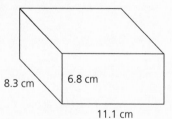

(b)

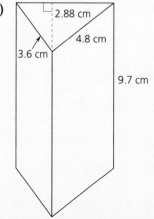

(c)

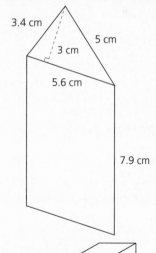

(d)

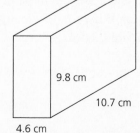

2. Find the surface area of each prism in Question 1.

3. Find the volume of a cube with one side measuring 5.1 m.

4. Find the surface area of a cube with one side measuring 4.5 cm.

5. Find the height of a rectangular prism with length 9.4 cm, width 6.3 cm, and volume 242.8 cm³.

6. A triangular piece of cheese has a volume of 146.4 cm³. Find the thickness, *t*, of the cheese.

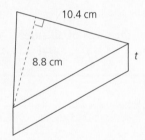

7. The dimensions of a room are shown.

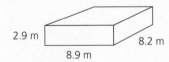

(a) Calculate the volume of the room.
(b) Calculate the total surface area of the room.
(c) The walls and ceiling are to be painted and a 4-L can of paint covers an area of 52.2 m². How many cans of paint are needed?

8. Find the volume and surface area of each figure.

(a)

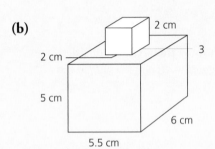

(b)

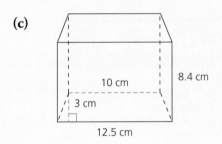

(c)

Measurement: Working with Formulas

Formulas are examples of equations that give relationships among different variables.

Example 1

Find the missing value.

$A = \pi r^2$ if $A = 63.585$ cm²
$\pi \doteq 3.14$

Solution

$A = \pi r^2$ —— Always write the formula as
$A = 63.585$ your first step.
$\pi \doteq 3.14$

$63.585 \doteq (3.14)(r^2)$
$20.25 = r^2$
$4.5 = r$

The radius of the circle is 4.5 cm.

Example 2

A rectangle has a perimeter of 128 m. If the length is 45 m, find the width.

Solution

$P = 2l + 2w$ —— Always write the formula as
$P = 128$ your first step.
$l = 45$
$128 = 2(45) + 2w$
$128 = 90 + 2w$
$38 = 2w$
$19 = w$

The width is 19 m.

Practise

1. Find the missing value.
   (a) $v = u + at$
   $v = 50$, $u = 25$, $a = 5$, $t = \blacksquare$
   (b) $l = Prt$
   $l = 117$, $P = 650$, $t = 2$, $r = \blacksquare$
   (c) $V = lwh$
   $V = 8192$, $l = 64$, $h = 16$, $w = \blacksquare$
   (d) $r = \frac{ab}{a + b + c}$
   $a = 7$, $b = 18$, $r = \blacksquare$, $c = 3$
   (e) $P^2 = l^2 + w^2$
   $l = 7$, $w = 24$, $P = \blacksquare$
   (f) $V = IR$
   $V = 1.5$, $R = 3$, $I = \blacksquare$
   (g) $P = I^2 R$
   $P = 9841.5$, $R = 1.5$, $I = \blacksquare$
   (h) $A = \frac{1}{2}bh$
   $A = 27.3$, $b = 6.5$, $h = \blacksquare$
   (i) $A = lw$
   $A = 3456$, $l = 72$, $w = \blacksquare$

2. An equilateral triangle has a perimeter of 725 cm. Write the measure of 1 side.

3. A square stamp has an area of 484 mm². Find its dimensions.

4. If the length of a rectangle is 31 cm and the area is 558 cm², find the width.

5. The volume of a room is 60 m³. If the length is 4 m and the width is 5 m, find the height.

6. The circumference of a circle is 75.36 cm. Find the radius.

7. One circle has a radius of 12 cm and another has a radius of 18 cm. Find the radius of a circle with an area the same as the sum of the areas of the given circles. Write your answer to one decimal place.

8. A triangle has an area of 250 m² and a base of 50 m. How high is it?

Geometry and Spatial Sense: Language of Geometry

To work with geometry, you have to understand the language of geometry.

The angles are named as ∠ABC. The complement of ∠ABC is 90° − 39° = 51°. The supplement of ∠ABC is 180° − 39° = 141°.

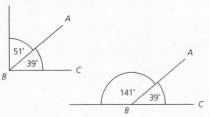

acute angle: $0° < x < 90°$;
right angle: $x = 90°$;
obtuse angle: $90° < x < 180°$

This exercise reviews other words in geometry that you need to know.

Practise

1. Match each diagram with the corresponding name. Use A, B, C, or D.
   A: Vertically opposite angles
   B: Supplementary angles
   C: Complementary angles
   D: Adjacent angles

   (a)

   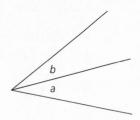

   (b)

   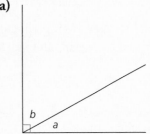

   (c)

   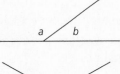

   (d)

   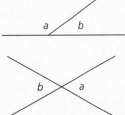

2. Name each angle as acute (A), right (R), obtuse (O), or straight (S).

   (a)   **(b)**

   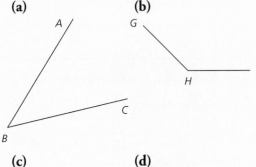

   (c)   **(d)**

   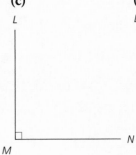

   (e)   **(f)**

   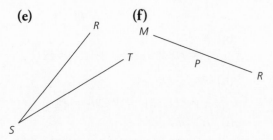

(g)

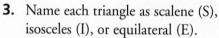

(h)

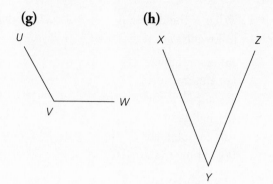

(g)

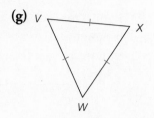

4. Name each triangle as acute-angled (A), right-angled (R), or obtuse-angled (O).

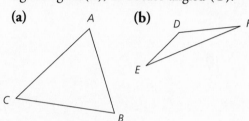

3. Name each triangle as scalene (S), isosceles (I), or equilateral (E).

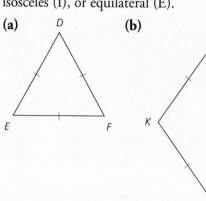

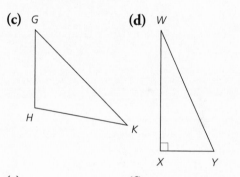

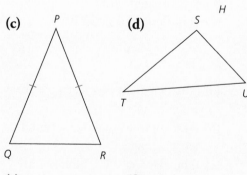

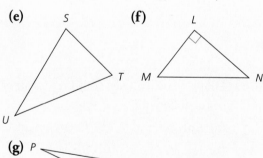

(g)

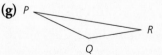

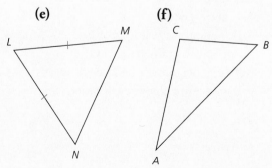

5. Write the complement for each angle.
   (a) 73°   **(b)** 27°   **(c)** 45°

6. Write the supplement for each angle.
   (a) 16°   **(b)** 72°   **(c)** 150°

7. Write A, B, C, D, E, or F for each figure.
A: parallelogram, B: rhombus, C: trapezoid, D: square, E: rectangle, F: kite

(a)   **(b)**

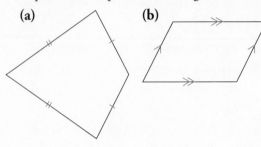

(c)   **(d)**

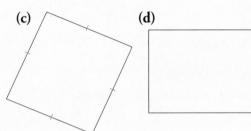

(e)   **(f)**

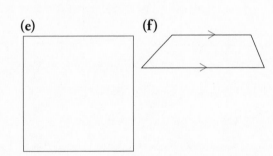

8. Draw a labelled diagram to represent each of the following.

  (a) line *AB*   **(b)** line segment *CD*

  (c) ray *MN*   **(d)** angle *QRS*

  (e) supplementary angles *EFG* and *GFH*

  (f) complementary angles *JKL* and *LKM*

  (g) parallel lines *CD* and *FG*

  (h) perpendicular lines *PQ* and *MN*

9. What is the degree measure of each of the following?

  (a) complement of 60°
  (b) quarter turn
  (c) supplement of 130°
  (d) half turn
  (e) complement of 20°
  (f) supplement of 40°

10. Draw and classify each angle.

  (a) 125°
  (b) 60°
  (c) 230°
  (d) 75°
  (e) 90°
  (f) 180°

11. Draw a labelled diagram for each of the following.

  (a) equilateral triangle *ABC*
  (b) scalene triangle *LMN*
  (c) acute triangle *FGH*
  (d) obtuse triangle *XYZ*
  (e) right triangle *JKL*
  (f) isosceles triangle *QRS*

12. Draw figures to check whether each statement is true.

  (a) The diagonals of a rectangle always intersect at right angles.
  (b) The opposite angles of a rhombus are always equal.
  (c) The diagonals of a rhombus are always equal.
  (d) The opposite angles of a parallelogram are always equal.
  (e) The diagonals of a kite are always perpendicular to each other.

Geometry and Spatial Sense: Angle Relationships

Here is a review of special angle relationships.

Complementary angles
$a + b = 90°$

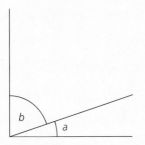

Supplementary angles
$a + b = 180°$

Vertically opposite angles
$a = b$
$c = d$

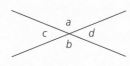

Isosceles triangle
$a = b$

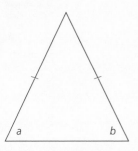

Sum of the angles of a triangle
$a + b + c = 180°$

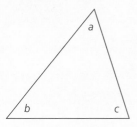

Exterior angle of a triangle
$a + b = c$

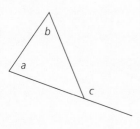

Transversal parallel lines
Alternate angles are equal.
$c = f, d = g$

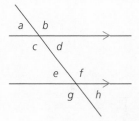

Corresponding angles are equal.
$b = f, a = e, d = h, c = g$

Co-interior angles are supplementary.
$d + f = 180°, c + e = 180°$

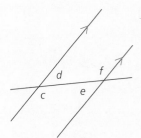

Practise

1. Find the measure of each unknown angle.

(a)

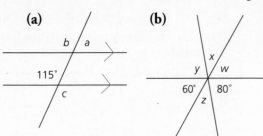

(b)

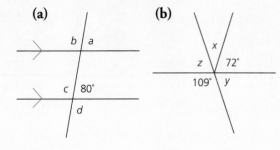

(c)

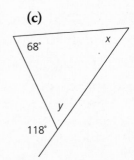

(d)

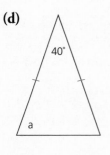

(e)

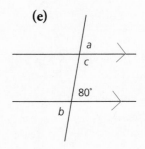

(f)

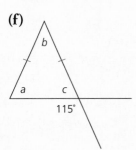

(g)

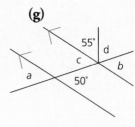

(h)

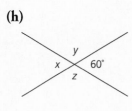

2. Find the missing measures.

(a)

(b)

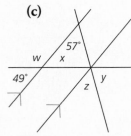

(c)

(d)

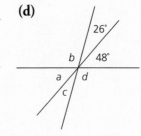

Chapter 6

Exploring Properties of Two-Dimensional Figures

Geometry is the study of the properties of shapes. We see geometry used everywhere, from buildings to railway tracks. It is used in architecture, engineering, and all forms of design. For instance, the designer of this textbook used geometric principles to give it a pleasing shape. Landscape architects use geometry to design gardens, and interior designers use it to design offices or homes.

The study of geometry involves discovering and verifying relationships between angles and lengths of sides for shapes and then applying them to solve problems.

In this chapter, you will:

- investigate, illustrate, explain, and apply the properties of angles related to parallel lines
- investigate, illustrate, and explain the properties of angles in a variety of polygons
- investigate, determine, and apply the properties of sides and diagonals of polygons
- test possible answers to questions about geometric relationships and confirm or deny statements about geometric relationships using dynamic geometry software.

353

Connections

The Chapter Problem

Which Properties Remain the Same?

Polygons and lines drawn on a flat surface have a variety of properties. The properties depend on, among other things, the type of shape and whether or not the lines in the shape are parallel. Which properties of two-dimensional shapes remain true when the shape is drawn on the surface of a sphere?

At the end of some lessons, questions will refer back to this problem. You will be able to use what you have learned to answer them. Keep a record of your answers to these questions in a project folder so that at the end of the chapter, you can provide a complete solution to the problem.

The Challenge

Do These Pentagonal Properties Remain the Same?

Draw pentagon *ABCDE* on a circle with centre *O*. Use diagonals to divide the pentagon into non-overlapping triangles. Draw the inscribed circle for each triangle. Two examples are shown.
- Prove that no matter how you divide the pentagon into triangles, the sum of the radii of the inscribed circles is always the same.
- Confirm or deny that the shape of the original pentagon has an effect on the sum.
- Determine whether a similar result is true for all polygons inscribed in a circle.

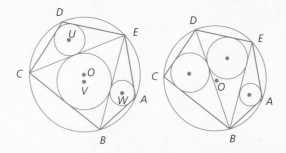

As you work through this chapter, you will be learning mathematics that you can apply to solving the Challenge. You may also need to do research in the library or on the Internet and use math knowledge you already have. You may want to discuss your plan with your teacher and with other students.

Getting Ready

In this chapter, you will need to be familiar with some basic geometric properties. These exercises will help you warm up for the chapter.

1. Match each drawing of an angle to the correct term:

   (a)

   (b)

   (c)

   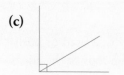

   (d)

   (e)

   (f)

   (g)

   i. acute
   ii. obtuse
   iii. right
   iv. complementary
   v. straight
   vi. supplementary
   vii. vertically opposite

2. Complete the sentences.
   (a) ■ lines never intersect.
   (b) ■ lines intersect at right angles.
   (c) Any enclosed figure with three or more sides is called a ■.
   (d) A four-sided polygon is called a ■.
   (e) Objects that are identical in size and shape are ■.

3. Draw the following:
   (a) a point
   (b) a ray
   (c) a line
   (d) a segment
   (e) a bisected angle
   (f) a diagonal
   (g) two intersecting lines
   (h) a rectangle
   (i) a square
   (j) a parallelogram
   (k) a rhombus
   (l) a trapezoid
   (m) a kite

4. Name the triangle that:
   (a) has no equal sides.
   (b) has all sides equal.
   (c) has two equal angles.
   (d) contains a 90° angle.
   (e) contains an angle greater than 90°.
   (f) has each of the three angles less than 90°.

5. How is each pair of items similar?
   (a) a square, a rhombus
   (b) a rectangle, a parallelogram
   (c) a rhombus, a parallelogram
   (d) an equilateral triangle, an isosceles triangle

6.1 Angle Properties of Parallel Lines

Hydraulic lifts have to keep the top platform parallel to the base during the full range of the lifting motion. Designers use parallel and intersecting lines to make sure this happens.

Hydraulic lifts are used to raise objects such as cars, crates, or wheelchairs. A lift is designed so that the top platform remains parallel to the base when it is lifting a load. Otherwise the load would fall off or the lift would tip.

Angles and Parallel Lines

You can model a hydraulic lift using stir sticks or Popsicle sticks joined with a brad or push-pin to provide a hinge as shown in the illustration. An elastic band joining the tops of the sticks represents the platform and a band joining the bottoms represents the base.

Think, Do, Discuss

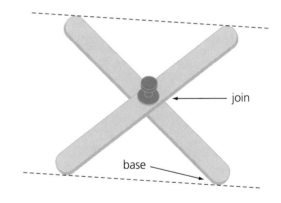

1. Begin with the sticks joined at their midpoints. Does the segment joining the two tops remain parallel to the base for all possible angles at the join?

2. Investigate if changing the position of the join affects whether or not the platform and base remain parallel. What conditions must be met to make sure they do remain parallel?

3. Draw two parallel line segments using both edges of a ruler or the lines on lined note paper. Draw a third segment that crosses the other two. Label all the angles formed to make them easier to refer to.
   (a) How many angles are formed by the intersecting segments?
   (b) Describe the positions of all angles that have equal measures.
   (c) Describe the relationship between the measures of the angles that are not equal.

4. Are the sizes of the angles or the relationships between them affected by the distance between the parallel lines or the slant of the line that crosses them? Examine several different cases to confirm your hypothesis.

5. Describe what happens to the relationships between the angles if the base and platform lines are not parallel to start with. Examine several different cases to confirm your hypothesis.

6. You probably noticed that models made from stir sticks or Popsicle sticks were not very accurate. Physical models are easy to make and they do model the various relationships well, but it is difficult to measure angles accurately. Several software programs have been designed to make constructing and manipulating geometric shapes easier. These programs also measure lengths and angles automatically and accurately.

The advantage of using this kind of "dynamic geometry software" (DGS) is that you can use it to examine a large number of variations of a situation. These programs allow you to "grab" a **vertex** and move it. As the angles or lengths of lines are changed by moving the vertex, the measurements are instantly updated on the computer screen.

Geometer's Sketchpad and *Cabri Geometry* are two DGS programs. Sample screens from each are shown.

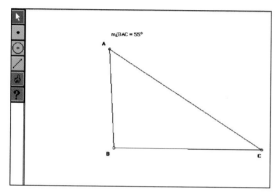

A triangle on the *Geometer's Sketchpad* screen.

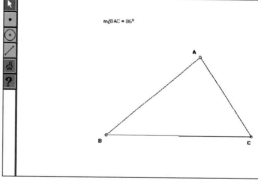

The same triangle after vertex *A* is dragged to a new position.

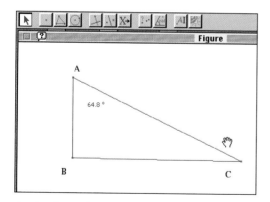

A triangle on the *Cabri Geometry* screen.

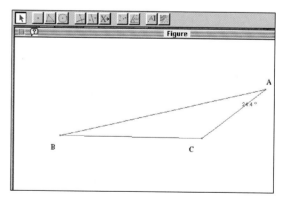

The same triangle after vertex *A* is dragged to a new position.

If you have access to dynamic geometry software, use it to carry out the investigations described above. Write a description of how you used the DGS to do the investigations and how it was different from doing it by hand. Discuss how this kind of software tool affects the confidence you have in your conclusions.

Focus

Key Ideas

- A line that intersects a pair of parallel lines is called a **transversal**. When angles are formed by two parallel lines and a transversal:
  - the corresponding angles are equal: $\angle 4 = \angle 8$, $\angle 3 = \angle 7$, $\angle 1 = \angle 5$, $\angle 2 = \angle 6$.
  - the alternate angles are equal: $\angle 3 = \angle 5$, $\angle 2 = \angle 8$.
  - the sum of the interior angles on the same side of the transversal is 180°: $\angle 2 + \angle 5 = 180°$, $\angle 3 + \angle 8 = 180°$.

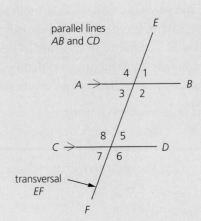

- Dynamic geometry software can be used to investigate the properties of angles formed by intersecting lines and in various polygons.

- An investigation can disprove a relationship by finding an example in which the relationship does not work. Such an example is called a **counter-example**. However, an investigation cannot *prove* that a relationship exists, because it may be that a counter-example exists but has not been found.

Example

If $AB \parallel EF$ and $\angle IJF = 59°$, find $\angle GIB$ and $\angle JIB$.

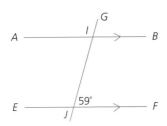

Solution

$AB \parallel EF$

$\therefore \angle GIB = \angle IJF$

$\qquad = 59°$

Also, since $AB \parallel EF$,

$\qquad \angle GIB + \angle JIB = 180°$

$\therefore \qquad 59° + \angle JIB = 180°$

$\therefore \qquad\qquad \angle JIB = 180° - 59°$

$\qquad\qquad\qquad \angle JIB = 121°$

Practise, Apply, Solve

Questions 1 to 3 all refer to the diagram on the right.

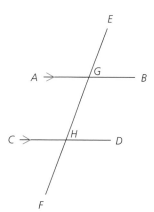

1. In the diagram, line segments *AB* and *CD* are parallel. A third line segment, *EF*, crosses the other two segments.
   (a) Describe where to find all angles equal to ∠*EGB*.
   (b) Describe where to find all angles equal to ∠*HGB*.
   (c) Describe the relationship between ∠*HGB* and ∠*GHD*.

2. Examine what happens when you move point *E* so that the angle at which the segment *EF* meets the parallel lines changes. Describe how this movement affects your answers to Question 1.

3. Suppose line segments *AB* and *CD* were not parallel.
   (a) Which of the results above would remain true and which would not?
   (b) How can you prove that some of the results will not be true if *AB* and *CD* are not parallel?
   (c) How can you prove that the results you think remain valid would stay true for lines that are not parallel?

4. Draw this diagram in your notebook. Explain how you drew segment *SU* so that it would be parallel to *RT*. List the drawing tools you used and how you used them.
   (a) What is the relationship between ∠*SRT* and ∠*QSU*? Why?
   (b) Is it possible for ∠*SRT* and ∠*QSU* to be equal and for segments *RT* and *SU* not to be parallel? Explain.

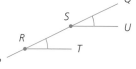

B

5. Write an explanation of how the properties of angles and parallel lines guarantee that the platform of the hydraulic lift will stay parallel to the base.

6. In each diagram, name all pairs of equal angles and all pairs of angles that add to 180°.

   (a)

   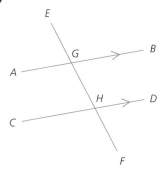

   (b)

   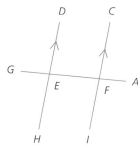

7. Study the figure on the right.
   (a) Determine if lines *k* and *m* are parallel.
   (b) State the reason for your answer.

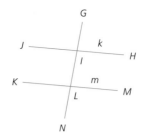

$$\angle MLI = 75°, \angle HIL = 105°$$

8. State the measure of each of the eight numbered angles.

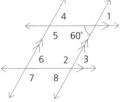

   (a) $\angle 1$ **(b)** $\angle 2$ **(c)** $\angle 3$ **(d)** $\angle 4$
   (e) $\angle 5$ **(f)** $\angle 6$ **(g)** $\angle 7$ **(h)** $\angle 8$

9. Use the diagram on the right to answer each question.

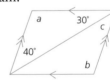

   (a) Find the measure of $\angle BCA$, $\angle ABC$, $\angle ACD$, and $\angle CDA$
       if $\angle BAC = 43°$ and $\angle CAD = 32°$.
   (b) Find the measure of $\angle BAC$, $\angle BCA$, $\angle ACD$, and $\angle CDA$
       if $\angle ABC = 135°$ and $\angle CAD = 25°$.
   (c) Name pairs of angles that are equal.
   (d) Name pairs of angles that are supplementary.

10. Find the values for *a*, *b*, and *c* for each diagram.

   (a) 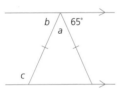   **(b)**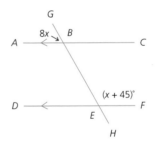

C

11. Use the diagram to find the measure
    of $\angle DEH$.

(diagram: G, A, B, C, D, E, F, H with $8x$ and $(x + 45)°$)

The Chapter Problem — Which Properties Remain the Same?

Refer back to the Chapter Problem at the beginning of the chapter.

1. How is a line on a sphere different from a line drawn on a flat surface?
2. What does it mean when two lines are parallel on a flat surface? How is
   the situation different on the surface of a sphere?
3. Suppose that there are two lines on a sphere that do not intersect. Is it
   possible for these lines not to be parallel? Define what it means for lines
   to be parallel on the surface of a sphere.

Angles Associated with Triangles

Angles in a Triangle

You have a toy robot turtle to which you can give simple travel instructions. It moves straight ahead until it hits an obstacle. It then stops and waits for instructions telling it through what angle it should turn. It turns through the angle you tell it and then moves straight ahead until it hits another obstacle, and so on.

You place your robot in a room and start it moving at an angle of 60° from one of the walls, as shown. When it hits the opposite wall, you instruct it to turn through 140° and it moves until it hits the wall again. Through what angle will you have to tell the robot to move for it to travel along the wall and return to its starting position?

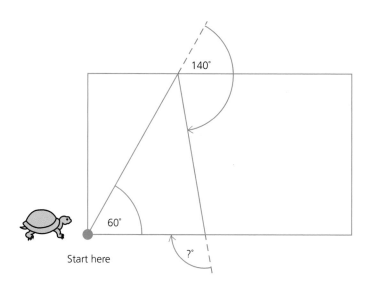

Think, Do, Discuss

1. Try the problem with several different travel route triangles. Use different starting angles and different angles at the first turn. What relationship exists that allows you to predict the final turn angle needed to return the robot home to its starting position?

   If you use DGS, you can construct one travel route triangle and then move vertices along the edges of the room to vary the angles at the vertices of the triangle.

2. Is the relationship you discovered true for all triangles? How can you be sure?

3. Draw a triangle on a piece of paper and label the vertices *ABC*. Carefully cut out the triangle. Tear off the angles at the vertices and put them together with a common vertex to form a single larger angle. What do you notice? Will this happen regardless of the type or size of triangle you start with?

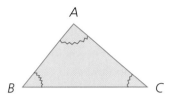

4. Describe the relationship that exists between the size of an angle at a vertex in a triangle and the length of the side opposite it.

5. State the algebraic relationship that exists between the angles at the vertices inside a triangle.

6. Suppose someone were to say that the relationship you described works only for triangles in which one of the angles is 60°. Describe how you could prove that statement was wrong.

7. Explain whether or not you have enough evidence to prove that this relationship holds for all possible triangles. Write a description of what someone would need to do to demonstrate that your conclusion was not always true.

Angles Outside a Triangle

In the previous investigation, you explored the relationship among the angles in a triangle. Does a similar relationship exist among the angles formed outside a triangle at each vertex?

Think, Do, Discuss

1. Draw several triangles with the sides extended to form outside angles at each vertex. (You can do this by hand or use dynamic geometry software.) For each triangle, investigate the relationships that exist among the measures of these angles.

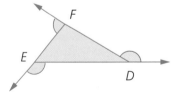

2. Investigate whether the size or shape of the original triangle affects the relationship that exists among the outside angles. Use DGS or do the following:

(a) Draw each triangle on a piece of paper. Extend the sides to form an outside angle at each vertex.

(b) Trace each outside angle onto another piece of paper. Carefully cut out the copies of the angles.

(c) Place the copies together to form a single larger angle with a common vertex.

(d) What do you notice?

(e) Repeat this process for several different triangles. Does the result remain the same?

3. How does the measure of one outside angle relate to the measures of the inside angles opposite it? Use several different triangles to investigate whether the shape or size of the original triangle affects this relationship. Use DGS or do the following:

(a) Draw each triangle on a piece of paper. Extend the sides to form an outside angle at each vertex.

(b) Trace each inside angle onto another piece of paper. Carefully cut out the copies.

(c) Place copies of the inside angles over the outside angles to see how the measures compare.

4. Write the algebraic relationship that connects the measures of the outside angles of a triangle. Write the algebraic expression that shows how the measure of an outside angle is related to the angles inside the triangle that are opposite it.

Parallel Lines and Triangles

In the previous investigations, you explored the relationships that exist among angles associated with triangles. Why are these relationships true? How can they be proved?

Think, Do, Discuss

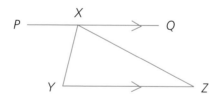

1. Trace a copy of the diagram onto a piece of paper. Make sure that *PQ* is parallel to the base of the triangle.

2. Carefully cut out copies of the angles at *Y* and *Z*. Place these so that their vertices meet at *X* and they form a single larger angle with ∠*YXZ*.

3. Write an explanation of how the angle formed relates to the base of the triangle.

Focus

Key Ideas

- The angles formed inside a polygon by two sides meeting at a vertex are called **interior angles**. When one side of a polygon is extended through the vertex, the angle formed at the vertex by the extended side and the original side is called an **exterior angle**.

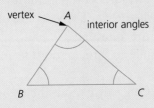

$$\angle A + \angle B + \angle C = 180°$$

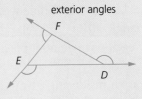

$$\angle D + \angle E + \angle F = 360°$$

- In a triangle:
  - the sum of the interior angles is 180°.
    $$\angle 1 + \angle 2 + \angle 3 = 180°$$
  - the sum of the exterior angles is 360°.
    $$\angle 4 + \angle 5 + \angle 6 = 360°$$
  - each exterior angle is equal to the sum of the interior angles at the opposite vertices. These are called **remote interior angles**.

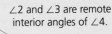

$\angle 2$ and $\angle 3$ are remote interior angles of $\angle 4$.

$$\angle 4 = \angle 2 + \angle 3$$
$$\angle 5 = \angle 1 + \angle 3$$
$$\angle 6 = \angle 1 + \angle 2$$

Example

If $DE \parallel AF$, $\angle DBA = 68°$, and $\angle BCF = 147°$, find the measure of $\angle ABC$.

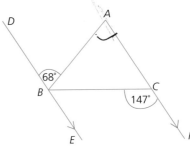

Solution

Since $DE \parallel AF$, $\angle BAC = \angle DBA$
$$= 68°$$

Since $\angle BCF$ is an exterior angle of $\triangle ABC$, $\angle ABC + \angle BAC = \angle BCF$.

$$\therefore \quad \angle ABC + 68° = 147°$$
$$\therefore \quad \angle ABC = 147° - 68°$$
$$= 79°$$

Practise, Apply, Solve

A

1. Find the value of x in each diagram.

(a)
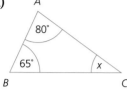

(b)
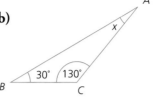

(c)
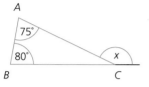

(d)
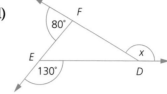

2. Find the value of each unknown.

(a)
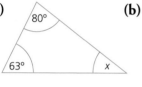

(b)

(c)
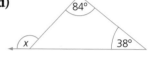

(d)
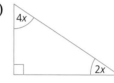

(e)
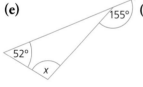

(f)
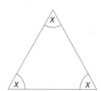

(g)
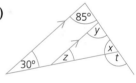

(h)

B

3. Determine the measure of x, y, and z in each diagram.

(a)
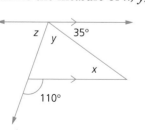

(b)
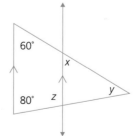

(c)
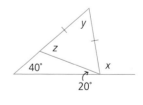

4. Find the measure of *x*.

(a)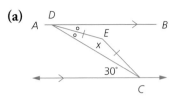

(b)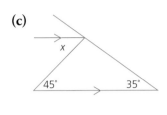

(c)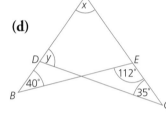

5. Think of the robot at the beginning of this section.
   (a) Suppose it travels a route in which all of the segments are the same length. Through what angle must it turn at every step?
   (b) Suppose it travels a route in which only two of the segments are the same length. What angles would be needed?

6. Find the size of each unknown angle.

(a)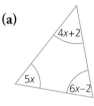

(b)

(c)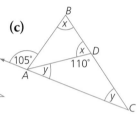

(d)

7. Given that *AB* ∥ *DF* and *BC* ∥ *DE*.
   (a) What is the relationship between ∠1 and ∠2?
   (b) Use DGS or several examples to provide evidence for your conclusions.
   (c) Write a clear expression for your answer.

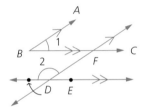

8. Determine the value for *x* and find the size of each of the angles represented by an algebraic expression.

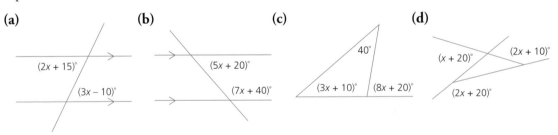

(a) $(2x + 15)°$ $(3x - 10)°$

(b) $(5x + 20)°$ $(7x + 40)°$

(c) $40°$ $(3x + 10)°$ $(8x + 20)°$

(d) $(x + 20)°$ $(2x + 10)°$ $(2x + 20)°$

9. Find the size of ∠*QSR*.

(a)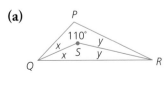

(b)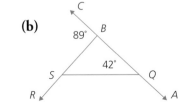

(c)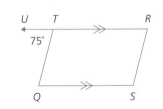

10. Find the value of *x*.

(a)

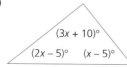

$(3x + 10)°$
$(2x - 5)°$ $(x - 5)°$

(b)

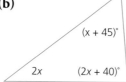

$(x + 45)°$
$2x$ $(2x + 40)°$

(c)

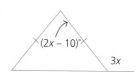

$(2x - 10)°$
$3x$

11. Identify the parallel lines. Explain why they are parallel.

(a)

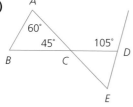

A
60°
45° 105°
B *C* *D*
E

(b)

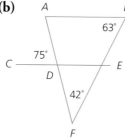

A *B*
63°
C 75°
D *E*
42°
F

(c)

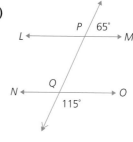

P 65°
L *M*
N *Q*
115° *O*

C

12. In $\triangle PQR$, the bisectors of $\angle Q$ and $\angle R$ meet at *S*. Prove that $\angle QSR = \left(\dfrac{180 + x}{2}\right)°$

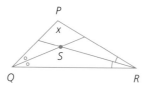

P
x
S
Q *R*

The Chapter Problem — Which Properties Remain the Same?

Refer to the Chapter Problem at the beginning of the chapter.

1. Describe how you can draw a triangle on the surface of a sphere.
2. Suppose you were doing geometry on a globe. Draw a triangle with its top vertex on the North Pole and its other vertices on the equator. How big are the base angles on the equator? What is the largest possible measurement for the top vertex angle?
3. How does the sum of the interior angles for a triangle drawn on a sphere differ from the sum of the interior angles of a triangle drawn on a flat surface?
4. Are the relationships involving the exterior angles different or the same?

6.3 Angles and Polygons

Tiling Patterns

You may not have considered this, but mathematics is involved in designing the shape of tiles used to cover floors. Floor tiles are examples of polygons. A polygon is a closed figure formed by three or more line segments. Many tiles are regular polygons. Regular polygons have equal side lengths. Not every regular polygon shape can be used. By itself, a regular pentagon cannot be used to tile a floor. Try it and see!

Think, Do, Discuss

1. Tiles are frequently square in shape. A square is one kind of rectangle. Can other rectangles be used for tiling? Are there any kinds of rectangles that could not be used for tiling? Make copies of several different rectangles and use them to determine the properties a rectangle must have for it to be used for tiling a flat surface.

2. Repeat Step 1 using triangles. Will equilateral triangles work? Can any shape of triangle be used for a tile or must it have special properties? Use DGS or cut out several different triangles to test your hypothesis.

3. What regular polygons can be used for tiling? Try regular pentagons, hexagons, and octagons. Which ones work and which do not? Describe what property a regular polygon must have for it to be usable in a tiling pattern.

Angles and Polygons

In the previous activity, you saw that the angles in a regular polygon determine whether it can be used for tiling. You already know a lot about the properties of angles associated with triangles. Now you will explore the properties of angles associated with various kinds of polygons.

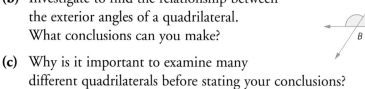

Think, Do, Discuss

1. **(a)** Investigate to find the relationship between the interior angles of a quadrilateral. Use several differently shaped quadrilaterals. What conclusions can you make?

   (b) Investigate to find the relationship between the exterior angles of a quadrilateral. What conclusions can you make?

   (c) Why is it important to examine many different quadrilaterals before stating your conclusions?

   (d) Suppose you examined 100 different quadrilaterals and got the same result each time. Would this be proof that your conclusion is always true?

2. **(a)** Investigate the angle relationships for various types of polygons. Be sure to try several different shapes for each type.

   (b) Summarize your results in a table like this:

Number of Sides	3	4	5	6	7	8	9	10
Sum of Interior Angles								
Sum of Exterior Angles								

   (c) Describe the relationship between the number of sides in the polygon and the sum of the interior angles. Use graphs to illustrate your conclusions.

   (d) Describe the relationship between the number of sides in a polygon and the sum of the exterior angles. Use graphs to illustrate your conclusions.

3. **(a)** Develop an algebraic model that can be used to predict the sum of the inside angles if you know the number of sides.

   (b) Develop an algebraic model that can be used to predict the sum of the outside angles if you know the number of sides.

   (c) Use your models to predict the results for a 20-sided polygon. Compare the predicted results against actual measured values.

   (d) Suppose measuring confirms your model's predictions. Is this a proof that your model is correct? Explain.

Focus

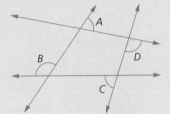
Example

Each interior angle of a regular polygon is 135°. How many sides does it have?

Solution

In a regular polygon, all the sides and angles are the same size. This diagram shows the neighbourhood of a vertex.

135° — exterior angle

Since each interior angle is 135°, each exterior angle must be $180° - 135°$ or 45°. Since the exterior angles in a polygon add to 360°, this means there must be 8 sides ($360 \div 45 = 8$). The polygon is a regular octagon.

Did You Know?

You can use regular shapes such as rectangles or hexagons to cover an area in a regular fashion without any overlap. But British mathematician Roger Penrose has discovered two tile shapes that together can completely cover an area in an irregular, or aperiodic, fashion. These Penrose tiles are shown here.

Tile A has interior angles of 36° and 144°, while tile B has interior angles of 72° and 108°. Use the library or the Internet to do some research on Penrose tiles. Why are they important in physics?

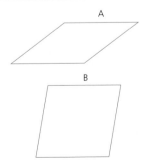

Practise, Apply, Solve

A

1. Find the value of *x* in each diagram.

(a)

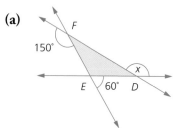

(b)

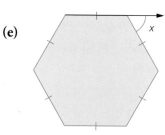

(c)

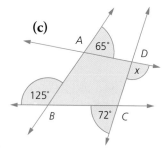

(d)

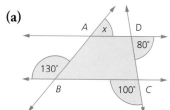

(e)

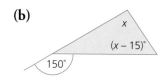

2. Determine how many sides a regular polygon has if each exterior angle measured is:

(a) 30°   **(b)** 45°   **(c)** 4°

B

3. One angle of a parallelogram is four times the measure of the exterior angle adjacent to it. Find the measure of all interior angles, then draw the diagram.

4. For each diagram, state the equation that expresses the relationship needed to solve the problem, then find the measure of the variable(s). Show the steps in the solution.

(a)

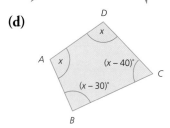

(b)

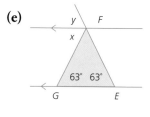

(c)

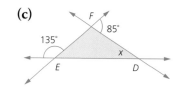

(d)

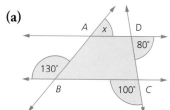

(e)

5. In a regular polygon, the ratio of the measure of the exterior angle to the measure of the adjacent interior angle is 4 to 1. How many sides does the polygon have?

6. When a regular polygon is used to tile a flat surface, the tiles have to join along edges or at vertices. Explain how the angles of a regular polygon affect the way the tiles can be joined. Why does this determine which regular shapes can be used as tiles and which cannot?

C

7. Find the value of each unknown angle.

(a)
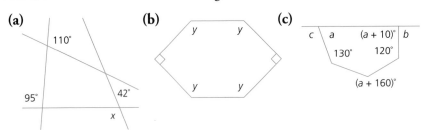

(b)

(c)

8. Explain why the opposite sides of a regular hexagon are parallel.

9. Explain why no sides of a pentagon are parallel.

10. The front profile of a barn is shown. Find the measure of each of the equal angles in the roof.

11. Suppose you are allowed to use two different regular polygons to tile a floor. Find a combination of tiles that will permit you to use an octagon and another shape. Find another pair of tile shapes that will allow you to use a regular polygon that cannot be used by itself. Is there a method you can use to find such pairs?

The Chapter Problem — Which Properties Remain the Same?

Refer to the Chapter Problem at the beginning of the chapter.

A soccer ball is an example of a tiling of a sphere. It is also the shape of a molecule called buckminsterfullerene. It is named after the inventor of the geodesic dome, Buckminster Fuller. Most scientists call this molecule a "bucky ball." What other shapes can be used to tile a sphere? Do they all have to be the same size?

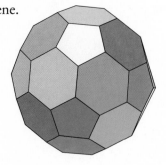

Did You Know?

The photograph with the Chapter Problem above shows Vancouver's Science World building. It is made up of triangles of special glass. This figure is a geodesic dome and was designed by Buckminster Fuller (1895–1983). Use the library or the Internet to find out more about geodesic domes and this architect.

Midpoints of Sides

Suppose you have to supervise the drilling of a tunnel through a mountain from point X to point Y, as shown in this diagram. The mountain blocks your view of the end point Y from the starting point X. How can you make sure you start drilling in the right direction?

See if you can explain why the following method works.

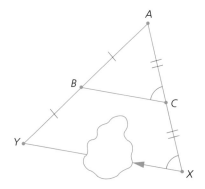

Pick another point, A, far enough from the mountain that you can see A from both X and Y. A has to be far enough away that if you stand at the midpoint of AX, you can see the midpoint of AY.

- Find the midpoints of AY and AX and label them B and C, respectively. Join them with a line segment.
- Measure $\angle ACB$ and transfer that measurement to X.
- That angle gives the direction you have to drill from X to reach Y.

Think, Do, Discuss

1. Repeat this investigation with several different triangles. You could use DGS to construct triangles, each with midpoints on two sides. What happens as you change the shape? Does the line segment formed by joining the midpoints of two sides always behave the same way? Does anything special happen when the original triangle is right-angled, isosceles, or equilateral?

2. Do the investigation again, this time starting with a square. You could use stir sticks, push-pins, and elastics to make a physical model as in Section 6.1. Alternatively, you could use DGS to see what happens as you vary the shape of the square.

3. Draw a square *ABCD*. Label the midpoints of the sides *E*, *F*, *G*, and *H*. Join them to form a new quadrilateral *EFGH*. Describe the shape you created by joining the midpoints. Does it have any properties that are similar to the shape you got joining the midpoints of two sides of a triangle? What is the same and what is different?

Popsicle sticks and push-pin model

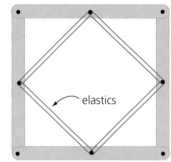

4. Repeat the investigation, but this time use a rectangle that is not a square. Try several different rectangles or use DGS to change the shape of the original rectangle. Describe how the result is the same as the one you found for a square. What is different?

5. Repeat the investigation for a rhombus, a parallelogram, a trapezoid, a kite, and a quadrilateral that has no special relationship between its angles or sides. What common results happen when you form a new quadrilateral by joining the midpoints of the sides of any quadrilateral?

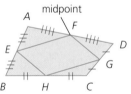

6. Write a summary of the results that are special for a square, rectangle, rhombus, parallelogram, or kite.

Did You Know?

The ancient Greeks felt that some rectangles were more pleasing to the eye than others. These special rectangles had a length-to-width ratio of about 8 : 5 $\left(\frac{8}{5}\text{ or } 1.6\right)$. Rectangles with this ratio are called **golden rectangles** and the ratio itself is called the **golden ratio**. Many examples of the golden rectangle can be seen in art and architecture from ancient Greece and in the modern world. The Parthenon in Athens is one example.

Painter Piet Mondrian (1872–1944) often used golden rectangles in his work. Do some research on Mondrian, either on the Internet or at the library. Examine his paintings for golden rectangles.

Diagonals

You have just completed an investigation that gave you information about the properties of the shapes formed by joining the midpoints of the sides of triangles and quadrilaterals.

Think, Do, Discuss

1. Conduct a similar investigation to discover relationships for the diagonals of various types of quadrilaterals.
2. Summarize your results in a table like this.

Type of Quadrilateral	Angle Relationships (vertex angles, angles formed by diagonals)		Length Relationships (sides, diagonals)	
	Size of Vertex Angles	Effect of Diagonals on Vertex Angles	Size of Diagonal Intersection Angles	Length of Diagonal Segments
square				
rhombus				
rectangle				
parallelogram				
trapezoid				
kite				

3. **(a)** Which quadrilaterals have diagonals that are equal in length?
   (b) What type of quadrilateral has 90° angles at the point of intersection of its diagonals?
   (c) Which quadrilaterals have equal angles at opposite vertices?
   (d) For which quadrilaterals do the diagonals break the angles at the vertices into equal parts?

4. Repeat Steps 1 to 3 for pentagons, hexagons, and octagons.
   (a) What happens only when the polygon is regular?
   (b) Which properties of the new figure seem to exist regardless of the number of sides of the original polygon? Which do not?

Focus

Key Ideas

• When the **midpoints** of the sides of a polygon are joined, a new polygon with the same number of sides as the original is created. This new polygon is an **inscribed polygon**. The segment that joins the midpoints of two adjacent sides is a **midsegment** of the polygon.

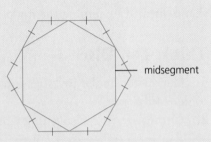
midsegment

• The midsegments of a quadrilateral form a parallelogram.

• A midsegment of a triangle is parallel to the opposite side. This midsegment is half the length of the parallel side.

Each type of quadrilateral has special properties associated with the diagonals and the angles at the vertices.

• The **diagonals** of a square are equal in length and bisect each other at right angles.

• The diagonals of a rhombus bisect each other at right angles and bisect the angles at the vertices.

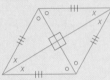

• The diagonals of a rectangle are equal and bisect each other.

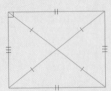

• The diagonals of a parallelogram bisect each other.

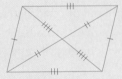

• The diagonals of a kite are perpendicular to each other.

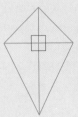

Example

Find the value of x.

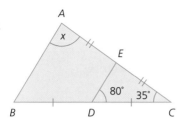

Solution

Since D and E are midpoints, then $DE \parallel AB$.
That means that $\angle BAC = \angle DEC$ because they are corresponding angles.
The angles in $\triangle DEC$ must add to $180°$.

As a result,
$\angle DEC = 180° - 80° - 35°$
$= 65°$

Therefore,
$\angle BAC = \angle DEC$
$= 65°$

Practise, Apply, Solve

1. Match each figure to the appropriate label.

(a)   (b)   (c)   (d)

(e)   (f)   (g)

i. equilateral triangle   **ii.** isosceles triangle   **iii.** kite   **iv.** trapezoid   **v.** rhombus
vi. rectangle   **vii.** square

2. Identify the parallelograms.
(a) trapezoid   (b) square   (c) rectangle   (d) kite   (e) rhombus

3. Construct a figure to match each description. Label diagrams appropriately with the name of the figure as well as parallel sides, congruent sides, and right angles.
(a) a parallelogram with diagonals that intersect at right angles
(b) a rhombus with a 90° angle
(c) a trapezoid with one pair of opposite sides equal
(d) a parallelogram with diagonals that are equal and intersect at right angles

4. Examine the polygons. Which are regular? Explain why the others are not regular.

(a)   (b)   (c)   (d)

(e)   (f)   (g)   (h)

5. True or False?
   (a) If the two pairs of opposite sides of a quadrilateral are equal, the figure must be a parallelogram.
   (b) The diagonals of a rhombus are perpendicular.
   (c) The diagonals of a square are perpendicular bisectors.
   (d) A square is a rhombus.
   (e) The diagonals of a parallelogram are always congruent.

6. Points *D* and *E* are the midpoints of sides *AC* and *AB* in △*ABC*.
   (a) Find the measure of ∠*ADE*.
   (b) State the reason for your answer.

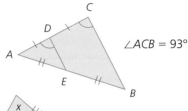

∠*ACB* = 93°

 B

7. Find the measure of angles *x*, *y*, and *z*.

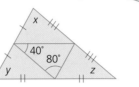

8. *DE* is a midsegment of triangle *ABC*. *CD* = 3.5 cm and *BE* = 3 cm
   (a) Find the length of *AD*.
   (b) Find the length of *AB*.
   (c) Find the measure of ∠*ADE*.
   (d) Find the measure of ∠*AED*.

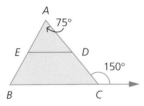

9. Find the measure of angles *x*, *y*, and *z*.

(a)
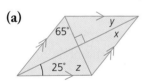

(b)

(c)
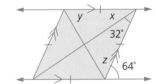

10. Find the lengths of:
   (a) *DE*
   (b) *BD*

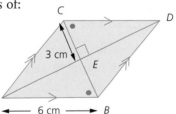

11. (a) Name the figure.
   (b) Find the measure of *x* and *y*.

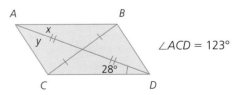

∠*ACD* = 123°

12. True or False? Support your answer with three examples.
   (a) If a polygon has equal sides, it also has equal angles.
   (b) If a polygon has equal angles, it also has equal sides.

13. Construct a triangle and connect the midpoints of two sides with a line segment. Measure the length of the midsegment and the length of the third side. Experiment by dragging the vertices. What conclusions can you reach?

14. Construct a trapezoid. Join the midpoints of the two non-parallel sides with a line segment. Measure the length of the segment and the lengths of the parallel sides.
    (a) Is the segment between the midpoints parallel to the two parallel sides?
    (b) State the relationship between the length of the segment and the lengths of the parallel sides.

15. Confirm or deny whether the results of the previous two questions hold for polygons with more than four sides.

16. Suppose that when you join the midpoints of the sides of a quadrilateral, the resulting figure is a rhombus. Is it possible for it not to be a square? Prove your hypothesis.

17. Suppose two quadrilaterals have the same perimeter. Will the quadrilaterals formed by joining the midpoints of the sides in each of the originals also have equal perimeters?

18. Suppose two quadrilaterals have the same perimeter. Will their diagonals add up to the same total length?

19. (a) Copy and complete the table. Find the number of diagonals that can be drawn from *one* vertex of a polygon followed by the number of triangles formed by the diagonals.
    (b) Explain how this result can be used to show what the sum of the interior angles must be for a given polygon.

Polygon	Number of Diagonals	Number of Triangles
triangle		
quadrilateral		
pentagon		
hexagon		
heptagon		
octagon		
nonagon		
decagon		
100-gon		
n-gon		

The Chapter Problem — Which Properties Remain the Same?

Refer to the Chapter Problem at the beginning of the chapter.

1. Draw a quadrilateral on the surface of a sphere in such a way that one diagonal is on the equator and the other lies along the line joining the North and South Poles. What has to be true for the quadrilateral to be a square? a rectangle? a parallelogram? a trapezoid?

2. Test the properties for angles and diagonals that you have discovered for quadrilaterals drawn on a flat surface. Which remain valid when the shapes are drawn on a sphere? Which produce similar, but different results? Which do not work at all?

6.5 Triangle Centres

When an artist constructs a mobile, she has to find the balance point for each suspended shape. Cut out several different shapes from a piece of poster board. Use a pin or sharp pencil to find the balance point for each shape. In the following activity, you will see if you can find a "geometric" method of predicting where the balance point will be.

Intersecting Medians

Think, Do, Discuss

1. Draw a triangle on a piece of cardboard or poster board. Cut out the triangle. Find the point at which you can balance the triangle on the point of a pencil. Mark that point with an *X*.

2. Suspend the triangle from a piece of string attached at a vertex. Use a pencil to extend the string line to the opposite side. Repeat this for each vertex. What do you notice?

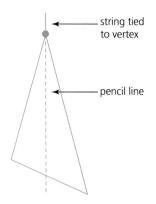

string tied to vertex

pencil line

3. Draw △*ABC*. Mark the midpoints of each side *D*, *E*, and *F*. Draw lines that join each vertex to the midpoint of the opposite side. These segments are called **medians**. Label their point of intersection *G*.

   (a) What do you notice about the way these new line segments intersect?

(b) What happens if you start with a triangle with a different shape?

(c) How does this relate to the balance point discussed above?

(d) The point of intersection divides each median into two segments. Compare the lengths of the shorter segment and the longer segment. What do you notice?

4. Draw an equilateral triangle *XYZ*. Draw lines that join each vertex to the midpoint of the opposite side.

(a) What do you notice about the way the medians meet the sides of the triangle?

(b) Change the shape of the triangle so that it is isosceles. What has changed about the way the medians meet the sides of the triangle? What has stayed the same?

5. Start with a shape other than a triangle. Which of the above methods can be used to find the balance point? Explain why some of the ideas only work for triangles and not for other shapes.

6. Draw a new triangle and mark the midpoint of each side. Draw a line perpendicular to each side through its midpoint. This line is called a **perpendicular bisector** for the side.

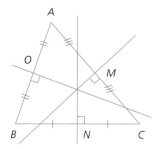

(a) Verify that all three perpendicular bisectors of a triangle intersect at a common point. Label this point *H*.

(b) Construct a circle with centre *H* that passes through each vertex of the triangle. Verify that the shape of the original triangle does not affect this result.

(c) Under what conditions will this point *H* and the point *G*, at which the medians intersect, be the same?

Did You Know?

To an observer on Earth, Sirius is the brightest star in the night sky. Rigel is actually brighter than Sirius, but appears dimmer because it is farther away. Astronomers compare stars by their **absolute magnitude**, the brightness they would have if they were all the same distance from Earth.

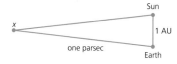

The distance from the Earth to the Sun is one **astronomical unit** (1 AU). Suppose a star is at point *x*. When $\angle x$ is equal to $\frac{1°}{3600}$, then the distance from the Earth to the star is about 3.216 light years, or one **parsec (1 pc)**. The absolute magnitude of a star is the brightness it would have if it were ten parsecs, or 32.16 light years, from Earth.

Intersecting Angle Bisectors

Draw $\triangle ABC$. Construct the **bisector** for the angle at each vertex. Extend each angle bisector so that it meets the side opposite the vertex. Label these points D, E, and F.

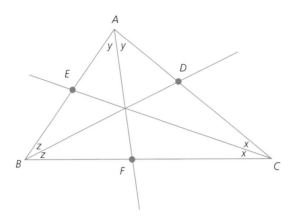

Think, Do, Discuss

1. Repeat the activity above for a number of triangles. Verify that the angle bisectors of any triangle intersect at a common point. Label this point J.

2. Draw a line segment from J to meet each side at 90°. Label the points where the perpendicular segments meet the sides M, N, and L. Confirm that $JM = JN = JL$.

3. Using J as a centre and JM as a radius, draw a circle. Describe what is special about this circle. Verify that changing the shape of the original triangle has no effect on the special properties of this circle.

4. Examine the special case in which $\triangle ABC$ is equilateral.
   (a) Describe how the angle bisectors meet the sides of the triangle.
   (b) How does the point J found in this activity relate to the point G, at which the medians intersect?
   (c) Describe what happens as the base of the triangle is stretched or compressed to form an isosceles triangle. What changes and what stays the same?

Intersecting Perpendiculars

Draw $\triangle ABC$. Draw the line segments from each vertex that meet the opposite side at 90°. These lines are called the **altitudes** of the triangle.

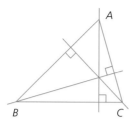

Think, Do, Discuss

1. Verify that the altitudes of any triangle all intersect at a single point. Label this point K.

2. Change the shape of $\triangle ABC$ by moving vertices.
   (a) For what kind of triangle will K always be inside the triangle?
   (b) For what kind of triangle will K be outside the triangle?
   (c) For what kind of triangle will K be on a side of the triangle?

3. For what kind of triangle will the point found in this activity be the same point found in the previous two activities? Check your conclusions. Write how you would explain this to a classmate who has never tried the activities on triangle centres.

Did You Know?

Bhaskara (1114–circa 1185) was a Hindu mathematician who proved the Pythagorean relation by cutting up a square into five pieces and rearranging them as shown. See if you can follow this proof.

$$c^2 = (a + b)^2 - 4\left(\frac{ab}{2}\right)$$
$$c^2 = a^2 + 2ab + b^2 - 2ab$$
$$c^2 = a^2 + b^2$$

Bhaskara provided another demonstration of the theorem by drawing the altitude on the hypotenuse and by using the properties of similar triangles.

$$\frac{c}{b} = \frac{b}{m} \quad \text{and} \quad \frac{c}{a} = \frac{a}{n}$$

Focus

Key Ideas

- When two or more lines intersect at a point, they are said to be **concurrent**.
- The medians of a triangle are concurrent. The point at which they intersect is called the **centroid** of the triangle. The centroid is the centre of mass of the triangle because it is the point at which the triangle can be balanced. The centroid divides each median in the ratio 1 : 2.
- The perpendicular bisectors of the sides of a triangle are concurrent. The point at which they intersect is called the **circumcentre**. It is the centre of a circle that passes through the vertices of the triangle. This circle is called the **circumscribed circle** or the **circumcircle** of the triangle. The circumcentre lies inside an acute triangle, outside an obtuse triangle, and on a side of a right-angled triangle.
- The bisectors of the vertex angles of a triangle are concurrent. The point at which they intersect is called the **incentre** of the triangle. It is the centre of a circle inside the triangle that meets each side at exactly one point. This circle is called the **inscribed circle** or the **incircle** of the triangle.
- The altitudes of a triangle are concurrent. The point at which they intersect is called the **orthocentre** of the triangle. The orthocentre lies inside an acute triangle, outside an obtuse triangle, and on a vertex of a right-angled triangle.
- When a triangle is equilateral, then all the centres are in the same location.

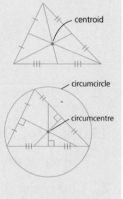

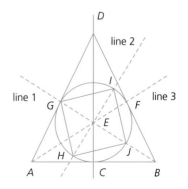

Example

You have been asked to design a logo for a company consisting of a square inscribed within a circle inscribed within an isosceles triangle. Describe how you would construct the logo.

Solution

Follow these steps using dynamic geometry software.

1. Draw segment *AB*.
2. Construct the perpendicular bisector of *AB* at *C*. In an isosceles triangle, the top vertex must lie along this line. Pick a point *D* to be that vertex. Join *DA* and *DB* to form the sides of the triangle.
3. Use the angle bisectors (line 1 and line 3) to find the incentre *E*. The radius of the inscribed circle must be *EC* because *EC* is already perpendicular to the base of the triangle.

4. The diagonals of a square are equal and perpendicular. *GJ* is a diameter. Draw a line (line 2) perpendicular to *GJ* at *E*. These are perpendicular diameters of the circle and can act as diagonals of the square.

5. Join the endpoints to form square *GHJI*.

Practise, Apply, Solve

Ⓐ

1. For each triangle, tell what:
   (a) segment *AB* is.   **(b)** the concurrent point *C* is.

   i.   **ii.**   **iii.**   **iv.**

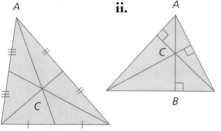
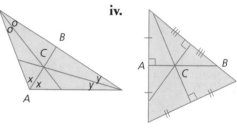

2. Match each construction to the related concurrent point.

Construction	Concurrent Point
(a) altitude	**i.** incentre
(b) median	**ii.** circumcentre
(c) perpendicular bisector	**iii.** orthocentre
(d) angle bisector	**iv.** centroid

3. Copy and complete the table. Enter "inside" the triangle, "outside" the triangle, or "on a side" of the triangle.

Triangle	Circumcentre	Orthocentre
acute		
obtuse		
right		
equilateral		
isosceles		

4. True or False?
   (a) The medians of a triangle intersect at a single point called an incentre.
   (b) The orthocentre of a triangle is always located inside the triangle.
   (c) The centroid of a triangle is always located inside the triangle.
   (d) The centroid, orthocentre, incentre, and circumcentre are concurrent for an equilateral triangle.
   (e) The angle bisector bisects the opposite side.
   (f) The length of the segment of a median, from the vertex to the centroid, is $\frac{2}{3}$ the length of the median.

B

5. Construct a right triangle. Draw a median from the hypotenuse. Measure the median. Compare its length to the length of the bisected hypotenuse segments.
   (a) Repeat with several right triangles. Write a conclusion about the results.
   (b) Find the length of BD, if $AC = 10$ cm.
   (c) Find the measure of $\angle BDC$.

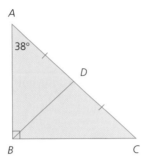

6. Construct a logo that consists of a circle inside a square inside an equilateral triangle.

7. Draw $\triangle ABC$. Construct an equilateral triangle on each side of the original triangle. Join each vertex of the original triangle to the top vertex of the equilateral triangle on the opposite side. Show that these line segments are concurrent.

8. Draw $\triangle ABC$. Find the point where the incircle meets each side. Join each vertex of the original triangle to the point where the incircle meets the opposite side. Show that these line segments are concurrent.

9. The mayors of three cities decide to pool their resources and build a recreational complex that is equidistant from all three city centres. The cities are located as shown.
   (a) Determine the best location.
   (b) How far will residents of the cities have to drive to get to the complex?

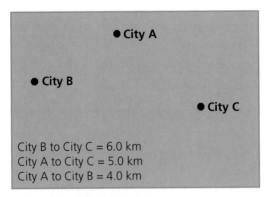

10. Draw $\triangle ABC$. Construct an equilateral triangle on each side of the original triangle. Show that the triangle formed by joining the centroids of the newly constructed equilateral triangles is also equilateral.

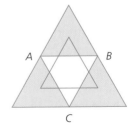

11. (a) Draw several different triangles on a piece of poster board. Mark the centroid on each one. Cut out the triangles. Balance each triangle on the end of a pencil at the centroid. What do you observe? Write down your observation.

(b) Find a way to locate the centroid of a quadrilateral. Verify that you have found the centroid using a balance-point test. (Hint: The median plays a major role.)

12. Point *F* is the centroid of △*ABC*. Suppose *BD* = 6 cm. Find the length of *BF*.

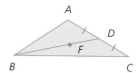

13. Verify that the following method can be used to find the centre of a circle.
  • Pick two points on the circle. Join them with a line segment to form a chord. Draw the perpendicular bisector of the chord.
  • Repeat the previous step using two different points.
  • The centre of the circle is at the intersection of the two bisectors.

Questions 14 to 16 refer to the triangle shown.

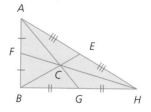

14. Given *CH* = 10*x* − 8 and *FC* = 3*x* − 2.
  (a) Find the value of *x*.
  (b) Find the length of *FH*.

15. Given *BC* = 2*x* + 3 and *BE* = 5*x* + 3.
  (a) Find the value of *x*.
  (b) Find the length of *BE*.

16. Given *AC* = 3*x* + 4 and *CG* = 4*x* − 8.
  (a) Find the value of *x*.
  (b) Find the length of *AG*.

The Chapter Problem — Which Properties Remain the Same?

Refer to the Chapter Problem at the beginning of the chapter.

1. Draw a triangle on the surface of a sphere. Put the top vertex on the North Pole and the base along the equator. Describe what you find when you draw:
  (a) the perpendicular bisectors of each side.
  (b) the altitudes from each vertex.
  (c) the medians.
  (d) angle bisectors at each vertex.

2. Describe the properties of this spherical triangle. How is it like a flat triangle? How is it different?

6.1 Angle Properties of Parallel Lines

- A line that intersects a pair of parallel lines is a
  transversal. When angles are formed by two
  parallel lines and a transversal:
  - the corresponding angles are equal: $\angle 4 = \angle 8$,
    $\angle 3 = \angle 7$, $\angle 1 = \angle 5$, $\angle 2 = \angle 6$.
  - the alternate angles are equal: $\angle 3 = \angle 5$,
    $\angle 2 = \angle 8$.
  - the sum of the interior angles on the same side
    of the transversal is 180°: $\angle 2 + \angle 5 = 180°$,
    $\angle 3 + \angle 8 = 180°$.

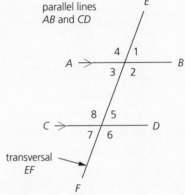

- Dynamic geometry software can be used to
  investigate the properties of angles formed by intersecting lines and in various polygons.

- An investigation can disprove a relationship by finding an example in which the relationship
  does not work. Such an example is called a **counter-example**. However, an investigation
  cannot *prove* that a relationship exists, because it may be that a counter-example exists but
  has not been found.

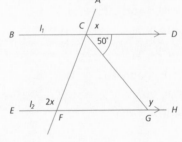

Example

Solve for x and y, given $l_1 \parallel l_2$.

Solution

Since $l_1 \parallel l_2$, then $y + 50° = 180°$
$\therefore y = 180° - 50°$
$\quad y = 130°$
Also, since $l_1 \parallel l_2$, $\angle EFC = \angle BCA$
$\therefore \angle BCA + \angle ACD = 2x + x$
$\qquad\qquad\qquad\quad = 3x$

However, $\angle BCA + \angle ACD = 180°$
$\therefore 3x = 180°$
$\dfrac{3x}{3} = \dfrac{180°}{3}$
$\quad x = 60°$

Extra Practice

1. Complete the sentence. If ■ angles or ■ angles are equal, two lines on a transversal must
   be parallel.
2. Complete the sentences.
   - **(a)** $\angle 1$ and $\angle 5$ are ■.
   - **(b)** $\angle 2$ and $\angle 8$ are ■.
   - **(c)** $\angle 2$ and $\angle 5$ are ■.
   - **(d)** $\angle 6$ and $\angle 2$ are ■.

3. Solve for x.

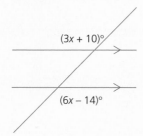

$(3x + 10)°$

$(6x - 14)°$

4. Solve for x.

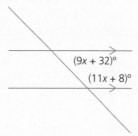

$(9x + 32)°$

$(11x + 8)°$

6.2 Angles Associated with Triangles ——————

- The angles formed inside a polygon by two sides meeting at a vertex are called **interior angles**. When one side of a polygon is extended through the vertex, the angle formed at the vertex by the extended side and the original side is called an **exterior angle**.

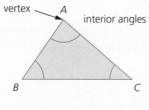

vertex — A interior angles

B C

$\angle A + \angle B + \angle C = 180°$

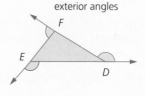

exterior angles

F

E

D

$\angle D + \angle E + \angle F = 360°$

- In a triangle:
    - the sum of the interior angles is 180°.
      $\angle 1 + \angle 2 + \angle 3 = 180°$
    - the sum of the exterior angles is 360°.
      $\angle 4 + \angle 5 + \angle 6 = 360°$
    - each exterior angle is equal to the sum of the interior angles at the opposite vertices. These are called **remote interior angles**.

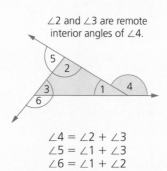

$\angle 2$ and $\angle 3$ are remote interior angles of $\angle 4$.

$\angle 4 = \angle 2 + \angle 3$
$\angle 5 = \angle 1 + \angle 3$
$\angle 6 = \angle 1 + \angle 2$

Example

Solve for x and y, given $AC \parallel DF$.

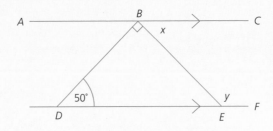

Solution

y is an exterior angle.

$\therefore y = \angle BDE + \angle DBE$
$\quad = 50° + 90°$
$\quad = 140°$

Since $AC \parallel DF$, $y + x = 180°$
$\therefore 140° + x = 180°$
$\quad \therefore x = 180° - 140°$
$\quad \quad \quad = 40°$

Extra Practice

5. Complete the sentences.
   (a) The sum of the interior angles of a triangle is ■.
   (b) In a triangle, the sum of two ■ interior angles equals the measure of their exterior angle.
   (c) The sum of the exterior angles of any polygon is ■.

6. Find the value of each variable.

   (a)
   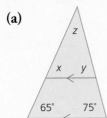

   (b)
   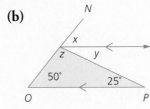

7. Which segments are parallel? Justify your answer.

   (a)
   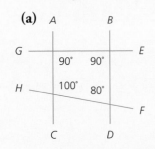

   (b)
   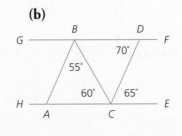

   (c)
   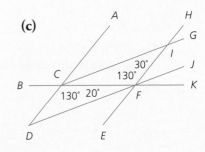

6.3 Angles and Polygons

- In a **quadrilateral**, the sum of the interior angles is 360°.

- In a **polygon** with n sides:
  - the sum of the interior angles is $180(n - 2)°$.
  - the sum of the exterior angles is 360°.

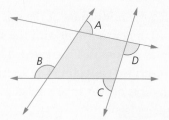

For example, in this diagram, the sum of the interior angles is $180(4 - 2)° = 360°$. The sum of the exterior angles is 360°.

- All **regular polygons** have equal side lengths and equal interior angles.

Example

What are the measures of the exterior angle and the interior angle at each vertex of a regular 18-gon?

Solution

The exterior angles are equal and must have a sum of 360°.
Therefore, if x is the value of each exterior angle, then

$$18x = 360°$$
$$x = \frac{360°}{18}$$
$$x = 20°$$

Therefore, each exterior angle is 20°.
Each interior angle must be:
$180° - 20° = 160°$

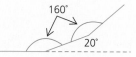

Extra Practice

8. Complete the sentence. The sum of the interior angles of an n-sided polygon is found by using the formula ■.

9. What angles must be found at the vertex of a regular 20-gon?

10. The interior angles of a regular polygon add to 1440°. How many sides does the polygon have?

6.4 Polygon Properties

- When the **midpoints** of the sides of a polygon are joined, a new polygon with the same number of sides as the original is created. This new polygon is an **inscribed polygon**. The segment that joins the midpoints of two adjacent sides is a **midsegment** of the polygon.

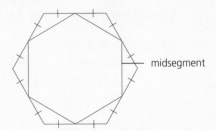
midsegment

- The midsegments of a quadrilateral form a parallelogram.

- A midsegment of a triangle is parallel to the opposite side. This midsegment is half the length of the parallel side.

Each type of quadrilateral has special properties associated with the diagonals and the angles at the vertices.

- The diagonals of a square are equal in length and bisect each other at right angles.

- The diagonals of a rhombus bisect each other at right angles and bisect the angles at the vertices.

- The diagonals of a rectangle are equal and bisect each other.

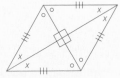

- The diagonals of a parallelogram bisect each other.

- The diagonals of a kite are perpendicular to each other.

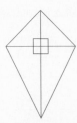

Example

In $\triangle ACD$, B and E are the midpoints of AC and AD.
$\angle ADC = 90°$.
Find the length of CD and the measure of $\angle AEB$.

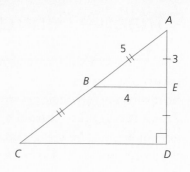

Solution

Since B and E are midpoints, $BE \parallel CD$ and $BE = \frac{1}{2}CD$.

Because $BE \parallel CD$, $\qquad CD = 2BE$

$\angle AEB = \angle ADC \qquad\qquad = 8$

$\qquad = 90°$

Extra Practice

11. Match each name to its definition. Use each name only once.
   (a) A quadrilateral with only one pair of parallel sides.
   (b) A parallelogram with four sides congruent and diagonals that intersect at right angles.
   (c) A parallelogram with diagonals that bisect each other and are equal in length.
   (d) A parallelogram that is both a rhombus and a rectangle.
   (e) A quadrilateral with two pairs of adjacent sides that are equal in length.

   i. trapezoid
   ii. square
   iii. rectangle
   iv. kite
   v. rhombus

12. Name each figure.
   (a) the figure formed by joining, in order, all of the midpoints on the sides of any quadrilateral
   (b) the quadrilateral whose diagonals are equal in length, bisect each other, and intersect at 90°
   (c) the quadrilateral whose diagonals are not equal to each other, bisect each other, and intersect at 90°

13. Sketch each quadrilateral and label it. List what you know about each shape.
   (a) rhombus   **(b)** parallelogram
   (c) kite   **(d)** trapezoid

14. List six properties of a square.

15. In quadrilateral $ABCD$,
   $\angle A = \angle D$ and $\angle B = \angle C$.
   Find x and y.

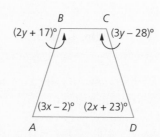

6.5 Triangle Centres

- When two or more lines intersect at a point, they are said to be **concurrent**.
- The medians of a triangle are concurrent. The point at which they intersect is called the **centroid** of the triangle. The centroid is the centre of mass of the triangle because it is the point at which the triangle can be balanced. The centroid divides each median in the ratio 1 : 2.

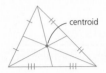
centroid

- The perpendicular bisectors of the sides of a triangle are concurrent. The point at which they intersect is called the **circumcentre**. It is the centre of a circle that passes through the vertices of the triangle. This circle is called the **circumscribed circle** or the **circumcircle** of the triangle. The circumcentre lies inside an acute triangle, outside an obtuse angle, and on a side of a right-angled triangle.

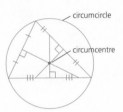
circumcircle
circumcentre

- The bisectors of the vertex angles of a triangle are concurrent. The point at which they intersect is called the **incentre** of the triangle. It is the centre of a circle inside the triangle that meets each side at exactly one point. This circle is called the **inscribed circle** or the **incircle** of the triangle.

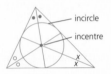
incircle
incentre

- The altitudes of a triangle are concurrent. The point at which they intersect is called the **orthocentre** of the triangle. The orthocentre lies inside an acute triangle, outside an obtuse triangle, and on a vertex of a right-angled triangle.

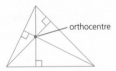
orthocentre

- When a triangle is equilateral, then all the centres are in the same location.

Example

Tell how to find the balance point for this paper pattern for the metal triangles of a mobile.

Solution

Find the midpoint of each side of the triangle. To do this, measure with a ruler or fold the edges or use dynamic geometry software.

Join each vertex to the midpoint of the opposite side. The intersection point of these lines (the medians) is the balance point, or centre of mass.

Extra Practice

16. Complete the sentences.
  (a) When three lines intersect at a common point, the lines are ■.
  (b) The centroid of a triangle is the concurrent point of the ■.
  (c) The incentre of a triangle is the concurrent point of the ■.
  (d) The point of concurrency of the altitudes for a triangle is the ■.
  (e) The point of concurrency for the perpendicular bisectors of a triangle is the ■.

17. Sketch triangles and clearly indicate how to find each point.
  (a) orthocentre   **(b)** incentre
  (c) circumcentre   **(d)** centroid

18. List at least one application for each point of concurrency:
  (a) incentre   **(b)** circumcentre   **(c)** centroid

19. Is there a triangle in which at least one of the altitudes is a side of the triangle? Is there a triangle in which exactly one of the altitudes is a side of the triangle? Explain.

20. Is there a triangle in which the perpendicular bisector of a side, an altitude, a median, and a bisector of one of the angles are on the same line? Explain.

21. Construct a large scalene triangle.
  (a) Locate and label the incentre *I*.
  (b) Locate and label the centre of gravity (centroid) *G*.
  (c) Locate and label the circumcentre *C*.
  (d) Locate and label the orthocentre *O*.
  (e) Three of these points should be collinear (in a straight line). Draw the line that contains the three points.

Chapter Summary

In this chapter, you investigated polygons and parallel lines to determine the geometric relationships between angles and line segments. You have seen that when a transversal crosses a pair of parallel lines, the alternate angles are equal, and so are the corresponding angles. The co-interior angles are supplementary. In a triangle, the medians, angle bisectors, and perpendicular bisectors all meet at different locations inside the triangle.

The relationship between the interior angles of a polygon depends on the number of sides in the polygon. The number of diagonals in a polygon also depends on the number of sides it has. In a quadrilateral, the manner in which the diagonals intersect depends on the shape of the quadrilateral.

You saw that using several examples to illustrate a relationship does not prove that it is always true. However, if an example can be found to show that the relationship does not hold (counter-example), this is enough to conclude that the relationship is not valid.

1. Solve for x.

   (a)   **(b)**

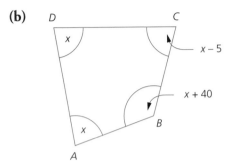

2. In a regular polygon, the ratio of the interior angles to the exterior angles is 3 : 1.
    (a) Find the measure of the interior angle.
    (b) How many sides are there?

Questions 3 to 6 refer to this diagram.

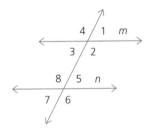

3. Answer "parallel" or "not parallel."
    (a) If $\angle 2 = \angle 5$, then lines m and n are ■.

    (b) If $\angle 3 = \angle 7$, then lines m and n are ■.

    (c) If $\angle 8 = 110°$ and $\angle 3 = 70°$, then lines m and n are ■.

4. Given that line m is parallel to line n and:
    $\angle 7 = 5x - 15$ and $\angle 1 = 3x + 30$.

    (a) Find the value of x.

    (b) Find the measure of $\angle 7$.

5. Name each pair of angles in the figure.
    (a) $\angle 2$ and $\angle 6$

    (b) $\angle 2$ and $\angle 8$

    (c) $\angle 3$ and $\angle 8$

Chapter Review Test

6. State the relationship between $\angle 2$ and $\angle 5$ in Question 3.

7. Find the measure of each angle in the figure.

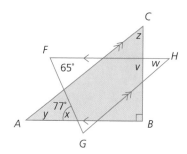

(a) $\angle v$ (b) $\angle w$ (c) $\angle x$ (d) $\angle y$ (e) $\angle z$

8. Three of the exterior angles of a pentagon measure 70°, 60°, and 90°. The other two angles are congruent. Find their measurement.

9. Points D and E are two midpoints of $\triangle ABC$. Point D is between A and C. E is between A and B. Complete the sentence.

   (a) If $AB = 12$, then $AE = \blacksquare$.   (b) If $DC = 7$, then $AC = \blacksquare$.

10. (a) Draw a parallelogram, a rectangle, a rhombus, and a square. In each figure, indicate the equal line segments and angles.

    (b) In each figure you drew in part (a), now draw the diagonals and indicate the equal line segments and angles.

11. Match each centre with the segments needed to find it.

   (a) centroid   **i.** altitude

   (b) incentre   **ii.** median

   (c) circumcentre   **iii.** perpendicular bisector

   (d) orthocentre   **iv.** angle bisector

12. Explain how to locate each point in a triangle.

   (a) centre of balance (gravity)

   (b) a point equidistant from the vertices

   (c) a point equidistant from the sides

13. Explain why angles x and y are congruent in this diagram.

14. Determine the measure of $\angle CFB$.

15. (a) Determine the measure of x.

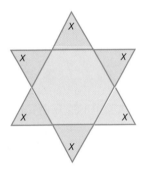

(b) Determine the measure of y.

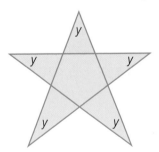

The Brock Monument at Queenston
Heights, Ontario, near Niagara-on-the-Lake

Chapter 7

Measurement Relationships in Three-Dimensional Figures

The Brock monument, shown here, consists of a large cylinder placed upon a rectangular prism, with a statue of General Brock on top. Inside the cylinder is a stairway that visitors can climb to the top and look out for kilometres in any direction. How could you find the volume of this cylinder? What is its surface area?

These are questions that you will be able to answer as you study this chapter and learn more about three-dimensional geometry.

In this chapter, you will:

- use methods for finding the area of two-dimensional figures to find the surface area of three-dimensional objects

- calculate the volume of three-dimensional objects

- solve real-world problems involving measurement of two-dimensional figures and three-dimensional objects

- apply graphical models and lines or curves of best fit to examine the relationships among different three-dimensional objects.

Connections

The Chapter Problem

What Is the Profit?

To earn money after school, John makes and sells candles. He has bought new moulds to make candles of different shapes and sizes. Now, he must order the candle wax. There are two types of wax. Paraffin is $1.50 for 500 mL and beeswax is $3.50 for 500 mL.

John wants to create a set of formulas to find the amount of wax needed for the ten different moulds he has bought. The sizes and shapes of the moulds are shown. Wicks sell for 0.5¢/cm plus 2¢ for each wick holder tab. John also needs to calculate the total cost of making and packaging each candle so he can find the selling price and his profit. The paper packaging in which he wraps the candles for sale costs $3.50/m². What is his profit on each type of candle?

Shape	Apothem/Radius	Height	Selling Price
square pillar	5 cm 4 cm 1.5 cm	9 cm 18 cm 25 cm	$5.50 $6.00 $12.00
hexagonal pillar	6 cm	12 cm	$9.50
octagonal pillar	7 cm 7 cm	15 cm 28 cm	$10.00 $15.00
decagonal pillar	4 cm	17 cm	$7.50
cylindrical pillar	3.8 cm 5 cm 2.5 cm	10 cm 15 cm 23 cm	$5.00 $6.50 $5.00

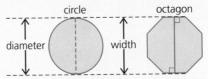

At the end of some lessons in this chapter, questions will refer back to this problem. You will be able to use what you have just learned to answer them. Keep your notes in a folder, so that at the end of the chapter, you can provide a full solution to the problem.

The Challenge

How High Is the Water?

What would happen if the ice caps at the North Pole and the South Pole melted? Specifically, how far up the CN Tower would you have to go to avoid getting wet?

To complete this Challenge, you may need to develop a research plan with your teacher or with other students. You may also need to do research outside the classroom.

In this chapter, you will be working with the geometrical properties of three-dimensional objects. These exercises will help you prepare for the work you will be doing in this chapter.

1. Copy this table and enter the correct formulas.

Shape	Perimeter/Circumference	Area
rectangle		$A = L \times W$
triangle		
circle		

2. Calculate the perimeter and area of each shape.

(a)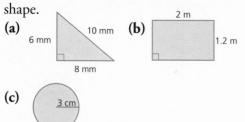

(b)

(c)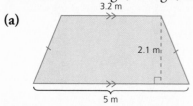

3. Calculate the area of each shape. Use only the formulas for rectangle, triangle, and circle.

(a)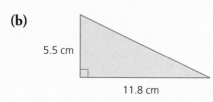

(b)

4. A right-angled triangle is shown. Use the Pythagorean theorem to calculate the length of the hypotenuse to one decimal place.

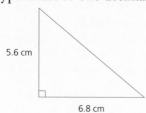

5. Find the equation of the line of best fit given this data.

x	2	3	5	4	1
y	−2	−1	1	0	−3

6. What is the area of this figure?

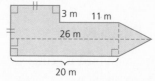

7. Ten metres of fencing was used to build a square dog kennel. What is the area of the kennel?

8. Calculate the area of the shaded region.

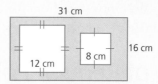

9. Air traffic controllers use radar to keep track of airplanes that land at their airport. The radar screen monitors a distance of 25 km around the airport in all directions. What area can the air traffic controller see?

10. Radio waves are broadcast from a tower and travel outward in a circular pattern. If the waves cover an area of 196 250 km², which towns will get the radio station on their radios?

Town	Distance from Radio Station (km)
Dundas	157
Georgetown	78
Sudbury	411
Kenora	1326
Niagara Falls	202

11. Find the volume of:
    (a) a rectangular prism 10 cm high with a base that is 3 cm by 5 cm.
    (b) a chocolate bar in the shape of a triangular prism that is 18 cm long. The base of the triangle is 3 cm and the height is 2 cm.

7.1 Area of Composite Figures and Regular Polygons

Area of Composite Figures

Marco needs to replace the siding on the front of his house. How can he determine the amount of siding he needs?

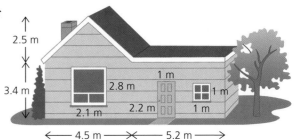

Think, Do, Discuss

1. What shapes combined together make the front profile of his house?
2. How can he determine the area of this combination of shapes?
3. How do the areas of the two windows and the door affect the amount of siding he needs? Using the dimensions from the diagram, determine the amount of siding Marco needs.

Area of Regular Polygons

Jean has a vase with a regular hexagon base. The distance between opposite sides is 10 cm. She wants to glue a piece of felt to the bottom to ensure that the vase will not scratch tables.

She needs to know how much felt to buy.

Think, Do, Discuss

1. Draw a regular hexagon on 1 cm or 0.5 cm graph paper. The distance from the centre of the hexagon to each side should be 5 cm. Estimate the perimeter and the area of the hexagon.

2. Divide the hexagon into six identical triangles that meet at the centre. Measure the base and the height of each triangle. The height of the triangles is also called the **apothem** of the hexagon. (The apothem of a regular polygon is like a circle's radius: it is a line drawn from the centre of the shape to meet any side at a right angle.) Record these measurements on each triangle. Calculate the area and perimeter of the hexagon.

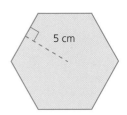

3. Cut out the six triangles and rearrange them into the shape of a parallelogram.
   (a) Explain how the area of the parallelogram compares to the area of the hexagon.
   (b) How is the height of the parallelogram related to the hexagon?
   (c) How is the base of the parallelogram related to the hexagon?
   (d) How can you use the formula for the area of a parallelogram,
       area = base × height,
       to develop a formula for the area of the hexagon?

4. Use the method in Questions 1 to 3 to determine the area of the base of Jean's vase. If felt costs $0.11/cm², how much will it cost Jean to cover the base?

5. Write a description of how you can use this method to find the area of any regular polygon with an even number of sides.

6. Draw a regular pentagon on 1 cm or 0.5 cm graph paper. Find the centre by drawing two perpendicular bisectors of the sides. Make the apothem of the pentagon 5 cm long. Estimate the perimeter and the area of the pentagon based on these measurements.

7. How many triangles can you divide the pentagon into if all the triangles must meet at the centre and have a side of the pentagon as base?

8. Draw these triangles on your diagram. Measure the base and height of each triangle. Record these measurements on each triangle. Calculate the area and the perimeter of the pentagon based on these measurements.

9. If the pentagon were cut into triangles, could they be rearranged to form a parallelogram? Why or why not?

10. (a) Into what four-sided figure could these triangles be rearranged?
   (b) Explain how the area of the four-sided figure compares to the area of the pentagon.
   (c) How is the height of this figure related to the pentagon?
   (d) How are the sides of this figure related to the pentagon?
   (e) How can the formula for the area of this figure be used to develop a formula for the area of the pentagon?

11. Describe how this method can be used to find the area of any regular polygon with an odd number of sides.

12. Any regular polygon can be rearranged to form a quadrilateral.
   (a) What are the two different types of quadrilateral that can be formed?
   (b) What determines the type of quadrilateral into which a regular polygon can be rearranged?
   (c) What is the general formula that can be used to determine the area of any regular polygon?

Focus

Key Ideas

- Two-dimensional shapes made from a combination of several different shapes are called **composite figures**.
- The area of a composite figure can be found by adding or subtracting the areas of each individual shape as required.
- The **apothem** of a regular polygon is the perpendicular distance from the centre of the polygon to each side.
- All regular polygons can be divided into isosceles triangles by drawing lines to connect the centre of the figure to each vertex of the polygon.
- The number of sides of a regular polygon determines the number of inscribed triangles in the polygon and the type of quadrilateral into which the polygon can be rearranged.
    - If the polygon has an even number of sides, the inscribed triangles can be rearranged to form a parallelogram with an area equal to the area of the polygon.
    - If the polygon has an odd number of sides, the inscribed triangles can be rearranged to form a trapezoid with an area equal to the area of the polygon.
- The formula for the perimeter, P, of a regular polygon is $P = nl$, where n is the number of sides and l is the length of one side.
- The general formula for the area, A, of any n-sided regular polygon is $A = \frac{Pa}{2}$, where P is the perimeter of the polygon and a is the apothem.
- Here is a summary of regular polygons with up to ten sides.

Number of Sides, n	Polygon	Diagram	Number of Sides, n	Polygon	Diagram
3	triangle		7	heptagon	
4	quadrilateral		8	octagon	
5	pentagon		9	nonagon	
6	hexagon		10	decagon	

Example

Calculate the area of the nonagon.

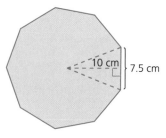

Solution

A nonagon has 9 sides. First, find the perimeter.

$$P = nl$$
$$P = (9)(7.5)$$
$$= 67.5$$

The perimeter of the nonagon is 67.5 cm.

Next, use the area formula to find the area of the nonagon.

$$A = \frac{Pa}{2}$$

$$A = \frac{(67.5)(10)}{2}$$

$$= \frac{675}{2}$$

$$= 337.5$$

The area of the nonagon is 337.5 cm².

Practise, Apply, Solve

A

1. How many sides does each polygon have?
   (a) pentagon   (b) octagon
   (c) quadrilateral   (d) heptagon

2. Determine the length of each side of each regular polygon.
   (a) a triangle with a perimeter of 18 cm
   (b) a hexagon with a perimeter of 27 cm
   (c) a nonagon with a perimeter of 108 mm
   (d) a decagon with a perimeter of 156 mm

3. Determine the perimeter of each regular polygon.

   (a)
   6.3 cm

   (b)
   2.5 mm

   (c)
   6.7 cm

4. Determine the area of each regular polygon by measuring one side length and where necessary the apothem, and then using the appropriate formula.

(a)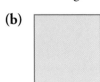

(b)

(c)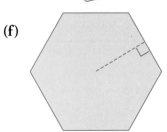

(d)

(e)

(f)

5. Calculate the area of each regular polygon using the measurements given and the formula $A = \frac{Pa}{2}$.

(a)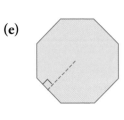
34 mm
41 mm

(b)
3.6 cm
2.3 cm

B

6. Calculate the area of each shape.

(a)
5.6 cm
3.2 cm
4.1 cm

(b)
3.8 cm
5.6 cm
5.6 cm

(c)
9.6 m
3.2 m
3.2 m

7. Calculate the perimeter and area of each shape.

(a)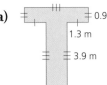
0.9 m
1.3 m
3.9 m

(b)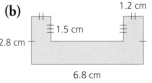
1.2 cm
1.5 cm
2.8 cm
6.8 cm

(c)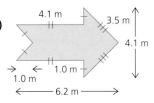
4.1 m
3.5 m
4.1 m
1.0 m
1.0 m
6.2 m

8. (a) Find the area of the shaded part of each diagram.

i.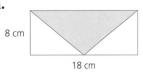
8 cm
18 cm

ii.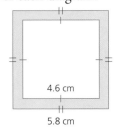
4.6 cm
5.8 cm

iii.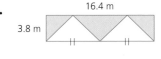
16.4 m
3.8 m

(b) Suggest another way to find each answer in part (a). Discuss it with a partner.

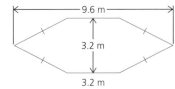

9. Calculate the area of each regular polygon.

(a)

7.2 cm

8.4 cm

(b)

20.4 cm

14.4 cm

(c)

17.4 cm

14.4 cm

10. A school field has the dimensions shown.

22.8 m

49.2 m

(a) Calculate the length of one lap of the track.
(b) If Amanda ran 625 m, how many laps did she run?
(c) Find the area of the field.

11. Calculate the area of each shaded region.

(a)

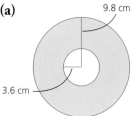

9.8 cm

3.6 cm

(b)

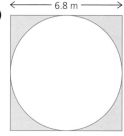

6.8 m

(c)

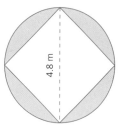

4.8 m

(d)

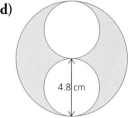

4.8 cm

(e)

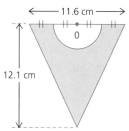

11.6 cm

0

12.1 cm

12. The total area, A, of the shaded region is given by $A = 2\pi R^2 + 2\pi r^2$.

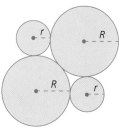

(a) Calculate the area if $R = 4.1$ m and $r = 2.8$ m.
(b) By how much does the area in part (a) increase if each radius is increased by 1.0 m?

13. Find the length of one side of each regular polygon.

(a)

1 cm

$A = 5.2$ cm^2

(b)

15 mm

$A = 758$ mm^2

14. Sari is building a hexagonal window with a side length of 1.16 m and an apothem of 1 m. Calculate the length of wooden framing and the area of glass needed.

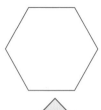

15. Mika is wallpapering a design on one of his bedroom walls. He decides to draw an octagon with triangles spreading out from each vertex. What area of wallpaper will just cover the design?

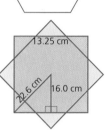

16. An irregular polygon is shown. Could you use the formula $A = \frac{Pa}{2}$ to find its area? Why or why not?

17. Determine the area of this shape.

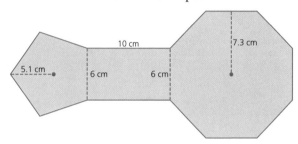

18. A designer's drawing of a road stop sign shows a regular octagon with a side length of 100 cm and an apothem of 120 cm. One can of the reflective paint used on these signs will cover 500 m². How many cans of paint should be ordered to cover 100 of these signs?

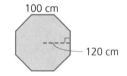

19. Michelle's elementary school class is going to construct a quilt. Each student is given a square piece of fabric that is 10 cm on each side. Michelle has created a pattern that each student can use to cut a regular octagon from each square. The pattern is shown here. The octagons will be sewn together to form a quilt. How much material will be left over each time an octagon is cut from a square?

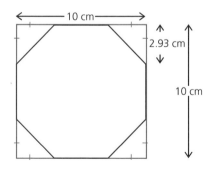

20. Suppose that you drew a number of regular polygons, each with an apothem of one metre.
   (a) Describe the relationship between the number of sides and the perimeter of each polygon.
   (b) Describe the relationship between the number of sides and the area of each polygon.
   (c) Describe what would happen to the perimeter and the area if the number of sides were allowed to increase without limits. What would the shape look like?

21. Suppose Antwan has a square piece of felt measuring 12 cm by 12 cm. What is the largest regular pentagonal-based vase that he can cover? (Hint: Try modelling this situation using dynamic geometry software.)

22. **(a)** A rectangle has an area of 96.0 cm^2. How many different rectangles can you construct with whole number measures for the sides?
   (b) A triangle has an area of 42 cm^2. How many different triangles can you construct with whole number measures for the base and height?

23. Calculate the shaded area of each figure.

(a)
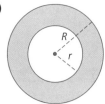

(b)
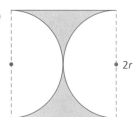

(c)
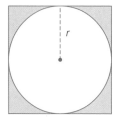

Leonard Euler (1707–1783)

Leonard Euler (pronounced "oiler") was born in Basel, Switzerland and became one of the world's most important mathematicians, especially in the field of analytic geometry. He was the first to use polynomial equations to represent the relationship between the number of vertices, v, faces, f, and edges, e, of a simple polyhedron:

$$v + f = e + 2$$

Although several other mathematicians also described this relationship, Euler was the first to state the relationship as a formula. Verify the formula. Use a cube to see if he was correct.

7.2 Volume of Regular Polygonal Prisms and Cylinders

Prisms

The hexagon is a common shape in nature. For instance, in their hives, bees store their honey in hexagonal prisms.

Suppose a particular kind of bee builds hexagonal prisms that are 1 cm on a side and 2 cm deep. How much honey can a hive with 5000 such hexagons hold?

Suppose that a packing plant places honey in cylindrical cans that are 10 cm long and have a radius of 5 cm. How many such cans can be filled from a single hive?

Think, Do, Discuss

1. Draw a diagram to show how a hexagonal-based prism can be divided into identical triangular prisms.

2. Use an accurate diagram to find the measurements you need to compute the volume of each triangular prism.

3. Explain how to use these volumes to find the volume of the hexagonal prism.

4. Find the total volume of honey in the hive.

5. The volume of a triangular prism is found using this formula:

$$\text{volume} = \text{area of base} \times \text{height}$$

   Explain how you can use this formula to find the volume of a regular hexagonal-based prism.

6. Write a description of how to determine the volume of any prism whose base is a regular polygon.

Cylinders

Horst uses a cylindrical container to store hamburgers. He uses lean ground beef to make each burger. The hamburgers are separated by a thin layer of wax paper so they don't stick together.

Suppose each hamburger is 1 cm thick. How many hamburgers can he store in the container? How much ground beef will the container hold?

Think, Do, Discuss

1. In the investigation for prisms, you developed the formula for determining the volume of a prism with a regular polygonal base. What two quantities in a prism does the volume depend on?

2. What is the shape of the pieces of wax paper that are used to separate the hamburgers? What is the shape of the bottom of each hamburger? What formula can be used to determine the area of each patty? Suppose the radius is 5.5 cm. Calculate the area of the bottom of each hamburger.

3. What is the thickness of each hamburger? What measurement does this correspond to in a prism? Using your knowledge of prisms, determine the volume of each hamburger.

4. Suppose the cylindrical container is 20 cm high. How many hamburgers can the container hold? What is the volume of the cylindrical container?

5. The formula for the volume of a cylinder is the same as the formula used to find the volume of a prism. Explain why this formula works for both types of figures.

6. Suggest a formula that you could use to calculate the volume of a cylinder.

7. Refer back to the beehive example at the beginning of this section. Determine the volume of each cylindrical honey can. Use it to estimate the total number of cans that can be filled from the hive. Write an explanation of how you did this.

Focus

Key Ideas

- A **prism** is a three-dimensional solid with two polygon-shaped faces (the base and the top) that are parallel and identical. The remaining sides, called lateral faces, are rectangular.
- The formula for finding the volume, V, of any regular prism is
  V = area of base × height.
- A **cylinder** is a three-dimensional solid with two circular faces that are parallel and identical.
- The formula for finding the volume, V, of any cylinder is
  V = area of base × height.
  A formula that is often used is $V = \pi r^2 h$.
  r is the radius of the base.
  πr^2 is the area of the base.
  h is the height of the cylinder.
- The volume formulas in this section apply only to three-dimensional shapes in which the area of cross-section is the same over the entire height. The **cross-section** is the two-dimensional shape produced when a plane cut is made through a solid, parallel to the base.

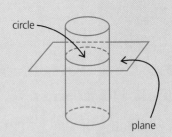

circle

plane

Example

Calculate the volume of each object. The base of the prism is a regular polygon.

prism

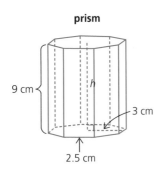

9 cm

h

3 cm

2.5 cm

cylinder

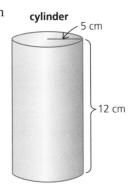

5 cm

12 cm

Solution

Prism:

V = area of base × height

$V = \left(\dfrac{1}{2}\right)(8)(2.5)(3) \times (9)$

$V = 270$

The volume of the prism is 270 cm³.

Cylinder:

V = area of base × height

$V = \pi \times (5)^2 \times 12$

$V = 300\pi$

$V \doteq 942.5$

The volume of the cylinder is about 942.5 cm³.

Practise, Apply, Solve

1. Which objects are prisms? cylinders?

(a)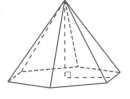

(b)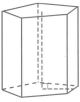

(c)

(d)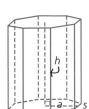

(e)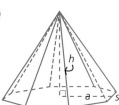

2. For which objects could you use $V = Ah$ to determine their volume?

(a)

(b)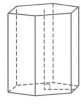

(c)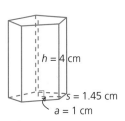

3. Find the volume of each object. The base of each prism is a regular polygon.

(a)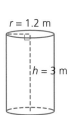

$r = 1.2$ m

$h = 3$ m

(b)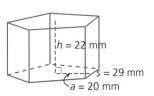

$h = 22$ mm

$s = 29$ mm

$a = 20$ mm

(c)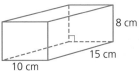

$h = 4$ cm

$s = 1.45$ cm

$a = 1$ cm

4. A box is designed to package rectangular 8 cm by 10 cm memo notes. Each memo note is 0.1 mm thick.
  (a) How many memo notes would fit into this box?
  (b) What volume of paper does the box hold?
  (c) How do your answers in parts (a) and (b) differ?

8 cm

15 cm

10 cm

5. What is the value of *x*?

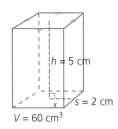

$h = 5$ cm
$s = 2$ cm
x
$V = 60$ cm³

6. A winemaker is mass-producing corks for wine bottles. The diameter of the opening of the bottle is 20 mm and the cork must be 38 mm high. What is the volume of the compressed cork?

7. Dairy Fresh packages two cartons of milk. The large carton is 8 cm by 8 cm by 18 cm. The small carton is 6 cm by 6 cm by 8 cm. How many small cartons of milk would fill one large one?

8. A gold bar is 15 cm by 8 cm by 3 cm and is worth $350 000. What is the volume of the bar in cubic centimetres? How much is one cubic centimetre worth?

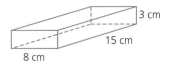

3 cm
15 cm
8 cm

9. A cylinder just fits inside a 10 cm × 10 cm × 10 cm box.
(a) Determine the volume of the box.
(b) Determine the volume of the cylinder.
(c) Determine the volume of the empty space in the box when the cylinder is placed inside.

10. Three tennis balls, each 8 cm in diameter, are stacked in a cylindrical container. Determine the minimum volume of this container.

11. The piston of an engine is 6 cm in diameter. The cylindrical combustion chamber in which the piston moves is 19.5 cm long.
(a) Determine the volume of the combustion chamber.
(b) Suppose the engine has four cylinders (pistons in combustion chambers). Determine the total volume of all the cylinders.
(c) The size of an engine is determined by the total volume of the combustion chambers. Use the fact that 1 cm³ = 1 mL and 1000 mL = 1 L to express the size of the engine in litres.
(d) What would the size of the engine be, in litres, if it had six cylinders?

6 cm
19.5 cm

12. **(a)** Suppose that a cylinder has a radius of 10 cm. Construct a mathematical model to describe the relationship between the height and the volume of the cylinder.
(b) Suppose the height of the cylinder is fixed at 10 cm. Construct a mathematical model to describe the relationship between the radius and the volume.

13. Use a standard-sized sheet of paper (21.5 cm by 28 cm) to make an open box or cylinder with the greatest possible volume.

14. Leslie wants to make her best friend a box of fudge for her birthday. She buys a beautiful heart-shaped box from the craft store and lines it with waxed paper. The box is 2 cm deep, 25 cm long, and 20 cm across at its widest point. Estimate the volume of fudge she will have to make to fill the box.

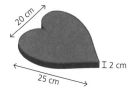

15. Tracy plans to create an ice sculpture for a table centrepiece at her friend's housewarming. The ice she will start with is shown. Calculate the volume of ice Tracy will need to make the sculpture.

16. To store his grain, Larry is building a cylindrical silo that must have a volume of 65 m³. The height of the silo must be 6 m. What is the radius?

17. Investigate the relationships between volume and apothem for prisms with regular polygonal bases when the height has a fixed value.

18. Investigate the relationships between volume and height for prisms with regular polygonal bases when the apothem has a fixed value.

The Chapter Problem — What Is the Profit?

Refer to the Chapter Problem at the beginning of the chapter.

1. Use the information in the table to find the volume of wax that each mould will hold.
2. Find the cost of paraffin and beeswax needed to make each candle.

Douglas Cardinal

Douglas Cardinal is one of Canada's foremost architects. He has designed such important buildings as the Canadian Museum of Civilization in Hull, Quebec, and has received many honours, both nationally and internationally. Do some research on Douglas Cardinal and his work. What other buildings has he designed? Why would an architect need to know mathematics?

7.3 The *Volume/Surface Area Explorer*

It is difficult to explore the relationship between the size and shape of three-dimensional objects. However, technology can make it easier. In this section, you will see how to use and work with the *Volume/Surface Area Explorer*. You can use the *Explorer* in many of the lessons in this chapter to investigate relationships and develop formulas related to surface area and volume.

Think, Do, Discuss

1. Open the *Volume/Surface Area Explorer*. This image will appear.

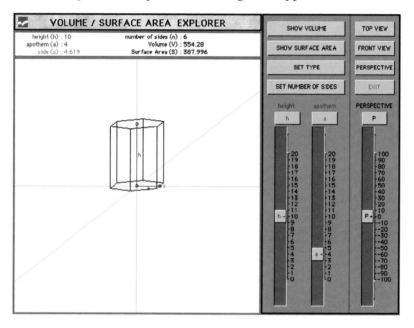

2. The graphics area displays the shape you are working with. Drag the *P* slider up and down. What happens to the prism?

3. Drag each of the *h* and *a* sliders up and down. What happens to the shape for each button?

4. Watch the values in the data box as you change the apothem and height of the shape. What do you notice?

5. Select SET TYPE . Notice that on the screen that appears you can select one of five types of objects. Complete these steps:

   (a) Select the right pyramid and select OK .

   (b) Now select SET NUMBER OF SIDES . On the screen that appears, select 6 , and then select OK .

6. Drag the height, apothem, and perspective sliders. How does the movement of each slider affect the values in the data box?

7. Change the view by selecting top view, front view, and perspective view. Describe what each view type shows about the figure.

Practise

1. Create a table of the similarities and differences between the five shapes that a[...] you select SET TYPE .

2. Create at least five different shapes with different apothem and height values. Rec[...] volumes.

3. Describe what each variable in the data box represents.

4. Form a six-sided right prism with a height of 12 units and an apothem of 8 units. Recor[...] the volume and surface area. Form a six-sided right pyramid with the same dimensions. Record the volume and surface area. Repeat these steps with seven-sided and eight-sided figures. Try to find a relationship between the volume and surface area of right pyramids and right prisms that share the same dimensions and number of sides.

5. Use the *Explorer* to determine the surface area of a basketball that is 30 cm in diameter.

6. A car cylinder is 20 cm long and the piston inside it is 6.5 cm in diameter. Use the *Explorer* to determine the volume of the piston chamber.

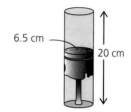
6.5 cm
20 cm

The Chapter Problem — What Is the Profit?

Refer to the Chapter Problem at the beginning of the chapter.

Use the information in the table and the *Volume/Surface Area Explorer* to find the volume of wax that each cylindrical mould will hold. Compare these answers with those from Section 7.2

Maria Mitchell (1818–1889)

Maria Mitchell was the first female astronomer in America. Her discovery of a new comet in 1847 brought her worldwide fame. In her studies of the stars, she used a type of geometry called trigonometry, which deals with right triangles. Trigonometry developed out of the study of the stars and was used long ago by the ancient Egyptians and Babylonians.

Trigonometry is often used in situations where measurements are difficult or impossible to take, such as finding the distance to a star.

e of Pyramids and Cones

...ppear when
...rd their

...re over 4000 years old. They are
...ere is enough stone in the three
...France 3.3 m high and 30 cm

...t World, the Great Pyramid of
...e that still stands. It covers five hectares,
...0.4 m square. It contains about 2.6 million
...with a mass of over two tonnes.

...er pyramids, it was built with incredible accuracy. For
...ce, it faces directly north, its base is only 17 cm out from being
a perfect square, and the stone blocks fit together so closely that a
knife blade cannot be inserted between them.

The Great Pyramid of Cheops

Pyramids

Look at the pyramid shown here. Notice that its base is a different
shape than the sides. All pyramids have triangular sides. The base can
be any polygon.

Think, Do, Discuss

1. Look at the pyramid inside the prism. Estimate how many times greater the
volume of the prism is than the volume of the pyramid.

2. Use the *Volume/Surface Area Explorer* to investigate the relationship between
the volume of a square-based prism and its corresponding pyramid. Collect data for at least
six different-sized prisms and pyramids. Each pair of figures should have the same height
and apothem. Copy and complete the table.

Dimensions	Volume of Prism	Volume of Pyramid

3. Graph the volume of the pyramids versus the volume of the prisms. If you use a graphing
calculator, enter the volumes for the prism in **L1** and the volumes for the pyramids in **L2**.
Graph the data you have collected with the volumes of the prisms on the x-axis and the
volumes of the corresponding pyramids on the y-axis.

4. Determine the equation of the line of best fit. How confident are you that the line represents this relationship accurately? What does this indicate about the relationship between the volume of a prism and its corresponding pyramid?

5. What does the slope of the line indicate?

6. Compare the slope of your line to the slope obtained by other students.

7. The volume formula for the prism is $V = Ah$, where A is the area of the base and h is the height of the prism. What is the formula for the volume of a pyramid?

8. Use the *Volume/Surface Area Explorer* to investigate the relationship between the volumes of prisms and pyramids with identical polygon bases. What happens if the height of the prism is the same as the height of the pyramid? What happens if the heights are different?

Cones

A cone is a solid figure with a circular base that gradually narrows to a point.

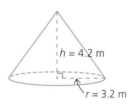

Think, Do, Discuss

1. Based on your conclusions from the section on pyramids, hypothesize a relationship between the volumes of a cylinder and a cone with equal heights and identical bases.

2. Test your hypothesis using the *Volume/Surface Area Explorer*. Record the volumes. Does your hypothesis hold true? What appears to be the relationship?

3. Write a formula for the volume of a cone.

Focus

Key Ideas

- The volumes of pyramids and prisms with equal heights and base areas are related. A pyramid with a given height, apothem, and number of sides has $\frac{1}{3}$ the volume of a prism with the same measurements.

- The formula for the volume of a pyramid is $V = \frac{1}{3}Ah$.
  A is the area of the base.
  h is the height of the pyramid.

- The volumes of cones and cylinders with equal heights and base areas are also related. A cone has $\frac{1}{3}$ the volume of a cylinder with the same radius and height.

- The formula for the volume of a cone is $V = \frac{1}{3}\pi r^2 h$.

- The vertical height of a pyramid or cone is the length of the line from the point at the top to the base.

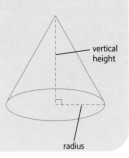

Example

As a wedding gift, John and Lisa received an oil lamp with a reservoir in the shape of a pyramid with a regular pentagonal base. The reservoir has a height of 8.1 cm and the oil comes in 750 mL bottles. How many times can they fill the lamp completely with one bottle of oil?

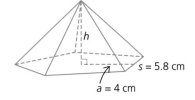

Solution

To find the area of the base, John performs these calculations:

$$A = \frac{1}{2}(\text{perimeter of base})(\text{apothem})$$

$$= \frac{1}{2}(5)(5.8)(4)$$

$$= 58$$

The area of the base is 58 cm².

$$V = \frac{1}{3}Ah$$

$$= \frac{1}{3}(58)(8.1)$$

$$\doteq 157$$

The volume is about 157 cm³.

$750 \div 157 \doteq 4.8$

Therefore, they can fill the lamp completely 4 times with one 750 mL bottle of oil.

Practise, Apply, Solve

1. Which solids are pyramids?

(a)

(b)

(c)

(d)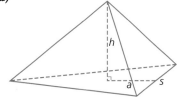

2. Calculate the volume of each solid.

(a)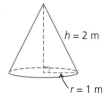

h = 2 m
r = 1 m

(b)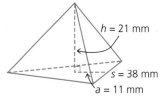

h = 21 mm
s = 38 mm
a = 11 mm

(c)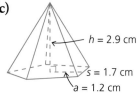

h = 2.9 cm
s = 1.7 cm
a = 1.2 cm

(d)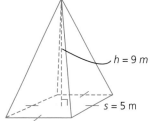

h = 9 m
s = 5 m

3. Determine the volume of water that would fill
   (a) a four-sided pyramid with apothem 4 cm and height 7.5 cm
   (b) a cone with radius 4 cm and height 7.5 cm.

4. (a) If each shape in Question 3 were filled with crushed ice, would the volumes you
        found in parts (a) and (b) still apply? Explain.
   (b) The volume of a liquid is expressed in litres. Express the volumes you determined
        in Question 3 in millilitres and litres. (Hint: 1 cm^3 = 1 mL and 1000 mL = 1 L)

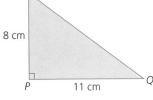

B

5. A cone can be generated by rotating a right triangle 360° about the right angle. Determine the volume of a cone formed by
   (a) rotating △PQR one full rotation about side PQ
   (b) rotating △PQR one full rotation about side PR.

6. Two pyramids have the same height and bases of the same shape. One has a volume of 27.2 cm³ and its base has an apothem of 4 cm. The base of the other has an apothem of 8 cm. What is its volume?

7. A cone-shaped paper cup has a radius of 6 cm and a height of 10 cm. Twice, the cone is filled with water and the water emptied into a cylindrical glass with a radius of 6 cm and a height of 10 cm. What percentage of the glass cylinder is filled with water?

8. A square pyramid has a volume of 100 cm³ and a base with an area of 40 cm². How high is the pyramid?

9. Sand for use on icy roads is stored in a conical pile 14.2 m high and with a base diameter of 34.4 m.
   (a) Calculate the volume of the pile.
   (b) If one sander can take 6.9 m³ of sand, how many sanders can be filled from the pile?

10. Salt is stored in a bin shaped like an inverted square-based pyramid. One side of the base is 2.8 m long. The bin is 1.8 m high. Determine the volume of salt in the bin.

11. A solid figure is said to be **truncated** when a portion of the bottom is cut and removed. The cut line must be parallel to the base. Many paper cups, such as the one shown here, are truncated cones. Calculate the volume of this paper cup.

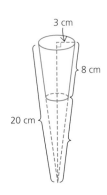

12. Here are four pyramids, each one 10 cm high and with an apothem of 4 cm. Which container holds the most? How would the volume of a cone with the same dimensions compare with these four figures?

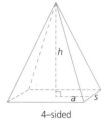  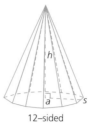 

4–sided   8–sided   12–sided   20–sided

13. What is the volume of this tent?

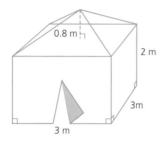

14. (a) Find an expression for the height of a cone in terms of its volume and radius.
    (b) A certain cone has a volume of 105 000 cm³ and a radius of 26 cm. How high is it?
    (c) Suppose the cone's height and radius are equal. How would the expression you wrote in part (a) change?

C

15. Create a mathematical model to show how the volume of a cone changes if its height remains constant, but its radius is allowed to vary.

16. Think about pyramids and a cone that all have the same height and equal apothems (or radius, in the case of the cone). Investigate how the difference between the volume of the cone and the volume of the pyramids change as the number of pyramid sides increase.

Did You Know?

In recent years, the record for the largest container of popcorn has been broken a number of times. At the time this book went to press, the current record holders, according to the 1998 *Guinness Book of Records*, were the students of Pittsville Elementary School, in Pittsville, Wisconsin. In 1996, they filled a container 12.2 m long by 8.5 m wide, with popcorn to a depth of 2 m.

How much popcorn is in a large bag, such as is sold at the movies? How many large bags would you need to fill the container mentioned above?

7.5 Volume of Spheres

At refineries, propane gas is stored in spherical tanks. The trucks used to transport propane store the propane in cylindrical tanks.

The Relationship Between a Sphere and a Cylinder

Earlier in this chapter, you used the relationship between a cone and a cylinder to determine the formula for the volume of a cone. You can also use the cylinder to find the formula for the volume of a sphere.

Archimedes, a famous mathematician of ancient Greece, was the first person to determine that a relationship exists between the volumes of a sphere and a cylinder.

Using a cardboard juice can and a ball of plasticene or playdough, perform this investigation.

1. Roll the dough into a perfect sphere that will just fit inside the can. Cover your playdough sphere in shrink-wrap to prevent it from getting wet.

2. Measure the diameter of the can.

3. Use scissors to cut the juice can to the same height as the diameter of the sphere. (Remember that the relationship between the cone and cylinder depended on them having the same height and radius.)

4. Place the sphere inside the can and confirm that the top of the can is at the same height as the top of the sphere. Remove the sphere. Now place the can in a bowl and fill it slowly to the top with water. Be careful not to spill any water into the bowl.

5. Very carefully, submerge the sphere completely into the can, letting the water spill out into the bowl. Remove the can and the sphere from the bowl. Remove the sphere from the can.

6. **Measurement 1:** Pour the excess water from the bowl into a measuring cup. Record the volume.

7. **Measurement 2:** Fill the can with water, then pour it into an empty measuring cup. Record the volume.

Think, Do, Discuss

1. What does measurement 2 represent?

2. What does measurement 1 represent?

3. What fraction of the water in the can was displaced by the sphere?

4. Compare your results with other students. Make a hypothesis about the relationship between the volume of a sphere and the volume of a cylinder whose diameter and height are equal to the diameter of the sphere.

5. Describe the mathematical relationship between the volume of a sphere and the volume of a cylinder with the same radius.

6. If the formula for volume of a cylinder is $V = \pi r^2 h$, write the formula for volume of a sphere with radius r.

Focus

Key Ideas

- A **sphere** is the set of points that are all the same distance, r, from a fixed point called the centre.

- The volume of a sphere is $\frac{2}{3}$ the volume of its corresponding cylinder (a cylinder with the same radius and height). For a sphere to fit exactly inside its corresponding cylinder, the diameter of the sphere must equal the height of the cylinder. This means that $d = h$ or $2r = h$.

$$\text{Volume of sphere} = \frac{2}{3} \times \text{volume of cylinder}$$

$$= \frac{2}{3}(\pi r^2 h)$$

$$= \frac{2}{3}(\pi r^2 (2r))$$

$$= \frac{2}{3}(2\pi r^3)$$

$$= \frac{4}{3}(\pi r^3)$$

- The formula for the volume of a sphere is $V = \frac{4}{3}\pi r^3$.

Example

Find the volume of the sphere to one decimal place.

diameter = 9.2 cm

Solution

Since the diameter of the sphere is 9.2 cm, the radius is 4.6 cm.

$$V = \frac{4}{3}\pi r^3$$

$$= \frac{4}{3}\pi(4.6)^3$$

$$= \frac{4}{3}\pi(97.336)$$

$$\doteq 407.7$$

The volume of the sphere to one decimal place is 407.7 cm³.

Practise, Apply, Solve

A

1. Find the volume of each sphere.

   (a)

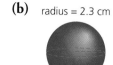

r = 32 mm

   (b) radius = 2.3 cm

   (c) diameter = 21 mm

2. A baseball has a radius of about 3.6 cm. Calculate its volume.

3. Calculate, to one decimal place, the volume of a sphere with

   (a) a radius of 1 cm

   (c) a diameter of 1.8 m

   (e) a circumference of 157.1 cm

   (b) a radius of 4.5 cm

   (d) a diameter of 14 mm

   (f) a circumference of 11.2 m.

B

4. Jim is a transportation manager for a company that produces ball bearings. He has two safety factors to consider when transporting the bearings: the volume of the box being used to hold the bearings and the weight limit of the truck transporting them. Each bearing has a diameter of 0.96 cm.

   (a) Each box can hold 8000 cm³ of ball bearings. How many ball bearings can each box hold?

   (b) Each ball bearing weighs 0.95 g. Determine the mass of each box.

   (c) What is the maximum number of boxes that can be loaded into a truck with a carrying capacity of 11 000 kg?

   (d) Besides the mass of the ball bearings, what else must be considered when loading the truck?

5. Ice cream is sold in stores in cylindrical containers. The containers are 21 cm high with a radius of 10 cm, and each scoop of ice cream is a sphere of diameter 4.2 cm.

   (a) How many scoops are in each container?

   (b) If one scoop sells for 86¢, how much money will the ice cream store make for each full cylinder of ice cream that it sells in cones?

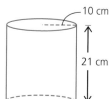

10 cm

21 cm

6. A candy company makes solid chocolate oranges. The oranges are packed in cube-shaped boxes, with all sides 7.5 cm. Each chocolate orange touches each face of the box.

   (a) What is the volume of chocolate enclosed?

   (b) What is the amount of empty space in the box?

7. The Party Team is a company that specializes in providing balloons for large parties and weddings. Each balloon is filled with helium so that it expands to a radius of 0.25 m.
   (a) How much helium is required to fill one balloon?
   (b) What is the cost to fill one balloon if helium costs $7.02/m³?

8. A toy company makes rubber balls. They currently manufacture balls with a diameter of 20 cm. How much rubber would they save if they made the balls with a diameter of 15 cm?

9. How much modelling clay will a student need to enlarge a sphere with a 10-cm diameter to create a larger sphere with a diameter of 13 cm?

10. A cube-shaped box fits exactly around a soccer ball with a diameter of 22.28 cm. What percent of the box is empty space?

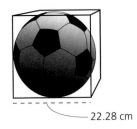

22.28 cm

11. Scott and Ashley sell single-scoop ice cream cones for $0.75 each. Their scoop makes spheres of ice cream that are 7 cm in diameter. Cones cost $0.12 each and each 4-L pail of ice cream costs $5. How much profit can they expect to make on each pail?

12. Determine the radius of a sphere with a volume of 117 cm³.

13. A hot-air balloon is about 21 m wide and 35 m high. Estimate the amount of helium needed to fill the balloon.

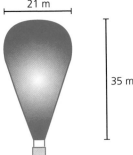

21 m

35 m

14. A farmer builds a cylindrical silo with a hemispherical top to contain wheat. The silo is 7.5 m tall from the ground to its peak and has a radius of 4 m. How much wheat can it hold? Answer to the nearest cubic metre.

7.5 m

4 m

C

15. Which has a larger volume: a sphere with radius *r* or a cube with length *2r*?

16. Suppose a balloon is in the shape of a sphere with a radius of 10 cm. What additional volume of air must be put into the balloon to expand it to twice its original size? three times its size?

17. A balloon is inflated to a radius of 10 cm. By how much will the radius increase if you add 1 L of air to the balloon?

Martin Gardner (b. 1914)

Martin Gardner spent most of his career teaching science and debunking non-science. Besides being a renowned scientist, he is also known for his mathematical abilities and his skills as a magician. He is probably best known for his math column in the magazine *Scientific American*. Here is one of his problems. Can you solve it?

Mrs. Perkins is creating a square quilt. She decides to use only squares, no two of which can be the same size, to create the quilt. The squares must have dimensions of whole centimetres. All of the squares must fit onto the quilt without any overlap or leftover space. How large will her quilt have to be before she can accomplish this, if the first square is 1 cm by 1 cm?

The solution appears in *Mathematical Carnival* (1975) by Martin Gardner, published by Alfred A. Knopf, New York.

Did You Know?

This painting by Raphael shows Plato and Aristotle in the "School of Athens." You can study the painting on the Internet in detail. Examine it for examples of symmetry, geometry, and ratios. How does the artist make a two-dimensional surface seem three dimensional?

In geometry, there are five solids called **Platonic solids**: the cube, the regular tetrahedron, the regular octahedron, the regular dodecahedron, and the regular icosahedron. They are named after the Greek scholar Plato (427–347 BCE). Each face of the solid is a regular polygon and all the polygons are congruent. Which regular polygon makes up each Platonic solid?

7.6 Surface Area of Prisms and Cylinders

One of the biggest challenges in our society is to reduce the amount of waste produced. We are running out of space for garbage disposal. So, there is a stronger focus today on recycling and reusing material and, especially, avoiding unnecessary over-packaging of consumer products.

Some companies have modified their packaging to reduce the amount of material used to package a product. There is also another incentive for packagers to use less material — it decreases the cost of packaging.

Product packagers need to consider how much material is needed for each packaging option. To figure this out, they need to know the **surface area** of each shape that could be used to package their product.

A **net** is a two-dimensional drawing of what a three-dimensional solid would look like if it were taken apart and laid out flat. The sum of the areas of each part of the net is the surface area. Here is an example of a 3-D triangular prism and its net.

Triangular Prism

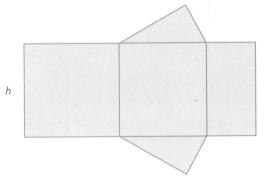

Net of Triangular Prism

Prisms

Sketch the net of a square-based prism in your notebook. Mark the dimensions on your drawing and explain how to find the total area with the least amount of computation.

Think, Do, Discuss

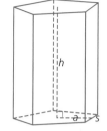

1. Draw the net of this regular prism and cut it out. Remove the pieces that correspond to the top and bottom. Describe a quick way to calculate the area of all the lateral faces.

2. Write a word equation to represent your description of how to find the total surface area of the prism.

3. Write a description of how to use this method to find the surface area of any prism with a regular polygon base.

Cylinders

There are many cylindrical objects around us. Paper towels, wrapping paper, and many other items come on tube-shaped cardboard with open ends. Juice cans are often metal or cardboard cylinders with metal tops and bottoms. How much material is used to make these cylinders?

Think, Do, Discuss

1. Find a cylindrical food container such as a coffee can, soup can, or pop can.

2. Measure and record the diameter and height of the cylinder. Calculate and record the radius.

3. Imagine that you cut out the top and bottom of the cylinder with a can opener. Then you cut the remaining portion along a vertical seam and pressed it flat. Draw the resulting net for this cylinder and label the dimensions.

4. Use the net to determine the surface area of the cylinder.

5. Write a formula for the surface area of a cylinder using the radius and height. Use h for the height of the cylinder and r for the radius.

Focus

Key Ideas

- A **net** is a two-dimensional picture of the surface of a three-dimensional solid.

- The **surface area** of any prism or cylinder is the sum of the areas of all the faces.

- In a prism or a cylinder, the surface area of the lateral faces is the product of the perimeter of the base and the height of the object.

- The surface area of a prism or a cylinder is twice the area of the base plus the area of the lateral faces.

- The formula for the surface area of a prism is $SA = 2(\text{area of base}) + (\text{perimeter of base} \times h)$.

- The formula for the surface area of a cylinder is $SA = 2\pi r^2 + 2\pi rh$.

Example

Calculate the surface area of this prism.

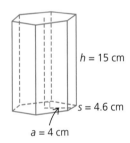

$h = 15$ cm
$s = 4.6$ cm
$a = 4$ cm

Solution

Draw the net and label each dimension.

$$SA = 2(\text{area of base}) + (\text{perimeter of base} \times h)$$
$$= 2\left[6\left(\tfrac{1}{2} \times 4 \times 4.6\right)\right] + [6(4.6)(15)]$$
$$= 2(55.2) + 414$$
$$= 110.4 + 414$$
$$= 524.4$$

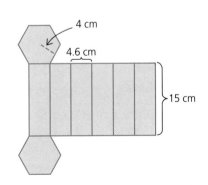

4 cm
4.6 cm
15 cm

The surface area of the hexagonal prism is 524.4 cm².

Did You Know?

A kite is an object that is flown in the air at the end of a line. The name comes from a graceful, soaring bird called a kite. Most kites are made from paper or cloth mounted on a frame made of sticks. There are hundreds of types of kites. The most basic types include flat kites, bowed kites, box kites, delta kites, and flexible kites.

The box kite was invented by Lawrence Hargrave of Australia in 1893. What three-dimensional shape does the box kite represent? What would the frame or skeleton look like?

Practise, Apply, Solve

A

1. Draw and label the nets of each figure.

(a)

$h = 32$ cm
$a = 10$ cm
$s = 20$ cm

(b)
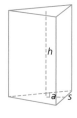
$h = 34$ mm
$a = 8$ mm
$s = 28$ mm

(c)

$h = 4.2$ m
$r = 0.9$ m

2. Calculate the surface area of each figure.

(a)
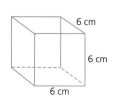
6 cm
6 cm
6 cm

(b)
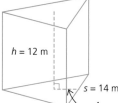
$h = 12$ m
$s = 14$ m
$a = 4$ m

(c)

$r = 12$ mm
$h = 29$ mm

3. A can of soup is 10.3 cm high and its diameter is 6.7 cm. How much paper is needed to make the label?

4. A can of peaches is 12.5 cm high and its diameter is 8 cm. Calculate the area of the label.

5. A wedge of cheese is in the shape of a triangular prism. It is 6 cm high and each triangular face has a side length of 10 cm and an apothem of 2.9 cm.
  (a) How much plastic wrap is needed to cover the cheese?
  (b) The plastic wrap costs $0.0005/cm². What is the cost to package the cheese?

B

6. Three golf balls are packaged in a box. If one ball has a radius of 2.1 cm, how much material is needed to make the box?

7. Acme Toothpick Company sells toothpicks in boxes and in cylindrical containers. Each box is 7.8 cm by 2.9 cm by 6.1 cm and each cylinder is 6.1 cm high and 2.7 cm in diameter. Which package uses less material?

8. Draw two cylinders with the same radius. Draw one cylinder so that its height is twice the height of the other.
(a) Determine the relationship between the surface areas of the two cylinders.
(b) Check your answer by finding the surface area of some sample packaging cylinders.

9. Find the surface area of each rectangular prism.

(a)
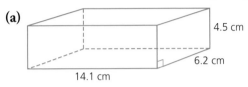
4.5 cm
6.2 cm
14.1 cm

(b)
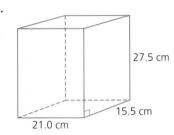
27.5 cm
15.5 cm
21.0 cm

(c)
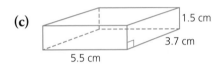
1.5 cm
3.7 cm
5.5 cm

(d)
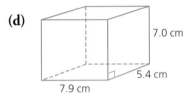
7.0 cm
5.4 cm
7.9 cm

10. (a) How much soup would fit into a can with a height of 14.5 cm and a diameter of 9 cm?
(b) How much paper would be needed to make the label?
(c) How much metal would be needed to make the can?

11. Determine the surface area for each prism. The base of each prism is a regular polygon.

(a)
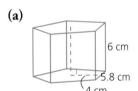
6 cm
5.8 cm
4 cm

(b)
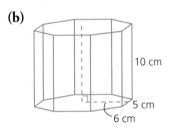
10 cm
5 cm
6 cm

(c)
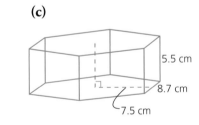
5.5 cm
8.7 cm
7.5 cm

(d)
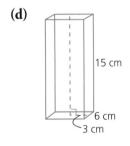
15 cm
6 cm
3 cm

(e)
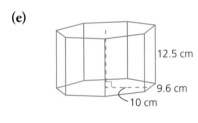
12.5 cm
9.6 cm
10 cm

C

12. A candy company wants to create a package that uses the least amount of packaging. The candy must be contained in a prism-shaped container with a height of 15 cm and an apothem of 3 cm. What shape should the base be to ensure that the least amount of material is used for the package?

13. A box with a square base must have a volume of 200 cm³. Find the dimensions of the box that minimizes the amount of material used.

14. What is the largest box that a sheet of wrapping paper 75 cm by 100 cm can cover?

15. Construct the net for any rectangular prism. Compute the surface area and the volume. Investigate the relationship between the surface area and the volume as the size of the prism is doubled, tripled, and so on.

The Chapter Problem — What Is the Profit?

Refer to the Chapter Problem at the beginning of the chapter.

1. Find the cost to package each candle in paper by calculating the surface area of each shape of candle.
2. Use the cost of the waxes and your cost answers from Question 1 to determine John's profit on each candle shape. Consider two cases: first, if John uses paraffin to make the candles; second, if he uses beeswax.

Career: Gemologist

As a gemologist, you would learn that all crystals have some form of symmetry or balanced arrangement of faces.

When crystals are cut to form gems, they usually break along some particular direction or plane to produce a flat surface. The way a crystal can be cut depends on how the atoms in the crystal are arranged.

Look for congruent triangles in the cut diamond. How many types can you find?

7.7 Surface Area of Pyramids and Cones

The Surface Area of a Pyramid

These are examples of different shapes of pyramids.

slant height (*l*)

height (*h*)

apothem (*a*)

To build your own pyramid, first draw an isosceles triangle. Measure its base and height.

Cut out the triangle and trace it four more times.

Cut out these triangles.

Draw a square base for the pyramid. The length of one side is the length of the base of one triangle. Tape enough pieces together to build your pyramid.

Think, Do, Discuss

1. Determine the area of the base of your pyramid.
2. Determine the surface area of your pyramid.
3. Why is the slant height of each triangular face not the same as the height of the pyramid? Write a description of how to use the measurements you have to calculate the height of the pyramid.
4. Using the same isosceles triangle for the sides, build a pyramid with a regular hexagon as its base. Find the surface area of this new pyramid.
5. Write a formula to express the surface area of a pyramid with a regular polygon base, in terms of the area of the base, the perimeter of the base, and the slant of the triangular faces.

Did You Know?

The Maya culture flourished in Mexico about a thousand years ago. The Maya were expert astronomers and mathematicians. As this photograph shows, they were also great architects. The photograph shows the large pyramid at Chichen Itza near Cancun.

When the Spaniards saw this pyramid for the first time, they thought that such an important structure must be connected with the king, so they called it "*el castillo*" (the castle). In fact, the pyramid is simply a very large calendar. It has 91 steps on each side and one step at the top, for a total of 365 steps, one for each day of the year.

Do some research, either in the library or on the Internet. Find out more about the Maya and their culture. Why did they build such a large pyramid? What is underneath it?

The Surface Area of a Cone

To create a cone, draw a circle and cut out a sector between 45° and 90°. Roll the larger piece into a cone shape and tape along the seams.

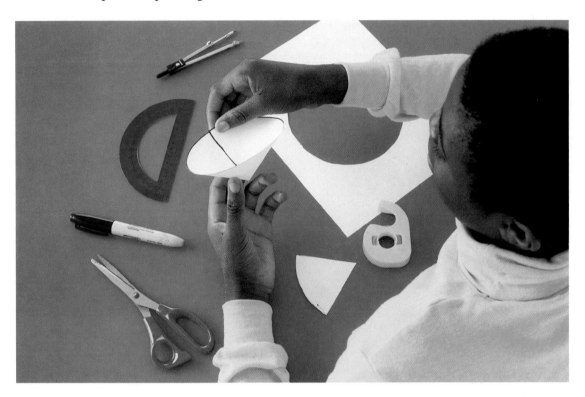

Think, Do, Discuss

1. Trace the base of the cone on another piece of paper and measure the radius, diameter, and circumference of the base.

2. The surface area of a pyramid is the sum of the area of the base and the area of all sides. The area of all the sides can be calculated by finding the product of the perimeter of the base and the slant height of the pyramid and dividing by 2. Can you use this method for a cone? Explain.

3. The general formula for the surface area of a pyramid is $SA = $ area of base $ + \frac{Pl}{2}$, where P is the perimeter of the base and l is the slant height. What shape is the base of the cone? What expression could replace "area of base" in this expression?

4. Write a formula to calculate the perimeter of the base of a cone.

5. Create a general formula to calculate the surface area of a cone.

6. Explain how you can use the radius and height of a cone to calculate the slant height of the cone.

Focus

Example

Calculate the surface area of this cone.

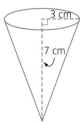

Solution

$$SA = \pi r^2 + \pi r l$$
$$= \pi(3)^2 + \pi(3)l$$

To find l, use the Pythagorean theorem:

$$l = \sqrt{h^2 + r^2}$$
$$= \sqrt{7^2 + 3^2}$$
$$= \sqrt{58}$$
$$\doteq 7.62$$

The slant height of the cone is about 7.62 cm.

$$SA = \pi(3)^2 + \pi(3)(7.62)$$
$$= 9\pi + 22.86\pi$$
$$= 31.86\pi$$
$$\doteq 100.1$$

The surface area is about 100.1 cm².

Practise, Apply, Solve

A

1. Sketch the net for each solid. The base of each pyramid is a regular polygon.

(a)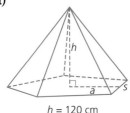

h = 120 cm
a = 7.8 cm
s = 11.3 cm

(b)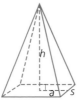

h = 12 m
a = 4 m
s = 8 m

(c)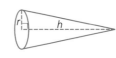

r = 4.1 cm
h = 20.2 cm

2. Calculate the slant height for each cone, where r is the radius and h is the vertical height.
   (a) $r = 6$ cm and $h = 8$ cm   (b) $r = 5$ cm and $h = 12$ cm
   (c) $r = 4.5$ cm and $h = 10$ cm   (d) $r = 21.2$ mm and $h = 24.5$ mm

3. Calculate the surface area of each cone in Question 2.

4. Calculate the surface area of each solid. The base of each pyramid is a regular polygon.

(a)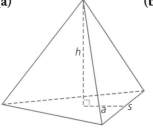

h = 10 cm
a = 4 cm
s = 13.9 cm

(b)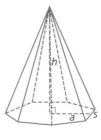

h = 10 cm
a = 4 cm
s = 3.9 cm

(c)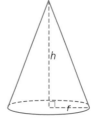

h = 10 cm
r = 4 cm

B

5. Some paper cups are shaped like cones.
   (a) What is the capacity of the paper cup shown here?
   (b) How much paper is needed to make the cup?

height = 12 cm
diameter = 9 cm

6. There are two sizes of containers for buying popcorn at the Fall Fair. Which one uses less material?

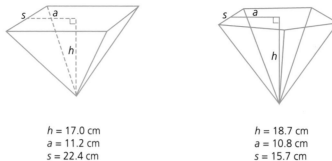

$h = 17.0$ cm
$a = 11.2$ cm
$s = 22.4$ cm

$h = 18.7$ cm
$a = 10.8$ cm
$s = 15.7$ cm

7. Janice and Wilson have bought a new house. They decide to paint the exterior of the house, including the door, and re-shingle the roof. One 4-L can of paint covers 35 m². One bundle of shingles covers 2.25 m².

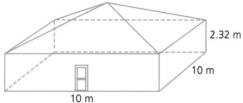

2.32 m

10 m

10 m

height from ground to peak = 4.32 m

(a) How many bundles of shingles do they need for the roof? (Hint: Find the slant height of the roof first.)

(b) How many cans of paint do they need?

(c) One can of paint is $29.95 and one bundle of shingles is $35.99. Find the total cost of the job. Include PST and GST in your answer.

8. Manufacturers often want to package their products in beautiful boxes, but still minimize the amount of material they use. Jim and Susan are designing a number of packaging options for their newest client, Scarves Are Us.

Scarves Are Us wants to package an expensive silk scarf in a box that could sit on a dresser and open to display the scarf. The box is to be made of silver cardboard with a hinged lid. Which box uses the least material?

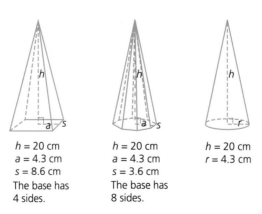

$h = 20$ cm
$a = 4.3$ cm
$s = 8.6$ cm
The base has
4 sides.

$h = 20$ cm
$a = 4.3$ cm
$s = 3.6$ cm
The base has
8 sides.

$h = 20$ cm
$r = 4.3$ cm

9. The Great Pyramid of Cheops was originally 147 m high, with a square base of side length measuring 230.4 m.
   (a) Calculate the surface area of the Great Pyramid, including the area of the base.
   (b) The outside surface of each block in the Great Pyramid is 2.3 m by 1.8 m. Determine the approximate number of blocks that make up the outside facing of the Great Pyramid.

The Sphinx and the Great Pyramid

10. Determine the surface area of each cone.

(a)

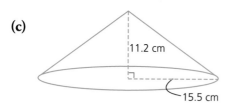

6 cm

8 cm

(b)

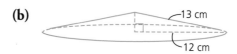

13 cm

12 cm

(c)

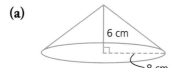

11.2 cm

15.5 cm

11. Determine the surface area of each pyramid.

(a)

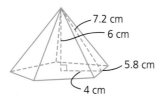

7.2 cm
6 cm
5.8 cm
4 cm

(b)

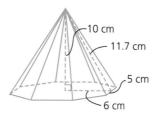

10 cm
11.7 cm
5 cm
6 cm

(c)

5.5 cm
9.3 cm
8.7 cm
7.5 cm

(d)

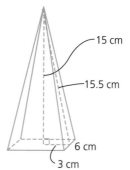

15 cm
15.5 cm
6 cm
3 cm

(e)

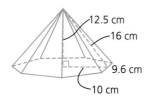

12.5 cm
16 cm
9.6 cm
10 cm

C

12. Estimate the surface area of this bottle of bleach.

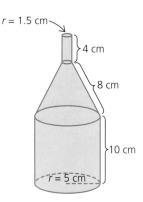

r = 1.5 cm

4 cm

8 cm

10 cm

r = 5 cm

13. A cone and a pentagonal pyramid are each 35 cm high. The cone has a radius of 13 cm and the pyramid has an apothem of 13 cm.
(a) Which object has the greater surface area?
(b) If the side length of the pyramid base is 18.9 cm, calculate the volume of each object.

The Chapter Problem — What Is the Profit?

Refer to the Chapter Problem at the beginning of the chapter.

1. John is investigating the production of candles in the shapes of pyramids and cones. Calculate his manufacturing and packaging costs for both types of candles, using both paraffin and beeswax.
2. Can he make a profit on any of these candles?

Career: Painting or Drafting

"… deal with nature by means of the cylinder, the sphere, and the cone, all placed in perspective, so that each side of an object or plane is directed toward a central point…. Lines perpendicular to the horizon give depth." Paul Cézanne (1839–1906)

Cézanne used these guidelines in his paintings, but they also apply to technical diagrams. Without perspective and a sense of depth, it would be impossible to show how to build such complicated objects as airplanes, boats, or buildings. The ability to read and create two-dimensional models of three-dimensional objects is an especially important skill for anyone involved in the fields of drafting and architecture. Spatial skills can develop the ability to visualize real objects from their plans.

Obtain copies of the plans for a building, a machine, or an invention. Analyze your plans and write an explanation of what all plans must have in common to clearly communicate the design to a builder or an engineer. How could you present your analysis to others?

Surface Area of a Sphere

Spheres occur everywhere around us — from oranges and grapefruit to baseballs and snowballs. The Earth is roughly spherical in shape, with a surface area of about 510 050 100 km^2. The diameter of the Earth can be estimated using the formula for the surface area of a sphere.

Think, Do, Discuss

1. Using an orange that is as close as possible to the shape of a sphere, estimate the surface area of the orange in square centimetres. Do not peel the orange. Write a description of the method you used.

2. Find the diameter of the orange.

3. Draw five circles on a piece of paper, each with the same diameter as the orange.

4. Peel the orange. Use the peelings, in a single layer, to cover one of the circles. When you have covered one circle completely and accurately, move on to another.

5. Record the number of circles that were covered by the peels from your orange. Compare your results with the results from other students in your class.

6. Suggest a formula that describes the relationship between the surface area of a sphere and the area of a circle with the same radius.

7. Use the *Volume/Surface Area Explorer* to create several spheres with radii of different lengths. Use these spheres to test your hypothesis.

Focus

Key Ideas

- The surface area of a sphere is related to the area of its cross-section at the equator.
- The cross-section of a sphere is a circle.
- The surface area of a sphere is four times the area of its cross-section at the equator.
- The formula for the surface area of the sphere is $SA = 4\pi r^2$.

Example

Find the surface area of this sphere.

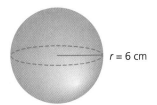

$r = 6$ cm

Solution

$$SA = 4\pi r^2$$
$$= 4\pi(6)^2$$
$$= 4\pi(36)$$
$$= 144\pi$$
$$\doteq 144(3.14)$$
$$\doteq 452.2$$

The surface area of the sphere is about 452.2 cm².

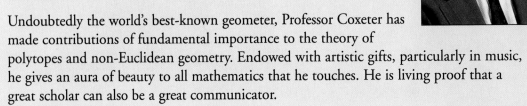

H.S.M. (Donald) Coxeter

Donald Coxeter was born and educated in England, but his professional connections with North America began early. In 1936, a few years after finishing his doctoral studies at Cambridge University, he joined the Faculty of the University of Toronto. Although he has taught as a visitor at centres around the world, he has remained there ever since.

Undoubtedly the world's best-known geometer, Professor Coxeter has made contributions of fundamental importance to the theory of polytopes and non-Euclidean geometry. Endowed with artistic gifts, particularly in music, he gives an aura of beauty to all mathematics that he touches. He is living proof that a great scholar can also be a great communicator.

Practise, Apply, Solve

1. Find the surface area of each sphere.

(a)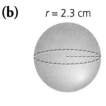
r = 32 mm

(b) r = 2.3 cm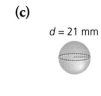

(c) d = 21 mm

2. Find the surface area of the sphere with each radius or diameter. Answer to two decimal places.

(a) $r = 12$ mm (b) $r = 3.5$ cm (c) $d = 16$ cm (d) $d = 7.8$ mm

3. (a) The circumference of the Earth is about 40 000 km. Based on this estimate, what is the surface area of the Earth? Answer to the nearest square kilometre.
(b) The Earth's surface area is about 510 050 100 km². Based on this estimate, what is the approximate radius of the Earth? Answer to the nearest kilometre.
(c) Do some research to determine which of the above estimates is more accurate.

4. A spherical gas storage tank has a diameter of 30 m. The paint needed to cover the exterior of the tank costs $30 per can and each can covers 100 m². Determine the number of cans of paint and the cost to paint the tank with one coat.

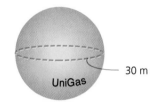
30 m

5. A baseball has an inner core covered with string. What is the surface area of the leather sewn on the outside of the ball if the circumference of the ball is between 23 and 23.5 cm?

6. A school supply company coats its cardboard globes with lacquer. Each globe has a circumference of 93 cm. One litre of lacquer covers 12 m². How many globes can be painted with 1 L of lacquer?

7. A golf ball has a diameter of 4.2 cm. Use the formula for the surface area of a sphere to find the surface area of a golf ball.

8. A ball bearing has a volume of 6.75 cm³. Determine its surface area.

9. Determine the radius of a sphere with each surface area. Answer to two decimal places.
(a) 320 cm² (b) 100 mm² (c) 314 m² (d) 1255 mm²

10. Find an expression for the radius of a sphere given its surface area.

C

11. Which has a larger surface area: a sphere with radius *r* or a cube with height, length, and width 2*r*?

12. In a previous section, you investigated the relationship between the volume of a sphere and the volume of the cylinder that exactly contained it. Conduct a similar investigation to determine the relationship between the surface areas of these two objects. Use the *Volume/Surface Area Explorer* to confirm your hypothesis.

13. SkyDome, in Toronto, is unique among domed stadiums around the world. It has a retractable roof. Engineers designed a system that allows the massive roof structure to open and close in about 20 min. The roof itself is a hemispherical shape made of a PVC shell and a metal alloy frame. The base of the stadium is made of steel and poured concrete.

    (a) Do some research to determine the dimensions of the stadium.
    (b) Determine the surface area of the roof.
    (c) Determine the volume inside the stadium with the roof closed.
    (d) SkyDome is home to the Blue Jays, Toronto's major league baseball team. If the roof were closed, how many baseballs would be needed to fill the stadium completely?

Gaspard Monge (1746–1818)

Gaspard Monge was born in Beaune, France. He was educated at the college of the Oratorians in Lyons where, at the age of sixteen, he became an instructor in physics. For entrance into military school as a draftsman, he constructed a large-scale map of his hometown. When asked to work out the gun emplacements of a proposed fortress, he solved the problem with a speedy geometric solution.

He cleverly represented three-dimensional objects by appropriate projections on the two-dimensional plane. This method was later taught as descriptive geometry.

Besides establishing the École Polytechnique in 1795, Monge is also known for his work with geometric solids. In 1809, he proved that the lines joining the midpoints of opposite edges of a tetrahedron intersect at the centre point or centroid of the tetrahedron.

Chapter Review

7.1 Area of Regular Polygons

- Two-dimensional shapes made from a combination of several different shapes are called **composite figures**.
- The area of a composite figure can be found by adding or subtracting the areas of each individual shape as required.
- The **apothem** of a regular polygon is the perpendicular distance from the centre of the polygon to each side.
- All regular polygons can be divided into isosceles triangles by drawing lines to connect the centre of the figure to each vertex of the polygon.
- The number of sides of a regular polygon determines the number of inscribed triangles in the polygon and the type of quadrilateral into which the polygon can be rearranged.
  - If the polygon has an even number of sides, the inscribed triangles can be rearranged to form a parallelogram with an area equal to the area of the polygon.
  - If the polygon has an odd number of sides, the inscribed triangles can be rearranged to form a trapezoid with an area equal to the area of the polygon.
- The formula for the perimeter, P, of a regular polygon is nl, where n is the number of sides and l is the length of one side.
- The general formula for the area, A, of any n-sided regular polygon is $A = \dfrac{Pa}{2}$, where P is the perimeter of the polygon and a is the apothem.
- Here is a summary of polygons with up to ten sides.

Number of Sides, n	Polygon	Diagram	Number of Sides, n	Polygon	Diagram
3	triangle		7	heptagon	
4	quadrilateral		8	octagon	
5	pentagon		9	nonagon	
6	hexagon		10	decagon	

Example

Calculate the area of this figure.

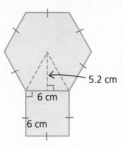

5.2 cm

6 cm

6 cm

Solution

Area of hexagon $= \dfrac{Pa}{2}$

$$= \dfrac{(6 \times 6)5.2}{2}$$

$$= 93.6 \text{ cm}^2$$

Area of square $= s \times s$

$$= 6 \times 6$$

$$= 36 \text{ cm}^2$$

Total area $=$ area of hexagon $+$ area of square

$$= 93.6 + 36$$

$$= 129.6$$

The area of the figure is 129.6 cm².

Extra Practice

1. The apothem and side of a regular hexagon measure 4 cm and 4.62 cm, respectively. What are the dimensions of a square with the same area as the hexagon?

2. Calculate the area of the shaded region.

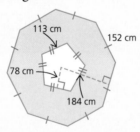

113 cm

152 cm

78 cm

184 cm

3. Joe and Bonnie are renovating their kitchen and have decided to use tiles on their countertop, which is 83 cm by 203 cm. The tiles are octagonal and square in a pattern where four octagons surround one square. The square tiles are 3 cm along one side.
   (a) Estimate the number of tiles they will need to cover the countertop.
   (b) Each square tile costs $0.55 and each octagonal tile costs $0.78. Estimate the cost of the tiles to cover the countertop.

7.2 Volume of Regular Polygonal Prisms and Cylinders

- A **prism** is a three-dimensional solid with two polygon-shaped faces (the base and the top) that are parallel and identical. The remaining sides, called lateral faces, are rectangular.
- The formula for finding the volume, V, of any regular prism is V = area of base × height.
- A **cylinder** is a three-dimensional solid with two circular faces that are parallel and identical.
- The formula for finding the volume, V, of any cylinder is V = area of base × height.
  A formula that is often used is $V = \pi r^2 h$.
  r is the radius of the base.
  πr^2 is the area of the base.
  h is the height of the cylinder.
- The volume formulas in this section apply only to three-dimensional shapes in which the area of cross-section is the same over the entire height. The **cross-section** is the two-dimensional shape produced when a plane cut is made through a solid, parallel to the base.

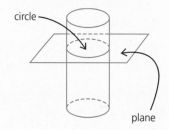

circle

plane

Example

Determine the volume of an oil drum that is 1.2 m high and has a diameter of 0.9 m.

Solution

$$r = \tfrac{1}{2}\,(\text{diameter})$$
$$= \tfrac{1}{2}(0.9)$$
$$= 0.45$$
$$V = \pi r^2 h$$
$$V = \pi(0.45)^2(1.2)$$
$$= 0.243\pi$$
$$\doteq 0.76 \text{ m}^3$$

The volume of the oil drum is about 0.76 m³.

Extra Practice

4. Some liquid products come in cylindrical cans of various dimensions. If a can holds 1 L of liquid, and its height must be equal to its radius, what are its dimensions?

5. How much water is needed to fill this hot tub?

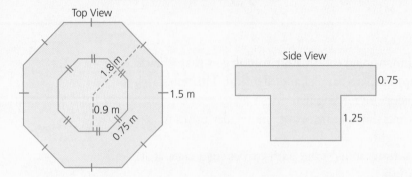

Top View

1.8 m

1.5 m

0.9 m

0.75 m

Side View

0.75

1.25

6. Elizabeth designed several new planter boxes. Her customers need to know how much topsoil to place in each planter. Calculate the amount of topsoil needed for each planter.

Planter 1: rectangular prism: 30 cm × 14 cm × 58 cm
Planter 2: pentagonal prism: apothem 26 cm, side length 38 cm, height 58 cm
Planter 3: cylinder: radius 31 cm, height 64 cm

7. An object is submerged in a rectangular container of water. This causes the water level to rise by 3 cm. The base of the container is 25 cm by 40 cm. Find the volume of the object.

7.3–7.4 Volume of Pyramids and Cones

- The volumes of pyramids and prisms with equal heights and base areas are related. A pyramid with a given height, apothem, and number of sides has $\frac{1}{3}$ the volume of a prism with the same measurements.

- The formula for the volume of a pyramid is $V = \frac{1}{3}Ah$.
  A is the area of the base.
  h is the height of the pyramid.

- The volumes of cones and cylinders with equal heights and base areas are also related. A cone has $\frac{1}{3}$ the volume of a cylinder with the same radius and height.

- The formula for the volume of a cone is $V = \frac{1}{3}\pi r^2 h$.

- The vertical height of a pyramid or cone is the shortest length of the line from the point at the top to the base.

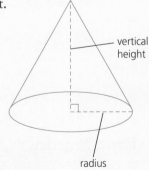

vertical height

radius

Example

Determine the volume of the cone.

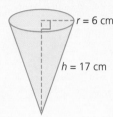

$r = 6$ cm

$h = 17$ cm

Solution

$$V = \frac{1}{3}\pi r^2 h$$

$$= \frac{1}{3}\pi(6)^2(17)$$

$$= 204\pi$$

$$\doteq 641$$

The volume is about 641 cm³.

Extra Practice

8. Calculate the volume of each figure. The base of each figure is a regular polygon.

(a)

$h = 9.9$ m
$a = 5.4$ m
$s = 7.8$ m

(b)

$r = 6.2$ cm
$h = 5.9$ cm

(c)

$h = 10.9$ mm
$a = 3.4$ mm
$s = 11.8$ mm

9. Given the height of each cone and its volume, calculate the radius of its base.

(a) $V = 141.6$ cm³, $h = 3.2$ cm
(b) $V = 528$ mm³, $h = 56$ mm
(c) $V = 2.1$ cm³, $h = 3.2$ cm

7.5 Volume of a Sphere

• A **sphere** is the set of points that are all the same distance, r, from a fixed point called the centre.

r

centre

• The volume of a sphere is $\frac{2}{3}$ the volume of its corresponding cylinder (a cylinder with the same radius and height). For a sphere to fit exactly inside its corresponding cylinder, the diameter of the sphere must equal the height of the cylinder. This means that $d = h$ or $2r = h$.

$$\text{Volume of sphere} = \frac{2}{3} \times \text{volume of cylinder}$$
$$= \frac{2}{3}(\pi r^2 h)$$
$$= \frac{2}{3}(\pi r^2 (2r))$$
$$= \frac{2}{3}(2\pi r^3)$$
$$= \frac{4}{3}(\pi r^3)$$

- The formula for the volume of a sphere is $V = \frac{4}{3}\pi r^3$.

Example

The radius of the Earth is about 6371 km.
Calculate its volume.

Solution

$$V = \frac{4}{3}\pi r^3$$
$$= \frac{4}{3}\pi(6371)^3$$
$$= \frac{1\ 034\ 386\ 411\ 000}{3}\pi$$
$$\doteq 1\ 083\ 206\ 917\ 000$$
$$\doteq 1.083 \times 10^{12}$$

The volume of the Earth is about
1.083×10^{12} km^3.

Extra Practice

10. Calculate the volume of each sphere.

(a)

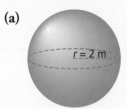

$r = 2$ m

(b)

$d = 3$ m

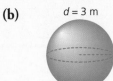

(c)

$r = 110$ cm

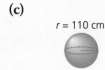

11. What impact does doubling the radius have on the volume of a sphere?

7.6 Surface Area of Prisms and Cylinders

- A **net** is a two-dimensional picture of the surface of a
  three-dimensional solid.

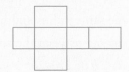

- The **surface area** of any prism or cylinder is the sum of the areas of all the faces.
- In a prism or a cylinder, the surface area of the lateral faces is the product of the perimeter of the base and the height of the object.
- The surface area of a prism or a cylinder is twice the area of the base plus the area of the lateral faces.
- The formula for the surface area of a prism is $SA = 2(\text{area of base}) + (\text{perimeter of base} \times h)$.
- The formula for the surface area of a cylinder is $SA = 2\pi r^2 + 2\pi rh$.

Example

Determine the surface area of this juice can.

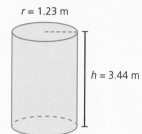

Solution

$$SA = 2\pi r^2 + 2\pi rh$$
$$= 2\pi(1.23)^2 + 2\pi(1.23)(3.44)$$
$$= 3.0258\pi + 8.4624\pi$$
$$= 11.4882\pi$$
$$\doteq 36.1$$

The surface area of the cylinder is about 36.1 m².

Extra Practice

12. The exterior of a cylindrical oil storage tank is to be painted white. The diameter of the tank is 15 m and the height is 20 m.
  (a) Calculate the surface area of the tank.
  (b) Six storage tanks are to be painted. How many litres of paint are needed, if 1 L covers 6.5 m²? Only the tops and sides of the tanks are to be painted.

7.7 Surface Area of Pyramids and Cones

- A **right pyramid** is a three-dimensional figure with a regular polygon as its base and lateral faces that are identical isosceles triangles meeting at a point.
- A **right cone** is a three-dimensional figure with a circular base and a curved surface that gradually narrows to a point that is directly above the centre of the circular base.
- The surface area of a pyramid or cone is the area of the base plus half the perimeter of the base times the slant height.
  - For a pyramid, this formula can be expressed as
  $SA = \frac{Pa}{2} + \frac{Pl}{2}$.

a is the apothem of the base.

P is the perimeter of the base, and *l* is the slant height of the pyramid.

- For a cone, this formula can be expressed as

  $SA = \pi r^2 + \pi r l.$

  r is the radius.

  l is the slant height of the cone.

- To find the slant height of a cone, use the Pythagorean theorem: $l = \sqrt{h^2 + r^2}$.

Example

Determine the surface area of this cone.

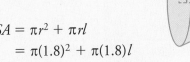

$r = 1.8$ cm

$h = 4.2$ cm

Solution

$$SA = \pi r^2 + \pi r l$$
$$= \pi(1.8)^2 + \pi(1.8)l$$

To determine the slant height, use the Pythagorean theorem.

$$l = \sqrt{(4.2)^2 + (1.8)^2}$$
$$= \sqrt{20.88}$$
$$\doteq 4.57$$

$$SA \doteq \pi(1.8)^2 + \pi(1.8)(4.57)$$
$$\doteq 11.47\pi$$
$$\doteq 36.03$$

The surface area is about 36.03 cm².

Extra Practice

13. When opened, a conical patio umbrella has a slant height of 1.5 m and a radius of 2.1 m. How much fabric was used in its construction?

14. A square-based tent in the shape of a rectangular pyramid over a rectangular prism covers a ground area of 4.9 m². It stands 1.5 m high around the perimeter of the tent and 2.5 m in the middle. Calculate the amount of canvas that was used to make the tent.

7.8 Surface Area of a Sphere

- The surface area of a sphere is related to the area of its cross-section at the equator.
- The cross-section of a sphere is a circle.
- The surface area of a sphere is four times the area of its cross-section at the equator.
- The formula for the surface area of the sphere is $SA = 4\pi r^2$.

Example

Determine the surface area of a balloon with a radius of 4.5 cm.

Solution

$$SA = 4\pi r^2$$
$$= 4\pi(4.5)^2$$
$$= 81\pi$$
$$\doteq 254$$

The surface area is about 254 cm².

Extra Practice

15. Mark McGwire's record-breaking home run baseball was placed in a spherical protective plastic case. The volume of the baseball is 226 cm³. How much plastic was needed to build the spherical case for the ball if a 3-cm clearance around the ball was required?

16. A spherical balloon is blown up from a radius of 8 cm to one of 24 cm. What is the change in its surface area?

17. A store sells two chocolate baseballs for the same price. One is a hollow sphere 10 cm in diameter on the outside, with a shell that is 1 cm thick. The other is a solid sphere with a diameter of 8 cm. Which sphere contains more chocolate?

Chapter Summary

In this chapter, you developed and applied formulas to determine the surface area and volume of a variety of 3-d shapes. Surface area is a measure of the outside surface of a three-dimensional shape. Surface area is always determined by finding the total area of all of the two-dimensional faces of the shape. Volume or capacity is a measure of the amount of space a three-dimensional figure occupies. For any prism or cylinder, the volume is determined by Volume = Area of the Base × Height. For any pyramid or cone, Volume = $\frac{\text{Area of the Base} \times \text{Height}}{3}$. A sphere's volume and surface area can be determined by using the formulas $V = \frac{4}{3}\pi r^3$ and $SA = 4\pi r^2$.

1. Find the area of each regular polygon.

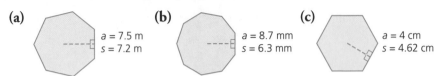

(a) $a = 7.5$ m, $s = 7.2$ m

(b) $a = 8.7$ mm, $s = 6.3$ mm

(c) $a = 4$ cm, $s = 4.62$ cm

2. Find the volume of each figure. The base of each figure is a regular polygon.

(a) $h = 7.9$ cm, $s = 9.2$ cm

(b) $h = 8.4$ cm, $s = 5$ cm, $a = 2.5$ cm

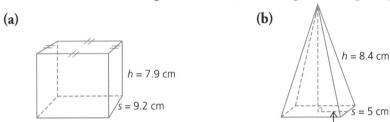

3. Find the surface area of each pyramid. The base of each pyramid is a regular polygon.

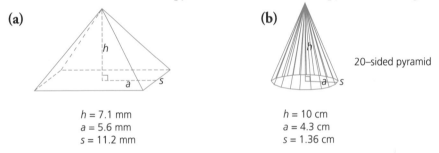

(a) $h = 7.1$ mm, $a = 5.6$ mm, $s = 11.2$ mm

(b) 20–sided pyramid, $h = 10$ cm, $a = 4.3$ cm, $s = 1.36$ cm

4. (a) How much helium is required to fill a spherical balloon so that its surface area is 900 cm²?
   (b) Helium costs $0.024/L and one balloon costs $0.07. What would 500 helium-filled balloons cost?

5. Animals produce heat in direct proportion to their body size. They lose heat in direct proportion to their surface area. Imagine that a polar bear lying stretched out is similar to a cylinder. Suppose it has a diameter of about 0.85 m and a length of 3.2 m. Calculate the surface area and the volume of the polar bear.

6. Popcorn is sold either in a cylindrical cup or cone. Each has the same round opening and the same height. The popcorn in the cylindrical cup costs twice as much as the popcorn in the cone. Which is the better buy?

7. A box in the form of a cube has sides of 40 cm. What is the volume of the largest cylinder that will fit inside the box?

8. A square-based prism has a volume of 1000 mL. What is the least surface area such a prism could have? (Hint: Make a table.)

9. A classroom is 10 m by 7 m by 3.5 m. If each person needs 5 m³ of air, how many people can occupy the classroom?

Chapter

8

The Geometry of Packaging

Packaging of products is used to influence us to buy one product over another. Yet, often we don't even pay attention to the packaging unless it is difficult to open.

Engineers and designers must develop packaging that protects the product while meeting the needs of the consumer and the manufacturer. Many decisions must be made when containers are designed and constructed. The weight, strength, flexibility, cost, and means of disposal have to be considered. The designer also has to think about the tools and machines that are needed to cut and assemble the container.

Many food products are packaged in rectangular boxes. Is there a reason for this?

What other package shapes are common in grocery stores? Why do you think different shapes are used?

In this chapter you will:

- identify, through investigation, the effect of varying the dimensions of a rectangular prism or cylinder on the volume or surface area of the object

- identify, through investigation, the relationships between volume and surface area of a given rectangular prism or cylinder

- explain the significance of optimal surface area or volume in various applications.

Connections

The Chapter Problem

What Shape Should the Gum Be?

As the design engineer for the Bubble Blaster Bubble Gum Company, you must choose the best shape for a new bubble gum. Each piece of gum must have a mass of 10 g. You have determined that each 10-g piece of gum will have a volume of 10 cm³. You plan to design a mould for the gum that will make the amount of wrapping for each piece as small as possible. Determine the shape and size of the mould.

At the end of some lessons in this chapter, questions will refer back to this problem. You will be able to use what you have just learned to answer them. Keep your notes in a folder, so that at the end of the chapter, you can provide a full solution to the problem.

The Challenge

What Can You Find Out About Packaging?

Investigate in depth some aspect of packaging. Some examples are given or you may choose one of your own. All statistical data should be analyzed and presented in an attractive and effective way.

- Choose a product and identify the most common type of packaging for this product. Research or investigate reasons (mathematical and other) for packaging it in this way. Then find an example of unusual packaging of the same product and investigate possible reasons for the unusual choice of packaging. Survey people on their preferences regarding packaging of the products. Report your findings, complete with suggestions for the manufacturers.

- Investigate which types of products are packaged in the most creative ways. Suggest reasons for your results. Discuss advantages and disadvantages of creative packaging. Survey people to develop some measure of the effectiveness of the creative packaging. Create a report of your findings for submission to the manufacturers.

- Invent a method to measure efficiency in packaging. Using your measure of efficiency, find examples of the most efficiently packaged and least efficiently packaged goods. Research possible reasons why manufacturers would choose inefficient packaging. Create a report with suggestions for manufacturers.

To complete this Challenge, you may need to develop a research plan with your teacher or with other students. You may also have to do research outside the classroom.

Getting Ready

In this chapter, you will be looking at packaging. These exercises will help you to prepare for the work.

1. **(a)** The perimeter of a square is 141 m. Find the length to two decimals of one side of the square.
   (b) One side of a rectangle is 17.1 m. The perimeter is 45.9 m. Calculate the measures of the other three sides.

2. **(a)** The frozen surface of a lake is nearly rectangular. It is 115 m wide and 145 m long, and will be used for skating. If half of this lake will be used for pleasure skating and the other half for hockey, how big will each area be?
   (b) One side of a rectangular field is 169.9 m. The perimeter is 486.6 m. Calculate the area of the field.

3. Calculate the area of each shape to one decimal.

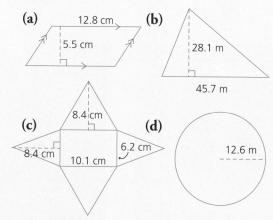

4. The measures of a square-based pyramid are shown.
   (a) Draw a net.
   (b) Find the area of each face.
   (c) Find the total surface area.

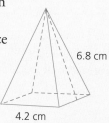

5. A satellite dish has a diameter of 7.1 m; find its circumference.

6. Solve.
   (a) $x + 5 = -10$ **(b)** $2x - 3 = -11$
   (c) $6 + \frac{1}{2}m = 8$ **(d)** $-5 = 2r - 7$
   (e) $0.4y - 1.3 = 2.7$ **(f)** $3x + 15 = 9$
   (g) $-3x + 4 = -26$ **(h)** $0.3y + 1 = 2.5$
   (i) $4.5x - 4 = 0$

7. Copy and complete the table for each prism.

	Height	Area of Base	Volume
(a)	17.4 cm	94.6 cm²	■
(b)	21.8 mm	■	198.32 mm³
(c)	■	157.1 m²	634.89 m³

8. Copy and complete the table for each cylinder.

	Radius	Height	Volume
(a)	■	65.1 m	232.9 m³
(b)	21.5 mm	26.9 mm	■
(c)	128.6 cm	■	718.38 cm³

9. Copy and complete the table for each cone.

	Radius	Height	Volume
(a)	■	35.7 cm	172.8 cm³
(b)	183.2 mm	59.3 mm	■
(c)	174.92 m	■	836.92 m³

10. Copy and complete the table for each sphere.

	Radius	Diameter	Volume
(a)	12.5 cm	■	■
(b)	■	28.4 mm	■
(c)	■	■	267.947 m³

11. Calculate the volume and surface area to two decimals.

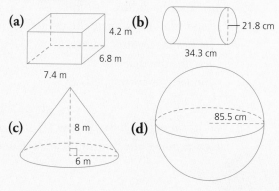

8.1 Investigating the Best Design: Cylinders

Many products come in cylinders. Is one size of cylinder more economical than another? Suppose a container must hold 1000 mL of juice. What size and shape of can would use the least amount of metal? Copy and complete this table.

Radius (cm)	Height (cm)	Surface Area (cm²)	Volume (1 cm³ = 1 mL)
1			1000
2			1000
3			1000
...			...
8			1000
9			1000
10			1000

Investigating with the *Volume/Surface Area Explorer*

Start the *Volume/Surface Area Explorer*. The *Explorer* displays a prism with a hexagonal base. Change the shape to a cylinder by clicking on **SET TYPE** and selecting "cylinder" on the screen that appears. Select **OK**.

Think, Do, Discuss

1. Use the *Explorer* to find the height of a cylinder with a capacity of 1000 mL and a radius of 1 cm. Complete the table using the *Explorer*.

2. Describe the nature of the relationship between the surface area and the radius. Use this relationship to estimate the radius that has the smallest surface area. Describe the shape of the cylinder that corresponds to that radius.

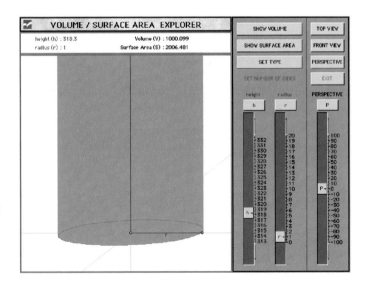

3. Write an explanation of how you can confirm that the cylinder found in Step 2 does, in fact, produce the minimum surface area for a volume of 1000 mL.

Improving the Accuracy of the Investigation by Using a Spreadsheet

One of the difficulties of doing an investigation like the previous one is that you may not be able to find the dimensions that give you the exact volume you want. It is possible, though, to set up a spreadsheet to find the height and surface area with improved accuracy, given the radius and the volume.

Think, Do, Discuss

1. Create a spreadsheet that contains the same information as the table of values on the opposite page.
2. Enter the formulas to calculate the height and the surface area in each row of the spreadsheet.
3. Explain how the spreadsheet data can be used to get a better estimate of the radius that minimizes surface area for cylinders.
4. A spreadsheet can be used to create a graph. Construct a graph that visually shows that the radius you found does actually minimize the surface area.

Generalizing the Results

What is the relationship between the dimensions of a cylinder that contains a given volume and has the smallest possible surface area?

Think, Do, Discuss

1. Repeat this investigation for several other volumes. In each case, describe the cylinder that contains the smallest possible surface area.
2. Make a general statement about the relationship between the dimensions of a cylinder with a given volume and has the minimum surface area.
3. Discuss why this relationship would interest designers in the packaging industry.
4. Do a quick visual survey of cylindrical packages in a store. Are most of them designed to use the smallest amount of packaging material? If not, why not? Write a report on your findings.

Extending the Results

Sometimes you know the amount of material that is available to construct a three-dimensional object and you want to maximize the volume.

Think, Do, Discuss

1. Suppose a cylinder has a surface area of 150 cm². Use the methods you have learned to determine the dimensions of the cylinder with this surface area and the largest possible volume.
2. Develop a formula that can be used to determine the dimensions of the cylinder with the maximum volume for a given surface area.

Focus

Key Ideas

Minimum Surface Area of a Cylinder

- For a cylinder with a given volume, there is always a radius and height that yield the smallest possible surface area. This area is called the **minimum surface area**.
- The minimum surface area for a given volume in a cylinder always occurs when the radius of the cylinder is half the height. In other words, the diameter of the cylinder equals the height of the cylinder ($2r = h$ or $d = h$).
- When the diameter of the cylinder equals the height, the front view of the cylinder has a square profile. This type of cylinder has the minimum surface area.

- For a given volume, the radius of a cylinder with the minimum surface area can be found by solving for r in the formula $V = 2\pi r^3$.

$$V = \pi r^2 h$$ This is the formula for volume.

$$V = \pi r^2(2r)$$ $h = 2r$ when the minimum surface area occurs.

$$V = 2\pi r^3$$

$$\frac{V}{2\pi} = r^3$$ Isolate the r^3 term by dividing both sides of the equation by 2π.

$$r = \sqrt[3]{\frac{V}{2\pi}}$$ Solve for r by taking the cube root of both sides of the equation.

Maximum Volume of a Cylinder

- For a cylinder with a given surface area, there is always a radius and height that yield the maximum possible volume.
- The maximum volume for a given surface area in a cylinder always occurs when the radius of the cylinder is half the height. In other words, the diameter of the cylinder equals the height of the cylinder ($2r = h$ or $d = h$).
- When the diameter of the cylinder equals the height, the front view of the cylinder has a square profile. This type of cylinder contains the maximum volume.

- The dimensions of a cylinder containing the maximum volume for a given surface area can be found solving the formula $SA = 6\pi r^2$ for r.
  SA is the known surface area.
  r is the radius of the cylinder and $2r$ is the height.

Example

Nalini is a design engineer and must design a cylindrical can for juice. Suppose the can must contain 350 mL of juice. Find the dimensions of the can that will use the least amount of metal.

Solution

Nalini knows that the can must have a square profile because the diameter of the can must equal the height, or twice the radius must equal the height ($h = 2r$).

$$V = \pi r^2 h$$ Use the formula for volume of a cylinder.

$$350 = \pi r^2 h$$ In this case the volume is 350 mL.

$$350 \doteq 3.14 r^2 (2r)$$ $\pi \doteq 3.14$ and $h = 2r$.

$$350 \doteq 6.28 r^3$$ Simplify.

$$\frac{350}{6.28} \doteq \frac{6.28 r^3}{6.28}$$ Solve for r.

$$55.732 \doteq r^3$$ Find the cube root of 55.732.

$$\sqrt[3]{55.732} \doteq r$$

$$r \doteq 3.82$$

When the radius is 3.82 cm, the height is twice this or 7.64 cm. These are the dimensions of a can that will hold 350 mL of juice, using the least amount of metal.

Practise, Apply, Solve

1. Evaluate.
   (a) $\sqrt{36}$ (b) $\sqrt{121}$ (c) $\sqrt{81}$ (d) $\sqrt{225}$
   (e) $\sqrt[3]{8}$ (f) $\sqrt[3]{27}$ (g) $\sqrt[3]{125}$ (h) $\sqrt[3]{216}$

2. Evaluate to the nearest hundredth.
   (a) $\sqrt{12}$ (b) $\sqrt{68}$ (c) $\sqrt{155}$ (d) $\sqrt{1028}$
   (e) $\sqrt[3]{18}$ (f) $\sqrt[3]{88}$ (g) $\sqrt[3]{144}$ (h) $\sqrt[3]{123.75}$

3. Solve each equation. Evaluate to one decimal place.
   (a) $x^2 = 25$ (b) $x^2 = 16$ (c) $x^2 = 121$ (d) $x^2 = 225$
   (e) $x^2 = 38$ (f) $x^2 = 96$ (g) $x^2 = 440$ (h) $x^2 = 1059$
   (i) $2x^2 = 72$ (j) $5x^2 = 500$ (k) $0.5x^2 = 2$ (l) $3x^2 = 54$
   (m) $x^2 - 2 = 47$ (n) $x^2 + 5 = 41$ (o) $2x^2 - 4 = 14$ (p) $4x^2 - 5 = 75$

4. Solve each equation. Evaluate to one decimal place.

(a) $x^3 = 1$ **(b)** $x^3 = 8$ **(c)** $x^3 = 64$ **(d)** $x^3 = -27$

(e) $x^3 = 12$ **(f)** $x^3 = 50$ **(g)** $x^3 = 135$ **(h)** $x^3 = 220$

(i) $2x^3 = 250$ **(j)** $5x^3 = -40$ **(k)** $0.5x^3 = 32$ **(l)** $3x^3 = 3000$

(m) $x^3 - 7 = 20$ **(n)** $x^3 + 16 = 15$ **(o)** $2x^3 - 3 = 5$ **(p)** $6x^3 - 10 = 110$

5. Determine the value of the missing variable. Evaluate to one decimal place.

(a)
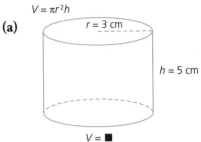
$V = \pi r^2 h$
$r = 3$ cm
$h = 5$ cm
$V = \blacksquare$

(b)
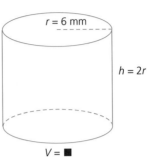
$r = 6$ mm
$V = 2\pi r^3$
$h = 2r$
$V = \blacksquare$

(d)
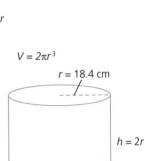
$V = 2\pi r^3$
$r = 18.4$ cm
$h = 2r$
$V = \blacksquare$

(c)
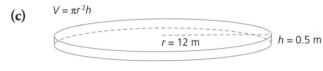
$V = \pi r^2 h$
$r = 12$ m
$h = 0.5$ m
$V = \blacksquare$

(e)
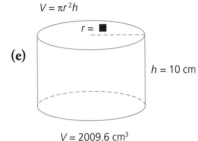
$V = \pi r^2 h$
$r = \blacksquare$
$h = 10$ cm
$V = 2009.6$ cm^3

(f)
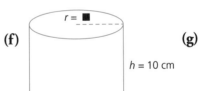
$V = 2\pi r^3$
$r = \blacksquare$
$h = 10$ cm
$V = 10\ 851.84$ mm^3

(g)
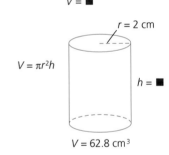
$r = 2$ cm
$V = \pi r^2 h$
$h = \blacksquare$
$V = 62.8$ cm^3

(h)
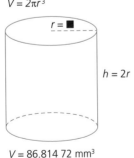
$V = 2\pi r^3$
$r = \blacksquare$
$h = 2r$
$V = 86.814\ 72$ mm^3

(i)
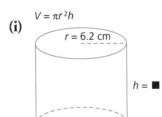
$V = \pi r^2 h$
$r = 6.2$ cm
$h = \blacksquare$
$V = 663.8588$ cm^3

(j)
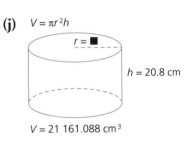
$V = \pi r^2 h$
$r = \blacksquare$
$h = 20.8$ cm
$V = 21\ 161.088$ cm^3

(k)
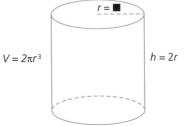
$r = \blacksquare$
$V = 2\pi r^3$
$h = 2r$
$V = 98.125$ m^3

6. Determine the dimensions of the cylinder that would have the minimum surface area for each volume. Evaluate to one decimal place.
(a) 785 cm³
(b) 4578.12 cm³
(c) 21 195 mL
(d) 12 265.625 mL

7. Determine the minimum surface area, to one decimal place, for each cylinder in Question 6.

8. A cylindrical juice can must hold 1 L of apple juice (1 L = 1000 cm³).
(a) Determine the dimensions of the can that will use the least amount of metal. Answer to the nearest tenth of a centimetre.
(b) Determine the surface area of this can.
(c) Suppose aluminum costs 0.1¢/cm², and there are 12 cans of juice in a case. Determine the cost of the aluminum used to make all the cans in a warehouse containing 2350 cases of juice.

9. Pineapple chunks are often packaged in cylindrical cans. If each can must contain 500 mL, determine:
(a) the dimensions, to one decimal place, of the can with the minimum surface area.
(b) the cost, to the nearest penny, of the least expensive can if aluminum costs $0.2¢/cm².

10. Determine the missing variable where $\pi \doteq 3.14$. Evaluate to one decimal place.
(a) $SA = 2\pi r^2 + 2\pi rh$. Determine SA, when $r = 2$ cm and $h = 5$ cm.
(b) $SA = 6\pi r^2$. Determine SA, when $r = 5$ mm.
(c) $SA = 2\pi r^2 + 2\pi rh$. Determine SA, when $r = 5$ cm and $h = 11.5$ cm.
(d) $SA = 6\pi r^2$. Determine SA, when $r = 3.8$ m.
(e) $SA = 2\pi r^2 + 2\pi rh$. Determine h, when $r = 4$ cm and $SA = 226.08$ cm².
(f) $SA = 6\pi r^2$. Determine r, when $SA = 1884.0$ mm².
(g) $SA = 2\pi r^2 + 2\pi rh$. Determine h, when $r = 15$ cm and $SA = 2543.4$ cm².
(h) $SA = 6\pi r^2$. Determine r, when $SA = 434.0736$ mm².

11. Solve for r.
(a) $A = \pi r^2$
(b) $SA = 6\pi r^2$
(c) $V = \frac{4}{3}\pi r^3$

12. Determine the dimensions of the cylinder that would have the maximum volume for each surface area. Evaluate to one decimal place.
(a) 1884 cm²
(b) 471 cm²
(c) 2491.59 cm²
(d) 923.16 cm²

13. Determine the maximum volume, to one decimal place, for each cylinder in Question 12.

14. A farmer wants to make a cylindrical water tank using metal. Suppose she has 75.36 m² of metal available. Determine:
(a) the dimensions of the tank that will hold the largest volume of water.
(b) the volume of water, to one decimal place, this tank could hold.

15. Mark, at the Fertilizer King, needs a plastic tank fitted into the back of his pickup truck so that he can spray fertilizer. Suppose his pickup truck is 1.8 m wide. Determine, to one decimal place:
(a) the dimensions of the largest vertical cylindrical tank that could fit into his truck and uses the least amount of plastic in its construction.
(b) the capacity of this tank.

C

16. A cylindrical drinking glass must be designed to hold the largest amount of liquid possible. Suppose the surface area of the glass must be 317.935 cm². Determine the dimensions of the glass. Evaluate to one decimal place.

17. Every day you encounter cylindrical containers that were not designed to have the minimum surface area or maximum volume. Why would these containers be designed in other ways?

18. In this section you investigated how to find the dimensions of a cylinder that contained a fixed volume with the minimum surface area. Repeat the investigation to determine a similar result for a cone. Create a presentation to explain your reasoning.

19. Chimes are a percussion instrument consisting of 18 to 20 tubes hung on a frame. The tubes are arranged with low notes on the left and high notes on the right. To produce a note, a player strikes the tubes with one or two mallets of pressed leather. To create each tube, the chime maker must know the formula for the volume of material in a hollow cylinder.

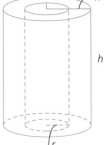

What mass would you need for a tube 0.05 m long, with an inner radius of 0.03 m and a hollow radius of 0.025 m? Answer to the nearest gram. (The density of aluminum is 2700 $\frac{\text{kg}}{\text{m}^3}$.)

The Chapter Problem — What Shape Should the Gum Be?

Refer to the Chapter Problem at the beginning of this chapter.

Suppose you decide to make the gum using a cylindrical mould. What dimensions will minimize the amount of wrapping?

Did You Know?

The cylindrical soft drink can is popular for many reasons. Its rounded edge makes it stronger than cans of the same size that have square or rectangular edges. Consumers prefer the look and feel of a curved surface.

Because cylindrical cans are made entirely from flat sheets of metal they are easy to make and recycle. The sheets of metal are cut into rectangles and disks. It takes one rectangle and two disks to make one can. The rectangle is rolled to make a tube and a disk is attached at each end.

The recycling of soft drink cans is an efficient process. Recycling saves money and materials and is good for the environment. A recycled aluminum can returns to the shelf as a new filled can in as little as 60 days.

The Relationship Between Surface Area and Volume in Rectangular Prisms

Exploring Minimum Surface Area with Interlocking Cubes

Interlocking cubes are a convenient tool for studying the effects that changing the dimensions of rectangular prisms has on surface area and volume.

Think, Do, Discuss

1. Copy this table into your notes.

Length	Width	Height	Volume	Surface Area
1 cube		1 cube		
2		1		
4		1		
8		1		

2. Using eight interlocking cubes, create a model of a prism for each of the lengths in the table. In each case keep the height of the prism fixed at one cube. In the table, record the width, height, volume, and surface area of each prism you create.

3. Which arrangement of interlocking cubes produces the prism with the smallest surface area? What shape does the base have in this situation?

4. Explain why the volume does not change even though the shape itself does.

5. Now create all the prisms you can with a height of two cubes, using all eight cubes. Add this data to your table.

6. Using eight cubes, can you create a prism with a height of three cubes? Explain.

7. Use eight cubes to create a prism with a height of four cubes. Add this data to your table. Can any other prisms be created with heights greater than four cubes? If so, create them and add the data to your table.

8. What are the dimensions of the prism with the smallest surface area? What type of prism is this?

9. Repeat this investigation using 64 interlocking cubes. Create a table like the one above to record your data. Start by creating prisms with a height of 1, then 2, and so on, until you have tried all the different arrangements.

10. Which arrangement of cubes produces the minimum surface area?

11. Based on your findings, predict the dimensions of the prism that would have the minimum surface area for each number of cubes:

    (a) 27   **(b)** 125   **(c)** 216

8.3 Investigating the Best Design: Rectangular Prisms

Investigating with a Spreadsheet

In Section 8.1, you saw that a cylinder can be designed with a minimum surface area for a given volume or a maximum volume for a given surface area. Is this also possible for a rectangular prism?

The volume formula for a cylinder has only two variables, height and radius. However, the volume formula for a rectangular prism has three variables, height, length, and width. In this investigation, you will hold one dimension of a prism fixed while varying the others.

Think, Do, Discuss

1. Set up a spreadsheet that will automatically calculate the surface area and volume of a rectangular prism, given its length, width, and height.

	A	B	C	D	E
1	**Length (cm)**	**Width (cm)**	**Height (cm)**	**Surface Area (cm²)**	**Volume (1000 cm³)**
2					
3					
4					
5					
6					

2. Consider a variety of rectangular prisms, all with a volume of 1000 cm³ and all the same height. Use the spreadsheet to investigate and find the length and width of the rectangular prism with the smallest surface area.

3. Now consider a variety of rectangular prisms, all with a volume of 1000 cm³, but of different heights. Extend your investigation from Step 2 to find the length and width of the rectangular prism with the smallest surface area.

4. Is the relationship between length and surface area linear or nonlinear? Use a graph to verify your conclusion. Find the length of the prism with the smallest surface area for a given height and volume. Describe the shape of the prism.

5. Form a general conclusion about what combination of length, width, and height gives the smallest surface area for a rectangular prism with a given volume.

6. Repeat the investigation for a rectangular prism with a fixed surface area of 1500 cm². Determine the dimensions of the prism with the largest possible volume.

7. Develop a formula to determine the dimensions of a prism with optimal volume for a given surface area.

8. Compare the results for a rectangular prism to the corresponding results for a cylinder.

9. You know how to find the surface area and volume for cylinders, rectangular prisms, and spheres. For a given volume, show which of these can be made to enclose the volume with the least surface area.

Paul Erdos (1913–1996)

Paul Erdos was in some ways the typical "absent-minded professor." Erdos could not open a box of cereal or balance a chequebook, and yet he was a great mathematician. He was called the "prince of problem solvers and the absolute monarch of problem posers." His work, in a branch of mathematics called combinatorics, led to the development of the CD and the computer chip.

Use the Internet or the library to find out more about Erdos or combinatorics.

Did You Know?

Simon Stevin (1548–1620) was a Dutch engineer and mathematician. He introduced innovations in bookkeeping, fortifications, and military engineering. He also led the way in the development of modern decimal notation. In Stevin's time, people worked with fractions. Even people who regularly used mathematics did not understand about using tenths, hundredths, and thousandths to simplify calculations. Stevin wrote a small book entitled "The Tenth," which explained for the first time how to do decimal arithmetic. His aim was to teach everyone a system of computation in which they would never have to use fractions again.

He used circled numbers to represent powers of $\frac{1}{10}$. He would have written 3.1416 like this:

$$\textcircled{0} \quad \textcircled{1} \quad \textcircled{2} \quad \textcircled{3} \quad \textcircled{4}$$
$$3 \qquad 1 \qquad 4 \qquad 1 \qquad 6$$

So, for instance, the circled 2 above the 4 represents the value $4 \times (\frac{1}{10})^2$ or 0.04.

For the general public, his greatest fame came when he invented a carriage that was propelled by sails and ran along the seashore. It carried 28 people and could easily outrun a galloping horse.

Focus

Key Ideas

Minimum Surface Area of a Rectangular Prism

- For a rectangular prism with a given volume, there is always a length, width, and height that will produce a minimum surface area.

- When the length, width, and height of the prism are equal, the front view of the prism has a square profile. This type of prism will have the minimum surface area.

- The minimum surface area for a given volume in a rectangular prism always occurs when the prism is a cube. The length, width, and height are equal.

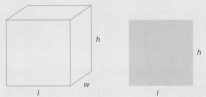

- For a fixed volume, the dimensions of the rectangular prism with minimum surface area can be found by solving for l in the formula $V = l^3$, where V is the volume and l is the length.

$V = lwh$	This is the formula for volume of a rectangular prism.
$V = l(l)(l)$	$w = l$ and $h = l$ produces the minimum surface area.
$V = l^3$	
$l = \sqrt[3]{V}$	

Maximum Volume of a Rectangular Prism

- For a rectangular prism with a given surface area, there is always a length, width, and height that will produce the maximum possible volume.

- The maximum volume for a given surface area in a rectangular prism always occurs when the prism is a cube. The length, width, and height are equal.

- When the length, width, and height of the prism are equal, the front view of the prism has a square profile. This type of prism contains the maximum volume.

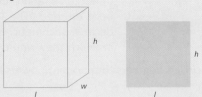

- The dimensions of a rectangular prism containing the maximum volume can be found by solving for l in the formula $SA = 6l^2$.
  SA is the known surface area.
  l is the length of each side of the cube.

Example

Salim is packaging teddy bears into boxes, then wrapping them in gift wrap for charity. He knows that the bears will fit into any shaped box with a capacity of at least 10 648 cm³. Find the dimensions of the box that will require the least amount of gift wrap.

Solution

Salim knows that the box that results in the minimum surface area for a given volume is a cube. Therefore,

$$V = l^3$$

$$10\ 468 = l^3$$

$$\sqrt[3]{10\ 468} = l$$

$$l = 22$$

The box must have a length, width, and height of 22 cm.

Practise, Apply, Solve

A

1. Evaluate to the nearest hundredth.

(a) $\sqrt{81}$ (b) $\sqrt[3]{216}$ (c) $\sqrt{288}$ (d) $\sqrt[3]{50}$

(e) $\sqrt{1856}$ (f) $\sqrt[3]{2092}$ (g) $\sqrt{12}$ (h) $\sqrt[3]{555}$

2. Solve each equation.

(a) $x^2 = 100$ (b) $x^3 = -64$ (c) $2x^2 = 162$

(d) $3x^3 = 24$ (e) $-5x^2 = -5$ (f) $2x^3 = -16$

(g) $x^2 + 12 = 21$ (h) $x^3 - 5 = -32$ (i) $x^3 + 12 = 137$

(j) $2x^2 - 12 = 20$ (k) $-x^3 + 12 = -15$ (l) $3x^3 - 1 = 23$

3. Determine the value of the unknown variable. Evaluate to one decimal place.

(a) $V = lwh$
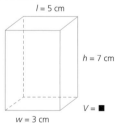
$l = 5$ cm, $h = 7$ cm, $w = 3$ cm, $V = \blacksquare$

(b) $V = lwh$
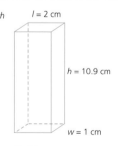
$l = 2$ cm, $h = 10.9$ cm, $w = 1$ cm, $V = \blacksquare$

(c) $V = lwh$
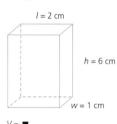
$l = 2$ cm, $h = 6$ cm, $w = 1$ cm, $V = \blacksquare$

(d) $V = lwh$
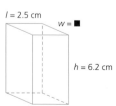
$l = 2.5$ cm, $w = \blacksquare$, $h = 6.2$ cm, $V = 52.7$ cm³

(e) $V = l^3$
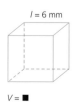
$l = 6$ mm, $V = \blacksquare$

(f) $V = l^3$
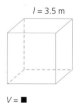
$l = 3.5$ m, $V = \blacksquare$

(g) $V = l^3$

$l = \blacksquare$

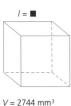

$V = 2744 \text{ mm}^3$

(h) $V = l^3$

$l = \blacksquare$

$V = 21.952 \text{ cm}^3$

B

4. Determine the dimensions of the rectangular prism that would have the smallest possible surface area for each volume. Evaluate to one decimal place where necessary.
   (a) 125 m^3
   (b) 3375 cm^3
   (c) 21.952 cm^3
   (d) 3112.136 m^3

5. Determine the minimum surface area for each prism in Question 4.

6. A popcorn company sells popcorn to movie theatres in bulk in cardboard boxes.
   (a) Each box has a volume of $28\ 800 \text{ cm}^3$. Determine the dimensions of the box that will require the least amount of cardboard to construct. Evaluate to two decimal places.
   (b) The worker filling the boxes uses a scoop that holds 1275 cm^3 of popcorn kernels. How many scoopfuls are needed to fill each box?

7. Sugar is sometimes packaged as cubes. Each cube of sugar must have a volume of 3.376 cm^3. Determine:
   (a) the dimensions of a cube, to one decimal place.
   (b) the volume of 64 cubes of sugar, to the nearest cubic centimetre.
   (c) the dimensions of the box that will hold 64 cubes made from the least possible amount of paper.

8. Determine the missing variable. Evaluate to the nearest hundredth.

(a) $SA = 2(lw + lh + wh)$

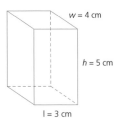

$w = 4 \text{ cm}$
$h = 5 \text{ cm}$
$l = 3 \text{ cm}$
$SA = \blacksquare$

(b) $SA = 2(lw + lh + wh)$

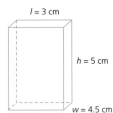

$l = 3 \text{ cm}$
$h = 5 \text{ cm}$
$w = 4.5 \text{ cm}$
$SA = \blacksquare$

(c) $SA = 2(lw + lh + wh)$

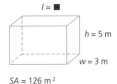

$l = \blacksquare$
$h = 5 \text{ m}$
$w = 3 \text{ m}$
$SA = 126 \text{ m}^2$

(d) $SA = 2(lw + lh + wh)$

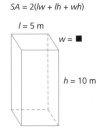

$l = 5 \text{ m}$
$w = \blacksquare$
$h = 10 \text{ m}$
$SA = 220 \text{ m}^2$

(e) $SA = 6l^2$

$l = 3$ cm

$SA = \blacksquare$

(f) $SA = 6l^2$

$l = 2.9$ m

$SA = \blacksquare$

(g) $SA = 6l^2$

$l = \blacksquare$

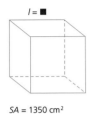

$SA = 1350$ cm^2

(h) $SA = 6l^2$

$l = \blacksquare$

$SA = 245.76$ mm^2

9. Determine the dimensions of the rectangular prism that would have the largest possible volume for each surface area. Evaluate to one decimal place where necessary.
  (a) 150 m^2 **(b)** 864 cm^2
  (c) 541.5 cm^2 **(d)** 4873.5 m^2

10. Determine the maximum volume for each prism in Question 9.

11. Susan wants to build a storage bin with a locking lid for firewood. She has 5.5 m^2 of plywood available. She designs the bin in the shape of a rectangular prism. Determine:
  (a) the dimensions of the bin with the largest possible volume, to two decimals.
  (b) the volume of Susan's bin, to two decimals.

12. The dimensions of $3\frac{1}{2}$" floppy disks measure 9 cm by 9 cm by 0.3 cm.
  (a) Determine the volume of one floppy disk.
  (b) Determine the volume of 30 floppy disks.
  (c) Design a box that will hold 30 floppy disks. Draw a diagram of the box and include the dimensions.

13. Manufacturers put soup in cans of different sizes. Suppose one company puts its soup in cans that are 11.3 cm high with a base diameter of 9 cm and are to be shipped in boxes of 12.
  (a) Find the dimensions of the box needed to ship the cans in one layer with three rows.
  (b) Find the dimensions of the box needed to ship the cans in two layers of two rows.
  (c) Which box and stacking arrangement uses the least amount of cardboard?
  (d) Can the 12 soup cans be packaged in a cube to minimize the amount of cardboard? Explain.

14. A cylinder just fits inside a 10 cm by 10 cm by 10 cm cubic box. Which shape has the smaller surface area? Verify your answer by determining the surface area of both shapes.

15. (a) Complete this table by finding the dimensions of each shape that will require minimum surface area. Using these dimensions, calculate the surface area of each shape to one decimal place.

Shape	Volume (cm³)	Dimensions (cm)	Surface Area (cm²)
rectangular prism	1000	$l = \blacksquare$	
cylinder	1000	$r = \blacksquare,\ h = \blacksquare$	
sphere	1000	$r \doteq \blacksquare$	

(b) Of the three shapes listed above, which has the smallest surface area for a fixed volume of 1000 cm³? Will this always be true for any volume?

16. (a) Complete this table by finding the dimensions of each shape that will maximize the volume. Using these dimensions, calculate the volume for each shape.

Shape	Surface Area (cm²)	Dimensions (cm)	Volume (cm³)
rectangular prism	1000	$l = \blacksquare$	
cylinder	1000	$r \doteq \blacksquare,\ h = \blacksquare$	
sphere	1000	$r = \blacksquare$	

(b) Of the three shapes listed above, which has the largest volume for a fixed surface area of 1000 cm²? Will this always be true for any surface area?

C

17. A rectangular box must be designed to package 12 cans of peas. Each can has a radius of 5 cm and a height of 10 cm. Determine the dimensions of the box that will require the least amount of cardboard. Is packaging 12 cans per box the most economical use of cardboard? Explain.

18. For a given volume, which shape would have the minimum surface area: a cylinder, a rectangular prism, or a sphere? Prove this using the formulas for volume and surface area using a fixed volume.

19. Investigate to determine the dimensions of a cone with the smallest possible surface area and a volume of 1000 cm³.

20. A jeweller has 1 cm³ of gold formed into a cubic box with 2-mm thick walls. Find the largest volume the box can contain if:
(a) it has a lid made of gold of the same thickness as the walls.
(b) it does not have a lid.

The Chapter Problem — What Shape Should the Gum Be?

Refer to the Chapter Problem at the beginning of this chapter.

1. Describe the shape into which the bubble gum pieces need to be moulded to minimize the amount of wrapping required for each piece.
2. Explain why this optimal shape is not often used by the packaging industry.

Chapter Review

8.1 Investigating the Best Design: Cylinders ———

Minimum Surface Area of a Cylinder

- For a cylinder with a given volume there is always a radius and height that allows the cylinder to be designed using the smallest possible surface area. This area is called the **minimum surface area**.

- The minimum surface area for a given volume in a cylinder always occurs when the radius of the cylinder is half the height. In other words, the diameter of the cylinder equals the height of the cylinder ($2r = h$ or $d = h$).

- When the diameter of the cylinder equals the height, the front view of the cylinder has a square profile. This type of cylinder has the minimum surface area.

- For a given volume, the radius of a cylinder with the minimum surface area can be found by solving for r in the formula $V = 2\pi r^3$.

$$V = \pi r^2 h$$ This is the formula for volume.

$$V = \pi r^2(2r)$$ $h = 2r$ when the minimum surface area occurs.

$$V = 2\pi r^3$$

$$\frac{V}{2\pi} = r^3$$ Isolate the r^3 term by dividing both sides of the equation by 2π.

$$r = \sqrt[3]{\frac{V}{2\pi}}$$ Solve for r by taking the cube root of both sides of the equation.

Maximum Volume of a Cylinder

- For a cylinder with a given surface area, there is always a radius and height that yield the largest possible volume.

- The maximum volume for a given surface area in a cylinder always occurs when the radius of the cylinder is half the height. In other words, the diameter of the cylinder equals the height of the cylinder ($2r = h$ or $d = h$).

- When the diameter of the cylinder equals the height, the front view of the cylinder has a square profile. This type of cylinder contains the maximum volume.

- The dimensions of a cylinder containing the maximum volume for a given surface area can be found by solving the formula $SA = 6\pi r^2$ for r.
  SA is the known surface area.
  r is the radius of the cylinder.

Example

Demetra is a design engineer who is designing a cylindrical can for juice. If the can must contain 500 mL of juice, find the dimensions of the can that will use the least amount of metal.

Solution

Demetra knows that the can with the least amount of metal will have a square profile. For this to happen, the diameter of the can must equal the height, or twice the radius equals the height ($h = 2r$).

$$V = \pi r^2 h \qquad \text{In this case, the volume is 500 mL.}$$

$$500 \doteq \pi r^2 h \qquad \pi \doteq 3.14 \text{ and } h = 2r.$$

$$500 \doteq 3.14r^2(2r) \qquad \text{Simplify.}$$

$$500 \doteq 6.28r^3$$

$$\frac{500}{6.28} \doteq \frac{6.28r^3}{6.28} \qquad \text{Solve for } r.$$

$$79.6178 \doteq r^3 \qquad \text{Find the cube root of 79.6178.}$$

$$\sqrt[3]{79.6178} \doteq r$$

$$r \doteq 4.3$$

When the radius is 4.3 cm, the height is twice this, or 8.6 cm. These are the dimensions of a can that will hold 500 mL of juice using the least amount of metal.

Extra Practice

1. Determine the unknown value to three decimal places.

(a) $V = 2\pi r^3$

(b) $V = \pi r^2 h$

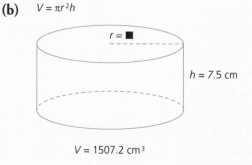

$r = 5.8$ cm

$h = 2r$

$V = \blacksquare$

$r = \blacksquare$

$h = 7.5$ cm

$V = 1507.2$ cm^3

(c) $V = 2\pi r^3$

$r = \blacksquare$

$V = 169.56 \text{ mm}^3$

(d) $V = \pi r^2 h$

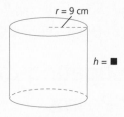

$r = 9 \text{ cm}$

$h = \blacksquare$

$V = 3942.27 \text{ cm}^3$

(e) $SA = 2\pi r^2 + 2\pi rh$

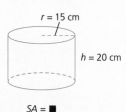

$r = 15 \text{ cm}$

$h = 20 \text{ cm}$

$SA = \blacksquare$

(f) $SA = 6\pi r^2$

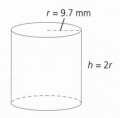

$r = 9.7 \text{ mm}$

$h = 2r$

$SA = \blacksquare$

(g) $SA = 2\pi r^2 + 2\pi rh$

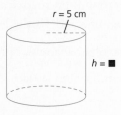

$r = 5 \text{ cm}$

$h = \blacksquare$

$SA = 408.2 \text{ cm}^2$

(h) $SA = 6\pi r^2$

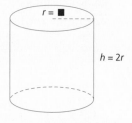

$r = \blacksquare$

$h = 2r$

$SA = 36\ 796.875 \text{ mm}^2$

2. Determine the dimensions of the cylinder that would have the minimum surface area for the given volume. Evaluate to three decimal places.
   (a) 572.265 cm³
   (b) 36 624.96 cm³
   (c) 2154.04 mL
   (d) 58.159 mL

3. Determine the minimum surface area for each cylinder in Question 2.

4. Determine the dimensions of the cylinder that would have the maximum volume for each of the given surface areas. Evaluate to three decimal places.
   (a) 678.24 cm²
   (b) 23.55 m²
   (c) 4823.04 cm²
   (d) 7536 cm²

5. Determine the maximum volume for each cylinder in Question 4.

6. A farm supply company needs a plastic tank fitted into the back of a pickup truck to transport liquid chemicals. The pickup truck is 165 cm wide. Determine:
   (a) the dimensions of the largest vertical cylindrical tank that could fit into the truck that uses the least amount of plastic in its construction.
   (b) the capacity of this tank.

7. Candles are moulded into cylindrical shapes. A candle has a volume of 1500 cm³. Determine the dimensions of the candle that will require the smallest amount of plastic wrap to package each candle. Answer to two decimal places.

8.2–8.3 Investigating the Best Design: Rectangular Prisms

Minimum Surface Area of a Rectangular Prism

- For a rectangular prism with a given volume, there is always a length, width, and height that will produce a minimum area.
- When the length, width, and height of the prism are equal, the front view of the prism has a square profile. This type of prism will have the minimum surface area.
- The minimum surface area for a given volume in a rectangular prism always occurs when the prism is a cube. The length, width, and height are equal.
- For a fixed volume, the dimensions of the rectangular prism with minimum surface area can be found by solving for l in the formula $V = l^3$, where V is the volume and l is the length.

$$V = lwh$$ This is the formula for volume of a rectangular prism.

$$V = l(l)(l)$$ $w = l$ and $h = l$ produces the minimum surface area.

$$V = l^3$$

$$l = \sqrt[3]{V}$$

Maximum Volume of a Rectangular Prism

- For a rectangular prism, with a given surface area, there is always a length, width, and height that will produce the maximum volume.
- The maximum volume for a given surface area in a rectangular prism always occurs when the prism is a cube. The length, width, and height are equal.
- When the length, width, and height of the prism are equal, the front view of the prism has a square profile. This type of prism contains the maximum volume.
- The dimensions of a rectangular prism containing the maximum volume can be found solving for l in the formula $SA = 6l^2$.
  SA is the known surface area.
  l is the length of each side of the cube.

Example

Siddarth is designing a box that must contain the largest possible volume. He has only 1350 cm² of metal for the box and the box must have a lid. Determine the dimensions he must use.

Solution

Siddarth knows that the box containing the maximum volume for a given surface area is a cube.

$$S = 6l^2$$
$$1350 = 6l^2$$
$$\frac{1350}{6} = \frac{6l^2}{6}$$
$$225 = l^2$$
$$\sqrt{225} = l$$
$$15 = l$$

The box must have a length, width, and height of 15 cm.

Extra Practice

8. Determine the unknown value.

(a) $V = lwh$ $l = 3.8$ cm

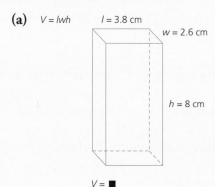

$w = 2.6$ cm

$h = 8$ cm

$V = \blacksquare$

(b) $V = lwh$

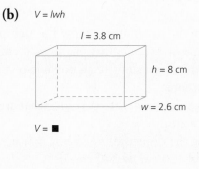

$l = 3.8$ cm

$h = 8$ cm

$w = 2.6$ cm

$V = \blacksquare$

(c) $V = lwh$

$l = 5.8$ cm

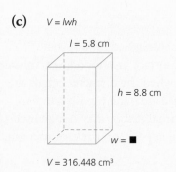

$h = 8.8$ cm

$w = \blacksquare$

$V = 316.448$ cm³

(d) $V = l^3$

$l = 6$ mm

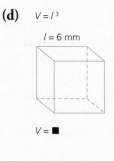

$V = \blacksquare$

(e) $V = l^3$

$l = \blacksquare$

$V = 3723.875 \text{ m}^3$

(f) $SA = 2(lw + lh + wh)$

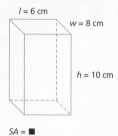

$l = 6 \text{ cm}$
$w = 8 \text{ cm}$
$h = 10 \text{ cm}$

$SA = \blacksquare$

(g) $SA = 2(lw + lh + wh)$

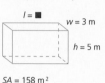

$l = \blacksquare$
$w = 3 \text{ m}$
$h = 5 \text{ m}$

$SA = 158 \text{ m}^2$

(h) $SA = 6l^2$

$l = 13.5 \text{ cm}$

$SA = \blacksquare$

9. Determine the dimensions of the rectangular prism that would have the smallest possible surface area for each volume.
   (a) 729 m³   **(b)** 9938.375 cm³   **(c)** 0.614 125 m³   **(d)** 551.368 m³

10. Determine the minimum surface area for each prism in Question 9.

11. Determine the dimensions of the rectangular prism with the largest possible volume for each surface area.
   (a) 1350 m²   **(b)** 433.58 cm²   **(c)** 8664 cm²   **(d)** 18 150 m²

12. Determine the maximum volume for each prism in Question 11.

13. The volume of a rectangular prism is 24 cm³.
   (a) Find the dimensions of all possible prisms with this volume that have whole number dimensions.
   (b) Among the answers to part (a), what are the dimensions of the prism with the least surface area?

14. Determine the dimensions of a box that has the largest possible volume made from a piece of plywood 120 cm by 240 cm, if:
   (a) the box has a lid.   **(b)** the box does not have a lid.

Chapter Summary

In this chapter, you have seen that both prisms and cylinders can be designed for a specific volume using the minimum surface area. The prism with the least surface area for a given volume is a cube. In the case of a cylinder, the most efficient shape occurs when the diameter equals the height. Both these shapes have a square profile. For a specific surface area, there exists a design that maximizes the volume for both prisms and cylinders. The optimal design may not be used because package designers have to consider other factors, like visual appeal and package strength.

Chapter Review Test

1. Determine the dimensions of the cylinder that would have the minimum surface area for a volume of 86 814.72 cm^3. Determine the minimum surface area for these dimensions.

2. Determine the dimensions of the rectangular prism that would have the smallest possible surface area for a volume of 32 768 cm^3. Determine the minimum surface area for these dimensions.

3. Determine the dimensions of the cylinder that would have the maximum volume for a surface area of 16 956 cm^2. Determine the maximum volume for these dimensions. Evaluate to three decimal places.

4. Determine the dimensions of the rectangular prism that would have the largest possible volume for a surface area of 12 150 cm^2. Determine the maximum volume for these dimensions.

5. A laundry detergent company plans to sell a "bargain box" that contains 10 L of detergent. Find the dimensions of the rectangular box that uses the smallest amount of cardboard.

6. Candles can be moulded into many different shapes. Suppose a candle must have a volume of 3500 cm^3. Determine the shape and dimensions of the candle that will require the smallest amount of shrink-wrap to package each candle. Your shapes are limited to either a cylinder, rectangular prism, or sphere. Evaluate to two decimal places.

7. Use technology to investigate the dimensions of a cylinder that would contain the maximum volume, made from a piece of metal that is 100 cm by 200 cm, if:
   (a) the cylinder has a top and bottom.
   (b) the cylinder has no top.
   (c) Prepare an argument to support your conclusions.

1. Examine each diagram. Use the information supplied to answer the questions.

   (a) Explain whether or not *AB* is parallel to *CD*.

   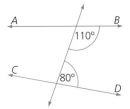

   (b) Determine the measure of ∠*BAC*. Give an explanation for your answer.

   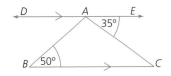

   (c) Determine the measure of ∠*CBA*.

   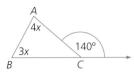

   (d) Points *A*, *B*, and *C* are three vertices of a regular polygon. Determine the number of sides in the polygon and the sum of the interior angles of the polygon.

   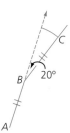

2. Draw △*ABC* with *D* the midpoint of *AB* and *E* the midpoint of *AC*. Join *DE*. Determine the measure of ∠*BCE* if ∠*ADE* = 45° and ∠*DAE* = 60°. Explain your solution.

3. Examine the diagram.

   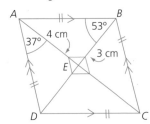

   (a) Determine the measure of ∠*BCD*. Explain your reasoning.
   (b) Calculate the area of *ABCD*.
   (c) Calculate the perimeter of *ABCD*.

Cumulative Review Test 3

4. An artist wants to balance the flat surface of a triangular piece of metal on a pole. The triangle has sides 50 cm, 70 cm, and 110 cm long. With the aid of a labelled diagram show how the artist would locate the balance point of the triangle.

5. A large stop sign in the shape of a regular octagon is made for a particularly dangerous intersection. The distance between opposite sides of the sign is 120 cm and each side is 50 cm long. What is the surface area for drivers to see?

6. One chocolate bar brand is marketed in the shape of a triangular prism. The face of the prism is an equilateral triangle of side length 3 cm. The chocolate bar is 18 cm long. Calculate the volume of the chocolate bar.

7. Golf balls are usually packaged three to a rectangular-shaped box.
   (a) If a golf ball has a diameter of 4.2 cm, determine the dimensions of a box that would just hold the three balls.
   (b) What is the surface area of the box?
   (c) An advertiser suggests the balls be packaged in a tubular package. What is the surface area of a container of this shape that would just hold the balls?
   (d) Which container has less surface area?
   (e) Suggest two reasons why golf balls are not usually sold in cylindrical packages.

8. A conveyor belt unloading salt from a ship makes a conical pile 10 m high with a base diameter of 20 m.
   (a) How much plastic sheeting would it take to just cover the pile of salt?
   (b) What is the volume of salt in the pile?
   (c) The salt is transported in trailers 5 m long by 2.5 m wide and 2 m high. If each trailer can carry only three quarters of its volume, how many trailer loads of salt are in the pile?

9. A glass-domed roof in the shape of a hemisphere covers a shopping mall food court. What is the area of glass if the dome is 20 m across?

10. A can of soup has a diameter of 7.5 cm and a height of 11 cm.
   (a) What is the volume of the can?
   (b) The manufacturer of the soup wants to reduce costs by minimizing the surface area of the can. In order to hold the same volume of soup, what will be the new dimensions of the can? Suggest a reason why soups are not usually packaged in a can of this shape.

Answers

Review of Essential Skills and Knowledge (Part I)

Number Sense and Numeracy: Decimals

1. (a) 260   (b) 270   (c) 1300
   (d) 1400   (e) 19 000   (f) 20 000
2. (a) 1.4   (b) 1.3   (c) 1.4
   (d) 0.24   (e) 0.23   (f) 1.2
   (g) 7.3   (h) 2.39
3. (a) 9.5   (b) 109.4   (c) 10.1
   (d) 18.1   (e) 21.0
4. (a) 11.9   (b) 4.9   (c) 36.0   (d) 70.8
5. (a) 120.1   (b) 171.2   (c) 62.3
   (d) 70.1   (e) 76.6
6. (a) 0.2   (b) 1.7   (c) 6.9
   (d) 0.4   (e) 5.0   (f) 0.6
7.

×	1.0317	1.043	8.07	0.18
10	10.317	10.43	80.7	1.8
10^2	103.17	104.3	807	18
0.1	0.103 17	0.1043	0.807	0.018

8.

÷	134.1	71.43	8.31	0.45
10	13.41	7.143	0.831	0.045
10^2	1.341	0.7143	0.0831	0.0045
0.1	1341	714.3	83.1	4.5

Number Sense and Numeracy: Fractions

1. (a) 6   (b) 4   (c) 16
   (d) 35   (e) 40   (f) 81
   (g) 4   (h) 11   (i) 1
2. (a) $\frac{4}{7}$ (b) $\frac{7}{9}$ (c) $\frac{1}{2}$
   (d) $\frac{4}{9}$ (e) $\frac{1}{2}$ (f) $\frac{3}{4}$
3. (a) $\frac{4}{9}$ (b) $\frac{7}{15}$ (c) $\frac{1}{15}$
   (d) $\frac{11}{24}$ (e) $\frac{7}{12}$ (f) $\frac{1}{6}$
4. (a) $3\frac{1}{3}$ (b) $3\frac{3}{5}$ (c) $5\frac{1}{2}$
   (d) $4\frac{1}{6}$ (e) 4   (f) $7\frac{3}{5}$
5. (a) $2\frac{1}{3}$ (b) $2\frac{1}{4}$ (c) $1\frac{3}{5}$
   (d) $\frac{3}{4}$ (e) $\frac{3}{11}$ (f) $\frac{4}{7}$
6. (a) $\frac{3}{10}$ (b) $\frac{21}{40}$ (c) 9

(d) $\frac{6}{11}$ (e) $\frac{2}{5}$ (f) $\frac{1}{2}$
7. (a) $\frac{15}{28}$ (b) $\frac{10}{33}$ (c) $\frac{6}{7}$
   (d) $\frac{10}{13}$ (e) 3   (f) $4\frac{1}{2}$
   (g) $\frac{1}{12}$ (h) $\frac{1}{14}$
8. (a) $\frac{1}{2}, \frac{5}{8}, \frac{3}{4}$ (b) $\frac{3}{4}, \frac{13}{16}, \frac{7}{8}$
   (c) $\frac{3}{5}, \frac{3}{4}, \frac{9}{10}$ (d) $\frac{2}{3}, \frac{5}{6}, \frac{8}{9}$

Number Sense and Numeracy: Ratio and Rate

1. (a) 3 : 7   (b) 5 : 6   (c) 7 : 3
   (d) 7 : 4   (e) 6 : 5   (f) 4 : 7
2. (a) 1 : 2   (b) 1 : 3   (c) 2 : 5
   (d) 2 : 7   (e) 3 : 5   (f) 5 : 7
   (g) 1 : 2 : 3   (h) 3 : 1 : 4   (i) 4 : 3 : 5
   (j) 4 : 3 : 5
3. (a) 4 : 7   (b) 2 : 3   (c) 2 : 5   (d) 2 : 3
4. (a) 7 : 30   (b) 17 : 60   (c) 500 : 1   (d) 1 : 4
5. (a) 4   (b) 9   (c) 14
   (d) 24   (e) 3, 8   (f) 3, 18
6. (a) 2 tins/dollar   (b) $9.38/h   (c) $1.33/novel
   (d) 19.75 km/h   (e) 0.75 goals/shot
7. (a) 1 : 17   (b) 25 : 1   (c) 1 : 5.49   (d) 0.41 : 1

Number Sense and Numeracy: Percent

1. (a) $\frac{49}{100}$ (b) $\frac{3}{4}$ (c) $\frac{1}{100}$
   (d) $\frac{1}{200}$ (e) $\frac{1}{3}$ (f) $\frac{3}{40}$
2. (a) 73%   (b) 30%   (c) 14%
   (d) 25%   (e) 62.5%   (f) 100%
3. (a) 43%   (b) 92%   (c) 22.5%
   (d) 107%   (e) 351%   (f) 0.5%
4. (a) 11.3   (b) 51   (c) 90
   (d) 1.2   (e) 1.1   (f) 20.6
5. (a) 73%   (b) 87%   (c) 38%
   (d) 52%   (e) 130%   (f) 126%
6. (a) 9   (b) 64   (c) 32
   (d) 5   (e) 1   (f) 65 536
7. (a) $180   (b) $127.50   (c) $7.50
   (d) $3.75   (e) $45   (f) $93.75
8. (a) 10%   (b) 20%   (c) 15%
   (d) 33.3%   (e) 45%   (f) 12.5%

Number Sense and Numeracy: Factors and Exponents

1. (a) 4   (b) 8   (c) 16
   (d) 9   (e) 27   (f) 81
   (g) 16   (h) 64   (i) 125

2. (a) 12 **(b)** 24 **(c)** 32 **(d)** 128
(e) 36 **(f)** 108 **(g)** 72 **(h)** 64
(i) 128 **(j)** 225

3. (a) base 2, exponent 3 **(b)** base 3, exponent 2
(c) base 2, exponent 4 **(d)** base 3, exponent 4
(e) base 5, exponent 2

4. (a) 3^5 **(b)** 2^4 **(c)** 5^3 **(d)** 4^6

5. (a) 5×5 **(b)** $2 \times 2 \times 2 \times 2 \times 2$
(c) $6 \times 6 \times 6 \times 6$ **(d)** $x \times x \times x$
(e) $y \times y \times y \times y$ **(f)** $2m \times 2m \times 2m$
(g) $3n \times 3n$ **(h)** $4 \times 4 \times 4$
(i) $3 \times 3 \times 3 \times 3$

6. (a) 8 **(b)** 81 **(c)** 25
(d) 1 **(e)** 0 **(f)** 256

7. (a) 10^2 **(b)** 10^3 **(c)** 10^5
(d) 10^6 **(e)** 10^1 **(f)** 10^7

8. (a) 2^2 **(b)** 2^4 **(c)** 2^6 **(d)** 2^8

9. (a) 53 **(b)** 32 **(c)** 24 **(d)** 36

10. (a) 4 **(b)** 4 **(c)** 8
(d) 12 **(e)** 11 **(f)** 4

11. (a) $2^2 \times 5^2$ **(b)** $2^2 \times 3^1$ **(c)** $2^2 \times 3^3$
(d) $5^2 \times 10^2$ **(e)** $3^2 \times 2^1$ **(f)** $2^3 \times 3^2$

Number Sense and Numeracy:
Integers—Addition and Subtraction

1. (a) -5 **(b)** -1 **(c)** 0
(d) -2 **(e)** -9 **(f)** -4

2. (a) -2 **(b)** 1 **(c)** -7 **(d)** -10
(e) 0 **(f)** 5 **(g)** -12 **(h)** -1 **(i)** -10

3. (a) 7 **(b)** -3 **(c)** 8 **(d)** 3
(e) 12 **(f)** 0 **(g)** -4 **(h)** 2

4. (a) -2 **(b)** 8 **(c)** -4 **(d)** -10
(e) 1 **(f)** 10 **(g)** -4 **(h)** -10

5. (a) 7 **(b)** -5 **(c)** 2 **(d)** -2
(e) 0 **(f)** -8 **(g)** 12 **(h)** 4
(i) -13 **(j)** -2

6. (a) $<$ **(b)** $=$ **(c)** $>$
(d) $=$ **(e)** $>$

7. (a) most: $4 - 3 - (-4)$, least: $-5 - 3 + 4$
(b) most: $-5 - (-2) + 4$, least: $-14 + 5 + 6$
(c) most: $9 - (-2) - 7$, least: $-5 - 3 + 6$
(d) most: $4 - (-3) - 7$, least: $5 - (-2) - 9$
(e) most: $-5 - 2 + 4$, least: $3 - 12 + 2$

Number Sense and Numeracy:
Integers—Multiplication and Division

1. (a) -6 **(b)** 36 **(c)** -12
(d) 21 **(e)** 20 **(f)** -14

2. (a) 14 **(b)** -24 **(c)** -35
(d) 35 **(e)** 36 **(f)** -36

3. (a) 3 **(b)** -4 **(c)** -3 **(d)** 3
(e) -1 **(f)** 4 **(g)** -5 **(h)** 2

4. (a) -10 **(b)** 3 **(c)** -5
(d) -8 **(e)** -1 **(f)** 2
(g) -2 **(h)** -3 **(i)** 2

5. (a) 16 **(b)** 16 **(c)** 81
(d) 25 **(e)** -25 **(f)** 64
(g) -64 **(h)** -32 **(i)** 9

6. (a) -18 **(b)** -32 **(c)** -135 **(d)** 36
(e) 72 **(f)** 100 **(g)** 75 **(h)** -75

7. (a) -12 **(b)** 72 **(c)** -9
(d) 8 **(e)** 4 **(f)** 2
(g) -4 **(h)** 1 **(i)** 6

8. (a) 35 **(b)** 2 **(c)** -576

Number Sense and Numeracy:
Order of Operations

1. (a) 6 **(b)** -1 **(c)** 14 **(d)** -2
(e) 8 **(f)** 3 **(g)** -4

2. (a) 26 **(b)** -16 **(c)** -11 **(d)** 6
(e) 16 **(f)** 101 **(g)** -1 **(h)** -30
(i) -41 **(j)** 6

3. (a) iv. **(b)** i. **(c)** v.
(d) ii. **(e)** iii.

4. -4 **5.** 3 **6.** 2 **7.** 4
8. -4 **9.** -5 **10.** 3 **11.** 8
12. -3 **13.** 0

Number Sense and Numeracy: Square Roots

1. (a) 5.2 **(b)** 6.4 **(c)** 9.6
(d) 10.1 **(e)** 3.5 **(f)** 8.1

2. (a) 5.9 **(b)** 2.8 **(c)** 7.1
(d) 8.8 **(e)** 10.3 **(f)** 2.1

3. (a) 0.3 **(b)** 0.6 **(c)** 1.2 **(d)** 0.5
(e) 0.9 **(f)** 1.3 **(g)** 0.8 **(h)** 1.4

4. (a) 15 **(b)** 18 **(c)** 22
(d) 36 **(e)** 21 **(f)** 17

5. 12 m × 12 m

6. 8.2 cm

7. (a) 13 cm **(b)** 24.5 cm **(c)** 14.3 mm
(d) 74.8 cm **(e)** 36 cm **(f)** 78.1 m

8. 54.5 m

Patterning and Algebra:
Variables and Substitution

1. (a) 21 **(b)** 2 **(c)** 20 **(d)** 0
(e) 12 **(f)** 2 **(g)** 8

2. (a) 23 **(b)** 11 **(c)** 3
(d) 3 **(e)** 6 **(f)** 3

3. (a) 10 **(b)** 14 **(c)** 44 **(d)** 20

4. (a) 23 **(b)** 7 **(c)** 15 **(d)** 12
(e) 11 **(f)** 7 **(g)** 75 **(h)** 5

5. (a) 144, 144 **(b)** same

6. (a) rectangle: $A = l \times w$;
(b) triangle: $A = \frac{1}{2} \times b \times h$
(d) square: $A = s^2$
(c) parallelogram: $A = b \times h$

7. (a) 24 cm^2 **(b)** 19.1 cm^2
(c) 86.5 cm^2 **(d)** 48.9 cm^2

8. (a) 3.14 **(b)** 12.56 **(c)** 50.24

Patterning and Algebra: Language in Mathematics

Note: "a" is the symbol for years.

1. (a) $2k$ (b) $k - 3$ (c) $k \div 6$ (d) $2k + 3$
   (e) $3 - 2k$ (f) $k + k$ (g) k^2
2. (a) $(c + 1)$ a   (b) $(c - 2)$ a
   (c) $2c$ a   (d) $(2c - 3)$ a
3. (a) $(m - 4)$ a   (b) $3(m - 2)$ a   (c) $(m + 1)$ a
4. (a) $8k¢$ (b) $17k¢$ (c) $50k¢$ (d) $46k¢$
   (e) $75k¢$ (f) $k¢$ (g) $100k¢$ (h) $nk¢$
5. (a) $10(d + 3)¢$ (b) $25(d + 3)¢$
   (c) $t(d + 3)¢$ (d) $100(d + 3)¢$
   (e) $200(d + 3)¢$ (f) $100m(d + 3)¢$
6. (a) $(p + 20)$ km/h   (b) $(p - 3)$ km/h
   (c) $2p$ km/h   (d) $\frac{2}{3}p$ km/h
7. $(2n - 3)$ 8. $(e - 2)$
9. $2(z + 3)¢$ 10. $3.96(2c - 3)¢$

Patterning and Algebra: Solving Equations

1. (a) $n = 4$ (b) $f = -3$ (c) $x = 6$
   (d) $g = -6$ (e) $n = 11$ (f) $z = 15$
2. (a) $x = 3$ (b) $n = 6$ (c) $c = -4$
   (d) $m = -5$ (e) $h = -5$ (f) $a = 5$
3. (a) $k = 3$ (b) $k = 7$ (c) $a = 5$
   (d) $y = -3$ (e) $z = 2$ (f) $p = 3$
   (g) $v = 2$ (h) $h = 0$ (i) $y = -2$
   (j) $y = 1$
4. (a) $\{12\}$ (b) $\{20\}$ (c) $\{-8\}$
   (d) $\{-32\}$ (e) $\{48\}$ (f) $\{0\}$
5. (a) $m = 6$ (b) $k = -15$ (c) $n = 20$
   (d) $e = 28$ (e) $h = 8$
6. (a) iii.   (b) i.   (c) iv.   (d) ii.
7. (a) $2x = 26$, $x = 13$ (b) $n - 5 = 2$, $n = 7$
   (c) $n - 4 = -9$, $n = -5$
   (d) $2x + 3 = 19$, $x = 8$

Patterning and Algebra: Working with Right Triangles

1. (a) 8.06   (b) 6.56   (c) 18.9
   (d) 16.2   (e) 2.35   (f) 0.94
2. (a) $h^2 = 4^2 + 3^2$ (b) $c^2 = 5^2 + 12^2$
   (c) $26^2 = 10^2 + k^2$ (d) $8^2 = 5^2 + w^2$
3. (a) 5   (b) 13   (c) 24   (d) 6.2
4. (a) $a = 10$ (b) $g = 12.2$ (c) $c = 11.5$
   (d) $n = 12$ (e) $y = 13.2$ (f) $h = 4.2$
5. 11 m   6. 2.0 m   7. 64.8 m

Data Management: Working with Statistics

1. (a) A, C, D   (b) A, E, F   (c) A, B, C, D, E
2. D
3. (a) 2%   (b) 1.8%
   (c) 6 no, 3 maybe, 2 yes, 0 maybe
4. (a) S   (b) S   (c) S   (d) P   (e) P
   (f) P   (g) S   (h) S
5. (a) S   (b) M   (c) N   (d) R   (e) C   (f) Y
   (g) Y   (h) M   (i) R   (j) S   (k) N

Data Management: Organizing and Representing Data

1. (a) Activity, Frequency: Movie, 17; Party, 15;
   Bowling, 7; Skating, 20; Hockey, 19
   (b)

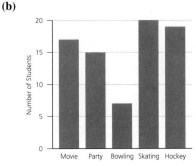

2. (a) 60
   (b) 28.3%, 36.7%   (c) 78°, 48°
3. (a) 20   (b) 25%   (c) 54°
4. $1.50, 3, 10°; $2, 7, 24°; $2.50, 17, 59°; $3,
   15, 52°; $3.50, 11, 38°; $4, 21, 73°; $4.50, 15, 52°;
   $5, 7, 24°; $5.50, 5, 17°; $6, 3, 10°

Data Management: Graphing Relationships

1. (a) 7   (b) 8   (c) 9
2. (a) 3.6   (b) 5.6   (c) 4.4
   (d) 10   (e) 15.4   (f) 13
3. (a)

Length vs. Mass

(graph: Length of Stretch (cm) vs Mass (g))

   (b) 2.4 cm, 8 cm,
       9 cm
   (c) 17.5 g, 27.5
       g, 39 g

Data Management: Measures of Central Tendency

1. (a) 68 kg   (b) 68 kg   (c) 67.6 kg   (d) 67.6 kg
2. (a) mean 15.3 a, median 15 a, mode 15 a
   (b) mode   (c) mean 24.2 a
3. (a) mean 58.4 m, median 56 m, mode 49 m and 63 m
   (b) Two measures each occur twice.
4. (a) No, because they are different types of shoes.
   (b) Yes, because they can be placed in order.
   (c) most: court and crosstrainers; least: basketball

Mental Mathematics and Estimation Strategies

(Actual values are given.)

Rounding Up/Rounding Down
(a) $13   (b) $10.51   (c) $26.77

Flexible Rounding
(a) $175.77   (b) $311.36   (c) $800.52

Compatible Numbers
(a) $21.07 (b) $30.80 (c) $50.52

Convenient Decimals
(a) $5.72 (b) $19.48 (c) $0.63

Clustering
(a) 30 L (b) $29.77 (c) 3060 kg

Rounding to the nearest Half
(a) about $1\frac{2}{3}$ (b) about $1\frac{1}{3}$ (c) about $\frac{47}{100}$

Front End Loading
(a) 20 865 (b) 18 864 (c) 78 887

Chapter 1

Getting Ready

1. (a) 2 (b) 78
   (c) 19 (d) 0
   (e) does not exist (f) 23
2. (a) 4 (b) 4 (c) 9.5
   (d) 10.5 (e) 74.5 (f) 100
3. (a) 6 (b) 7 (c) 19.8
   (d) 52.9 (e) 50 (f) 12.9
4. (a) mode 13, median 14, mean 14
   (b) mode 20, median 20, mean 32
   (c) does not exist, median 802, mean 727
   (d) mode 0, median 0, mean 13
   (e) mode 12, median 43, mean 43.3
   (f) mode 99, median 20, mean 43.8
5. (a) 4.5, 4.5, 4.5 (b) 3, 3, 5
   (c) does not exist, 520.5, 549.25
   (d) 0, 32, 32 (e) 0.3, 0.75, 1
   (f) does not exist, 76, 71
6. (a) *example*: Since most people buy their computers from computer stores, surveying all computer stores in Canada will yield an accurate idea of which computer was sold most often.
   (b) *example*: Advantage: short and easy to understand survey requiring little time on the part of the store owners being surveyed. Disadvantage: entire survey would be very time consuming, since there are many computer stores in Canada.
   (c) *example*: Get data from consumer magazines and computer publications.
   (d) *example*: When the data being collected is much more important than the time the data takes to be collected.
   (e) *example*: A census is probably less biased than other forms of data collection because no one is excluded from the sample pool of a census. If questions in the census are biased, however, then the census procedure can be biased.

7. (a)

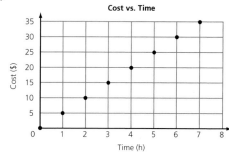

(b)

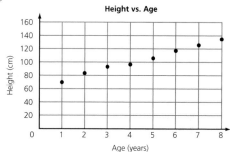

(c)

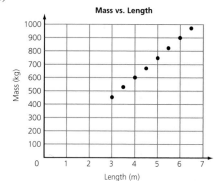

(d)

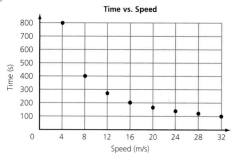

(e)

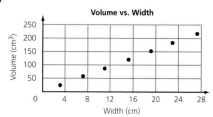

(f)

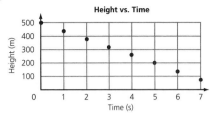

Height vs. Time

1.2 Recognizing and Reducing Bias

Practise, Apply, Solve

1. **(a)** biased, because only bus-riders are asked
   (b) non-biased
   (c) non-biased
   (d) biased, because only those who watch and are interested will vote

2. *examples*:
   (a) Not a random sample. Latecomers may have different viewpoints.
   (b) not a good cross-section of the population
   (c) The students in each class might not be randomly selected.
   (d) People with bad attitudes towards homework might not be home.
   (e) not a random sample
   (f) not a random sample
   (g) not a random sample

3. *examples*:
   (a) biased, because only patrons may vote, and some may vote multiple times
   (b) biased, because class representatives are not a random sample
   (c) biased, because many people are not home on a Wednesday morning

4. **(a)** biased, because not every member of the population has a chance to vote
   (b) biased, because not every member of the population has a chance to vote
   (c) non-biased

5. **(a)** *example*: asking teenagers at school
   (b) Teenagers would be in the sample group. They are readily available at school. Not everyone would be surveyed (would take too long).
   (c) *example*: Convenience sampling is taking a sample group of people that match the survey category and are easy to survey (since they tend to be easily accessible).
   (d) *example*: advantages: easy for pollster, information can be gathered quickly; disadvantages: the sample group is basically at one location (the school). Teenagers from different schools should also participate for any meaningful conclusions to be reached.
   (e) *example*: The sampling procedure is biased, since a more varied sample group is needed.

6. **(a)** Yes, all of the names were in the hat so everyone had a chance of being selected.

   (b) This sample is random because everyone who was selected was selected by chance.
   (c) Yes, it is the same as in part **(a)**.
   (d) *example*: have a computer select names at random
   (e) *example*: advantages: generally, non-biased groups are selected; disadvantages: sometimes a more specific sample should be selected
   (f) No, since everyone has an equal chance of being selected.

7. **(a)** *example*: If there are 15 boys and 20 girls, then select 3 boys and 4 girls
   (b) *example*: hair colour
   (c) *example*: advantages: useful for comparing how different groups respond to a question; disadvantages: may create bias if the survey question involves different groups

8. **(a)** *example*: The publisher wants to get a large enough sample group.
   (b) *example*: Yes, because no other schools have input.
   (c) *example*: advantages: gives representative sample group for each area of the population; disadvantages: not useful for widespread surveys
   (d) *example*: select ten students from each of ten schools
   (e) *example*: a form of sampling in which large groups of people from several locations make up the sample group

9. **(a)** random sampling of the school's students
   (b) convenience sampling among those involved in fine arts
   (c) convenience sampling among those involved in athletics

10. **(a)** non-biased *example*: Assign every student a number, then randomly select ten numbers.
    (b), (c) non-biased *example*: the students involved in these activities know more about their success or failure than other students.

11. *example*: biased: ask ten friends. Non-biased: Assign everyone numbers, then randomly select ten.

12. A random selection of students and staff should be at the meeting to represent the needs and interests of the school population.

13. Any random method of selection is suitable.

14. *example*:
    (a) Ask mainly young male drivers.
    (b) Ask very few young male drivers.
    (c) Ask as many young male drivers as compared to the rest of the survey respondents.

15. *example*:
    (a) Do you chew gum? What kind of gum would you most highly recommend?
    (b) 20 people selected at random from a phone book
    (c) telephone survey
    (d) a bar graph, each bar representing a type of gum

16. *example*:
    (a) Would you chew a gum that is tastier than any other gum?
    (b) candy-shop patrons
    (c) personal interviews

1.4 Drawing Conclusions from Data

Practise, Apply, Solve

2. *example*:
   (a) We cannot say how often they use it, or whether they prefer it to other brands.
   (b) This majority may represent a single group, such as council members.
   (c) This is not a representative sample.
   (d) It does not say what they prefer it to.
4. (a) *example*: Products that are unavailable cannot be compared with those that are.
   (b) The survey could have been biased by asking only friends of the lobby group members.
6. *example*:
   (a) It is assumed that all 513 people read the paper. The sample size is inappropriately large.
   (b) It is assumed that the proportions of this very small survey will be the same for a larger one. The sample size is too small to give representative results.
7. (a) No. This sample was not representative, and the students may have non-Canadian heroes.
   (b) It is assumed that a Canadian teen's hero must be Canadian.
8. (a) *example*: geographic location, different amounts of time spent with each parent
   (b) *example*: Possibly there was not a large enough sample of different neighbourhoods to obtain precise conclusions.
   (c) *example*: The age of the children may affect their opinions. The article only mentioned numerical statistics for Grade 5 students, which may be misleading.
9. (a) promoters of beef consumption
   (b) *example*: No. Just because heme iron is absorbed "more readily" does not mean that we require it in our diets more than non-heme iron. Also, we are not told how much iron we actually need, and whether there are foods other than beef that are also very rich in iron.
11. The graph does not present data reliably. In it, Brand A appears to be four times more popular than Brand D. Start the graph at zero to present the data reliably.

1.6 The Process of Designing an Experiment

Practise, Apply, Solve

1. (a) decide on a method to collect the data
   (b) organize the data
   (c) graph the data
   (d) collect the data
   (e) decide on a method to collect the data
   (f) decide on a method to collect the data
2. *examples*:
   (a) There exists a direct linear relationship between height and "arm stretch."
   (b) by direct measurement
   (c) random sampling
   (d) measuring with a ruler or a tape measure
   (e) twenty samples in a table
   (f) in a graph, a line graph or scatter plot
   (g) Represent "arm stretch" on the horizontal axis, height on the vertical axis.
   (h) As height increases, "arm stretch" also increases.
   (i) advantage: direct measurement is usually reliable; disadvantage: human error may have affected the accuracy of measurements
   (j) Selected students at random.
4. *example*: The experiment may involve having subjects listen to different types of music for specific time periods. Each subject will then have his or her heart rate measured before the music starts playing, at several points during the music, and after the music stops playing. Doctors can use the results to create a calmer atmosphere for patients undergoing medical operations. Other people who deal with stress, such as students studying for an exam, may find the results helpful.
5. *example*: To investigate the relationship, it may be easier to deal with a simpler problem. An example would be trying to figure out the approximate interest rate needed if you invest $360/year, instead of $30/month. Any results would be imprecise, but it would give you an idea of the range of values you should be thinking about.
9. *examples*:
   (a) a survey
   (b) direct measurement or research
   (c) research
10. *examples*:
    (a) hamburgers, french fries, hot dogs, onion rings
    (b) a random survey of people in the neighbourhood
    (c) Onion rings were the most popular fast food. Hot dogs were the least popular fast food.
    (d) mostly onion rings, then hamburgers and fries, and maybe a few hot dogs.
    (e) In the neighbourhood, since the data on which foods are most popular will not change. If it cannot be in the neighbourhood, then it should be built in another area where people like the same types of food. More surveys would have to be conducted to figure out which other areas are best.
11. *examples*:
    (a) Holding your wrist and counting the number of beats in 15 s, then multiplying by 4 to get the number of beats in a minute, or feeling your neck and doing the same, are two different methods for taking your pulse.
    (f) When resting before exercise, the pulse rate is relatively slow. Exercise raises the pulse rate to varying degrees, depending on the type of exercise and how long one exercises. Then resting after exercise lowers the pulse rate once again.

12. *examples*:

    (a) One aspect of student physical fitness may be how many pushups each student can do in a row. Since there is not enough time for an impartial observer to count the number of pushups each student does separately, the data will have to come from students counting how many pushups other students did. The only likely source of error is dishonesty on the part of the counter.

    (b) Maybe a random sample of about 20% of each grade in the school would be enough to make valid conclusions about the school's fitness level. The data can be collected by having the subjects gather in groups at a time when they have done nothing physically strenuous beforehand. Then half of them can do their pushups while the other half counts, and vice versa. The data can then be collected and organized.

    (c) A bar graph may be the best choice because it would be easy to figure out the average performance of the student body.

13. **(a)** *example*: The plants will grow taller if more water is given to them each day.

    (b) *example*: amount of water, amount of sunlight, type of soil, temperature, the use of fertilizer

    (c) amount of water

    (d) amount of sunlight, type of soil, temperature, the use of fertilizer

    (e) Keep the conditions in (d) the same for all of the plants in the experiment. That way only the factor being studied (the amount of water) will affect the height of the plants.

    (f) *example*: Put all of the plants in an environment where the factors in (d) are the same for every plant (i.e. on a windowsill indoors). Group the plants into *n* groups, where *n* is the number of different amounts of water you want to test. There should be an equal number of plants in each group, and each group should have more than one plant to increase the accuracy of the experiment. Water and measure the height of each plant every day, and record the data.

    (g) *example*: Organize the data in several tables.

    (h) *example*: A line graph would be most appropriate, so that height of each group of plants can be compared on a day-to-day basis.

    (i) Bias was avoided by making sure that the factors in (d) did not affect the results of the experiment.

1.8 Drawing and Interpreting Scatter Plots

Practise, Apply, Solve

1. **(a)** You would set up a table with number of hours spent watching TV per night in one column, and math marks in the other.

    (b) You would label number of hours spent watching TV nightly on the horizontal axis, and math marks on the vertical axis.

(c) (3, 90)

(d) The graph would probably slope down to the left because math marks would generally decrease with number of TV hours watched increasing.

2. **(a)** Jodi is correct.

    (b) Reduce your height values by 1.

3. **(a)**

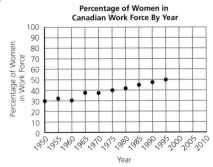

(b), (c) As the year increases, the percentage of women in the Canadian work force increases.

(d) *example*: If the graph keeps rising at its current rate, about 60%. However, it is possible the graph could level off or decrease.

4.

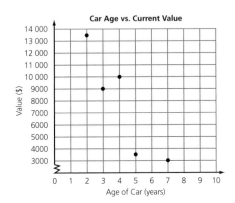

5. **(a)**

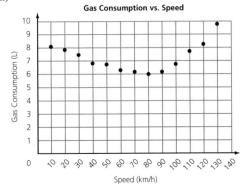

(b) This plot could be reasonable; the curve is smooth, and the engine might perform more efficiently at higher speeds.

(c) The amount of gas consumed decreases until 80 km/h is reached, then increases.

(d) *example*: engine manufacturer designing a more efficient engine

6. *example*: As the air becomes less clean, the number of allergies increase.

7. (a), (b) *example*:

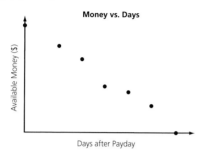

Money vs. Days

Available Money ($) — Days after Payday

(c) *example*: The available money is at its highest value on payday (i.e., 0 days after payday), and then the amount of money decreases with time as the money is spent.

8. (a)

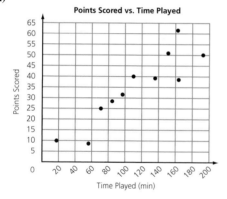

Points Scored vs. Time Played

Points Scored — Time Played (min)

(b) Generally the number of points scored increases with the number of minutes played.

9. (a)

Birth Rate by Year

Birth Rates Per 1000 People — Year

○ ON
■ NF
◇ PE
+ NS

(b) The graph consists of points, because not all of the data points fall on a straight line.

(c) As height increases, so does weight.

(d) No. Eventually you stop growing taller.

10. (b) Birth rates are decreasing in Canada and in the provinces identified.

(c) extinction

(d) *example*: No, because the birth rate should eventually stabilize.

11. (a)

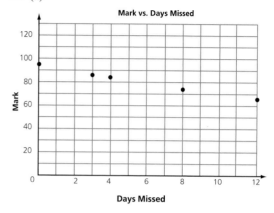

Mark vs. Days Missed

Mark — Days Missed

(b) As a student misses more days of school, the student's mark decreases.

1.10 The Line of Best Fit

Practise, Apply, Solve

3. (a) The greater the number of hours of TV watched, the lower the test mark.

7. (a) around 16 minutes
   (b) around 14 points

8. (b) about 4 field goals made
   (d) about 16 points made

9. (c) around 13 cm
   (d) around 18 cm

10. Doug's line is not reasonable because there are nine points below his line, and only five points above it.

11. (a) about 160 m
   (b) about 36 s
   (c) It would not be reasonable to use the graph to estimate the time for Alex to run large distances, such as 3000 m. Alex can go much faster sprinting short distances than he can running for long distances. Since his speed would be different in each of the situations, the corresponding times would not be related in the same way to the different distances, so the graph cannot be used.

12. (a) about 1020 seats; about 495 seats
   (b) about 11 days
   (c) no

1.12 Interpreting Correlation Value

Practise, Apply, Solve

1. (a) negative correlation
   (b) positive correlation
   (c) no correlation
   (d) negative correlation
2. (c) *example*: Those who live farther from the school take more time to get to school.
   (d) There is a positive correlation between distance from the school and time taken to get to school.
   (e) *example*: The scatter plot should display a strong positive correlation. Any inconsistencies may be explained by some students using different means of transportation to get to school.
3. (a) negative correlation
   (b) no correlation
   (c) positive correlation
   (d) no correlation
   (e) negative correlation
4. (a) positive correlation
   (b) negative correlation
   (c) positive correlation
   (d) negative correlation
   (e) positive correlation
5. (a) The first student will not be able to make a prediction based on these lines. The second student correctly drew the line of best fit. The third student incorrectly drew the line of best fit. Thus, the second student is correct.
   (b) The first student simply connected the points, rather than drawing a line of best fit. The third student's line was too low to correctly fit the data.
6. (a) *example*: number of wrinkles
   (b) *example*: hearing ability
   (c) *example*: hair length
8. (a) *examples*: study time, time spent asking teacher questions
   (b) *examples*: amount of TV watched, lack of attendance
   (c) *examples*: type of clothing, number of CDs owned
11. They are both examples of positive correlation; Figure A has a stronger correlation than Figure B.
12. (a) iv.   (b) 2   (c) iii.
    (d) i.   (e) ii.
13. (b) The scatter plot shows a negative correlation between latitude and average temperature.
    (c) *example*: Find the average temperature of a city with latitude 47°N.
14. (c) There is a positive correlation between height and hand span.

1.14 Drawing the Mean Fit Line

Practise, Apply, Solve

1. (a) (6.75, 8.5)   (b) (3, 6.67)
   (c) (363.75, 212.5)

2. (a) i. positive correlation, ii. strong positive correlation, iii. negative correlation
3. (b) The farther Dawn is from the net, the less shots she makes. Strong negative correlation.
   (c) *example*: If she stood 1 m from the net, she would make 27 shots. If she stood 12 m from the net, she would not make any shots.
4. (b) This point is the average ratio of wrist circumference to shoe length for your class.
   (e) This line represents the relationship between wrist circumference and shoe length for your class.
5. Find the mean of the first set of data, then find the mean for the second set of data. Plot this mean point on your graph. Draw a line of best fit through this point, which best represents the relationship or correlation you see in your data. Try to get the same number of points above the line as there are below the line.
6. It is easier to see the correlation when the number of data points increases. However, it is then more difficult to draw the line of best fit, since there are more points that must fall above or below the line.
7. *examples*: Find the mean point. (1987.5, 7.9) What is the relationship (strong positive correlation)? Extrapolate car efficiency in 1992 (10).
9. Predictions are made by interpolation or extrapolation.
10. A strong correlation means that all of the data points occur on or very near to the line of best fit. A weak correlation means that the data points vary from the line of best fit.
11. Scatter plots are used to relate two sets of data. Once all data points are plotted, find the mean point and draw the mean fit line. The graph can now be used to interpolate or extrapolate values for unknown data. In real life, scatter plots would be used to show relationships between things like age and physical activity, etc.
12. (c) In $2\frac{3}{4}$ h, 550 soft drinks would be sold.
    (d) In 3.5 h, 700 soft drinks would be sold.
13. (c) 78   (d) 54
14. (a) *example*: As height increases, so does shoe size.
    (b) *example*: As movie admission price increases, movie attendance decreases.
    (c) *example*: Test for correlation between a person's first initial and their height. Gather the data by random sampling. No correlation would be found.
15. (c) 76 cm
16. (c) 75
    (d) The line of best fit without the point (0, 0) is more precise, since (0, 0) is not part of the original data set.

Chapter Review

1. by random selection

2. (a) *example*: unbiased: random sample of students throughout the school; biased: only students from a specific class or grade are surveyed
   (b) *example*: unbiased: random sample of students with equal numbers of male and female students in the sample; biased: a sample of students that consists of more males than females, or vice versa
   (c) *example*: unbiased: random sample of students throughout the school; biased: a sample that is made up of members of a school sports team

3. (a) No. The sample may have been biased, and the questions asked might have been unclear.
   (b) How did you select your sample? What kind of survey did you conduct? What questions did you ask?
   (c) If the sample was large enough and randomly selected, and if the questions asked were clear and straightforward.

4. (a) There is a bias because only parents attending that meeting will be asked. An appropriate sample will be randomly selected from all parents, teachers, and students.
   (b) There is a bias because students who are bused to school may not vote. An appropriate sample will be selected randomly from the entire student population.

5. (a) No. Although there is evidence to show that these movies are the highest-grossing movies of the year, there is no evidence that they are the "best movies of the year." Also, this does not necessarily imply that filmgoers prefer action and suspense over comedy or romance.

6. (a) The fact that more than half the respondents to the poll thought that it is "at least somewhat likely" that aliens have visited Earth does not imply that they would not be surprised if they landed in their backyards. Also, the statistics suggest that less than 38% of Canadians actually believe that aliens exist. Thus, the conclusion is not justified.
   (b) The most convincing data is that which does not reveal the actual statistics, but uses words like "many." This leads us to believe that a majority feel this way, although this may be untrue.

8. (b) The points rise from left to right. The pattern shows that there is a weak positive correlation between the amount a student makes and the amount they save.

9. (b) The points rise from left to right. The pattern show that there is a strong positive correlation between the student's test mark and their course grade.

10. (b) There is no pattern shown in the data points.

11. (b) The number of hours practised daily seems to rise slightly from left to right. There is a very weak positive correlation.

12. (b) The points generally rise from left to right. This suggests that the bigger the movie budget is, the more the movie might gross.

13. (c) No, since the correlation is very weak.

14. (b) 580 km   (c) 200 km
    (d) For part (b) extrapolation was used because the graph was extended beyond its known data values. For part (c) interpolation was used because a value between two known values was estimated.
    (e) The amount of gasoline used to travel a distance can vary depending on the speed of the car, whether the car is going up or down hill, and so on. This would cause points on the graph to vary from the line of best fit.

15. (c) 3.0 cm   (d) 30 mL   (e) 9.0 cm

16. (c) 110 cm
    (d) No, this is a graph of Mary's height as she is growing. Presumably she will not be growing this fast when she is 18 years old. This line of best fit would not be suitable.
    (e) Yes, the line of best fit may only be used to estimate values close to the known values. As seen in this example, the line of best fit cannot be used to extrapolate values far greater than the known values because people stop growing after they reach a certain age.

17. (b) line slopes upward
    (c) positive correlation

18. (b) ii., iii., i., iv.
    (c) For some of the graphs the line of best fit lies close to all the points. Predictions can easily be made for these graphs. For the other graphs the points are scattered all around the line of best fit. Predictions based on those graphs are not very accurate.

19. (a) As one variable increases the other variable also increases.
    (b) As one variable increases the other variable decreases.
    (c) No relationship can be seen between the two sets of data.

21. (a) (13, 8)   (b) (10, 7)   (c) (4, 3)

22. (a) negative correlation   (b) positive correlation

23. (b) negative correlation   (c) strong
    (d) (5.5, 70.5)

24. (a) Divide the number of cans in the recycling bins by the total number of cans used.

(b) and (c)

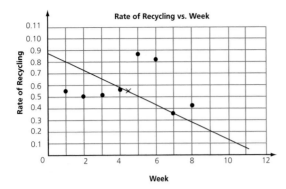

Rate of Recycling vs. Week

(horizontal axis: Week; vertical axis: Rate of Recycling)

(d) No, the student council was not successful. Except for weeks 5 and 6, there is a negative correlation between the number of cans recycled and the total number of cans used.

Chapter Review Test

1. (b) negative correlation
(c) As the temperature increases, the number of bacteria decreases.

2. (a) People at the Ottawa airport may be biased towards the Ottawa hockey team. A better way would be to choose random samples throughout Canada.
(b) People at that particular drugstore may have a different preferred toothpaste brand than those at other drugstores. Random samples of people in different locations would work better.
(c) People at a subway stop may not be as concerned about gasoline taxes, since they usually take public transit. A wide range of people, from drivers to those who take public transportation, should be surveyed.

3. *example*: Bias includes any influence on data collection that leads to imprecise or misleading conclusions. For example, a sample of Grade 1 students from a specific school is asked what their favourite toy is. The sample size is too small to yield accurate conclusions.

4. (a) *example*: money paid and time spent working
(b) *example*: planet temperature and distance from the sun
(c) *example*: number of hairs on a person's head and high school mathematics marks

5. (b) 163.33 cm   **(c)** 176.58 cm
(e) As the boys' heights increase, their fathers' heights increase (a positive correlation).
(f) 191 cm   **(g)** 171 cm

6. *example*: A random sample may not have been the best sample to choose, as perhaps some people in the random sample do not go to movie theatres at all.

7. *example*: The mean fit line is a better line of best fit. Since the mean coordinates of the mean fit line are constant, this provides an ideal standard from which everyone can make predictions from. Lines drawn by visual estimation do not portray the data as accurately as the mean fit line.

8. (a) 113 books   **(b)** her 8th book
(c) Adrienne's 16th book should sell more than 200 copies, so she will have written 16 books in all.

9. (a) Yes, it is biased. Only adults were asked, and they were adults randomly located throughout the community.
(b) A better sample group would include a random sample of both adults and children who live in the western region of the community.

Chapter 2

Getting Ready

1. (a) 9   **(b)** 20   **(c)** 3
(d) 10   **(e)** 1   **(f)** 6
(g) 2   **(h)** 14

2. (a) $\frac{11}{15}$ **(b)** $\frac{5}{6}$ **(c)** $\frac{3}{14}$
(d) $5\frac{11}{12}$ **(e)** $\frac{2}{15}$ **(f)** $1\frac{13}{15}$
(g) $2\frac{7}{20}$ **(h)** $\frac{2}{9}$

3. (a) 4   **(b)** 8   **(c)** −4   **(d)** −36
(e) 21   **(f)** −3   **(g)** 8   **(h)** −8
(i) 30   **(j)** −6   **(k)** −48   **(l)** −13
(m) 1   **(n)** 19   **(o)** −3   **(p)** −2

4. (a) 0.08   **(b)** 0.15   **(c)** 0.075
(d) 0.005   **(e)** 0.236   **(f)** 1.03
(g) 0.586   **(h)** 0.0004

5. (a) $\frac{1}{2}$, 0.5   **(b)** $\frac{4}{5}$, 0.8
(c) $\frac{12}{7}$, 1.7143   **(d)** $\frac{5}{8}$, 0.625
(e) $\frac{3}{4}$, 0.75   **(f)** $\frac{7}{8}$, 0.875
(g) $\frac{2}{3}$, 0.$\overline{6}$ **(h)** $\frac{11}{8}$, 1.375

6. (a) $2.00/tin   **(b)** $9.38/h
(c) 39.5 km/h   **(d)** $10.99/CD
(e) 7 m/s   **(f)** $6.58/book
(g) $14.17/dinner   **(h)** 1.7 min/lap

7. (a) 21   **(b)** 7   **(c)** −3   **(d)** 7
(e) 1   **(f)** 5   **(g)** −2   **(h)** −2
(i) 3   **(j)** 0

8. (a) $x = 4$ **(b)** $b = 37$ **(c)** $y = 3$
(d) $c = -92$ **(e)** $b = 6$ **(f)** $x = 5$
(g) $x = 27$ **(h)** $d = -18$ **(i)** $y = 40$
(j) $c = 7$ **(k)** $b = -3$ **(l)** $m = 78$

2.1 Graphing a Relationship

Practise

(a)

	A	B
1	t	D
2	-4	0
3	-3	5
4	-2	10
5	-1	15
6	0	20
7	1	25

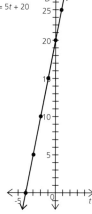

$D = 5t + 20$

(b)

	A	B
1	m	C
2	-1	-23
3	0	2
4	1	27
5	2	52

$C = 25m + 2$

(c)

	A	B
1	r	H
2	-2	$-\frac{1}{3}$
3	-1	$\frac{1}{3}$
4	0	1
5	1	$1\frac{2}{3}$
6	2	$2\frac{1}{3}$
7	3	3

$H = \frac{2}{3}r + 1$

(d)

	A	B
1	x	y
2	-2	-2
3	-1	4
4	0	10
5	1	16

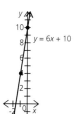

$y = 6x + 10$

(e)

	A	B
1	x	y
2	-1	-35
3	0	0
4	1	35

$y = 35x$

(f)

	A	B
1	x	y
2	-2	-1.25
3	-1	-1
4	0	-0.75
5	1	-0.5
6	2	-0.25
7	3	0
8	4	0.25

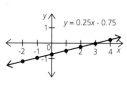

$y = 0.25x - 0.75$

2.2 Tables of Values, Patterns, and Graphs

Practise, Apply, Solve

1. a straight line
2. (a), (c), (d)
3. **(a)** distance   **(b)** cookies made
   (c) total fire alarms
4. **(a)** number of sweaters   **(b)** pages printed
   (c) cans of juice
5. false, the labels on the axes should be switched
7. **(a)** independent variable is the hours worked,
   dependent variable is the cost
   (b)

h	Cost
0	$20
1	60
2	100
3	140
4	180

(c)

Cost vs. Hours

(d) $120

8. (a)

Time (min)	Height (m)
0	1500
1	3600
2	5700
3	7800
4	9900
5	12 000
6	14 100
7	16 200
8	18 300
9	20 400
10	22 500

(b)

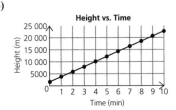

Height vs. Time

(c) The balloon rises at 2100 m per minute. This is a straight line or linear relationship.

(d) 6.4 min

9. (a)

Books Sold	Royalties
0	$0
5000	1250
10 000	2500
15 000	3750
20 000	5000
25 000	6250

(b)

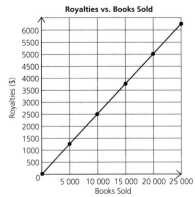

Royalties vs. Books Sold

(c) This is a linear relationship. The royalties increase at $1250 per 5000 books.

(d) $5375

10. (a)

Week	Bank Balance
0	$900
1	800
2	700
3	600
4	500
5	400
6	300
7	200
8	100
9	0

(b)

Balance vs. Week

(c) The graph decreases by $100 every week. This relationship is linear.

(d) 9 weeks

(e) These are all linear relationships. The graph decreases. The rest are increasing graphs.

11. (a)

Hours	Earnings
0	$0
5	45
10	90
15	135
20	180
25	225
30	270
35	315
40	360
45	427.50
50	495

(b)

(c) This relationship is not linear because the graph is not a straight line.

(d) The line changes at 40 h because, for every hour Anne works over 40 h, she gets paid at a higher rate.

12. (a)

Time (min)	Depth (m)
0	0
5	50
10	100
15	150
20	200
25	250
30	300

(b)

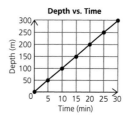

(c) This is a linear relationship. The submarine descends at 10 m/min or 50 m/5 min.

13. (a)

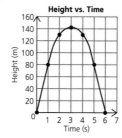

(b) The relationship is not linear since it is not a straight line.

(c) both 108 m

(d) The rocket reaches 80 m once on the way up and once on the way down.

(e) The rocket's height would be −112 m or 112 m down into the ground after 7 s.

14. (a) No, the graph is not a straight line.

(b) $40

(c) $60

(d) 2 days

(e) No, the first two days are $20 a day; after that the cost of renting is $10 a day.

2.3 Graphing an Equation

Practise

(a)

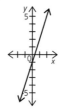

(b)

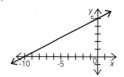

(c)

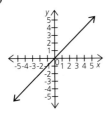

(d)

(e)

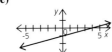

2.4 Connecting Equations and Graphs

Practise, Apply, Solve

1. (a) Cost = 5 + 5 × time in hours, $C = 5 + 5t$
  (b) Charge = 10 × time in hours, $C = 10t$
  (c) Baskets = 20 × time in hours, $B = 20t$
  (d) Cost = 25 + 19 × tonnes of sand,
     $C = 25 + 19t$
  (e) Gas left = 75 − 0.125 × Distance travelled in
     km, $G = 75 − 0.125d$
  (f) Earnings = 15 × time in hours, $E = 15t$

2. (a), (d), (e)

3. (a) Y1 = 5 + 5X   **(b)** Y1 = 10X
  (c) Y1 = 20X   **(d)** Y1 = 25 + 19X
  (e) Y1 = 75 − 0.125X   **(f)** Y1 = 15X

4. Red is a direct variation; blue is a partial variation.

5. (a) false   **(b)** false
  (c) true   **(d)** false

6. (a) Cost = 20 + 40 × time in hours, $C = 20 + 40t$
  (b) *example*: cell formula = 20 + 40*A2

	A	B
1	*t*	*C*
2	0	$20
3	1	60
4	2	100
5	3	140

  (c) Y1 = 20 + 40X, Y = 20 + 40X, *x* represents
     time in hours and *y* represents total cost.
  (d) This is a partial variation since the cost will
     never be zero as there is a flat rate of $20.

(e)

	A	B
1	*t*	*C*
2	0	$20
3	1	60
4	2	100
5	3	140
6	4	180
7	5	220
8	6	260

  (f) $C = \$440$

7. (a) Height = 1500 + 35 × time in seconds,
     $H = 1500 + 35t$, or Height = 1500 + 35 × 60
     seconds per minute × time in minutes,
     $H = 1500 + 2100t$
  (b) Y1 = 1500 + 2100X, Y = 1500 + 2100X,
     x represents the time in minutes because time is
     the independent variable, *y* represents the height
     reached by the balloon. *y* is the dependent
     variable.
  (c) *example*: cell formula = 1500 + 2100*A2

	A	B
1	Time (min)	Height (m)
2	0	1500
3	1	3600
4	2	5700
5	3	7800
6	4	9900
7	5	12 000
8	6	14 100
9	7	16 200
10	8	18 300
11	9	20 400
12	10	22 500

  (d) This is a partial variation since the graph never
     passes through zero on the *y*-axis.
  (e) For every second that passes the graph rises
     35 m, or for every minute that passes the balloon
     rises 2100 m.
  (f) $H = 12\ 000$ m

8. (a) Earnings = 0.25 × number of books sold,
     $E = 0.25b$
  (b) Y1 = 0.25X, Y = 0.25X, *x* represents the
     number of books sold, which is the independent
     variable. *y* represents the amount earned which
     is the dependent variable.

(c) *example*: cell formula = 0.25*A2

	A	B
1	Books Sold	Royalties
2	0	$0
3	5000	1250
4	10 000	2500
5	15 000	3750
6	20 000	5000
7	25 000	6250
8	30 000	7500
9	35 000	8750
10	40 000	10 000
11	45 000	11 250

(d) This is a direct variation since the graph passes through the *y*-axis at zero.

(e) The graph rises $1250 for every 5000 books sold.

(f) $E = \$250\ 000$

9. (a) Bank balance = 900 − 100 × time in one week intervals, $B = 900 - 100t$

(b) Y1 = 900 − 100X, Y = 900 − 100X, *x* represents the time that passes in one week intervals, which is the independent variable. *y* represents the dependent variable, or the bank balance.

(c) *example*: cell formula = 900 − 100*A2

	A	B
1	Time (weeks)	Bank Balance
2	0	$900
3	1	800
4	2	700
5	3	600
6	4	500
7	5	400
8	6	300
9	7	200
10	8	100
11	9	0

(d) This is a partial variation because the graph does not pass through the *y*-axis at zero.

(e) For every week that passes, $100 is withdrawn from the bank account. The graph moves over 1 time interval and down $100 on each rate triangle.

(f) $B = \$300$

10. (a) Depth of submarine = 50 × time in 5 min intervals, $D = 50t$, or Depth = 10 × time in minutes, $D = 10t$

(b) Y1 = 10X, Y = 10X, *x* represents the time in 1 min intervals or the independent variable. *y* represents the depth that the submarine has reached or the dependent variable.

(c) *example*: cell formula = 10*A2

	A	B
1	Time (min)	Depth (m)
2	0	0
3	5	50
4	10	100
5	15	150
6	20	200
7	25	250
8	30	300
9	35	350
10	40	400

(d) This is a direct relationship, since the graph passes through the *y*-axis at zero.

(e) For every minute the graph moves over it rises 10 m, or for every 5 minutes the graph moves over it rises 50 m.

11. (a) Plan A: Cost = 0.75*g*,
Plan B: Cost = 10 + 0.50*g*

(b) Plan A: Cost = $15, Plan B: Cost = $20

(c) Plan A: Cost = $30, Plan B: Cost = $30

(d) 30 beverages a month use Plan A, 50 beverages a month use Plan B

14. (a)

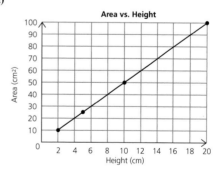

(b) Area = 5*h*

15. (a) $2y = 4x - 8$ or $y = 2x - 4$

(b) $3y + 6 = 12x$ or $y = 4x - 2$

(c) $10x - 5 = 5y$ or $y = 2x - 1$

(d) $8x = 4y - 20$ or $y = 2x + 5$

2.6 Graphing in Four Quadrants

Practise, Apply, Solve
1. (a) $U(2, 2)$ **(b)** $B(-5, 2)$ **(c)** $C(2, -3)$
 (d) $V(-2, -2)$ **(e)** $G(5, -7)$ **(f)** $K(-7, 2)$
 (g) $E(-5, 5)$ **(h)** $N(0, -6)$
2. (a) A **(b)** S **(c)** T
 (d) I **(e)** Q **(f)** L
3. (a) MAT
4. (a) P$(-6, 0)$, Q$(2, 0)$
 (b) Both P and Q have a zero y-coordinate, and lie on the horizontal axis.
5. (a) W$(0, 6)$, L$(0, 2)$, N$(0, -6)$
 (b) They all have a zero x-coordinate, they lie on the vertical axis.
6. D, F, J, V
7. origin $(0, 0)$
8. D, H, J, U, V
9. I, E
10. (a) first quadrant **(b)** second quadrant
 (c) fourth quadrant **(d)** second quadrant
 (e) third quadrant
11. (a) $L(0, 2)$, $W(0, 6)$ **(b)** $N(0, -6)$
 (c) $Q(2, 0)$, $M(5, 0)$ **(d)** $P(-6, 0)$

12. (c) $(-1, -2)$, $(0, 0)$, $(1, 2)$
 (e) triangle
13. (b) linear   **(c)** $(0, 1)$, $(7, 8)$
14. (a)

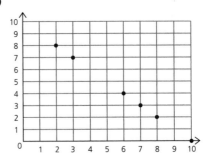

(b) straight line
(c) $(0, 10)$, $(1, 9)$, $(4, 6)$, $(5, 5)$, $(9, 1)$
15. (a) sum = 9   **(b)** a straight line

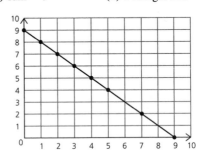

(c) $(6, 3)$, $(8, 1)$ **(d)** a linear relation
16. (a)

x	y
-2	1
-1	2
0	3
1	4
2	5

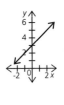

(b)

x	y
-2	-4
-1	-2
0	0
1	2
2	4

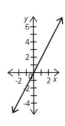

500 ANSWERS

(c)

x	y
−2	−7
−1	−5
0	−3
1	−1
2	1

(h)

x	y
−2	−4.5
−1	−4.25
0	−4
1	−3.75
2	−3.5

(d)

x	y
−2	−4
−1	−1
0	2
1	5
2	8

17. (a)

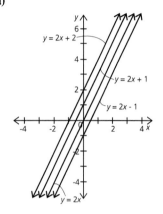

(b) The graphs are all parallel. They all intersect the x-axis and the y-axis in different spots.

18. (a)

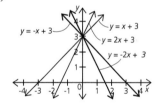

(e)

x	y
−2	8
−1	4
0	0
1	−4
2	−8

(b) The graphs all pass through point (0, 3). They all intersect the x-axis in different spots.

19. (a) This is a straight line graph. The graph represents a linear relation.

(f)

x	y
−2	11
−1	6
0	1
1	−4
2	−9

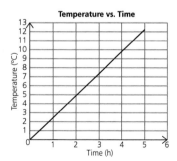

(g)

x	y
−2	−1
−1	−0.5
0	0
1	−0.5
2	1

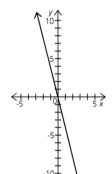

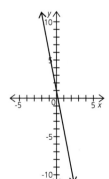

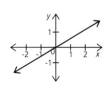

20. (a) *example*: a straight line graph, linear relation

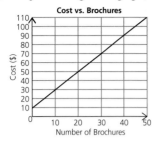

21. (a)

x	y
−3	13
−2	12
−1	11
0	10
1	9
2	8
3	7

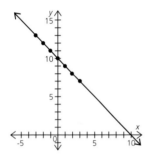

(b)

x	y
−2	12
−1	10
0	8
1	6
2	4

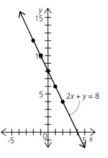

(c)

x	y
−5	−6
−1	−3.6
0	−3
1	−2.4
5	0

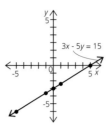

22. (a) 10 lines   **(b)** 15 lines

23. (a)

Number of Toppings (t)	Price of the Pizza (P)
0	9
1	9.75
2	10.50
3	11.25
4	12
5	12.75

(b)

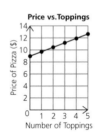

There is a linear relationship.

(c) $13.50

(d) No, since the number of toppings on a pizza has to be a whole number.

24. (a)

x	y
−3	−16
−2	−13
−1	−10
0	−7
1	−4
2	−1
3	2

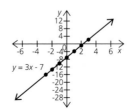

(b)

x	y
-2	$5\frac{3}{4}$
-1	$4\frac{1}{4}$
0	$2\frac{3}{4}$
1	$1\frac{1}{4}$
2	$-\frac{1}{4}$

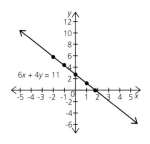

$6x + 4y = 11$

(c)

x	y
-2	$\frac{1}{3}$
-1	$\frac{5}{12}$
0	$\frac{1}{2}$
1	$\frac{7}{12}$
2	$\frac{2}{3}$

$x - 12y = -6$

2.7 The Roles of *m* and *b* in *y* = *mx* + *b*

The Steepness of a Line

1.

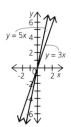

$y = 5x$

$y = 3x$

2. The graphs are both linear relations since they are straight lines. They have different slopes.

3. $y = 5x$ is the steeper line

4. **(a)** $y = 10x$ is the steepest line.
   (b) $y = 0.5x$ is the least steep line.

5. $y = 5x - 3$ is the steeper line. The graphs are both linear relations. They have different slopes.

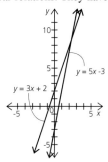

$y = 5x - 3$

$y = 3x + 2$

6. $y = 5x - 3$ and $y = 3x - 2$ have different intersection points with the axes than the graphs from Question 1.

7. **(a)** The larger *m* is in the equation of a line, the steeper the graph will be.
   (b) The line will cross the *y*-axis at *b*.

8. The vertical side of the rate triangle tells how much the graph rises and the horizontal side tells how much the graph moves over. As the vertical side increases and the horizontal side decreases, the steeper the graph becomes.

The Direction of a Line

1.

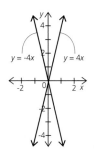

$y = -4x$

$y = 4x$

2. The graphs intersect the axes at the same point. $y = 4x$ moves up 4 and right 1 unit on the rate triangle. $y = -4x$ moves down 4 and right 1 unit on the rate triangle.

3. A negative number in front of *x* makes the graph of a line slope downwards.

2.8 The Roles of Slope and Intercepts

Practise, Apply, Solve

1. **(a)** false   **(b)** true
   (c) false   **(d)** true

2. **(a)** $m_1 = \frac{1}{2}$, $m_3 = 0.75$, $m_2 = 6$, $m_4 = 10.5$
   (b) $m_3 = -0.25$, $m_1 = -1$, $m_2 = -5$, $m_4 = -11$

3. **(a)** $y = 6x + 8$ **(b)** $y = -4x - 6$
   (c) $y = 19x - 4$ **(d)** $y = 6x + 4$

4. **(a)** $b = 14$, $m = -6$ **(b)** $b = 14$, $m = 14$
   (c) $b = 20$, $m = 3$ **(d)** $b = 10$, $m = -16$

5. **(a)** iii.   **(b)** iv.   **(c)** ii.   **(d)** i.

6. (a) amount Joe had in earnings when he started working, time when Joe had no earnings, how much Joe earns per hour he works

(b) flat rate to rent the banquet hall, not applicable, cost for lunch per person

(c) value of a new copier, age of a worthless copier, rate of depreciation per year for a copier

7. (a) $y = 10x$ **(b)** $y = 5x + 150$

(c) $y = -x + 7$

8. (a) slope $= 7500$, represents the value increase per year of the house

(b) y-intercept $= 125\,000$, represents the starting value, or the value of the new house

(c) $177\,500$

9. (a) slope $= -1360$, represents the depreciation value of the car per year

(b) y-intercept $= 17\,000$, represents the price of the new car

10. (a) slope $= 0.03$, represents the percentage she gets of her weekly sales

(b) y-intercept $= 350$, represents her base salary for the week

(c) 3200

11. (a) slope $= 1.25$, represents the amount he is paid per tire made

(b) y-intercept $= 0$, represents the amount he is paid if he makes no tires

12. (a) $b = 0$, slants upward, fairly steep

(b) $b = 5$, slants upward, very steep

(c) $b = 0$, slants downward, steep

(d) $b = -1$, slants downward, slightly steep

(e) $b = 0$, slants upward, very gradual

(f) $b = -4$, slants downward, slightly steep

13. (a)

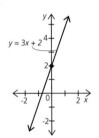

(b)

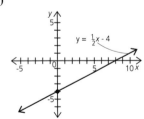

(c)

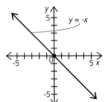

(d)

(e)

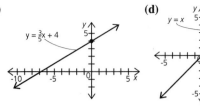

(f)

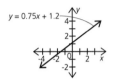

14. (a) 0.75/km   **(b)** $y = 1.2 + 0.75x$

(c)

(d) the base fee to call a taxi

15. (a) 5.25/child   **(b)** $F = 5.25c + 50$

(c)

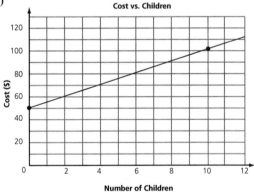

(d) the base to fee to hire the clown

2.9 Finding the Equation of a Given Line

Practise, Apply, Solve

1. (a) true   **(b)** false

(c) false   **(d)** true

2. 0.2

3. (a) 18 cm   **(b)** 100 cm   **(c)** 0.72

4. (a) 1   **(b)** -7 **(c)** -3

(d) 5   **(e)** 3   **(f)** -12

6. (a) $m = 1$ **(b)** $m = \dfrac{1}{5}$ **(c)** $m = -34$

(d) $m = 9$ **(e)** $m = 3$ **(f)** $m = -1$

(g) $m = -\dfrac{3}{4}$

7. (a) $y = 3x + 6$ (b) $y = \frac{3}{2}x + 7$

    (c) $y = -\frac{3}{2}x + 8$ (d) $y = 4x - 3$

    (e) $y = \frac{5}{6}x + 13$ (f) $y = -\frac{3}{4}x$

    (g) $y = \frac{2}{5}x - 2$

8. (a) $m = -1, b = 7, y = -x + 7$
    (b) $m = -1, b = -7, y = -x - 7$
    (c) $m = 2, b = 1, y = 2x + 1$
    (d) $m = \frac{3}{4}, b = 3, y = \frac{3}{4}x + 3$
    (e) $m = -5, b = 0, y = -5x$
    (f) $m = -2, b = 12, y = -2x + 12$

9. (a) $y = \frac{2}{3}x - 3$ (b) $y = \frac{1}{3}x - 2$

    (c) $y = -\frac{1}{4}x - \frac{1}{4}$ (d) $y = 2x - 7$

10. (a) independent variable is time, dependent variable is distance

    (b)

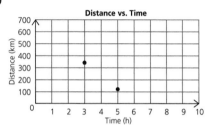

    (c) $y = -110x + 680$
    (d) slope represents the speed at which they are travelling, y-intercept represents their starting position

11. (a) rate = \$1556 per year
    (b) $y = 1556x - 3\,060\,671$
    (c) income = \$66 889

12. (a) cost   (b) rate = \$0.55/km
    (c) $y = 0.55x + 50$
    (d)

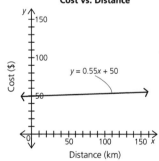

    (e) \$77.50, \$121.50, \$325.00

13. (a) maximum heart rate in a stress test for a newborn
    (b) the rate of decline of maximum heart rate in a stress test over the years
    (c) $y = -0.81x + 185$
    (d) maximum heart rate = 138 beats/min

14. (a) $y = 0.75x + 6.75$ (b) cost = \$6.75
    (c) cost = \$10.50

15. (a) $y = 0.03x$ (b) cost = \$0.75
    (c) cost = \$5.70   (d) 200 min

16. (a) cost = \$3.50 per meal
    (b) rental cost = \$100   (c) $y = 3.5x + 100$
    (d) cost = \$397.50

17. value = $-316.67x + 1750$, where x represents age

18. (a) $y = 1\,811\,250x + 36\,225\,000$
    (b) \$61 582 500

19. $y = -10x + 48$

2.10 Slopes and Equations of Lines: Special Cases

Special Case I

(a)   (b)

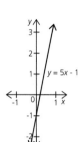

Special Case II

(a)

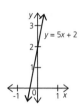

Practise, Apply, Solve

1. (a)

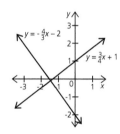

    (b)

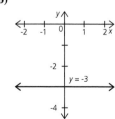

(c)

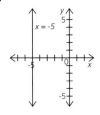

(d)

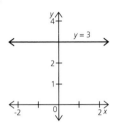

(e)

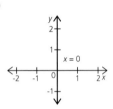

(f)

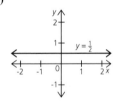

2. The vertical change is equal to zero for a horizontal line.

3. The horizontal change is equal to zero for a vertical line.

4. (a) $m = 0$, $y = -2$ **(b)** slope undefined, $x = -2$
   (c) $m = 0$, $y = 2$ **(d)** slope undefined, $x = 3$

5. (a) false   **(b)** true
   (c) false   **(d)** true

6. (a) perpendicular   **(b)** neither
   (c) parallel   **(d)** perpendicular
   (e) neither   **(f)** neither

7. (a) parallel   **(b)** perpendicular
   (c) perpendicular   **(d)** neither
   (e) parallel   **(f)** neither

8. (a) $y = 6$ **(b)** $x = 4$ **(c)** $x = 3$
   (d) $y = 1$ **(e)** $x = -1$ **(f)** $y = 5$

9. (a) $x = -4$ **(b)** $y = 5$
   (c) $y = -3$ **(d)** $x = 1$

10. (a) $y = -2x - 5$ **(b)** $-\frac{2}{3}x - 2 = y$

   (c) $y = \frac{5}{3}x$ **(d)** $y = 5x - 6$

   (e) $y = \frac{-1}{3}x - 6$

11. (a) Sarah: $y = 10 + 8x$; Latoya: $y = 8x$
   (b) parallel
   (c)

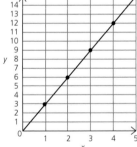

   (d) Latoya will never catch Sarah.

12. (b) Slope of $FG = 1$; slope of $FH = -1$. They run at the same speed. Since these are negative reciprocals, FG is perpendicular to FH.

13. (a) $y = $ constant   **(b)** $x = $ constant

14. $k = -\frac{4}{3}$ or $k = -\frac{3}{4}$

15. (a) $y = 12$ **(b)** $y = 2$ **(c)** $x = -1$

2.11 Conditions for Linear Relationships

Practise, Apply, Solve

1. (a) linear   **(b)** nonlinear   **(c)** linear
   (d) nonlinear   **(e)** nonlinear   **(f)** nonlinear
   (g) linear   **(h)** nonlinear   **(i)** nonlinear
   (j) linear   **(k)** linear   **(l)** nonlinear

2. (a)

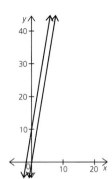

(b)

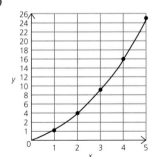

(c)

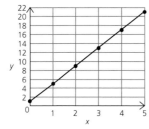

(d)

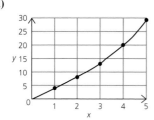

(e)

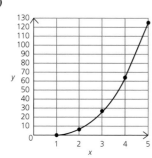

(f)

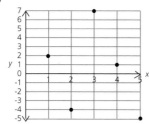

(g)

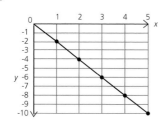

(h)

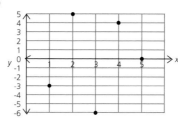

(i)

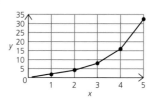

(j)

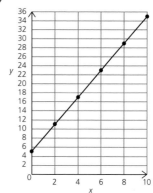

(k)

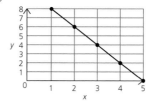

(l)

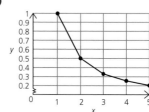

3. (a) $y = 3x$ **(c)** $y = 4x + 1$ **(g)** $y = -2x$
(j) $y = 3x + 5$ **(k)** $y = -2x + 10$

4. (a) nonlinear

(b)

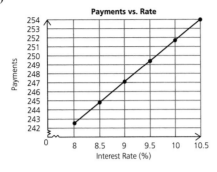
Payments vs. Rate

(c) $243.63   **(d)** 10.76%

5. (a) nonlinear

(b)

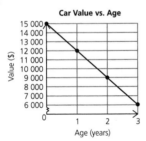
Height vs. Time

(c) 33.75 m   **(d)** 3 s

(e) These are the points where the ball is at ground level.

6. (a) linear

(b)

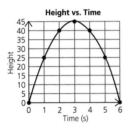
Car Value vs. Age

(c) $y = -3000x + 15\ 000$

(d) $10 500

(e) According to the graph, the car will be worthless after five years. This is not realistic because the car's depreciation will slow down, never reaching zero.

7. (a)

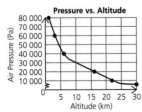
Pressure vs. Altitude

(b) As the altitude increases, the air pressure decreases, although the rate of decrease slows down with increasing altitude.

(c) nonlinear   **(d)** around 13 000 Pa

8. (a)

Time (h)	0	1	2	3	4	5
Bacteria	500	750	1125	1688	2532	3798

(b)

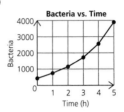
Bacteria vs. Time

(c) nonlinear   **(d)** around 3.4 h

9. (a)

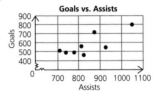
Goals vs. Assists

(b) nonlinear

(c) We cannot make predictions because the data does not follow any recognizable pattern.

10. (a)

x	y
1	1
2	4
3	9
4	16
5	25
6	36
7	49
8	64

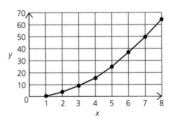

(b)

x	y
1	1
2	8
3	27
4	64
5	125
6	216
7	343
8	512

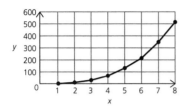

(c)

x	y
1	1
2	0.5
3	0.33
4	0.25
5	0.2
6	0.17
7	0.14
8	0.13

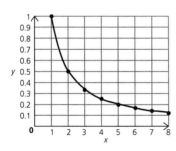

(d)

x	y
1	1
2	1.41
3	1.73
4	2
5	2.23
6	2.45
7	2.65
8	2.83

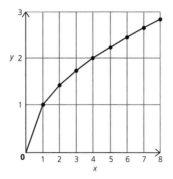

(e)

x	y
1	20
2	10
3	6.67
4	5
5	4
6	3.33
7	2.86
8	2.5

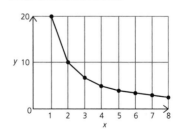

11. none

12. (a) $y = |x^3|$ **(b)** $y = 5x$ **(c)** $y = \frac{1}{x}$

2.13 Finding the Line of Best Fit

Practise, Apply, Solve

1. **(a)** $y = 1.65x + 1.84$ **(b)** $y = 3.38x + 8.34$
   (c) $y = 2x + 8$ **(d)** $y = 1.57x - 0.72$
2. **(e), (c), (b), (a), (d)**
3. **(a)** years   **(b)** $y = -0.911x + 253.817$
   (c) The line is a good representation because the absolute value of the correlation coefficient is close to 1.
   (d) around 213.7 s
4. **(a)**

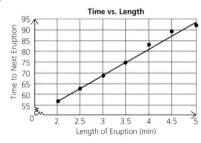

Time vs. Length

   (b) $y = 12.43x + 31.64$
   (c) 90.68 min
   (d) This equation will make very accurate predictions, as the correlation coefficient is very close to 1.
5. **(a), (c)**

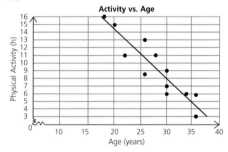

Activity vs. Age

   (b) The scatter plot shows a weak negative correlation between age and the length of time spent exercising per week.
   (e) $y = -0.62x + 26.64$
6. **(a), (c)**

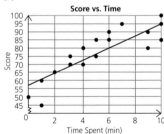

Score vs. Time

   (b) The scatter plot indicates a positive correlation.
   (f) $y = 3.79x + 56.87$

(g) The graphing calculator will give us more accurate predictions.
(h) 76%
7. **(a)** $y = 0.65x + 27.11$, where y is the student's science mark, x is the student's mathematics mark.
   (b) There exists a positive correlation between marks from the two subjects.
   (c) 82%   **(d)** no
9. No. The line of best fit indicates a never-ending increase in height, but this would not happen.

2.14 Finding the Point of Intersection

Practise
   (a) $(2, -3)$ **(b)** $(4, 3)$
   (c) $(-1, 5)$ **(d)** $(5, 1)$

2.15 Finding and Interpreting the Point of Intersection

Practise, Apply, Solve

1. **(a)** $(2, 2)$ **(b)** $(2, 3)$ **(c)** $\left(\frac{4}{7}, \frac{4}{7}\right)$
2. **(a)** one point
   (b) when the lines are parallel
3. **(a)** yes   **(b)** yes
   (c) no   **(d)** no
4. **(a)** yes   **(b)** no
   (c) no   **(d)** yes
   (e) yes   **(f)** no
5. **(a)** $(5, 19)$ **(b)** $(5, 3)$
   (c) none   **(d)** $(5, 21)$
   (e) $(0, 0)$ **(f)** $(-1, 2)$
   (g) $(3, -1)$ **(h)** none
6. **(a)** Movies To Go: $C = 2.5v$,
       Videorenters: $C = 10 + 2v$
   (b) The point of intersection is $(20, 50)$.
   (c) In this case, the point of intersection represents the number of videos that have to be rented (20) to yield the same price ($50) at both video stores.
   (d) If a customer is going to rent more than 20 videos in a year (assuming that the membership fee for Videorenters is an annual fee), then the customer should use Videorenters. If the customer is going to rent less than 20 videos in a year, then the customer should use Movies To Go.
7. **(a)** Ontario Express: $P = 5 + m$,
       Day by Day Delivery: $P = 3.5 + 1.25m$
   (c) The point of intersection is $(6, 11)$. It represents the mass that the package has to have (6 kg) to yield the same price ($11.00) at Ontario Express and Day by Day Delivery.
   (d) Ontario Express is less expensive than Day by Day Delivery when a package weighs more than 6 kg. Ontario Express is more expensive than

Day by Day Delivery when a package weighs less than 6 kg.

9. **(a)** $C = 1.2 + 0.06j$ **(b)** $R = 0.10j$

   (d) The point of intersection, (30, 3), represents the break-even point for Bill. When he sells 30 cups of lemonade, his total costs equal \$3, and his total revenue is also \$3.

   (e) i. loss   **ii.** profit   **iii.** profit

10. **(a)** Bill cannot make a profit if he does not increase his selling price. Now the cost of producing a cup is equal to the selling price of each cup (\$0.10). Therefore, the cost and revenue are increasing at the same rate. But there is an initial cost of \$1.20, which means that Bill will never make that initial \$1.20 back because he gains the same amount per cup that he spent.

    (b) The cost line will be steeper, since its slope will be 0.10 now. Since its slope is identical to the slope of the revenue line, both lines will be parallel.

    (c) To maintain the same break-even point, 30 cups of lemonade, Bill should sell the lemonade at \$0.14 per cup.

11. **(a)** The break-even point for Plan A and Plan B is (100, 40). 100 km must be driven to yield the same cost (\$40) for both plans.

    (b) Plan A is the better deal when more than 100 km is driven per day.

    (c) Plan B is the better deal when less than 100 km is driven per day.

12. $\left(\dfrac{44}{5}, \dfrac{74}{5}\right)$

13. **(a)** The slope of both lines is -4.

    (b) The y-intercept of both lines is -2.

    (c) The two lines are identical. Every point that satisfies one equation satisfies the other, therefore any point lying on the line may be considered a point of intersection.

14. **(a)** $\left(\dfrac{1}{6}, -1\dfrac{2}{3}\right)$ **(b)** $\left(\dfrac{1}{4}, \dfrac{1}{4}\right)$

    (c) the two lines are identical, any point on that line is a point of intersection

Chapter Review

1. **(a)**

Year	Earnings (\$M)
0	6
1	10
2	14
3	18
4	22
5	26

(b)

(c) A linear relationship exists in the data.

2. **(a)**

Month	Balance
0	500
1	750
2	1000
3	1250
4	1500
5	1750

(b)

(c) A linear relationship exists in the data.

3. **(a)** The athlete earns \$4 million per year, plus \$6 million to start. $E = 6 + 4Y$ (in millions of dollars).

   (b) $y_1 = 4x_1 + 6$, $y = 4x + 6$, where y represents the athlete's earnings (the dependent variable) and x represents the number of years that the athlete has played for the team (the independent variable).

(c)

Years	Earnings ($M)
0	6 + 4*A1
1	6 + 4*A2
2	6 + 4*A3
3	6 + 4*A4
4	6 + 4*A5
5	6 + 4*A6
6	6 + 4*A7
7	6 + 4*A8
8	6 + 4*A9
9	6 + 4*A10

Years	Earnings ($M)
0	6
1	10
2	14
3	18
4	22
5	26
6	30
7	34
8	38
9	42

(c)

Month	Balance
0	500 + 250*A1
1	500 + 250*A2
2	500 + 250*A3
3	500 + 250*A4
4	500 + 250*A5
5	500 + 250*A6
6	500 + 250*A7
7	500 + 250*A8
8	500 + 250*A9
9	500 + 250*A10

Month	Balance
0	500
1	750
2	1000
3	1250
4	1500
5	1750
6	2000
7	2250
8	2500
9	2750

(d) This is a partial variation when the data is graphed, the y-intercept will occur at $y = 6$.

(e) Using a rate triangle, we find that for every step to the right we make four steps up, reflecting the fact that the athlete earns an extra $4 million every year.

4. (a) Lita has $500 in her account, plus $250 for every month that has passed. $L = 500 + 250M$.

(b) $Y_1 = 500 + 250x_1$, $Y = 500 + 250x$, x is the number of months Lita has been putting money in the account (independent variable) and y is how much money she has in the bank (dependent variable).

(d) This is a partial variation because the y-intercept of the graph will occur at $y = 500$.

(e) Using a rate triangle, we see that for every one step to the right we make 250 steps up. This reflects the fact that Lita puts $250 in her account every month.

5. $D(-6, -4)$

6. (a) $y = 5x - 5$

x	1	2	3	4	5	6	7
y	0	5	10	15	20	25	30

(b), (c)

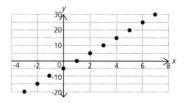

(d) $(-3, -20)$; $(-2, -15)$; $(-1, -10)$

(e) $\left(\frac{1}{2}, -2\frac{1}{2}\right)$ **(f)** none

7. (a) $y = 3x + 5$

x	−2	−1	0	1	2
y	−1	2	5	8	11

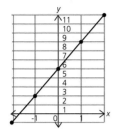

(b) $y = 2x - 6$

x	−2	−1	0	1	2
y	−10	−8	−6	−4	−2

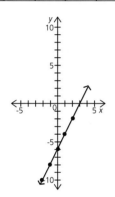

(c) $y = -4x - 3$

x	−2	−1	0	1	2
y	5	1	−3	−7	−11

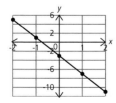

(d) $y = 7x + 3$

x	−2	−1	0	1	2
y	−11	−4	3	10	17

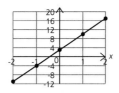

(e) $y = -x - 2$

x	−2	−1	0	1	2
y	0	−1	−2	−3	−4

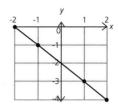

(f) $y = -2x + 1$

x	−2	−1	0	1	2
y	5	3	1	−1	−3

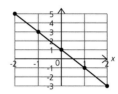

(g) $y = \frac{1}{2}x - 4$

x	−2	−1	0	1	2
y	−5	$-4\frac{1}{2}$	−4	$-3\frac{1}{2}$	−3

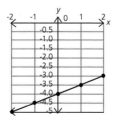

(h) $y = \frac{1}{4}x + 1$

x	−2	−1	0	1	2
y	$\frac{1}{2}$	$\frac{3}{4}$	1	$1\frac{1}{4}$	$1\frac{1}{2}$

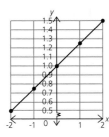

8. (a) 13; −3   **(b)** 15; 11
    (c) −20; 2   **(d)** 1; −18

9. (a) The slope of the line is −5500, which means that the truck's value will decrease by $5500 every year.
    (b) The y-intercept of the line is 125 000, which means that the truck was initially worth $125 000.

10. (a) $y = 2x - 4$

    (b) $y = -3x + 2$

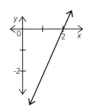

    (c) $y = \frac{3}{4}x - 3$

    (d) $y = 4x - 6$

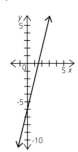

11. (a) $y = 25x + 200$
    (b) $1000, $1325, $1525

12. (a) $y = 5x + 4$ **(b)** $y = \frac{3}{2}x + 4$
    (c) $y = -\frac{1}{2}x + 2$ **(d)** $y = -3x + 5$

    (e) $y = -\frac{3}{4}x + 3$

13. (a) $m = 3; y = 3x + 1$ **(b)** $m = 1; y = x + 1$
    (c) $m = -2; y = -2x$ **(d)** $m = 4; y = 4x + 5$

14. (a) $0.50 per topping   **(b)** $8.75
    (c) $y = 0.5x + 8.75$ **(d)** $11.25

15. (a) $x = 2$

    (b) $y = 5$

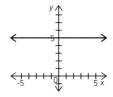

    (c) $x = -3$

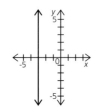

    (d) $y = 1$

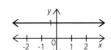

    (e) $y = 0$

    (f) $x = -4$

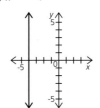

16. (a) 0   **(b)** undefined
    (c) They are equal.
    (d) They are negative reciprocals.

17. (a) $y = -5x - 11$ **(b)** $y = -\frac{1}{4}x + 5$

(c) $y = \frac{3}{4}x - 2$ **(d)** $y = 2x - 3$

(e) $y = -\frac{1}{2}x - 2$

18. (a) linear

Δx	Δy
1	4
1	4
1	4
1	4

(b) nonlinear

Δx	Δy
1	3
1	5
1	7
1	9

(c) linear

Δx	Δy
1	4
2	8
1	4
4	16

(d) nonlinear

Δx	Δy
1	6
1	18
1	54
1	162

19. (a) nonlinear

(b)

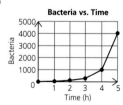

(c) 32   **(d)** around 5 h 36 min

20. (a) linear

(b)

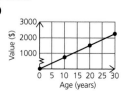

(c) $y = 75x + 0.25$ **(d)** $1125.25

21. $y = -1.08x + 15.38$

22. (a)

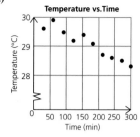

(b) There exists a negative correlation between temperature and time.

(e) $y = -0.01x + 30.01$

23. (a) (3, 1)   **(b)** (2, −1)   **(c)** (−1, 3)

(d) $\left(3\frac{1}{2}, -3\right)$ **(e)** (4, −6)   **(f)** $\left(3\frac{1}{5}, 7\frac{4}{5}\right)$

24. (a) Faster Fitness: $C = 90 + 5n$, Drop-In Fitness $C = 35n$

(b) (3, 105)

(c) The point of intersection represents the number of classes that have to be taken (3 classes) in order to pay the same amount of money ($105) at both Faster Fitness and Drop-In Fitness.

(d) If someone is to take less than 3 instruction classes in a year, then Drop-In Fitness is the best choice. If someone wishes to take more than 3 instruction classes a year, than Faster Fitness is the better choice.

Chapter Review Test

1. (a) Added mass is the independent variable, stretch is the dependent variable.

(b)

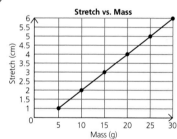

(c) linear

(d) direct variation

(e) 2.4 cm; 8 cm; 9 cm

(f) 17.5 g; 27.5 g; 39 g

(g) $m = 1/5$; $b = 0$. This means that the elastic band is not stretched at all when it has no attached masses, and it stretches 1 cm for each 5 g added to it.

(h) $y = \frac{1}{5}x$

2. (a) $m = 4$ **(b)** $y = 4x - 7$

(c) $m = 4$ **(d)** $m = -\frac{1}{4}$

3. (a)

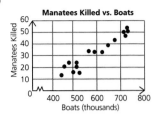

(b) A positive correlation exists in this data, so environmentalists can claim that powerboats are killing the manatee population.

(d) $y = 0.13x - 44.19$

(e) around 86 manatees

4. (a) $x = 5$

(b) $y = -2$

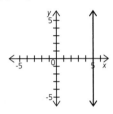

(c) $y = \frac{3}{4}x - 2$

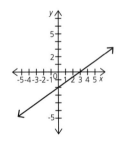

(d) $y = -5x - 4$

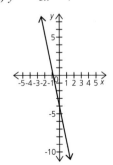

5. (a) $y = 1$ **(b)** $y = -2x + 11$

(c) $y = -\frac{5}{2}x + 5$ **(d)** $y = \frac{1}{2}x + 4$

6. (a) $m = -\frac{7}{6}$ **(b)** $b = -\frac{1}{3}$

(c) $y = -\frac{7}{6}x - \frac{1}{3}$ **(d)** 6

(e) $b = 0$ **(f)** $m = \frac{6}{7}$

7. (a) Time is the independent variable, distance is the dependent variable.

(b)

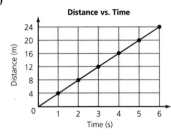

(c) linear   **(d)** direct variation

(e) 10 m; 25 m; 32 m   **(f)** 0.75 s; 5.25 s; 9 s

(g) $m = 4$; $b = 0$. This means that when no time has passed, no distance has been travelled. The distance increases at a rate of 4 m every second.

(h) $y = 4x$

8. (a) $y = -41$ **(b)** $y = -\frac{2}{3}x$

(c) $y = 3x + 6$ **(d)** $y = \frac{3}{4}x + 3$

Chapter 3

Getting Ready

1. (a) -16 **(b)** 17   **(c)** $\frac{1}{6}$

(d) $\frac{19}{36}$ **(e)** 0.011   **(f)** -14

2. $a = 7$

3. (a) 128   **(b)** -325 **(c)** -25 **(d)** 0

4. 32.76 cm²

5. 12 m

6. (a) 81   **(b)** 32   **(c)** 36   **(d)** 64

(e) 27   **(f)** 64   **(g)** 125   **(h)** 16

7. 2.3 cm

8. (a) $x = 5$ cm   **(b)** $x = 6$ cm

9. (a) -30 **(b)** 9

(c) -14 **(d)** -43

10. (a) $-13, -17, -21$ **(b)** $45, 51, 57$

(c) $\frac{1}{16}, \frac{1}{32}, \frac{1}{64}$

(d) 0.000 01, 0.000 001, 0.000 000 1

(e) 256, 1024, 4096   **(f)** 81, -243, 729

(g) 250, 1250, 6250   **(h)** 13, 21, 34

11. (a) $y = 2x$ **(b)** $y = -x$

(c) $y = x + 3$ **(d)** $y = 2x + 1$

3.2 Introduction to Rational Numbers

Practise, Apply, Solve

1.

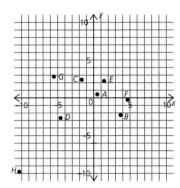

2. (a) $-10.3, -5.5, -4\frac{2}{3}, -1\frac{3}{4}, \frac{1}{2}, 1.5, 3\frac{3}{5}, 4.75$

   (b) $-9.5, -2\frac{7}{8}, -2\frac{1}{5}, -0.1, \frac{1}{3}, 2.25, 2\frac{1}{2}, 2.9$

3. (a) 0.125, terminates   **(b)** 3.6, terminates
   (c) $7.8\overline{3}$, repeats, period = 3
   (d) $4.6\overline{3}$, repeats, period = 63
   (e) $-0.\overline{7}$, repeats, period = 7
   (f) -0.35, terminates
   (g) $-4.\overline{142857}$, repeats, period = 142857
   (h) $-0.\overline{923076}$, repeats, period = 923076

4. (a) $\frac{27}{100}$ **(b)** $1\frac{11}{20}$

   (c) $-2\frac{39}{40}$ **(d)** $-3\frac{3}{16}$

5. Vito is correct.
   Jasmine's error: $\frac{-2 \times 2 - 1}{2} = \frac{-4 - 1}{2} = \frac{-5}{2}$

6. (a) False, rational numbers include fractions, which are not integers.
   (b) True, rational numbers include the whole numbers.
   (c) True, rational numbers include integers.
   (d) True, rational numbers include natural numbers.
   (e) True, decimal numbers are rational numbers.
   (f) True, all rational numbers can be expressed as terminating or repeating decimals.

7.

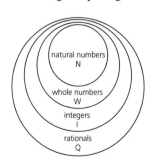

8. (a)

x	y
-1	-3
-0.5	-1
0	1
0.5	3
1	5

(b)

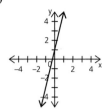

9. (a) False, if the denominator was 0, the quotient would be undefined.
   (b) True, any decimal or fraction is a rational number but not an integer.
   (c) False, all integers are rational numbers.
   (d) False, there is no other integer between two consecutive integers.
   (e) True, any rational number can be found between two other rational numbers.
   (f) False, there are many equivalent fractional forms of rational numbers.
   (g) False, mixed fractions can be expressed as improper fractions and are thus rational numbers.
   (h) False, zero is an integer and is therefore a rational number.

10. (a) The Chinese value of $\frac{355}{113}$ is closest to the present day value of π.
   (b) π is not rational because it is a non-repeating, non-terminating decimal.

12. $0.75 = \frac{75}{100} = \frac{75 \div 25}{100 \div 25} = \frac{3}{4}$ but $0.\overline{75} = \frac{25}{33}$ because it is a repeating decimal.

13. Any fractions with denominators that are not factors of 10, 100, 1000, and so on, repeat.
   examples are: $\frac{2}{11} = 0.\overline{18}, \frac{9}{13} = 0.\overline{692307}$

14. (a) $\frac{3}{11}$ **(b)** $\frac{41}{333}$
   (c) $\frac{1}{30}$ **(d)** $-2\frac{2}{165}$

15. (a)

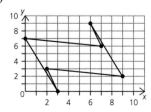

They all form closed shapes, but have different patterns.

3.4 Rational Number Operations

Practise, Apply, Solve

1. Group 1: $\frac{9}{8}$, $1\frac{1}{8}$, $\frac{-9}{-8}$; Group 2: $\frac{-9}{8}$, $-\frac{9}{-8}$

2. $-\frac{16}{3}$, $-3\frac{1}{4}$, -2.87, $-1.\overline{4}$, 0.95, $1\frac{5}{8}$

3. (a) $-1\frac{1}{12}$ **(b)** $-\frac{2}{15}$ **(c)** $-\frac{1}{12}$ **(d)** $\frac{1}{7}$

(e) $1\frac{1}{4}$ **(f)** $-5\frac{9}{10}$ **(g)** $-5\frac{1}{2}$ **(h)** $\frac{2}{3}$

(i) 7 **(j)** $\frac{9}{10}$ **(k)** $-\frac{7}{8}$ **(l)** $-3\frac{1}{3}$

4. (a) $2\frac{5}{8}$ h **(b)** $-11\frac{3}{8}$

5. (a) $-3\frac{49}{60}$ **(b)** $1\frac{4}{5}$ **(c)** $-\frac{23}{24}$

(d) $8\frac{7}{16}$ **(e)** $3\frac{9}{56}$ **(f)** $-1\frac{19}{20}$

6. (a) $\frac{23}{48}$ **(b)** $5\frac{1}{2}$ **(c)** $\frac{11}{12}$

(d) $\frac{11}{12}$ **(e)** $\frac{247}{576}$ **(f)** $1\frac{11}{12}$

(g) $\frac{16}{33}$ **(h)** $-17\frac{1}{3}$ **(i)** $-17\frac{1}{3}$

7. (a) -2.6 **(b)** -15.3 **(c)** -2.73

(d) -2.73 **(e)** -5.07 **(f)** -3.6

(g) $-0.\overline{619047}$ **(h)** $-0.\overline{692307}$

(i) $-0.\overline{692307}$

8. (a) Left Side $= 3x - 7$

$$= 3\left(\frac{1}{3}\right) - 7$$
$$= 1 - 7$$
$$= -6$$

Right Side $= -6$

L.S. $=$ R.S., so $x = \frac{1}{3}$ is the solution.

(b) Left Side $= \frac{3}{4}x - 1$

$$= \frac{3}{4}(-8) - 1$$
$$= -6 - 1$$
$$= -7$$

Right Side $= -7$

L.S. $=$ R.S., so $x = -8$ is the solution.

(c) Left Side $= -\frac{3}{4}x + 2$

$$= -\frac{3}{4}\left(-1\frac{1}{3}\right) + 2$$
$$= -\frac{3}{4}\left(-\frac{4}{3}\right) + 2$$
$$= 1 + 2$$
$$= 3$$

Right Side $= 3$

L.S. $=$ R.S., so $x = -1\frac{1}{3}$ is the solution.

9. In parts (a) and (c) a calculator might interpret fractions such as $\frac{1}{3}$ and $-1\frac{1}{3}$ as repeating decimals, 0.3 and -1.3, producing erroneous values (e.g., $3(0.3) = 0.9$, instead of $3\left(\frac{1}{3}\right) = 1$). In part (b)

there are no repeating decimals in the equation, so part (b) should not be a problem for the calculator.

10. (a) 10 **(b)** 8

11. (a) 1 **(b)** about 0.348

(c) -1 **(d)** $76\frac{1}{3}$

12. (a) $1 + \cfrac{1}{1 + \cfrac{1}{1 + \cfrac{1}{2}}} = 1 + \cfrac{1}{1 + \cfrac{1}{\frac{3}{2}}} = 1 + \cfrac{1}{1 + \frac{2}{3}} = 1 + \cfrac{1}{\frac{5}{3}}$

$$= 1 + \frac{3}{5} = 1\frac{3}{5}$$

(b) $1 + \cfrac{1}{1 + \frac{1}{4}} = 1\frac{4}{5}$

(c) one term: $1 + \frac{1}{2} = 1\frac{1}{2}$

two terms: $1 + \cfrac{1}{2 + \frac{1}{2}} = 1\frac{2}{5}$

three terms: $1 + \cfrac{1}{2 + \cfrac{1}{2 + \frac{1}{2}}} = 1\frac{5}{12}$

four terms: $1 + \cfrac{1}{2 + \cfrac{1}{2 + \cfrac{1}{2 + \frac{1}{2}}}} = 1\frac{12}{29}$

five terms: $1 + \cfrac{1}{2 + \cfrac{1}{2 + \cfrac{1}{2 + \cfrac{1}{2 + \frac{1}{2}}}}} = 1\frac{29}{70}$

(d) the square of the result with one term:

$$\left(1\frac{1}{2}\right)^2 = \frac{9}{4} = 2\frac{1}{4}$$

the square of the result with two terms:

$$\left(1\frac{2}{5}\right)^2 = \frac{49}{25} = 1\frac{24}{25}$$

the square of the result with three terms:

$$\left(1\frac{5}{12}\right)^2 = \frac{289}{144} = 2\frac{1}{144}$$

the square of the result with four terms:

$$\left(1\frac{12}{29}\right)^2 = \frac{1681}{841} = 1\frac{840}{841}$$

the square of the result with five terms:

$$\left(1\frac{29}{70}\right)^2 = \frac{9801}{4900} = 2\frac{1}{4900}$$

As the number of terms in the denominator increases, the square of the continued fraction approaches 2. Therefore, the continued fraction itself must be approaching the positive square root of 2, since it is always positive.

(e) The square of the continued fraction approaches 5, therefore the continued fraction approaches the square root of 5.

14. (a) $p = 2(l + w)$

Expand the parentheses. $p = 2l + 2w$

(b) $p = 2(l + w)$

Expand the parentheses.

$p = 2l + 2w$

Subtract $2l$ from both sides.

$p - 2l = 2w$

Divide both sides by 2.

$\frac{1}{2}(p - 2l) = w$

Switch both sides of the equation.

$w = \frac{1}{2}(p - 2l)$

(c) $p = 2(l + w)$ Expand the parentheses.

$p = 2l + 2w$ Subtract $2w$ from both sides.

$p - 2w = 2l$ Divide both sides by 2.

$\frac{p - 2w}{2} = l$

Switch both sides of the equation.

$l = \frac{p - 2w}{2}$

15. length $21\frac{1}{3}$ m, width $5\frac{1}{3}$ m

3.6 Models of Movement

Practise, Apply, Solve

1. (a) iii.   **(b)** i.   **(c)** iv.   **(d)** ii.

2. (a) The object is stopped from 20 s − 26 s. Its slowest speed while actually moving is from 8 s − 16 s.

(b) The object begins to return to its starting point at the 26 s mark, and reaches its starting point at the 32 s mark.

(c) The slope of the graph between 20 s and 26 s is 0 m/s.

(d) A zero slope (0 m/s) means that the object is not moving during a particular time interval.

4.

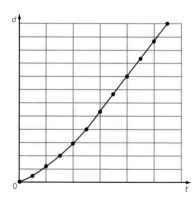

5. (a)

Time (s)	Distance (m)	Differences (m)
0	0	
1	9.3	9.3
2	37.2	27.9
3	83.7	46.5
4	148.8	65.1
5	232.5	83.7
6	334.8	102.3
7	455.7	120.9

The data represents a nonlinear relationship.

(b)

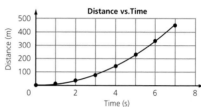

(c) The driver is accelerating, since the difference in distance in each time interval is increasing.

6. i. linear, constant velocity

ii. nonlinear, decelerating

iii. nonlinear, accelerating

iv. nonlinear, constant, then accelerating, then decelerating

7. (a)

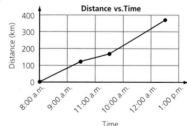

(b) The car travels fastest from 10:30 a.m. to 12:30 p.m. The car travels slowest from 9:30 a.m. to 10:30 a.m.

(c) nonlinear

(d) about 82 km/h

8. (a) nonlinear

(b)

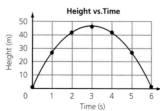

(c) 34.75 m

(d) at the 2.37 s mark or the 3.63 s mark

(e) in the time interval from 3 s to 6 s

(f) in the time interval from 0 s to 3 s

(g) at 3 s   **(h)** 46 m

(i) gravity accelerates the ball downwards

9. (a)

Speed (km/h)	Time (h)
100	1
75	$1\frac{1}{3}$
50	2
25	4
12.5	8
10	10
1	100

(b)

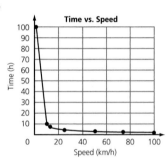

Speed is the independent variable, while time is the dependent variable.

(c) *example*: Pick three points (25, 4), (50, 2), and $\left(75, 1\frac{1}{3}\right)$.

Rate triangle 1: $\text{Slope} = \dfrac{2 - 4}{50 - 25} = -\dfrac{2}{25}$

Rate triangle 2: $\text{Slope} = \dfrac{1\frac{1}{3} - 2}{75 - 50}$

$= -\dfrac{\frac{2}{3}}{25} = -\dfrac{2}{75}$

The values are different.

(d) The relationship is nonlinear.

10. (a) The positive slopes represent time intervals when the race car is accelerating.

(b) The negative slopes represent time intervals when the race car is decelerating.

(c) The horizontal parts of the graph represent time intervals when the race car is at a constant speed.

11. *examples*:

(a)

(b)

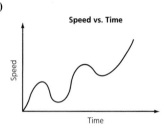

(c)

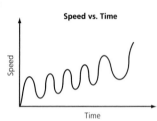

(d)

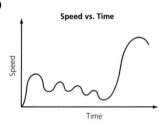

12. (a)

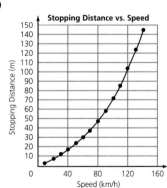

(b) Rate triangle 1: $\text{Slope} = \dfrac{37.9 - 29.8}{70 - 60} = \dfrac{8.1}{10}$
$= 0.81$

Rate triangle 2: $\text{Slope} = \dfrac{47.5 - 37.9}{70 - 60} = \dfrac{9.6}{10}$
$= 0.96$

(c) The rate of change in stopping distance also increases as the speed increases.

(d) This is not an accurate observation on Sheila's part, as the relationship is nonlinear. She will need to leave more than twice the distance if she drives twice as fast.

3.7 Creating Difference Tables

Practise

(a)

x	y	Differences
2	12	
4	24	12
6	36	12
8	48	12
10	60	12
12	72	12
14	84	12

(b)

x	y	Differences
2	8	
4	14	6
6	22	8
8	27	5
10	38	11
12	53	15
14	44	−9

(c)

x	y	Differences
6	53	
7	50	−3
8	47	−3
9	44	−3
10	41	−3
11	38	−3
12	35	−3

(d)

x	y	Differences
1	3	
2	9	6
3	12	3
4	5	−7
5	11	6
6	13	2
7	8	−5

3.8 Relationships in Geometric Figures

Practise, Apply, Solve

1. (b) 1: Length of top: 1, Width of top: 1,
Perimeter of top: 4, Area of top: 1
2: Length of top: 2, Width of top: 2,
Perimeter of top: 8, Area of top: 4
3: Length of top: 3, Width of top: 3,
Perimeter of top: 12, Area of top: 9
4:

Length of top: 4, Width of top: 4,
Perimeter of top: 16, Area of top: 16
5:

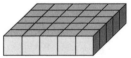

Length of top: 5, Width of top: 5,
Perimeter of top: 20, Area of top: 25
6:

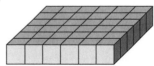

Length of top: 6, Width of top: 6,
Perimeter of top: 24, Area of top: 36

(c) i.

Length of Top	Width of Top	Differences
1	1	
2	2	1
3	3	1
4	4	1
5	5	1
6	6	1

This relationship is linear.

ii.

Length of Top	Perimeter of Top	Differences
1	4	
2	8	4
3	12	4
4	16	4
5	20	4
6	24	4

This relationship is linear.

iii.

Length of Top	Area of Top	Differences
1	1	
2	4	3
3	9	5
4	16	7
5	25	9
6	36	11

This relationship is nonlinear.

iv.

Perimeter of Top	Area of Top	Differences
4	1	
8	4	3
12	9	5
16	16	7
20	25	9
24	36	11

This relationship is nonlinear.

(d) i.

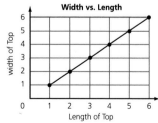

ii.

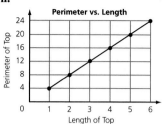

iii.

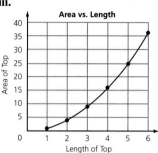

iv.

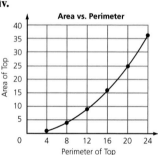

2. (a) Number of Cubes: 1, Number of Exposed Faces: 5
Number of Cubes: 2, Number of Exposed Faces: 8
Finite Differences: 3
Number of Cubes: 3, Number of Exposed Faces: 11
Finite Differences: 3
Number of Cubes: 4, Number of Exposed Faces: 14
Finite Differences: 3

Model: Number of Cubes: n
Number of Exposed Faces: $3n + 2$

(b) linear

(c) The number of faces not covered is $3n + 2$, where n represents the number of cubes.

3. (a) Length of Top: 2, Width of Top: 1, Area of Top: 2
Length of Top: 4, Width of Top: 2, Area of Top: 8,
Finite Difference: 6
Length of Top: 6, Width of Top: 3, Area of Top: 18,
Finite Difference: 10
Length of Top: 8, Width of Top: 4, Area of Top: 32,
Finite Difference: 14
Model: Length of Top: $2n$, Width of Top: n,
Area of Top: $2n^2$

(b) nonlinear

(c) The area of the top is $2n^2$ square units, where n represents the width of the top.

4. (a) $x = 10.0$ **(b)** $x = 13.0$ **(c)** $x = 12.7$
   (d) $x = 7.5$ **(e)** $x = 11.2$ **(f)** $x = 10.0$

5. (a) Length: 1, Width: 9, Area: 9
   Length: 2, Width: 8, Area: 16,
   Finite Differences: 7
   Length: 3, Width: 7, Area: 21,
   Finite Differences: 5

(b) nonlinear

(c) Area = length $\times$ width

(d)

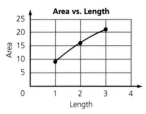

6. (b) linear

(c)

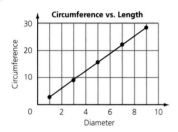

7. (a)

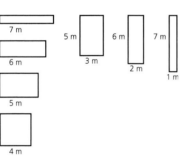

(b)

Length (m)	Width (m)	Area (m)
1	7	7
2	6	12
3	5	15
4	4	16
5	3	15
6	2	12
7	1	7

(c) nonlinear

(d)

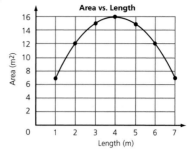

(e) When the length and width are both 4 m, the
maximum area of 16 m² is obtained. This is
shown by the highest point on the graph.

(f) $w = 8 - l$

(g) $A = l(8 - l)$ or $A = 8l - l^2$

8. (a)

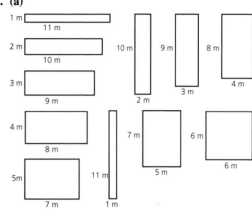

(b)

Length (m)	Width (m)	Area (m)
1	11	11
2	10	20
3	9	27
4	8	32
5	7	35
6	6	36
7	5	35
8	4	32
9	3	27
10	2	20
11	1	11

(c) nonlinear

(d)

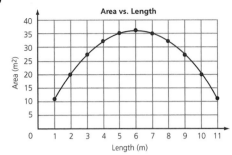

Area vs. Length

(e) When the length and width are both 6 m, the maximum area of 36 m² is obtained. This is shown by the highest point on the graph.

    (f) $w = 12 - l$

    (g) $A = l(12 - l)$ or $A = 12l - l^2$

9. When the length and width are both 16 m, the maximum area of 256 m² is obtained.

10. 5.8 m

11. 42.0 m

12. 100.2 km

13. (a) $w = 5 - l$ (b) $w = 8 - l$
    (c) $w = 12.5 - l$ (d) $w = 17.5 - l$

14. (a) $w = 25 - l$ (b) $l = 37.5 - w$ (c) $l = 0.5p - w$

15. $x = 12.5$ cm

16. (a) $2, \sqrt{5}$
    (b) continue the pattern for two more triangles

3.9 Models of Growth

Practise, Apply, Solve

1. (a) exponential (b) linear   (c) linear
    (d) exponential (e) linear   (f) exponential

2. (a) 10^3 (b) 2^3 (c) 5^4
    (d) 3^5 (e) $(-2)^2$ (f) $(-4)^4$

3. (a) $7; (7)(7)(7)$ (b) $-7; (-7)(-7)(-7)$
    (c) $7; -(7)(7)(7)$ (d) $6; \left(\frac{1}{6}\right)\left(\frac{1}{6}\right)\left(\frac{1}{6}\right)$
    (e) $-6; \left(-\frac{1}{6}\right)\left(-\frac{1}{6}\right)\left(-\frac{1}{6}\right)$
    (f) $6; -\left(\frac{1}{6}\right)\left(\frac{1}{6}\right)\left(\frac{1}{6}\right)$ (g) $a; (a)(a)$
    (h) $-a; (-a)(-a)$ (i) $a; -(a)(a)$

4. (a) $\left(\frac{1}{2}\right)^1$ (b) $\left(\frac{1}{3}\right)^2$ (c) $\left(\frac{1}{5}\right)^2$
    (d) $\left(\frac{1}{4}\right)^3$ (e) $\left(\frac{1}{a}\right)^2$ (f) $\left(\frac{1}{b}\right)^3$

5. (a) 2187   (b) 16   (c) 1 000 000
    (d) 512   (e) 512   (f) 64
    (g) 1   (h) 1   (i) -1
    (j) $\frac{1}{9}$ (k) 0.125   (l) 0.0625
    (m) $\frac{1}{9}$ (n) 1   (o) -1
    (p) 1   (q) -1 (r) $-0.031\ 25$
    (s) $\frac{1}{36}$ (t) $-\frac{1}{36}$

6. (a) 6561 (b) 512   (c) 1   (d) 1
    (e) -32 (f) 25   (g) 1   (h) -1

    (i) 0.031 25   (j) $0.\overline{1}$ (k) 0.0625
    (l) 0.008   (m) $-0.015\ 625$ (n) 1

7. (a) 2.3×10^3 (b) 1.35×10^5 (c) 8.5×10^{-2}
    (d) 2.37×10^{-3} (e) 1.2×10^7 (f) 1.25×10^2
    (g) 8.54×10^{-6} (h) $7.652\ 34 \times 10^5$
    (i) 1.234×10^6 (j) 2.3004×10^4
    (k) 4.0×10^{-8} (l) $2.220\ 02 \times 10^5$
    (m) 2.35×10^3 (n) 4.0×10^{-6}
    (o) 1.283×10^8 (p) 1.267×10^{-2}

8. (a) 120   (b) 256 700   (c) 0.013 45
    (d) 24 900 000 (e) $-0.000\ 0367\ 8$
    (f) 1.25   (g) 0.6712   (h) 0.000 285
    (i) $-2\ 456\ 000$ (j) 0.002 300 4 (k) 500 000
    (l) $-0.000\ 006$

9. (a) greater than one   (b) less than one
    (c) greater than one   (d) less than one

10. (a) 4 350 000 000   (b) 0.000 060 53
    (c) 16 300 000 000
    (d) 0.000 000 000 004 521

11. (a) 358.8   (b) 3.1464

12. (a) $\frac{29}{45}$ (b) $13\frac{1}{2}$ (c) $\frac{11}{16}$
    (d) 71 663 616 (e) $\frac{5}{6}$ (f) 169

13. (a) 6 million   (b) 1 h   (c) 96 million
    (d)

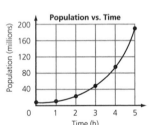

Population vs. Time

14. (a) 4   (b) $-\frac{5}{6}$ (c) 4
    (d) $-\frac{1}{8}$ (e) $3\frac{2}{3}$ (f) $\frac{1}{4}$

15. For 10 d, the $1000/d plan is better. For 20 d, the $1000/d plan is better. For 30 d, the plan that doubles the previous day's earnings starting from $0.01 on the first day is better.

16. (a) from the Earth to the moon

17. about 4.82 h

3.10 Powers with Rational Bases

Practise, Apply, Solve

1. (a) 12.3   (b) -300.76 (c) 37 330.104
    (d) 0.0005   (e) $-0.000\ 29$

2. (a) 5^1 (b) 7^1 (c) 10^2 (d) 8^2

3. (a) $\frac{8}{125}$ (b) $\frac{9}{16}$ (c) $\frac{3}{2}$ (d) $\frac{1}{1}$
    (e) $\frac{49}{16}$ (f) $\frac{64}{81}$ (g) $-\frac{64}{343}$ (h) $\frac{8}{1}$

4. (a) Initial mass = 500 g
    (b) Half-life = 1 year
    (c) after 2 years $M = 125$ g; 8 years $M = 1.953$ g; 20 years $M = 4.768 \times 10^{-4}$ g
    (d) last year $M = 1000$ g; 4 years ago $M = 8000$ g

5. (a) original principal = \$4500

(b) interest calculated 4 times per year

(c) invested for 10 years

(d) interest rate is 8%

(e) $A = \$9936.18$

6. (a)

time t	0	35	70	105
mass g	100	50	25	12.5
time t	140	175	210	...
mass g	6.25	3.125	1.563	
time t	315	350		
mass g	0.195	0.098		

(b) $A = 100\left(\dfrac{1}{2}\right)^{\frac{350}{35}} = 100\left(\dfrac{1}{2}\right)^{10}$
$\doteq 0.097\ 656\ 25$ g

7. (a) 0.781 25 g **(b)** $1.818\ 99 \times 10^{-10}$ g

(c) 75 days

8. (a)

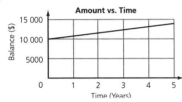

(b) nonlinear **(c)** exponential

(d) Balance = $10\ 000(1.07)^t$, where t is time in years

(e) in another three years, Balance = \$17 182

9. (a) nonlinear **(b)** exponential decay

(c)

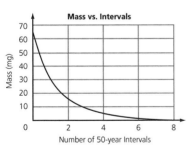

(d) Mass = $64\left(\dfrac{1}{2}\right)^t$, where t is the number of 50-year intervals

(e) 200 years, 350 years, 450 years

10. (a) simple interest is linear, compound interest is exponential

(b)

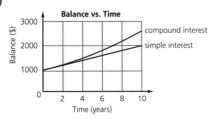

(c) Simple interest balance = $1000 + 100t$, where t is the time in years

Compound Interest balance = $1000(1.1)^t$, where t is the time in years

11. (a) \$607.75 **(b)** \$2191.12 **(c)** \$6341.21

(d) \$2188.10 **(e)** \$632.43 **(f)** \$1106.33

(g) \$1026.58

12. It will take 33 years for the investment to grow to \$1 000 000.

13. $C = 5.0421 \times 10^{-5}$

14. (a) $P = 2426$

(b) The town population decreases 7% a year.

15. Smartmoney Trust Co. is the better investment.

16. computer value = \$530.83

3.11 Exponent Laws

Practise, Apply, Solve

2. (a) 2^5 **(b)** 3^6 **(c)** 5^4 **(d)** 4^{12}

3. (a) 2^3 **(b)** 4^3 **(c)** 7^5 **(d)** 10^2

4. (a) 3^8 **(b)** 9^{12} **(c)** 2^{15} **(d)** 10^{36}

5. (a) $2^7 = 128$ **(b)** $4^1 = 4$ **(c)** $5^2 = 25$

(d) $3^3 = 27$ **(e)** $2^{-5} = \dfrac{1}{32}$ **(f)** $10^1 = 10$

(g) $(-2)^5 = -32$ **(h)** $3^2 = 9$

6. (a) $2^3 = 8$ **(b)** $4^3 = 64$

(c) $10^5 = 100\ 000$ **(d)** $2^{-7} = \dfrac{1}{128}$

(e) $3^{-1} = \dfrac{1}{3}$ **(f)** $3^4 = 81$

(g) $10^9 = 1\ 000\ 000\ 000$

(h) $5^1 = 5$

7. (a) $2^6 = 64$ **(b)** $3^6 = 729$ **(c)** $4^{-2} = \dfrac{1}{16}$

(d) $5^2 = 25$ **(e)** $10^{-6} = 0.000\ 001$

(f) $10^6 = 1\ 000\ 000$ **(g)** $6^1 = 6$

(h) $28^0 = 1$

8. (a) m^6 **(b)** n^2 **(c)** x^{-6} **(d)** r^6

(e) w^{-13} **(f)** m^1 **(g)** p^3 **(h)** b^{-5}

(i) x^8 **(j)** y^{-12} **(k)** m^6 **(l)** p^{-8}

(m) m^4 **(n)** y^{10} **(o)** x^{-3}

(p) s^9 **(q)** t^{16} **(r)** h^1

9. (a) $16y^{12}$ **(b)** $9x^{10}$ **(c)** $\dfrac{1}{5y^6}$ **(d)** $\dfrac{64}{y^{21}}$

(e) $1000b^{24}$ **(f)** $\dfrac{1}{100c^6}$

(g) $\dfrac{-y9}{8}$ **(h)** $16m^8$

10. (a) -473 **(b)** 32

(c) 9.0×10^9 **(d)** -100.001

11. (a) $\dfrac{1}{8}$ **(b)** $\dfrac{1}{7^{16}}$ **(c)** 1

(d) $2666\dfrac{2}{3}$ **(e)** 35 **(f)** 150

12. (a) 7.2×10^{-23} **(b)** 1.4×10^2

(c) 1.0×10^{19}

13. (a) $15\dfrac{3}{4}$ **(b)** $25\dfrac{1}{125}$

(c) $\dfrac{1}{3}$ **(d)** $100\dfrac{9}{10}$

14. (a) 524 288 **(b)** $\dfrac{7}{12}$

15. (a) 6 **(b)** 3 **(c)** 4 **(d)** 12

16. (a) 2^{10} **(b)** 3^{12} **(c)** 3^{12} **(d)** $(-5)^{21}$

17. (a) 256 **(b)** 125 **(c)** $\frac{1}{27}$ **(d)** 256

18. (a) x^7y^8 **(b)** x^2y^3 **(c)** x^1y^3 **(d)** $\frac{1}{x^5y^2}$

   (e) $x^{12}y^{16}$ **(f)** $\frac{x^4}{y^{10}}$ **(g)** $\frac{y^8}{x^4}$ **(h)** y^1

19. (a) -8 **(b)** 1 **(c)** 4 **(d)** 4 **(e)** -2

20. (a)

Kilometres	Metres	Centimetres	Millimetres
10^0 km	10^{-3} km	10^{-5} km	10^{-6} km
10^3 m	10^0 m	10^{-2} m	10^{-3} m
10^5 cm	10^2 cm	10^0 cm	10^{-1} cm
10^6 mm	10^3 mm	10^1 mm	10^0 mm

   (b) 5×10^5 cm **(c)** 6×10^{-1} cm
   (d) 4.0×10^4 cm³

Chapter Review

1. (a) False, the set of integers also includes negative numbers.
   (b) True
   (c) False: $\pi = 3.14159...$ is neither an integer nor a rational number.
   (d) False: 1, 2, ... belong to the natural numbers, whole numbers, integers, and rational numbers. Also, 0 is not a natural number.
   (e) False: $-9 + 5 = -4$ does not belong to the set of natural numbers.

2. (a) *example*

x	y
-1	$3\frac{1}{2}$
$-\frac{4}{5}$	$3\frac{2}{5}$
0	3
$\frac{1}{3}$	$2\frac{5}{6}$
1	$2\frac{1}{2}$

   (c)

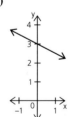

3. (a) $-1\frac{2}{5}$ **(b)** $-2\frac{1}{20}$ **(c)** $32\frac{7}{24}$ **(d)** $1\frac{1}{6}$
   (e) $-\frac{11}{24}$ **(f)** $6\frac{7}{10}$

5. (a) linear **(b)** nonlinear **(c)** linear

6. (a) speed is the dependent variable, time is the independent variable

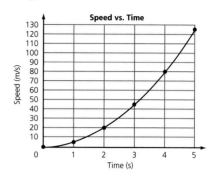

   (b) nonlinear, since the graph is not a straight line
   (c) As the rock is falling, it is gaining speed.

7. (b)

Polygon	Triangle	Quadrilateral	Pentagon	Hexagon
Number of Diagonals	0	2	5	9

   (c) seven sides: 14 diagonals; eight sides: 20 diagonals
   (d) nonlinear
   (e)

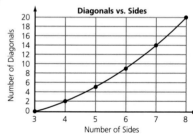

   (f) $D = \frac{(S-3)(S)}{2}$

8. about 574 m
9. about 1106 km
10. (a) 81 **(b)** -32 **(c)** -81 **(d)** $\frac{8}{27}$
   (e) $\frac{1}{16}$ **(f)** $\frac{1}{1000}$ **(g)** $36n^2$ **(h)** $-128y^7$
   (i) $27m^3$ **(j)** $-\frac{8}{27}k^3$
11. (a) $\frac{12}{35}$ **(b)** $\frac{1281}{16}$ **(c)** 2 **(d)** -117
12. (a) 6.3×10^8, 6.3×10^{-8}
   (b) 7.21×10^{10}, 7.21×10^{-10}
13. (a) 4.964×10^7 **(b)** 1.43×10^{-33}
14. (a) 1.999 005 **(b)** 19 990.05
   (c) 7776 **(d)** 6561
   (e) 2.8531 **(f)** -3125
15. (a) nonlinear

(b)

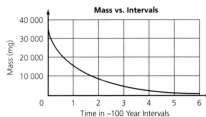

(c) Balance $= 32\ 768\left(\dfrac{1}{2}\right)^t$, where t is the time in 100-year intervals

(d) mass = 32 mg

16. (a) nonlinear   **(b)** linear
   (c) nonlinear   **(d)** linear

17. (a) \$2360.28   **(b)** \$3183.96
   (c) \$563.41   **(d)** \$35 769.22
   (e) \$9933.61   **(f)** \$2268.70

18. (a) $2^8 = 256$ **(b)** $5^2 = 25$ **(c)** $3^{-3} = \dfrac{1}{27}$

   (d) $8^{-2} = \dfrac{1}{64}$ **(e)** $7^2 = 49$ **(f)** $5^1 = 5$

   (g) $10^9 = 1\ 000\ 000\ 000$ **(h)** $2^6 = 64$

   (i) $6^2 = 36$ **(j)** $35^0 = 1$ **(k)** $5^{-3} = \dfrac{1}{125}$

   (l) $10^8 = 100\ 000\ 000$

19. (a) m^8 **(b)** x^4 **(c)** p^4 **(d)** 1
   (e) y^{12} **(f)** w^{-6} **(g)** x^8 **(h)** t^{13}
   (i) m^{-9} **(j)** x^{-15}

20. (a) $16t^6$ **(b)** $-125x^{15}$
   (c) $10\ 000y^{20}$ **(d)** x^{-100}

21. (a) 128   **(b)** 3   **(c)** 4

Chapter Review Test

1. (a) $3\dfrac{4}{15}$ **(b)** $-\dfrac{19}{40}$ **(c)** $-11\dfrac{11}{12}$

   (d) -12 **(e)** $3\dfrac{47}{75}$

2. Natural numbers (N) are the numbers used for counting, 1, 2, 3... Whole numbers (W) are the numbers used for counting and also zero, 0, 1, 2, 3... Integers (Z) are positive and negative natural numbers as well as zero, ...−3, −2, −1, 0, 1, 2, 3... Rational numbers (Q) are numbers of the form $\dfrac{a}{b}$ where a and b are both integers, with b not equal to zero.

3. (a) 243   **(b)** 1   **(c)** −128   **(d)** $\dfrac{1}{27}$

   (e) 15625   **(f)** 27   **(g)** −49   **(h)** $\dfrac{1}{36}$

4. (a) 4.37×10^{11} **(b)** 1.35×10^{-10}

5. 4.0×10^7 s

6. (a) between D and E
   (b) Shasta is resting.
   (c) after 10 min
   (d) 4 min
   (e) Shasta ran 125 m/min on her way home.

7. perimeter = 56.6 m

8. (a) The graph is not a straight line, so the relationship is nonlinear.

(b)

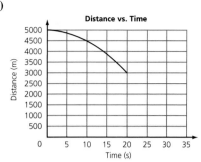

(c) The hailstone hits the ground about 32 s after it starts to fall.

9. (a) bacteria population $= 20(3)^t$, where t is the time in hours
   (b) after 24-h population $= 5.649 \times 10^{12}$

10. \$67 126.60

11. $\dfrac{x}{y^9}$

Cumulative Review Test 1

1. (a) $-\dfrac{1}{21}$ **(b)** $-6\dfrac{49}{99}$ **(c)** $-4\dfrac{1}{5}$ **(d)** $1\dfrac{3}{5}$

2. (a) -4 **(b)** -3
   (c)

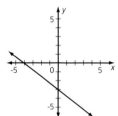

   (d) $-\dfrac{3}{4}$

3. $y = -4x - 2$

4. $y = -x + 2$

5. (a)

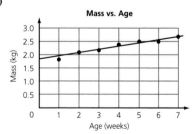

(c) 0.9

(d) The rate of change of mass per week is about 0.15 kg/week. This represents the slope of the line of best fit.

(e) The mass of the puppy at birth was about 1.75 kg. This represents the y-intercept of the line of best fit.

(f) The equation of the line of best fit is $y = 0.15x + 1.75$, where x represents the age of the puppy in weeks, and y represents the mass of the puppy in kilograms.

(g) 3.25 kg

(h) No. When the puppy is 50 weeks old, the puppy may not continue to grow at the same rate as it did during the first few weeks after birth.

6. Answers may vary. *Examples:*

  (a) targetted sampling

  (b) The results of the sampling are not indicative of the preference of the general school population. The sample group is only composed of Sarah's classmates in her Grade 9 math class, which biases the sampling procedure.

  (c) Sarah can randomly select an equal number of students from each grade in the school to participate in her survey. If she selected 20 students at random from each grade, the results would not be biased.

7. **(a)** High Energy Gas: $C = 0.1V + 12$

  New Gas: $C = 0.09V + 20$

  C represents the total cost per month in dollars, and V represents the volume of gas used in cubic metres.

  (b) The independent variable is V, the volume of gas used. The dependent variable is C, the total cost per month.

  (c)

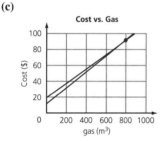

  (d) When the cost for either company is the same, 800 m³ of gas are consumed.

  (e) The cost at the point of intersection is $92.

8. **(a)** 1500, 1725, 1984, 2281, 2624; nonlinear

  (b)

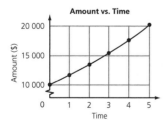

9. The data is nonlinear, because the finite differences are not constant.

Length of Shadow (m)	2	4	6	8	10
Distance from Tip to Tip	5.4	6.4	7.8	9.4	11.2
Finite Differences		1	1.4	1.6	1.8

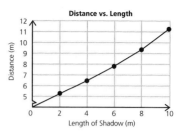

10. $751.82

Chapter 4

Getting Ready

1. **(a)** -3 **(b)** -12 **(c)** -4 **(d)** -15
  (e) 8 **(f)** 7 **(g)** 5 **(h)** -24
  (i) 8 **(j)** 10 **(k)** -13 **(l)** 1

2. **(a)** 12.55 **(b)** -1 **(c)** -6.1 **(d)** -6.55
  (e) -2.4 **(f)** 15.42 **(g)** -12.2 **(h)** 0.8
  (i) 0.5 **(j)** 0.5 **(k)** 8.48 **(l)** -0.1
  (m) -1.5 **(n)** -3.51

3. **(a)** $1\frac{1}{4}$ **(b)** $-\frac{1}{4}$ **(c)** $-1\frac{7}{24}$ **(d)** $\frac{1}{24}$
  (e) $6\frac{1}{8}$ **(f)** $-1\frac{1}{8}$ **(g)** -4 **(h)** $3\frac{9}{40}$

4. **(a)** -18 **(b)** 5.1 **(c)** -19.67
  (d) 0 **(e)** 132 **(f)** 11

5. **(a)** -7 **(b)** 49 **(c)** $-\frac{1}{8}$
  (d) 26 **(e)** -0.017 **(f)** 9
  (g) -10 **(h)** 9 **(i)** -4

6. **(a)** $x = -17$ **(b)** $x = 8$ **(c)** $m = -2$
  (d) $r = \frac{2}{9}$ **(e)** $y = 10$ **(f)** $x = 2$
  (g) $x = 1$ **(h)** $y = 3\frac{2}{3}$ **(i)** $x = 2$

7. **(a)** $w = 5$ m **(b)** $P = 46$ cm **(c)** $t = 2$

8. **(a)** x^8 **(b)** x^5 **(c)** x^6
  (d) $x^{-3}y^7$ **(e)** $x^{-7}y^{-2}$ **(f)** $x^{10}y^{-20}$

4.1 Adding and Subtracting Simple Polynomials

Practise, Apply, Solve

1. **(a)** 5 **(b)** -3 **(c)** -7 **(d)** 1
  (e) -4.3 **(f)** -6 **(g)** -1 **(h)** $\frac{3}{4}$

2. **(a)** binomial **(b)** monomial
  (c) trinomial **(d)** monomial
  (e) binomial **(f)** trinomial

3. **(a)** $3x, -2x$ **(b)** $-2g, -5g$ **(c)** $6m, -1.5m$
  (d) $-\frac{1}{2}y, 2\frac{1}{2}y$ **(e)** $-2.1y^3, -0.8y^3$
  (f) $-3.75rs, 4.25rs$

4. **(a)** $5l$ **(b)** $-3m$ **(c)** $-8x$ **(d)** $3r$
  (e) $-3y$ **(f)** $-4p$ **(g)** $9y^2$ **(h)** $6x^2$
  (i) $5m^3$ **(j)** $4s^2$ **(k)** $-\frac{3}{4}w^2$

5. **(a)** $7m - 2n$ **(b)** $7s - 3t$ **(c)** $-3x - 4y$
  (d) $3x^2 + 4y$ **(e)** $5h + 6$ **(f)** $-3n + 4$

(g) $-12x - 6$　　**(h)** $\frac{11}{20}a - \frac{1}{10}b$
(i) $-m - 7n + 11$　　**(j)** $-0.9x + 0.2y$
(k) $5x^3 + x^2$　　**(l)** $-9x^3 + 9xy - 3$

6. (a) $7h - 5$　**(b)** $7x - 2$　**(c)** $5x - 2y$
(d) $7m - n$　　**(e)** $-3y^2 + 2y + 1$
(f) $9x^2 - 12xy + 3y^2$

7. (a) $3h + 11$　**(b)** $3x + 14$　**(c)** $2x - 6y$
(d) $6m + 9n$　**(e)** $8y^2 - 4y + 4$
(f) $-3x^2 + 4xy + 9y^2$

8. (a) $4h - 3$　**(b)** $6h + 19$　**(c)** $7x - 16y$
(d) $3m + 4n$　**(e)** $6x^2 - 12xy - 4y^2$

9. (a) $43.5x + 35$　　**(b)** $38.75x + 41$
(c) $82.25x + 76$　　**(d)** \$734.00

10. (a) $160t - 100$　　**(b)** $40t - 25$
(c) $200t - 125$　　**(d)** \$875.00
(e) No, the single polynomial in **(c)** is only valid if they work the same number of tables.

11. (a) $4f + 5g + 6h$　　**(b)** $-5f - g - 3h$
(c) $-f + 4g + 3h$　　**(d)** 10

12. (a) $18.05h + 21.65$　　**(b)** $-0.47x - 1.7$
(c) $5.4m - n$　　**(d)** $14.24y + 4.14$
(e) $-\frac{1}{5}m - n$　　**(f)** $\frac{1}{20}s - \frac{3}{14}t$

13. (a) Monday: boys $250P$, girls $306P$
Tuesday: boys $410P - 3N - 2D$,
girls $455P - 2N - Q$
Wednesday: boys $613P - 11N - 6D - 5Q$,
girls $715P - 10N - 2D - 3Q - 2T$
Thursday:
boys $851P - 15N - 20D - 11Q - 4L - 2T$,
girls $938P - 25N - 11D - 8Q - 5L - 3T$
(c) girls　　**(d)** \$79.38

4.2 The Distributive Property

Practise, Apply, Solve

1. (a)

t	$C = 8.00 + 0.50t$	$2C$	$3C$
0	\$8.00	\$16.00	\$24.00
1	8.50	17.00	25.50
2	9.00	18.00	27.00
3	9.50	19.00	28.50

(b) Column $2C$ represents the cost of 2 pizzas.
(c) $3(8.00 + 0.50t) = 24.00 + 1.50t$. This represents the cost of 3 pizzas. If all three pizzas have 2 toppings, the cost is \$27.

2. (a) 1, 2
(b) Since 2 and b are multiplied together, they consist of one term, not two terms.

3. (a) $6h$　　**(b)** $-2x$　　**(c)** $7x$
(d) $-6m$　　**(e)** $-20r$　　**(f)** $-72q$
(g) $8cd$　　**(h)** $-12b$　　**(i)** $-24abc$

4. (a) $-4m$　　**(b)** $-4n$　　**(c)** $5a$
(d) $-4r$　　**(e)** $-2m$　　**(f)** r

5. (a) 4　　**(b)** -2　　**(c)** $3y$

(d) $-7a^2$　　**(e)** $4x^3$　　**(f)** $-6n^3$

6. (a) $15h + 10$　　**(b)** $-24h + 18$
(c) $12x - 8y$　　**(d)** $10a - 15b + 40$
(e) $-6n + 9m - 12s$　**(f)** $-2x - 5$
(g) $-x^2 + 3x - 7$　　**(h)** $12x^2 + 20x - 36$
(i) $2y^2 + 2y + 2$

7. (a) $4h + 3$　　**(b)** $-5m + 1$　　**(c)** $6n - 4p$
(d) $4x - 3y - 1$　　**(e)** $5a + 4b - 2c$
(f) $5l - 6m + 3n$

8. (a) 3　　　　　　**(b)** $x - y$
(c) 2　　　　　　**(d)** $4x^2 - 3y^3$
(e) -5　　　　　**(f)** $-35a^4 + 36a^3$
(g) $2x$　　　　　**(h)** y

9. (a) $5(x - 3)$　　　**(b)** $3(2x - y)$
(c) $5(2x - 3y - 6)$　　**(d)** $-4(x - 2y)$
(e) $6(3x^2 - 4x + 2)$　**(f)** $7(3y - 4x - 2z)$
(g) $15(3a - 2b + 4c)$　**(h)** $5(9x^3 - 10x^2 + 3y)$
(i) $7x - 5y + 3$

10. (a) $3 + x$　　　　**(b)** $-5x + 3$
(c) $\frac{5}{12}m - \frac{15}{32}n + \frac{15}{64}$
(d) $-13.12a - 4.16b + 8.64$
(e) $-3\frac{1}{2}r + 5\frac{3}{4}s$　　**(f)** $3\frac{1}{2}t - 8u$

11. (a) $26c + 88$　　**(b)** $-2x - 39y$
(c) $12x + 32y$　　**(d)** $21a + 11b + 7c$
(e) $-26m + 45n - 10$　**(f)** $-4x^2 + 6x + 15$
(g) $4x^2 + 17x - 21$　**(h)** $4x + 30$
(i) $18p + 4$　　**(j)** $9x^2 - 2x$
(k) $-p - k$

12. (a) $\frac{3}{10}a - 3\frac{1}{3}b$　　**(b)** $\frac{7}{10}a - \frac{1}{18}b$
(c) $-3\frac{3}{32}a + 10\frac{7}{8}b$
(d) $-1\frac{4}{21}a - 1\frac{3}{14}b$　**(e)** $-6.455m + 4.13n$
(f) $1\frac{3}{4}a - 1\frac{3}{4}b$

13. (a) D1 = $5h + 7$, E1 = $h + 3$, F1 = $-h - 3$,
G1 = $7h + 17$, H1 = $1\frac{1}{2}h + 4\frac{1}{2}$
(b) For $h = 3$, $5h + 7 = 22$, $h + 3 = 6$,
$-h - 3 = -6$, $7h + 17 = 38$, $1\frac{1}{2}h + 4\frac{1}{2} = 9$.
For $h = 4$, $5h + 7 = 27$, $h + 3 = 7$,
$-h - 3 = -7$, $7h + 17 = 45$,
$1\frac{1}{2}h + 4\frac{1}{2} = 10\frac{1}{2}$.
For $h = 5$, $5h + 7 = 32$, $h + 3 = 8$,
$-h - 3 = -8$, $7h + 17 = 52$, $1\frac{1}{2}h + 4\frac{1}{2} = 12$.
(c) B1 = 14, C1 = 8, D1 = 22, E1 = 6, F1 = -6,
G1 = 38, H1 = 9
B2 = 17, C2 = 10, D2 = 27, E2 = 7,
F2 = -7, G2 = 45, H2 = 10.5
B3 = 20, C3 = 12, D3 = 32, E3 = 8,
F3 = -8, G3 = 52, H3 = 12
(d) They are identical.

14. (a) $9a + 24 = 51$　　**(b)** $-2a + 25 = 19$
(c) $-2a^2 - 10a - 14 = -62$
(d) $a^3 - a^2 - 2a = 12$

15. (a) $20x + 50$　　**(b)** $4x + 30$
(c) 90 square units　**(d)** 32 units

16. (a) $-38\ 100x + 308\ 700$
(b)

	A	B	C	D
1	Number of Years	Value of One Sedan	Value of One Sport Utility	Total Value
2	0	$19 600	$24 500	$308 700
3	1	17 200	21 400	270 600
4	2	14 800	18 300	232 500
5	3	12 400	15 200	194 400
6	4	10 000	12 100	156 300
7	5	7600	9000	118 200
8	6	5200	5900	80 100

(c) The company paid $73 500 for sport utilities and $235 200 for the sedans.
(d) The sport utilities are depreciating at a faster rate.
17. (a) the term with the t coefficient
(b) $V = 101\ 550t + 12\ 370\ 000$
(c) $12\ 877\ 750$
18. (a) 6 **(b)** 4 **(c)** 3
(d) 8 **(e)** -3

4.3 Factoring Polynomials

Practise
(a) $2(4x + 1)$ **(b)** $3(x - 5)$ **(c)** $4(x + 3)$
(d) $2(3 - x)$ **(e)** $5(x - 5)$ **(f)** $2x(x + 2)$
(g) $3(3x^2 - 1)$ **(h)** $x(x + 4)$ **(i)** $6(x - 4)$
(j) $4x(x + 1)$ **(k)** $7(x + 2)$ **(l)** $8(1 - 2x)$

4.4 Extending Algebra Skills with Polynomials

Practise, Apply, Solve
1. (a) $10xy$ **(b)** $5r^3$ **(c)** $6mn^2$
(d) $6abc^2$ **(e)** $6m^2n^3$ **(f)** $56mn^2pq^2$
2. (a) $8ab$ **(b)** $-30xy$ **(c)** $3m$
(d) $-3b$ **(e)** $-27mn$ **(f)** $-3y$
(g) $-24xyz$ **(h)** $35abc$ **(i)** 9
(j) $-5x^2$ **(k)** $2m^3$ **(l)** $-45ab^2c^2d$
(m) $30a^2bc^2d^2$ **(n)** $3bc^2$
3. (a) $5n + 3n^2$ **(b)** $2R^2 - 10R$
(c) $6k^2 + 3k$ **(d)** $-4y^2 - 7y$
(e) $10d^3 - 5d^2 - 15d$ **(f)** $-12c + 15c^2 - 3c^3$
(g) $-3s^3 + 5s^2 - 2s$ **(h)** $14t^2 - 8t^3 + 2t^4$
4. (a) $xy - 2$ **(b)** $m^2 - 2$
(c) $-2a^2 - 3c^2$ **(d)** $3y^3 - 2z^2 + 5$
(e) $2p - 3r + 4k$ **(f)** $1 - y$
5. (a) 4 **(b)** $4c$ **(c)** $2y$ **(d)** $3x^2$
6. (a) $40n^2p^2$ **(b)** $-24j^2k^2$ **(c)** $12x^5y$
(d) $-10m^8n^3$ **(e)** $12ax^4y^4$ **(f)** $56fg^5h^3$
(g) $-30r^3st^2$ **(h)** $56a^4b^6$

7. (a) $5ab$ **(b)** $-3x^3yz$ **(c)** $-5mn^3p^7$
(d) $4r^{10}s^5$ **(e)** $-3ab^2c^3$ **(f)** $2e^5g^3$
8. (a) $18x^5 + 6x^4$ **(b)** $10y^7 + 15y^5 + 5y^3$
(c) $12a^3b^4 - 18a^2b^5$
(d) $14m^4n^6 + 35m^3n^7 - 21m^5n^4p$
(e) $3x^2 - 2$ **(f)** $3p - q$
(g) $5mn^3 - 2m^3n^2$ **(h)** $3xy - 4x^4 + 5x^2y^2$
9. (a) $-k + 2k^2$ **(b)** $6t^2 - 2t$
(c) $-8a^2 + 11a$ **(d)** $2p + 9p^2$
(e) $-2s^3 + 28s^2 - 10s$ **(f)** $26b^3 + 14b^2 - 13b$
10. (a) $5xy + 4y$ **(b)** $3x^2 - 5x$
(c) $10x^2 - 8xy - 14y^2$
(d) $12x^2 - 15y^2 + 11xy - 8x + 9y$
(e) $7a^3 + a^2 + 3a^2b$
(f) $4x^2 + 14xy - 15x^2y$
(g) $-9a^2 + 7ab - b - 5b^2$
(h) $12a - 9b$
(i) $10x^2 + 3xy + 2x$
(j) $3a^4 + 5a^3 + 3a^2 + 16a$
11. (a) y **(b)** $3ac$ **(c)** $2x^2$
(d) x^3y^4 **(e)** $5x^4y^3$ **(f)** $2x^4y^2$
12. (a) $2x + 1$ **(b)** $5n - m$
13. (a) $4(2x + 1)$ **(b)** $5b(3ac - 1)$
(c) $8mp(2n + 3q)$ **(d)** $2x(2x^2 + 3x - 4)$
(e) $7y^2(2y^2 - 3y + 4)$ **(f)** $4x^2y^2(3xy^2 - 1 + 2xy^3)$
(g) $5a^3b^3(5a^2 + 7b - 4ab^2)$
(h) $3g^4k^4(1 - 3g + 6k)$
14. $4x^3y^3 - 3x^2y$
15. (a) $4x^2y - 3xy$ **(b)** $900\ \text{cm}^2$
16. (a) $x^2 + 7x + 10$ **(b)** $x^2 - 36$
(c) $x^2 + 2x - 15$ **(d)** $6x^2 + 5x - 6$
(e) $2x^2 + 5xy + 3y^2$ **(f)** $4x^2 - 20x + 25$
17. (a) $2(2W + L + Q)$ **(b)** $2(3s + b)$
18. (a) $\dfrac{y + 2x}{xy}$ **(b)** $\dfrac{4x - 1}{2x^2}$ **(c)** $\dfrac{2x}{x^2 - 1}$

Chapter Review
1. (a) $5x$ **(b)** $2y$ **(c)** $-6m - 3n$
(d) $-3r$ **(e)** $14a$ **(f)** $4b$
(g) $-\dfrac{5}{12}m$ **(h)** $-3\dfrac{1}{10}p$
2. (a) $5a + b$ **(b)** $5x + 2y$ **(c)** $-x + 3y$
(d) $13a - 5b$ **(e)** $2m - n$ **(f)** $-\dfrac{1}{6}x + \dfrac{1}{4}y$
(g) $-1\dfrac{1}{8}m - \dfrac{3}{10}n$
(h) $-1.4r + 7.5s - 7.3t$
3. (a) $-2m - 7n$ **(b)** $x - 3y + 2z$
(c) $3m$ **(d)** $9k - 2n - 5m$
(e) $10k - 13$ **(f)** $-5x + 7y$
(g) $0.5x - 13.85$ **(h)** $-\dfrac{11}{35}a - \dfrac{23}{35}b$
4. $(28m + 6)$ m of fencing is needed.
5. (a) $48b$ **(b)** $24a$ **(c)** $-12x$
(d) $-4b$ **(e)** $-6m$ **(f)** $5n$
(g) $-11m$ **(h)** $-15n$
6. (a) $3x + 6$ **(b)** $-175 + 28w$
(c) $-16m + 16$ **(d)** $3r + 2s$
(e) $-10a + 15b + 20c$

(f) $6m - 9n + 15p$

(g) $0.3C - 0.12f + 0.72g$

(h) $-\frac{1}{2}x + \frac{1}{4}y - 6z$

7. (a) $9x + 18$ **(b)** $14x - 28$

(c) $-x - 19$ **(d)** $13x^2 + 20xy - 16x$

(e) $4a^3 - 6a^2$ **(f)** $-12x^2y - 17x^2 - 31xy$

(g) $3ab^2 - 3$

8. (a) $5(2x + 1)$ **(b)** $7bc(a - 3)$

(c) $12mp(2n + q)$ **(d)** $3x(x^2 + 2x - 3)$

(e) $7y^2(3y^2 - 2y + 4)$ **(f)** $2x^2y^2(xy^2 - 3 + 5xy^3)$

(g) $12a^3b^3(6a^2 + 3b - 4ab^2)$

(h) $4g^4k^4(7 - 13g + 11k)$

Chapter Review Test

1. (a) $3h + 3k - 9$ **(b)** $-0.4x + 0.9y - 2.9$

(c) $m + 9$ **(d)** $\frac{5}{12}n + 1\frac{1}{12}p$

(e) $9x - 2$

(f) $6x^2 - 6xy + 4y^2 + 2x - 12y$

2. (a) $5(3x^2 - x + 2)$ **(b)** $a^2(b^2 + b - 1)$

(c) $5y(3x^2 - 2xy + 6y^2)$

(d) $7m^2n^2(3m + 2n - 5)$

3. (a) $x^2 - 6xy - 1$ **(b)** $-3a^3 - 4ab^2 - 4b^3$

(c) $2x^2 + 7x - 2$ **(d)** $3a^2 + 4ab + b^2$

4. (a) $7s - 6r$ **(b)** $33m - 22n$

(c) $-3a - 17b + 26$ **(d)** $\frac{1}{3}x + 10$

(e) $-1.25r + 3.75t - 5.25$

(f) $-20x + 18y - 3$

5. (a) $7n$ **(b)** $125n$

(c) $\$5.00$

Chapter 5

Getting Ready

1. (a) $4\frac{5}{12}$ **(b)** $\frac{7}{8}$ **(c)** $-\frac{3}{20}$ **(d)** $5\frac{3}{8}$

(e) 14 **(f)** $1\frac{31}{32}$ **(g)** $-6\frac{1}{3}$ **(h)** $-1\frac{1}{16}$

2. (a) -2 **(b)** 2 **(c)** 13 **(d)** 2

(e) 4 **(f)** 40 **(g)** -4 **(h)** 49

(i) 4 **(j)** 1 **(k)** 28 **(l)** 0

3. (a) 20 **(b)** 50 **(c)** -1 **(d)** -5

(e) $1\frac{1}{2}$ **(f)** 0.125 **(g)** -1 **(h)** 10

4. (a) $x = -5$ **(b)** $y = -9$ **(c)** $w = 2$

(d) $x = 4$ **(e)** $x = -6$ **(f)** $t = -4$

(g) $z = 2$ **(h)** $a = 1$ **(i)** $b = -1$

(j) $y = 2\frac{1}{3}$ **(k)** $x = -7$ **(l)** $w = -4$

5. (a) $x = -1, x = 2$; x is less than or equal to 2

(b) $y = 3, y = 5$; y is greater than 2

(c) $a = -\frac{1}{2}, a = 0$; a is greater than -1 and less than 1

(d) $b = -6, b = -3$; b is less than or equal to -3

(e) $w = -5, w = 2$; w is greater than or equal to -5

(f) $x = -1, x = \frac{1}{2}$; x is greater than or equal to -1 and less than or equal to 2

(g) $y = -4, y = -3$; y is greater than -5 and less than or equal to -3

(h) $z = 0, z = 9$; z is greater than or equal to 0 and less than 10

6. (a)

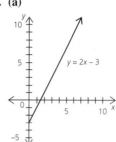

(b)

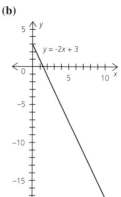

(c)

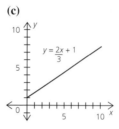

(d)

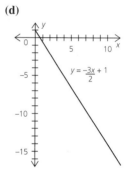

(e)

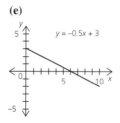

(f)

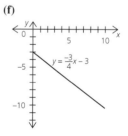

(g)

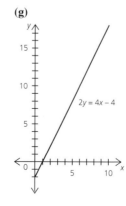

(h)

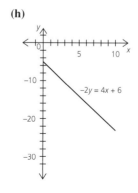

7. (a) $3x + 5 = 10$ **(b)** $5(3 + x) = 12$

(c) $\frac{1}{3}x + 2x = 2$ **(d)** $2x = 7$

(e) $\frac{1}{4}x = 5^2$ **(f)** $3x - 4 = 13$

(g) $2x \div 7 = 5$ **(h)** $3x = 5 + x$

5.1 Relationships with Two Variables

Practise, Apply, Solve

1. (a) volume of concentrate plus volume of water equals 10 L

(b) 1 L   **(c)** 0.2 L

(d) intercepts are (0, 10) and (10, 0)

2. (a) $30/kg times mass of almonds plus $8/kg times mass of raisins is $150

(b) $30a + 8r = 150$ **(c)** 15 kg of raisins

(d) 1 kg of almonds

(e) The intercepts are (5, 0) and (0, 18.75) or (0, 5) and (18.75, 0).

3. (a)

Tables	Chairs
0	20
1	17
2	15
3	13
4	10
5	8
6	6
7	3
8	1

(b) 20 chairs   **(c)** 8 tables

(d) The values chosen in this situation must be integers because only completed tables and chairs are paid for.

(e)

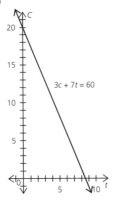

(f) (0, 20) and (8.6, 0).

4. (a)

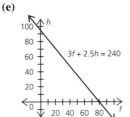

Figure Skates	Hockey Skates
0	96
15	78
45	42
60	24
80	0

(b) 96 hockey skates

(c) 80 figure skates

(d) The values must be integers because Henri can only sharpen complete pairs of skates.

(e)

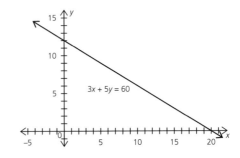

(f) (0, 96) and (80, 0).

5. (a)

x	y
−5	15
0	12
5	9
20	0

(b) The x-intercept is at (20, 0) and the y-intercept is at (0, 12).

(c) x would have to be greater than zero and less than 20. y would have to be greater than zero and less than 12.

6. (a) $10 000   **(b)** $16 666.67

(c)

Clothing Store	Hardware Store
$5000	$7000
$10 000	$4000
$15 000	$1000

(d)

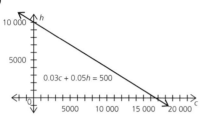

(e) Additional points are not necessary to complete the graph since the relation is linear.

(f) (16 666.67, 0) and (0, 10 000). They represent the sales at each store for Christine to make $500.

7. (a) 1200 km   **(b)** 720 km

(c)

Highways	Country Roads
2	10
7	5
11	1

(d)

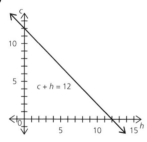

(e) (12, 0) and (0, 12). They represent the maximum possible time Gregor can drive on either the highway or the country road.

(f) 1040 km

8. (a) 96 quarters

(b) 480 nickels

(c)

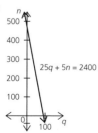

i. 80 nickels and 80 quarters

ii. 48 quarters and 240 nickels

9. (a)

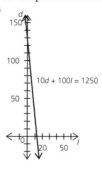

maximum value of d is 125, maximum value of l is 12.5; $d = 15$

(b)

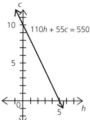

maximum value of h is 5, maximum value of c is 10; $c = 7$

(c)

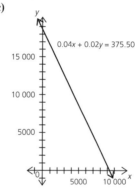

maximum value of x is 9387.5, maximum value of y is 18775; $x = 8887.5$

11. (a)

A	B
5	10
7.5	8.75
8	8.5
9	8
11	7

(b) The minimum Part B score is 12.5 to pass.

(c) You cannot pass the exam with only a Part A score. Part A is out of 20 marks and is multiplied by 2 to find the percentage. 2 times 20 is only 40, you need 50 to pass.

(d)

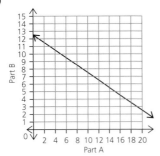

(e)

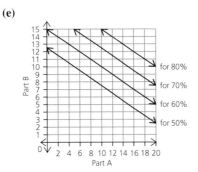

5.2 Solving Simple Equations

Practise

(a) $x = -2$ **(b)** $c = 1$ **(c)** $z = 5$ **(d)** $x = -3$
(e) $x = -3\frac{1}{3}$ **(f)** $a = -\frac{1}{3}$ **(g)** $y = 2\frac{2}{5}$ **(h)** $w = -1$

5.3 Finding Values That Satisfy a Linear Relation

Practise, Apply, Solve

1. **(a)** $x = 20$ **(b)** $m = 12$ **(c)** $p = -25$
   (d) $s = 16$ **(e)** $m = -14$ **(f)** $r = 1$
   (g) $x = 12$ **(h)** $x = 13$ **(i)** $m = 29$
   (j) $p = 23$ **(k)** $x = 18$ **(l)** $k = -8$
2. **(a)** $m = 4$ **(b)** $y = 3$ **(c)** $p = -2$
   (d) $k = -3$ **(e)** $n = 6$ **(f)** $x = 12$
   (g) $k = 4$ **(h)** $m = -8$ **(i)** $h = -7$
   (j) $y = 17$ **(k)** $x = 2.4$ **(l)** $x = -9$
3. **(a)** $x = 24$ **(b)** $a = 8$ **(c)** $b = -15$
   (d) $w = -16$ **(e)** $c = 12$ **(f)** $k = 48$
   (g) $x = -14$ **(h)** $b = -24$ **(i)** $x = -10$
   (j) $x = 10$ **(k)** $a = -12$ **(l)** $y = 30$
4. **(a)** $m = 4$ **(b)** $p = 3$ **(c)** $q = 2$
   (d) $t = 3$ **(e)** $k = 3$ **(f)** $p = 9$
   (g) $a = 2$ **(h)** $c = 5$ **(i)** $n = 9$
   (j) $x = 2$ **(k)** $x = -2$ **(l)** $y = 5$
5. **(a)** $k = 9$ **(b)** $x = 28$ **(c)** $b = 30$
   (d) $n = 4$ **(e)** $x = 32$ **(f)** $k = 27$
   (g) $x = 10$ **(h)** $y = 12$ **(i)** $d = 45$
   (j) $x = 16$ **(k)** $x = 4$ **(l)** $x = 28$

6. **(a)** $x = 3$ **(b)** $y = 7\frac{1}{3}$ **(c)** $p = 1$
   (d) $k = -2$ **(e)** $x = -1$ **(f)** $y = \frac{-13}{15}$
   (g) $c = -2$ **(h)** $m = 0.25$ **(i)** $k = 3\frac{5}{8}$
   (j) $m = 5.2$ **(k)** $x = 1.9$ **(l)** $m = 1.8$
7. **(a)** $3a + r = 15$, where $r = 7.5$
   (b) $3a + (7.5) = 15$, substitute the value of r
   $3a = 15 - 7.5$, subtract 7.5 from both sides to isolate the variable
   $3a = 7.5$, simplify
   $\frac{3}{3}a = \frac{7.5}{3}$, divide both sides of the equation by the numerical coefficient
   $a = 2.5$, You need 2.5 kg of almonds for the mix.
8. **(a)** $3c + 7t = 60$, where $t = 3$
   (b) $3c + 7(3) = 60$, substitute
   $3c + 21 - 21 = 60 - 21$, simplify and subtract 21 from both sides to isolate the variable
   $3c = 39$, simplify
   $\frac{3}{3}c = \frac{39}{3}$, divide both sides to make the coefficient of the variable 1
   $c = 13$, Jamie made 13 chairs last week.
9. **(a)** $0.03c + 0.05h = 800$, where $c = 2500$
   (b) $0.03(2500) + 0.05h = 800$, substitute
   $75 - 75 + 0.05h = 800 - 75$, simplify and isolate the variable
   $0.05h = 725$, simplify
   $\frac{0.05}{0.05}h = \frac{725}{0.05}$, divide to make the coefficient 1
   $h = 14\ 500$, Her sales totalled \$14 500 at the hardware store.
10. **(a)** $250 = 10q + 2n$, where $q = 17$
    (b) $250 = 10(17) + 2n$, substitute
    $250 - 170 = 170 - 170 + 2n$, simplify and isolate the variable
    $80 = 2n$, simplify
    $40 = n$, Nathan bought 40 rolls of nickels.
11. **(a)** $3c + 7t = 60$, where $c = 10.25$, $t = 4.18$
    (b) $c = 14\frac{5}{9}$ **(c)** $c = 1.7$
12. **(a)** $h = \$14\ 718.70$ **(b)** $c = \$19\ 541.33$
    (c) $c = \$11\ 250$
13. **(a)** $n = 15$ rolls **(b)** $q = 17$ rolls
    (c) $d = 39$ rolls
14. **(a)** $a = -4$ **(b)** $b = 5$ **(c)** $c = -6$
    (d) $d = -30$ **(e)** $e = -7$ **(f)** $t = 12$
    (g) $g = \frac{1}{3}$ **(h)** $h = 15$ **(i)** $i = 15$
    (j) $j = 12$ **(k)** $k = 1.06$ **(l)** $n = 0.55$
    (m) $m = 1.8$ **(n)** $w = 3.17$ **(o)** $y = -3$
15. **(a)** $a = 3$ **(b)** $b = 5$ **(c)** $c = -5$
    (d) $d = 1\frac{3}{5}$ **(e)** $e = -2$ **(f)** $f = -2$
    (g) $g = 33$ **(h)** $h = \frac{3}{8}$ **(i)** $i = 1\frac{1}{5}$
    (j) $j = 1\frac{1}{3}$ **(k)** $k = \frac{8}{27}$ **(l)** $l = \frac{2}{3}$
    (m) $m = 4$ **(n)** $n = 0.3$ **(o)** $p = 1.2$

16. (a)

t	3	6	9	12	15
h	20	16	12	8	4

(b)

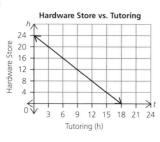

Hardware Store vs. Tutoring

(c) The intercepts in the form (t, h) are (0, 24) and (18, 0). They represent the time in hours Abimael works entirely at one of the jobs to make \$180. The intercepts are the limits on the variables because a negative variable would represent Abimael paying money, instead of making it.

(d) i.

He must tutor 11.5 h.

ii. $t = 11.375$ h

17. (a) $x = 3$ **(b)** $a = 72$ **(c)** $q = 30$
(d) $d = 240$ **(e)** $c = 3$ **(f)** $x = 4750$
(g) $a = 1\frac{1}{4}$ **(h)** $m = 1$

18. (a) $y = 12$ **(b)** $y = -1$ **(c)** $m = -2$
(d) $y = -4$ **(e)** $k = -2$ **(f)** $x = 1$
(g) $y = 4$ **(h)** $y = 36$ **(i)** $m = 5$
(j) $p = 3$ **(k)** $y = 3$ **(l)** $y = 5$

19. (a) $m = 2$ **(b)** $t = -2$ **(c)** $r = -3$
(d) $y = 5$ **(e)** $m = 7$ **(f)** $y = \frac{3}{2}$
(g) $x = -20$ **(h)** $x = 13$ **(i)** $x = -19$
(j) $k = 8$

20. 16 m, 11 m, 10 m

21. (a)

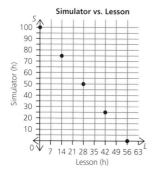

Simulator vs. Lesson

(b)

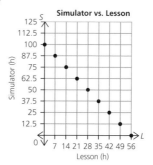

Simulator vs. Lesson

(c)

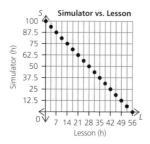

Simulator vs. Lesson

(d) The graph would become a straight line.

(e) paying by the hour: lesson time = 44 h, simulator time = 21 h; paying every half hour: lesson time = 43.5 h, simulator time = 22 h; paying every quarter hour: lesson time = 43.75 h, simulator time = 21.75 h; paying every minute: lesson time = 43.75 h, simulator time = $21.8\overline{6}$ h

5.5 Rearranging the Equation of a Line

Practise, Apply, Solve

1. (a) $o = 10 - g$ **(b)** $g = 10 - o$

2. (a) $a = \dfrac{75 - 4r}{15}$ **(b)** $r = \dfrac{75 - 15a}{4}$

3. (a) $h = \dfrac{240 - 3f}{2.5}$ **(b)** $f = \dfrac{240 - 2.5h}{3}$

4. (a) $y = 5 - 3x$, x-intercept $\left(\dfrac{5}{3}, 0\right)$, y-intercept (0, 5), slope -3

(b) $y = \dfrac{-10 - 2x}{5}$, x-intercept $(-5, 0)$, y-intercept $(0, -2)$, slope $-\dfrac{2}{5}$

(c) $y = \dfrac{-12 + 4x}{3}$, x-intercept (3, 0), y-intercept $(0, -4)$, slope $1\dfrac{1}{3}$

(d) $y = 0.75 - x$, x-intercept (0.75, 0), y-intercept (0, 0.75), slope -1

(e) $y = \dfrac{1 - 0.25x}{0.5}$, x-intercept (4, 0), y-intercept (0, 2), slope -0.5

(f) $y = \dfrac{0.4x - 3.5}{0.2}$, x-intercept (8.75, 0), y-intercept $(0, -17.5)$, slope 2

(g) $y = 8 - \dfrac{2}{3}x$, x-intercept (12, 0), y-intercept (0, 8), slope $-\dfrac{2}{3}$

(h) $y = 12 - \frac{4}{5}x$, x-intercept $(15, 0)$, y-intercept $(0, 12)$, slope $-\frac{4}{5}$

(i) $y = 25 + 3\frac{1}{8}x$, x-intercept $(-8, 0)$, y-intercept $(0, 25)$, slope $3\frac{1}{8}$

5. (a) $y = \frac{60 - 3x}{5}$

(b) slope $-\frac{3}{5}$, x-intercept $(20, 0)$, y-intercept $(0, 12)$

(c)

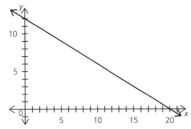

6. (a) $a = \frac{20 + 5b}{2}$

(b)

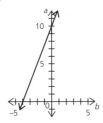

(c) slope 2.5, intercepts $(0, 10)$ and $(-4, 0)$

(d) $b = \frac{2a - 20}{5}$

(e)

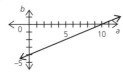

(f) slope $\frac{2}{5}$, intercepts $(0, -4)$ and $(10, 0)$

(g) The slopes of the two graphs are inverses.

7. (a) $a = 35 - 2b$

(b) slope -2, intercepts $(0, 35)$ and $(17.5, 0)$

(c)

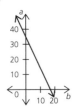

8. (a) $d = \frac{3.2 - 1.4c}{2.8}$

(b) intercepts $(0, 1.1)$ and $(2.3, 0)$, slope -0.5

(c)

9. (a) $z = \frac{0.02 - 2.25w}{3.15}$

(b) intercepts $(0, 0.006)$ and $(0.009, 0)$, slope -0.71

(c)

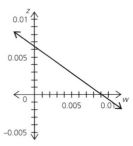

10. (a)

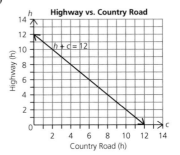

(b) If you use 160 kg of All Grow and 80 kg of No Weed, the ratio is $2 : 1$.

(c) $800 = 2.5A + 5N$, find where $A = N$
$800 = 2.5A + 5A$, if $A = N$ then substitute
$800 = 7.5A$, simplify
$\frac{800}{7.5} = \frac{7.5}{7.5}A$, divide by the numerical coefficient
$106.\overline{6} = A$, Use $106.\overline{6}$ kg of All Grow and No Weed each for \$800.

11. (a)

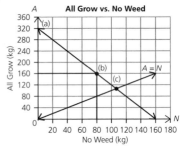

(b)

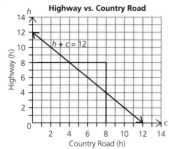

Highway vs. Country Road

from graph: (8,4) therefore distance $= 100h + 60c = 100(8) + 60(4) = 800 + 240 = 1040$ km

(c)

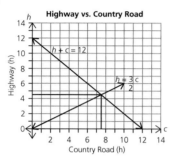

Highway vs. Country Road

For equal distance on each road, $100h = 60c$ or $h = \frac{3}{5}c$. Graph this line on the existing graph $12 = h + c$; substituting gives: $12 = \frac{3}{5}c + c$; simplifying gives: $12 = 1\frac{3}{5}c$; solving: $c = 7\frac{1}{2}$, $h = 4\frac{1}{2}$ h

12. (a) linear, intercepts $(0, -3)$ and $(5, 0)$, slope $\frac{3}{5}$

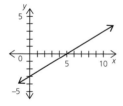

(b) linear, intercepts $(0, 7)$ and $\left(1\frac{3}{4}, 0\right)$, slope -4

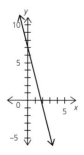

(c) nonlinear

(d) linear, intercepts $(0, -4)$ and $(-1\frac{1}{3}, 0)$, slope -3

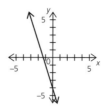

(e) linear, intercepts $(0, -8)$ and $(-6\frac{2}{3}, 0)$, slope $-1\frac{1}{5}$

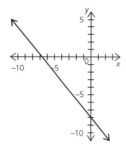

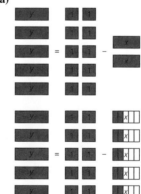

(f) nonlinear

13. (a) linear   **(b)** nonlinear
(c) linear   **(d)** nonlinear
(e) linear   **(f)** nonlinear
(g) linear   **(h)** nonlinear

14. (a)

(b) The tiles are difficult to use for this process since you cannot take sections of tiles.
(c) If you draw every x-tile as 5 fifths, you can break the x-tile into parts.

(d)

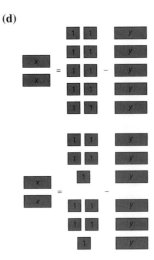

15. At least 708 digital watches and 472 dial watches should be produced.
16. large candy 14¢, small candy 8¢
17. 1424 left-handed, 178 right-handed

5.6 Solving Polynomial Equations

Practise
(a) $y = -8$ (b) $x = 5$ (c) $t = 10$
(d) $x = 7$ (e) $n = -5$ (f) $x = 6$
(g) $p = 2$ (h) $q = 4$ (i) $m = 9$

5.7 Solving Polynomial Equations

Practise, Apply, Solve
1. (a) $x = 6$ (b) $x = 2$ (c) $x = 1$ (d) $x = -1$
   (e) $x = 2$ (f) $x = 9$ (g) $x = 2$ (h) $x = -\frac{1}{2}$
2. (a) $x = 6$ (b) $c = -10$ (c) $d = -8$
   (d) $x = 7$ (e) $x = 4$ (f) $x = 4$
3. (a) $x = 7$ (b) $n = -5$ (c) $t = 3$
   (d) $d = -2$ (e) $k = -15$ (f) $y = -2$
   (g) $z = -3$ (h) $u = 5$ (i) $b = 3$
   (j) $a = 3$ (k) $j = -4$ (l) $k = 1$
   (m) $p = 2$ (n) $s = -4$
4. (a) $x = 5$ (b) $x = -14$ (c) $x = 7$
   (d) $x = 18$ (e) $x = -3\frac{3}{4}$ (f) $s = 72$
   (g) $k = 22\frac{1}{2}$ (h) $r = -\frac{1}{2}$ (i) $y = -3$
5. (a) $y = 1$ (b) $p = 6$ (c) $d = -3$
   (d) $n = 3$ (e) $x = -1$ (f) $h = 2$
   (g) $z = 4$ (h) $v = -8$
6. (a) $q = -1$ (b) $n = 9$ (c) $p = 2$
   (d) $z = 4$ (e) $c = 1$ (f) $v = -4$
7. (a) $h = 1$ (b) $m = -16$ (c) $n = 1$
   (d) $p = 3$ (e) $u = -5$ (f) $a = \frac{7}{2}$
   (g) $q = 1.99$ (h) $y = 3$ (i) $r = -2.76$
   (j) $z = 3\frac{3}{8}$ (k) $w = 5$
8. (a) $y = 21$ (b) $x = 3\frac{2}{3}$ (c) $x = 3\frac{1}{5}$

9. (a) $x = 7$ (b) $y = -4\frac{2}{3}$ (c) $y = 2\frac{3}{7}$
10. (a) $x = 4$ (b) $y = \frac{3}{5}$ (c) $y = 1\frac{29}{31}$
11. (a) $x = 1$ (b) $y = 1$ (c) $c = -12$
12. (a) $d = -1\frac{15}{77}$ (b) $h = 2\frac{19}{96}$ (c) $j = 8$
13. (a) $8.98(b - 6)$ (b) $17.96   (c) 12
14. $k = 2$
15. $x = 7\frac{5}{22}$
16. $x = -1\frac{659}{878}$
17. Use 125 kg of the $8/kg grade and 75 kg of the $10/kg grade for the new blend.
18. $3600
19. 60 mL

5.8 Standard Form of a Linear Equation

Practise, Apply, Solve
1. (a) neither   (b) neither
   (c) neither   (d) neither
   (e) standard form   (f) neither
   (g) neither   (h) neither
   (i) standard or slope-y-intercept form
   (j) standard form   (k) neither
   (l) neither   (m) slope-y-intercept form
   (n) neither   (o) slope-y-intercept form
2. (a) $y = -0.3x - 2$ (b) $4x - 3y - 12 = 0$
   (c) $x + y - 38 = 0$ (d) $y = 0.06x + 150$
   (e) $46x + 53y - 7600 = 0$
   (f) $y = 2x + 1.5$ (g) $y = \frac{4}{3}x - 10$
3. (a) x-intercept 5, y-intercept -2
   (b) x-intercept 5, y-intercept 4
   (c) x-intercept 5, no y-intercept
   (d) no x-intercept, y-intercept -2
   (e) x-intercept 0, y-intercept 0
   (f) x-intercept 9, y-intercept -9
   (g) x-intercept 0, y-intercept 0
   (h) x-intercept 5, y-intercept 4
   (i) x-intercept 4, y-intercept -5
4. (a) $y = \frac{2}{5}x - 2$, slope is $\frac{2}{5}$
   (b) $y = -\frac{4}{5}x + 4$, slope is $-\frac{4}{5}$
   (c) $x = 5$, slope is undefined
   (d) $y = -2$, slope is 0
   (e) $y = -x$, slope is -1
   (f) $y = x - 9$, slope is 1
   (g) $y = -\frac{2}{3}x$, slope is $-\frac{2}{3}$
   (h) $y = -\frac{4}{5}x + 4$, slope is $-\frac{4}{5}$
   (i) $y = 1\frac{1}{4}x - 5$, slope is $1\frac{1}{4}$
5. (a) $3x - y + 5 = 0$ (b) $2x + y + 11 = 0$
   (c) $2x - 3y - 12 = 0$ (d) $x - 6y + 15 = 0$
   (e) $x - 6y + 5 = 0$ (f) $5x + 12y - 35 = 0$
   (g) $x - 2y + 7 = 0$ (h) $30x - 9y - 4 = 0$
   (i) $x + 2y + 5 = 0$

6. (a) $4x + 14y + 7 = 0$; x-intercept $-1\frac{3}{4}$, y-intercept $-\frac{1}{2}$

(b) $7x - y - 3 = 0$; x-intercept $\frac{3}{7}$, y-intercept -3

(c) $6x - 4y - 7 = 0$; x-intercept $1\frac{1}{6}$, y-intercept $-1\frac{3}{4}$

(d) $y - 2 = 0$; y-intercept 2, there is no x-intercept

(e) $68x + 51y - 6 = 0$; x-intercept $\frac{3}{34}$, y-intercept $\frac{2}{17}$

(f) $13x - 21y + 18 = 0$; x-intercept $-1\frac{5}{13}$, y-intercept $1\frac{1}{7}$

7. (a) $y = 5x - 50$; the slope represents the rate at which Tiffany is paid back, the y-intercept represents the Tiffany's initial amount, and the x-intercept represents the day when Tiffany is completely repaid.

(b) $y = 20x + 200$; the slope represents the amount Andrew earns for each problem fixed, the y-intercept represents Andrew's base salary.

(c) $5x + 4y + 12 = 0$

(d) $1.2x + 2.1y = 33.6$; the y-intercept represents the maximum number of \$2.10 packs Brad can buy, the x-intercept represents the maximum number of \$1.20 packs Brad can buy.

(e) $x + y = 12$; the intercepts represent the maximum number of hours Peggy can spend on each type of lesson.

(f) $y = -4200x + 210\ 000$; the slope represents the rate at which the value of the house is depreciating, the y-intercept represents the purchase price of the house.

8. No, the planes will not collide.

9. (a) Let x be the number of correct answers, and y be the number of incorrect answers.
$x - 0.25y = 34.75$ or $y = 4x - 139$

(b)

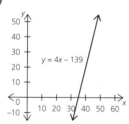

(c) $x + y = 41$

(d)

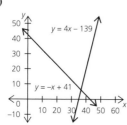

(e) The point of intersection is (36, 5).

(f) These coordinates mean that Aline answered 36 questions correctly and 5 questions incorrectly.

(g) $4x - y - 139 = 0$, $x + y - 41 = 0$

10. (a) Let x be the number of tire installations, and y be the number of gear assemblies.
$x + y = 40$

(b) $2x + 5y = 110$ or $y = -\frac{2}{5}x + 22$

(c)

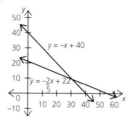

(d) The point of intersection is (30, 10). This tells us that Ralph did 30 tire installations and 10 gear assemblies.

(e) $x + y - 40 = 0$, $2x + 5y - 110 = 0$

11. (a) Let x be the mass of the chocolate-coated almonds in kilograms, and y be the mass of the chocolate-coated raisins in kilograms.
$x + y = 19$ or $y = -x + 19$

(b) $10.5x + 5y = 150$ or slope-y-intercept form: $y = -2.1x + 30$

(c)

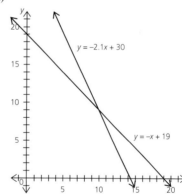

(d) The point of intersection is (10, 9). This tells us that in the candy mixture there are 10 kg of chocolate-coated almonds and 9 kg of chocolate-coated raisins.

(e) $x + y - 19 = 0$, $21x + 10y - 300 = 0$

12. (a) $d + r = 4800$; standard form:
$d + r - 4800 = 0$;
slope-y-intercept form: $r = 4800 - d$

(b) $32d + 20r = 116\ 400$; standard form:
$32d + 20r - 116\ 400 = 0$
slope-y-intercept form: $r = -1.6d + 5820$

(c)

Running Shoes vs. Dress Shoes

(d) The coordinates of the point of intersection are (1700, 3100). This tells us that 1700 pairs of dress shoes and 3100 pairs of running shoes were made.

(e) $r + d - 4800 = 0$, $8d + 5r - 29\,100 = 0$

13. (a) $2w + t = 83$; standard form: $2w + t - 83 = 0$
slope-y-intercept form, $t = 83 - 2w$

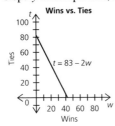

Wins vs. Ties

(b) $w + t = 48$; standard form: $w + t - 48 = 0$
slope-y-intercept form: $t = 48 - w$

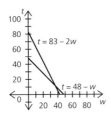

(c) The coordinates of the point of intersection are (35, 13). This tells us that Raymond's team won 35 games and had 13 ties.

14. clothing store $5000, hardware store $10 000

15. 30 kg of hard candy and 30 kg of soft candy are needed.

16. Cathy sold low-risk stocks worth $5250 and high-risk stocks worth $9000.

5.9 Problem Solving and Linear Equations

Practise, Apply, Solve

1. (a) $(-1, 2)$ **(b)** $(-3, -1)$ **(c)** $(5, -\frac{1}{2})$

(d) $(-15, 10)$ **(e)** $(13\frac{1}{2}, -7)$ **(f)** $(-90, -31)$

2. (a) $(-4, -2)$ **(b)** $(-5, -44)$

(c) $(a, b) = (1, 7)$ **(d)** $(7, 1)$

(e) $(6.8, 5.7)$ **(f)** $(13\frac{1}{7}, -3\frac{3}{7})$

(g) $(1, -4)$ **(h)** $(3, 36)$

(i) $(-10, -17)$ **(j)** $(1, -1.4)$

(k) $(1\frac{1}{4}, 7\frac{1}{4})$ **(l)** $(0, -5)$

(m) $(5, 7)$ **(n)** $(r, s) = (20, 14)$

(o) $(x, t) = (2, 7)$ **(p)** $(-3, -13)$

(q) $(-2\frac{2}{7}, 5)$ **(r)** $(-\frac{3}{7}, -\frac{9}{35})$

3. (a) $x = 24$ **(b)** $x = 6\frac{2}{5}$ **(c)** $x = 0.2$

(d) $x = -\frac{7}{15}$ **(e)** $x = -1\frac{11}{15}$ **(f)** $r = 1\frac{7}{51}$

(g) $r = \frac{22}{25}$ **(h)** $y = -\frac{1}{43}$ **(i)** $g = 2$

(j) $s = \frac{49}{90}$

4. 30 tire installations, 10 gear assemblies

5. 10 kg almonds, 9 kg raisins

6. 10 figure skates, 84 hockey skates

7. 195 minutes on the highway, 525 minutes on other roads

8. 80 kg All Grow, 120 kg No Weed

10. $3000 at 10%, $5000 at 12%.

11. 88 km/h

12. The clerk would have to make $3000 in sales.

13. 15 L of 40% solution and 5 L of 80% solution

14. Gretchen worked for 12 h at her first job and for 7 h at her second job.

Chapter Review

1. (a) 20 wreaths **(b)** 35 candles

(c)

Wreaths	Candles
12	14
8	21
16	7

(d)

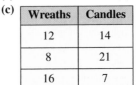

Candles vs. Wreaths

(e) 4 wreaths

2. (a) 24 **(b)** 72

(c)

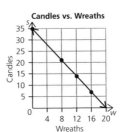

Popsicles vs. Chips

(d) 12 chips, 36 popsicles

3.(a) Let x be the number of times he

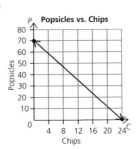

3. (a) Let x be the number of times he travelled by bus, y the number of times by car.

Then, $1.5x + 1.2y = 26.4$ and $x = 12$.

So, $1.5(12) + 1.2y = 26.4$

$$18 + 1.2y = 26.4$$
$$1.2y = 8.4$$
$$y = \frac{8.4}{1.2}$$
$$y = 7 \text{ times}$$

(b) $1.5x + 1.2(12) = 26.4$

$$1.5x + 14.4 = 26.4$$
$$1.5x = 12$$
$$x = \frac{12}{1.5}$$
$$x = 8 \text{ times}$$

(c) $1.2x + 0.8y = 20,\ y = 10$

$$1.2x + 0.8(10) = 20$$
$$1.2x + 8 = 20$$
$$1.2x = 12$$
$$x = \frac{12}{1.2}$$
$$x = 10 \text{ times}$$

4. Let x be the number of tickets bought in advance, y the number of tickets bought at the door.

(a) $6.5x + 8y = 177.5,\ y = 10$

$$6.5x + 8(10) = 177.5$$
$$6.5x + 80 = 177.5$$
$$6.5x = 97.5$$
$$x = \frac{97.5}{6.5}$$
$$x = 15 \text{ tickets}$$

(b) $6.5(10) + 8y = 249$

$$65 + 8y = 249$$
$$8y = 184$$
$$y = \frac{184}{8}$$
$$y = 23 \text{ tickets}$$

(c) $\frac{4}{5}(6.5)(5) + 8y = 98$

$$26 + 8y = 98$$
$$8y = 72$$
$$y = \frac{72}{8}$$
$$y = 9 \text{ tickets}$$

5. 400 gum, 200 chocolate

6. (a) $y = -\frac{6}{11}x - 1\frac{9}{11}$ x-intercept $-3\frac{1}{3}$, y-intercept $-1\frac{9}{11}$, slope $-\frac{6}{11}$

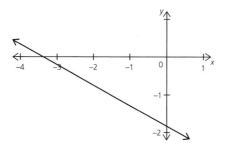

(b) $y = -3\frac{1}{5}x + 2$ x-intercept $\frac{5}{8}$, y-intercept 2, slope $-3\frac{1}{5}$

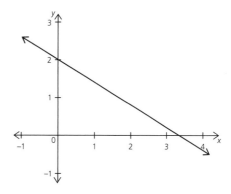

(c) $y = -3x + 100$

x-intercept $33\frac{1}{3}$, y-intercept 100, slope -3

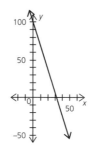

(d) $y = -\frac{14}{155}x + \frac{5}{31}$

x-intercept $1\frac{11}{14}$, y-intercept $\frac{5}{31}$, slope $-\frac{14}{155}$

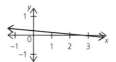

(e) $y = -\frac{4}{7}x + 2\frac{2}{7}$

x-intercept 4, y-intercept $2\frac{2}{7}$, slope $-\frac{4}{7}$

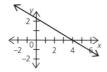

(f) $y = 9x$

x-intercept 0, y-intercept 0, slope 9

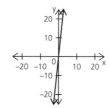

7. (a) $x = -1\frac{5}{6}y - 3\frac{1}{3}$

x-intercept $-3\frac{1}{3}$, y-intercept $-1\frac{9}{11}$, slope $-1\frac{5}{6}$

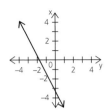

(b) $x = -\frac{5}{16}y + \frac{5}{64}$

x-intercept $\frac{5}{64}$, y-intercept $\frac{1}{4}$,

slope $-\frac{5}{16}$

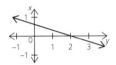

(c) $x = -\frac{1}{3}y + 33\frac{1}{3}$

x-intercept $33\frac{1}{3}$,

y-intercept 100, slope $-\frac{1}{3}$

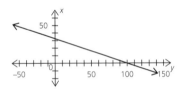

(d) $x = -11\frac{1}{14}y + 1\frac{341}{434}$

x-intercept $1\frac{341}{434}$, y-intercept $\frac{5}{31}$, slope $-1\frac{11}{14}$

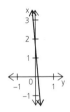

(e) $x = -1\frac{3}{4}y + 4$

x-intercept 4, y-intercept $2\frac{6}{21}$,

slope $-1\frac{3}{4}$

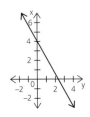

(f) $x = \frac{1}{9}y$

x-intercept 0, y-intercept 0, slope $\frac{1}{9}$

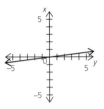

8. (a) $n = 10\frac{2}{3}$ **(b)** $r = 7\frac{1}{5}$ **(c)** $q = 9$

(d) $n = -2.6$ **(e)** $x = 1\frac{1}{23}$ **(f)** $p = -1\frac{17}{21}$

(g) $y = 3$ **(h)** $b = 3.2$

9. (a) $x = 1\frac{17}{20}$ **(b)** $x = -\frac{1}{7}$

10. 50 guests

11. (a) $-5x + 3y - 6 = 0$ **(b)** $3x + 4y - 2 = 0$
  (c) $2x - 3y - 12 = 0$ **(d)** $9x - 8y - 6 = 0$

12. (a) $-\frac{3}{4}, \frac{5}{4}$ **(b)** $-\frac{7}{3}, -\frac{1}{3}$ **(c)** $\frac{3}{5}, \frac{2}{5}$

13. (a) $p + l = 15$
  (b) $315p + 105l = 3675$
  (c)

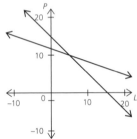

(d) The point of intersection tells us how many portraits and how many landscapes Denise must have painted to have painted 15 pictures and earned $3675. She painted 10 illustrations and 5 pieces of technical art.

14. (a) $x = 3.5, y = -2.5$ **(b)** $x = 1, y = 0.25$
  (c) $x = 6, y = 10$ **(d)** $x = 1, y = 12$

Chapter Review Test

1. (a) $y = -8$ **(b)** $x = 5$ **(c)** $y = -4$
  (d) $x = 3$ **(e)** $n = 1$ **(f)** $n = -1$
  (g) $x = 20$ **(h)** $x = 16$ **(i)** $a = 16$

2. (a) x-intercept -4.176, y-intercept 8.875, slope 2.125
  (b)

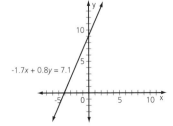

3. (a) $(-1, 4)$ (b) $(3, -2)$ (c) $(0, 3)$

4. (a) $n = 1\frac{1}{4}m - 20$ (b) $m = \frac{10}{21}(n + 1)$

5. (a) $4x + 9y - 30 = 0$ (b) $-\frac{4}{9}, \frac{10}{3}$

6. (a) All six possible combinations are given.

Number of Hours Worked at First Job ($14/h)	Number of Hours Worked at Second Job ($11/h)
7	82
18	68
29	54
40	40
51	26
62	12

(b)

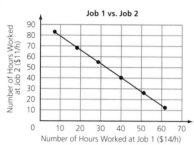

7. (a) Costs $= 5n + 378$, Revenue $= 26n$, where n is the number of cakes sold.

(b)

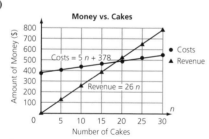

(c) 18 cakes

8. (a) $x = \frac{35}{41}$ (b) $r = \frac{1}{2}$

(c) $a = \frac{6}{5}$ (d) $x = -\frac{7}{3}$

9. (a) $x = 7\frac{3}{5}$ (b) $x = \frac{1}{4}$

10. 200 pairs of skates

11. 1887.1 k•Wh

12. 85 racing bikes, 120 mountain bikes

13. $a = 9$

Cumulative Review Test 2

1. (a) -25 (b) $\frac{1}{32}$ (c) 1   (d) 100

(e) 60   (f) 64   (g) $-25\frac{26}{27}$ (h) $2\frac{5}{6}$

2. (a) m^2 (b) y^{12}

(c) $\frac{1}{1000x^6}$ (d) x^7y^9

(e) $5ab$ (f) $-5a + b - 2c$

(g) $7x^2 + 31x - 45$ (h) $-3x^4 - 11x^3$

(i) $-20m^5n^5$ (j) $4r^{15}s^{12}$

(k) $2y^2 - 1\frac{1}{2}x^3 + 3xy^2$

3. (a) $8xz(2y + 3w)$ (b) $4g^2h^3(2g^2h^2 - 3)$

4. (a) $x = 2$ (b) $x = -1$ (c) $s = 2$

(d) $p = 2\frac{10}{11}$ (e) $a = \frac{1}{4}$ (f) $x = -5$

5. (a) Line segment BC shows her fastest speed, as this line segment has the steepest slope.

(b) Line segment DE shows she is not moving, as her distance does not change during this time.

(c) Line segment EF shows she is sprinting towards the school. You know she is moving towards the school because her distance from the school is decreasing.

(d) Line segments AB and FG show her running at 50 m/min.

6. (a) Let H represent the number of hours spent on the Internet in one month. Then the cost per month for Information Technology Co. is $20 + 2H$, and the cost per month for The World Around Us Co. is $10 + 2.5H$.

(b) Information Technology Co.: $0.9(20 + 2H) = 18 + 1.8H$; The World Around Us Co.: $0.85(10 + 2.5H) = 8.5 + 2.125H$

(c) i. 35 h; Information Technology Co.: $81; The World Around Us Co.: $82.88
ii. 60 h; Information Technology Co.: $126; The World Around Us Co.: $136

(d) 29.2 h

7. (a) $0.1j + 0.09t = 900$ (b) $3600.00

8. $(-1, 2)$

9. $1, -1, \frac{-5}{3}$

Review of Essential Skills and Knowledge (Part II)

Measurement: Area and Perimeter

1. (a) 105 m²   (b) 729 cm²   (c) 102 cm²
(d) 180 cm²   (e) 237.7 cm²   (f) 828 cm²

2. (a) 4.8 cm   (b) 2.16 cm

3. 856.3 cm²

4. (a) 598 m   (b) 260 m

5. (a) 70.4 cm²   (b) 642.1 cm²
(c) 12.7 m²   (d) 1009.2 cm²
(e) 80 cm²

6. (a) 50 cm²   (b) 96 cm²   (c) 48 cm²

Measurement: Working with Circles

1. (a) D: 32.2 cm; C: 101.1 cm; A: 813.9 cm²
(b) R: 4.7 m; C: 29.5 m; A: 69.4 m²

(c) R: 4.0 cm; D: 8.0 cm; A: 50.2 cm²
(d) R: 5.0 m; D: 10.0 m; C: 31.4 m
(e) R: 3.2 m; D: 6.5 m; A: 33.1 m²
(f) R: 6.3 cm; D: 12.6 cm; C: 39.6 cm
2. (a) 102.4 cm   (b) 834.3 cm²
3. (a) 30.8 m   (b) 75.4 m²
4. (a) 8.2 cm   (b) 211.1 cm²
5. 5805.9 cm²
6. 135.0 km
7. 415.3 m²
8. (a) dime 5.3 cm, nickel 6.6 cm, quarter 7.2 cm
   (b) dime 2.3 cm², nickel 3.5 cm², quarter 4.2 cm²
   (c) 1.9 cm   (d) 0.7 cm²
9. (a) 62.7 cm²   (b) 58.5 cm²
   (c) 71.77 cm²   (d) 80 cm²
   (e) 57.125 cm²   (f) 21.98 cm²
   (g) 377.585 cm²

Measurement: Volume and Surface Area

1. (a) 626.5 cm³   (b) 83.8 cm³
   (c) 66.4 cm³   (d) 482.4 cm³
2. (a) 448.1 cm²   (b) 157.0 cm²
   (c) 127.4 cm²   (d) 398.3 cm²
3. 132.7 cm³   4. 121.5 cm²
5. 4.1 cm   6. 3.2 cm
7. (a) 211.6 m³   (b) 245.1 m²   (c) 5 cans
8. (a) $V \doteq 472.5$ cm³; $SA \doteq 358.925$ cm²
   (b) $V = 177$ cm³; $SA = 201$ cm²
   (c) $V = 283.5$ cm³; $SA = 311.1$ cm²

Measurement: Working with Formulas

1. (a) 5   (b) 0.09   (c) 8
   (d) 17   (e) 25   (f) 0.5
   (g) 81   (h) 8.4   (i) 48
2. 241.7 cm   3. 22 mm × 22 mm
4. 18 cm   5. 3 m   6. 12 cm
7. 21.6 cm   8. 10 m

Geometry and Spatial Sense: Language of Geometry

1. (a) C   (b) D   (c) B   (d) A
2. (a) A   (b) O   (c) R   (d) S
   (e) A   (f) S   (g) O   (h) A
3. (a) E   (b) I   (c) I   (d) S
   (e) I   (f) S   (g) E
4. (a) A   (b) O   (c) O   (d) R
   (e) A   (f) R   (g) O
5. (a) 17°   (b) 63°   (c) 45°
6. (a) 164°   (b) 108°   (c) 30°
7. (a) F   (b) A   (c) B   (d) E
   (e) D   (f) C
8. (a)   (b)

(c)   (d)

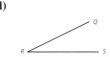

(e)   (f)

(g)   (h)

9. (a) 30°   (b) 90°   (c) 50°   (d) 180°
   (e) 70°   (f) 140°
10. (a) obtuse   (b) acute
   (c) obtuse   (d) acute
   (e) right   (f) straight
11. (a)   (b)

(c)   (d)

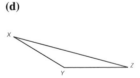

(e)   (f)

12. (a) no   (b) yes   (c) yes   (d) yes
   (e) yes

Geometry and Spatial Sense: Angle Relationships

1. (a) $a = 65°$, $b = 115°$, $c = 115°$
   (b) $w = 60°$, $x = 40°$, $y = 80°$, $z = 40°$
   (c) $x = 50°$, $y = 62°$
   (d) $a = 70°$

(e) $a = 80°$, $b = 80°$, $c = 100°$
(f) $a = 65°$, $b = 50°$, $c = 65°$
(g) $a = 50°$, $b = 50°$, $c = 50°$, $d = 75°$
(h) $x = 60°$, $y = 120°$, $z = 120°$
2. (a) $a = 80°$, $b = 100°$, $c = 100°$, $d = 100°$
(b) $x = 37°$, $y = 71°$, $z = 71°$
(c) $w = 131°$, $x = 49°$, $y = 74°$, $z = 57°$
(d) $a = 48°$, $b = 106°$, $c = 26°$, $d = 106°$

Chapter 6

Getting Ready

1. (a) iii.   (b) i.   (c) iv.   (d) ii.
(e) vi.   (f) v.   (g) vii.
2. (a) parallel   (b) perpendicular
(c) polygon   (d) quadrilateral
(e) congruent
4. (a) scalene   (b) equilateral
(c) isosceles   (d) right-angled
(e) obtuse   (f) acute
5. (a) similarities: both are quadrilaterals, are parallelograms, and have equal sides; differences: square's sides intersect at 90°, rhombus's sides intersect at varying angles
(b) similarities: both are quadrilaterals, are parallelograms; differences: rectangle's sides intersect at 90°, parallelogram's sides intersect at varying angles
(c) A rhombus is a parallelogram. It has 4 equal sides.
(d) similarities: both are types of triangles; differences: equilateral triangle has 3 sides of equal length and 3 equal angles of 60°, and is always an acute triangle; an isosceles triangle has 2 sides of equal length and the 2 angles opposite the equal sides are also equal, can be either acute or obtuse.

6.1 Angle Properties of Parallel Lines

Practise, Apply, Solve

1. (a) $\angle EGB = \angle GHD$ corresponding
$\angle EGB = \angle AGH$ vertically opposite
$\angle EGB = \angle CHF$ alternate exterior
(b) $\angle HGB = \angle FHD$ corresponding
$\angle HGB = \angle AGE$ vertically opposite
$\angle HGB = \angle CHG$ alternate interior
(c) $\angle HGB$ and $\angle GHD$ are interior angles on the same side of the transversal and their sum is 180°.
2. This does not affect the relationships as stated above. If EF is moved so that it is perpendicular to AB and CD then all angles created would be equal.
3. (a) If AB and CD are not parallel then only the vertically opposite or supplementary angle relationships will be true.

(b) It can be proven by counter-example that some of the relationships are false.
(c) It can be proven that the vertically opposite or supplementary angle relationships will remain true since these relations do not depend on the lines being parallel.
4. You will need a compass, ruler, and pencil. First draw PQ, then draw RT off of PQ using the compass to reproduce the angle. To draw SU parallel to RT, construct a perpendicular to RT. Construct another perpendicular to this line and call it SU.
(a) $\angle SRT$ and $\angle QSU$ are equal angles on the same side of the transversal since SU and RT are parallel and PQ intersects both lines.
(b) If the angles are equal then the lines must be parallel.
5. The platform will always stay parallel to the base because the alternate interior angles formed are equal.
6. (a) $\angle EGB = \angle GHD = \angle CHF = \angle AGH$, $\angle AGE = \angle HGB = \angle CHG = \angle FHD$, any angle from the first group plus any angle from the second group will add to 180°.
(b) $\angle GED = \angle EFC = \angle HEF = \angle IFA$, $\angle GEH = \angle DEF = \angle EFI = \angle AFC$, any angle from the first group plus any angle from the second group will add to 180°.
7. (a) k and m are parallel.
(b) Since $\angle MLI + \angle HIL = 180°$ then by the alternate interior angle relationship the lines must be parallel.
8. (a) $\angle 1 = 60°$ (b) $\angle 2 = 120°$ (c) $\angle 3 = 60°$
(d) $\angle 4 = 60°$ (e) $\angle 5 = 120°$ (f) $\angle 6 = 60°$
(g) $\angle 7 = 120°$ (h) $\angle 8 = 60°$
9. (a) $\angle BCA = 32°$, $\angle ABC = 105°$, $\angle ACD = 43°$, $\angle CDA = 105°$
(b) $\angle BAC = 20°$, $\angle BCA = 25°$, $\angle ACD = 20°$, $\angle CDA = 135°$
(c) $\angle ABC$, $\angle ADC$; $\angle BAC$, $\angle ACD$; $\angle CAD$, $\angle BCA$; $\angle BAD$, $\angle BCD$
(d) $\angle BAD$, $\angle ADC$; $\angle BAD$, $\angle ABC$; $\angle ABC$, $\angle BCD$; $\angle BCD$, $\angle CDA$
10. (a) $a = 50°$, $b = 65°$, $c = 115°$
(b) $a = b = 110°$, $c = 40°$
11. 60°

6.2 Angles Associated with Triangles

Practise, Apply, Solve

1. (a) 35°   (b) 20°   (c) 155°
(d) 150°
2. (a) $x = 37°$ (b) $x = 30°$ (c) $x = 15°$
(d) $x = 122°$ (e) $x = 103°$ (f) $x = 65°$
(g) $x = 60°$
(h) $t = 115°$, $x = 65°$, $y = 85°$, $z = 30°$
3. (a) 35°, 75°, 70°   (b) 60°, 40°, 100°
(c) 100°, 60°, 60°
4. (a) 150°   (b) 20°   (c) 45°

5. (a) Each interior angle will be 60°. So the robot must turn 120° at every wall.

(b) The two interior angles at the ends of the equal lines will be equal.

6. (a) $x = 12°$ **(b)** $x = 30°, y = 60°, z = 30°$
(c) $x = 70°, y = 35°$ **(d)** $x = 72°, y = 73°$

7. (a) $\angle 1 + \angle 2 = 180°$
(c) $\angle 1 = \angle BFD$ since they are alternate interior angles and $\angle 2 + \angle BFD = 180°$ since they are interior angles on the same side of a transversal. Therefore, $\angle 1 + \angle 2 = 180°$.

8. (a) $x = 25°, 65°, 65°$ **(b)** $x = 10°, 70°, 110°$
(c) $x = 6°, 28°, 68°$
(d) $x = 62°, 82°, 134°, 144°$

9. (a) 145°   **(b)** 133°   **(c)** 105°
10. (a) 30°   **(b)** 19°   **(c)** 42.5°
11. (a) AB and DE **(b)** AB and CE **(c)** LM and NO

6.3 Angles and Polygons

Practise, Apply, Solve

1. (a) $x = 150°$ **(b)** $x = 105°$
(c) $x = 98°$ **(d)** $x = 120°$ **(e)** $x = 120°$
2. (a) 12 sides   **(b)** 8 sides   **(c)** 90 sides
3. The two different interior angles are 36° and 144°.
4. (a) $130° + 80° + 100° + x = 360°, x = 50°$
(b) $x + x - 15° = 150°, x = 82.5°$
(c) $135° + 85° + (180 - x)° = 360°, x = 40°$
(d) $x + x + x - 30 + x - 40° = 360°, x = 107.5°$
(e) $x = 63°, x + y = 126, y = 63°$
5. 10
6. The internal angles of a polygon determine the way a polygon can be tiled. When polygons meet at vertices they form a 360° angle. Therefore, any regular polygon whose internal angle does not divide 360° cannot be used as tiles.
7. (a) $x = 113°$ **(b)** $y = 135°$
(c) $a = 80°, b = 90°, c = 100°$
10. $x = 144°$
11. You can tile a floor using an octagon and a square at each vertex. You could also use pentagons with a decagon at each vertex.

6.4 Polygon Properties

Practise, Apply, Solve

1. (a) vii.   **(b)** v.   **(c)** i.   **(d)** ii.
(e) iii.   **(f)** vi.   **(g)** iv.
2. (a) no   **(b)** yes   **(c)** yes
(d) no   **(e)** yes
3. (a) Student may also draw a square.

rhombus

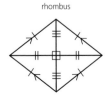

(b)
square

(c)
regular trapezoid

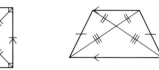

(d)
square

4. regular: (a), (b), (e), (f); Figures (c), (d), (g), (h) are not regular because their sides are not all equal in length.
5. (a) true   **(b)** true   **(c)** true
(d) true   **(e)** false
6. (a) $\angle ADE = 93°$
(b) Since D and E are midpoints of AC and AB, DE is a midsegment of $\triangle ABC$ and is parallel to BC. Since DE and BC are parallel, $\angle ACB$ and $\angle ADE$ are corresponding angles, and are therefore equal.
7. $\angle x = 80°, \angle y = 60°, \angle z = 40°$
8. (a) $AD = 3.5$ cm   **(b)** $AB = 6$ cm
(c) $\angle ADE = 30°$ **(d)** $\angle AED = 75°$
9. (a) $\angle x = 25°, \angle y = 25°, \angle z = 65°$
(b) $\angle x = 60°, \angle y = 60°, \angle z = 30°$
(c) $\angle x = 32°, \angle y = 58°, \angle z = 58°$
10. (a) $DE = 3\sqrt{3}$ cm   **(b)** $BD = 6$ cm
11. (a) parallelogram   **(b)** $\angle x = 28°, \angle y = 29°$
12. (a) True. *Examples:* a regular square, a regular triangle, and a regular pentagon.
(b) False. *Examples:* a rectangle that is not a square, an octagon or hexagon with one pair of opposite sides shorter than the rest but with equal angles of 135° or 120°.
13. The length of the midsegment is always half the length of the third side of the triangle.
14. (a) The segment between the midpoints is parallel to the two parallel sides of the trapezoid.
(b) The sum of the lengths of the two parallel sides of the trapezoid is always twice the length of the midsegment.
15. The results of the previous two questions do not hold for polygons with more than four sides.
16. The quadrilateral can also be a rectangle that is not square.
17. *example*: No. Counter-example: a 9-by-5 rectangle and a 7-by-7 square.
18. *example*: No. Counter-example: a 9-by-5 rectangle and a 7-by-7 square.

19. (a)

Polygon	Number of Diagonals	Number of Triangles
triangle	0	1
quadrilateral	1	2
pentagon	2	3
hexagon	3	4
heptagon	4	5
octagon	5	6
nonagon	6	7
decagon	7	8
100-gon	97	98
n-gon	$n - 3$	$n - 2$

(b) Since every triangle's interior angles add up to 180°, the sum of the interior angles for any polygon is simply the sum of the interior angles of all triangles formed by the diagonals from one vertex. So for an n-sided polygon, the sum of the interior angles is $180° \times (n - 2)$.

6.5 Triangle Centres

Practise, Apply, Solve

1. (a) i. median **ii.** altitude **iii.** angle bisector **iv.** perpendicular bisector
(b) i. centroid **ii.** orthocentre **iii.** incentre **iv.** circumcentre

2. (a) iii. **(b)** iv. **(c)** ii. **(d)** i.

3.

Triangle	Circumcentre	Orthocentre
acute	inside	inside
obtuse	outside	outside
right	on a side	on a side
equilateral	inside	inside

4. (a) false **(b)** false **(c)** true
(d) true **(e)** false **(f)** true

5. (a) The median has the same length as one of the bisected hypotenuse segments.
(b) $BD = 5$ cm
(c) $\angle BDC = 76°$

9. (a) The best location is at the circumcentre of the triangle.
(b) about 3.02 km

11. (a) Each triangle can be balanced on the end of a pencil at the centroid.
(b) Draw the perpendicular bisectors of each side. The centroid is at the point where the perpendicular bisectors intersect. (See note on text about this question.)

12. $BF = 4$ cm
14. (a) $x = 1$ **(b)** $FH = 3$
15. (a) $x = \frac{3}{4}$ **(b)** $BE = 6\frac{3}{4}$
16. (a) $x = 4$ **(b)** $AG = 24$

Chapter Review

1. alternate interior, alternate exterior
2. (a) corresponding **(b)** equal
(c) supplementary **(d)** corresponding
3. $x = 8$
4. $x = 7$
5. (a) 180° **(b)** remote **(c)** 360°
6. (a) $x = 65°, y = 75°, z = 40°$
(b) $x = 50°, y = 25°, z = 105°$
7. (a) $AC \parallel BD$ since same-side interior angles add to 180°.
(b) $AB \parallel CD$ since alternate interior angles are equal.
(c) $AD \parallel HE$ since same-side interior angles add to 180°, $CG \parallel DJ$ since alternate interior angles are equal.
8. sum of interior angles $= 180(n - 2)$, where n is the number of sides of the polygon
9. interior 162°, exterior 18°
10. 10
11. (a) i. **(b)** v. **(c)** iii.
(d) ii. **(e)** iv.
12. (a) parallelogram
(b) square **(c)** rhombus
14. *example*: equal side lengths, all interior angles are 90°, diagonals are equal in length, diagonals bisect each other, diagonals intersect at 90°, opposite sides are parallel
15. $x = 25°, y = 45°$
16. (a) concurrent
(b) medians
(c) angle bisectors
(d) orthocentre **(e)** circumcentre
17. (a) **(b)**

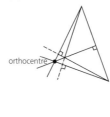
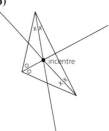

(c) **(d)**

18. (a) the centre of a circle that will touch each side of the triangle at exactly one point
(b) the centre of a circle that passes through the vertices of the triangle
(c) the centre of mass of the triangle
19. Yes, only right-angled triangles have two of the altitudes as a side of the triangle.
20. Yes, these are all true for equilateral triangles.
21.

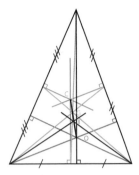

Chapter Review Test

1. (a) $50°$ **(b)** $81.25°$
2. (a) $135°$ **(b)** 8
3. (a) parallel   **(b)** parallel
     (c) parallel
4. (a) $x = 22.5°$ **(b)** $\angle 7 = 97.5°$
5. (a) corresponding   **(b)** alternate interior
     (c) supplementary
6. same-side interior angles of a transversal
7. (a) $v = 90°$ **(b)** $w = 38°$ **(c)** $x = 65°$
     (d) $y = 38°$ **(e)** $z = 52°$
8. $70°$
9. (a) 6 **(b)** 14
10. (a), (b)

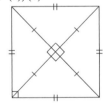
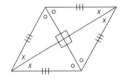
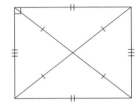
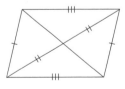

11. (a) ii.   **(b)** iv.   **(c)** iii.   **(d)** i.
12. (a) centroid   **(b)** circumcentre   **(c)** incentre
13. Use the alternate interior angle relation. Since the triangle is isosceles, then by the corresponding angle relation, x and y are congruent.

14. $\angle CFB = 105°$
15. (a) $x = 60°$ **(b)** $y = 36°$

Chapter 7

Getting Ready

1.

Shape	Perimeter Circumference	Area
rectangle	$P = 2L + 2W$	$A = L \times W$
triangle	$P = a + b + c$	$A = \frac{1}{2}b \times h$
circle	$C = \pi d, C = 2\pi r$	$A = \pi r^2$

2. (a) $A = 24$ mm^2; $P = 24$ mm
     (b) $A = 2.4$ m^2; $P = 6.4$ m
     (c) $A \doteq 28.3$ cm^2; $P \doteq 18.8$ cm
3. (a) $A = 8.61$ m^2 **(b)** $A = 32.45$ cm^2
4. $h \doteq 8.8$ cm
5. $y = x - 4$
6. $A = 165$ m^2
7. $A = 6.25$ m^2
8. $A = 288$ m^2
9. $A \doteq 1962.5$ km^2
10. Dundas, Georgetown, and Niagara Falls
11. (a) $V = 150$ cm^3 **(b)** $V = 54$ cm^3

7.1 Area of Composite Figures and Regular Polygons

Practise, Apply, Solve

1. (a) 5 **(b)** 8 **(c)** 4 **(d)** 7
2. (a) 6 cm   **(b)** 4.5 cm   **(c)** 12 mm   **(d)** 15.6 mm
3. (a) 25.2 cm   **(b)** 12.5 mm   **(c)** 53.6 cm
4. (a) 4.29 cm^2 **(b)** 3.24 cm^2 **(c)** 5.25 cm^2
     (d) 7.5 cm^2 **(e)** 4.4 cm^2 **(f)** 8.1 cm^2
5. (a) 5576 mm^2 **(b)** 41.4 cm^2
6. (a) 15.5 cm^2 **(b)** 42.0 cm^2 **(c)** 20.5 m^2
7. (a) 17.4 cm, 8.6 m^2 **(b)** 22.2 cm, 2.4 cm^2
     (c) 19.2 m, 1.9 m^2
8. (a) i. 72 cm^2 **ii.** 12.5 cm^2 **iii.** 31.2 cm^2
9. (a) 181.4 cm^2 **(b)** 734.4 cm^2 **(c)** 1002.2 cm^2
10. (a) 170.0 m   **(b)** 3.7 **(c)** 1530 m^2
11. (a) 260.87 cm^2 **(b)** 9.94 m^2 **(c)** 6.57 m^2
     (d) 36.17 cm^2 **(e)** 57.0 cm^2
12. (a) 154.80 m^2 **(b)** about 100 m^2
13. (a) $1.7\overline{3}$ cm   **(b)** around 14.44 mm
14. Length of frame $= 6.96$ m; Area of glass $= 3.48$ m^2
15. 1175.2 cm^2
16. *example:* No, because it does not have an apothem.
17. 311.7 cm^2
18. one can
19. 17.2 cm^2

20. (a) The perimeter decreases as the number of sides increases.

(b) If n is the number of sides, s is the length of each side, and a is the length of the apothem, then $A = \frac{1}{2}nsa$.

(c) The perimeter would approach $2\pi a$, and the area would approach πa^2. The shape would look like a circle, with the apothem as the circle's radius.

21. area of about 94.63 cm^2, with sides of length 7.42 cm

22. (a) 12   **(b)** 12

23. (a) $\pi r^2 - \pi r^2$ **(b)** $4r^2 - \pi r^2$
(c) $4r^2 - \pi r^2$

7.2 Volume of Regular Polygonal Prisms and Cylinders

Practise, Apply, Solve

1. prisms: (b) and (e), cylinders: (c) and (d)

2. (b)

3. (a) $V \doteq 13.6$ m^3 **(b)** $V = 31\ 900$ mm^3
(c) $V = 14.5$ cm^3

4. (a) 800 notes   **(b)** 1200 cm^3
(c) In part (a), only the thickness of the box is considered. In part (b), the length and width are also considered.

5. $x = 3$

6. 11.9 cm^3

7. 4

8. $V = 360$ cm^3. Each cubic centimetre is worth about \$972.22.

9. (a) $V = 1000$ cm^3 **(b)** $V \doteq 785.4$ cm^3
(c) $V \doteq 214.6$ cm^3

10. $V \doteq 1206.4$ cm^3

11. (a) $V \doteq 551.3$ cm^3 **(b)** $V \doteq 2205.4$ cm^3
(c) $V \doteq 2.2$ L   **(d)** $V \doteq 3.3$ L

12. (a) $V \doteq 314.2h$ **(b)** $V \doteq 31.4r^2$

14. about 750 cm^3 **15.** about 75.7 cm^3

16. about 1.86 m   **17.** $\frac{V}{a} = \frac{Ph}{2}$

18. $\frac{V}{h} = \frac{Pa}{2}$

7.3 The *Volume/Surface Area Explorer*

Practise

4. Six-sided right prism: Volume: 2660.544; Surface Area: 1108.56; Six-sided right pyramid: Volume: 886.848; Surface Area: 621.409; Seven-sided right prism: Volume: 2588.88; Surface Area: 1078.7; Seven-sided right pyramid: Volume: 862.96; Surface Area: 604.671; Eight-sided right prism: Volume: 2544.768; Surface Area: 1060.32; Eight-sided right pyramid: Volume: 848.256; Surface Area: 594.368; Volume of prism = 3 × Volume of pyramid; Surface area of prism $\doteq$ 1.784 × Surface area of pyramid

5. 2827.4 cm^2 **6.** 663.66 cm^3

7.4 Volume of Pyramids and Cones

Practise, Apply, Solve

1. (b) and **(d)**

2. (a) $V \doteq 2.09$ m^3 **(b)** $V = 4389$ mm^3
(c) $V = 4.93$ cm^3 **(d)** $V = 75$ m^3

3. (a) $V = 160$ cm^3 **(b)** $V \doteq 125.66$ cm^3

4. (a) The volumes would be unchanged.
(b) $V = 160$ mL or 0.16 L, $V \doteq 125.66$ or 0.125 L

5. (a) $V \doteq 737.23$ cm^3 **(b)** $V \doteq 1013.69$ cm^3

6. 108.8 cm^3 **7.** 66.7%   **8.** 7.5 cm

9. (a) $V \doteq 4399.2$ m^3 **(b)** 637 sanders

10. 4.704 m^3

11. about 147.87 cm^3

12. The 4-sided pyramid holds most. A cone with the same dimensions will have a smaller volume than any of these figures.

13. 20.4 m^3

14. (a) $h = \frac{3V}{\pi r^2}$ **(b)** $h \doteq 148.3$ cm   **(c)** $h = \sqrt[3]{\frac{3V}{\pi}}$

7.5 Volume of Spheres

Practise, Apply, Solve

1. (a) 137 258.28 mm^3 **(b)** 50.97 cm^3
(c) 4849.05 mm^3

2. 195.43 cm^3

3. (a) 4.2 cm^3 **(b)** 381.7 cm^3
(c) 3.1 m^3 **(d)** 1436.8 mm^3
(e) 65 475.3 cm^3 **(f)** 23.7 m^3

4. (a) 17 269 ball bearings
(b) 16 405.55 g or 16.405 55 kg
(c) 670 boxes
(d) example: shape of the boxes

5. (a) 170 scoops   **(b)** \$146.20

6. (a) 220.89 cm^3 **(b)** 200.98 cm^3

7. (a) 0.065 45 m^3 **(b)** \$0.46

8. 2421.64 cm^3/ball   **9.** 626.75 cm^3

10. 47.64%   **11.** \$8.86 on each pail

12. 3.03 cm

13. Estimates may vary. *Example:* About 5000 m^3 of helium

14. 310 m^3

15. the cube

16. 29 321.53 cm^3, 108 908.55 cm^3

17. by 0.740 cm

7.6 Surface Area of Prisms and Cylinders

Practice, Apply, Solve

1. Nets may vary, although numbers should be in the correct positions. *Examples:*

(a)

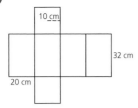

(b)

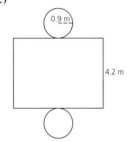

(c)

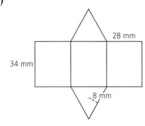

2. **(a)** 216 cm² **(b)** 672 m² **(c)** 3091.33 mm²
3. 216.80 cm²
4. 314.16 cm²
5. **(a)** 267 cm² **(b)** $0.13
6. 246.96 cm²
7. the cylinder
8. **(a)** The taller cylinder's surface area is two times the surface area of the shorter cylinder less the surface area of the two circular bases.
9. **(a)** 357.54 cm² **(b)** 2658.5 cm²
   (c) 68.3 cm² **(d)** 271.52 cm²
10. **(a)** 922.45 cm³ **(b)** 409.98 cm²
    (c) 537.21 cm²
11. **(a)** 290 cm² **(b)** 640 cm²
    (c) 678.6 cm² **(d)** 432 cm²
    (e) 1512 cm²
12. The base should be circular.
13. A box that is a 5.85 cm × 5.85 cm × 5.85 cm cube would minimize the amount of material used.
14. The largest box that can be covered is a 35.4 cm × 35.4 cm × 35.4 cm cube.

7.7 Surface Area of Pyramids and Cones

Practise, Apply, Solve

1. **(a)**

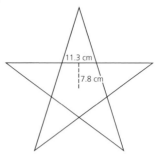

(b)

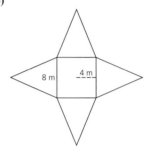

(c)

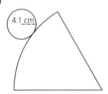

2. **(a)** 10 cm **(b)** 13 cm
   (c) 10.97 cm **(d)** 32.40 mm
3. **(a)** 301.59 cm² **(b)** 282.74 cm²
   (c) 218.70 cm² **(d)** 3569.85 mm
4. **(a)** 307.96 cm² **(b)** 201.62 cm²
   (c) 185.61 cm²
5. **(a)** 254.47 cm³ **(b)** 181.18 cm²
6. the pentagon-based pyramid
7. **(a)** 48 bundles of shingles
   (b) 3 cans of paint
   (c) $2089.98
8. the cone-shaped box
9. **(a)** 139 144.08 m² **(b)** about 33 610 blocks
10. **(a)** 452.39 cm² **(b)** 942.48 cm²
    (c) 1685.96 cm²
11. **(a)** 162.4 cm² **(b)** 354.0 cm²
    (c) 438.48 cm² **(d)** 222 cm²
    (e) 873.6 cm²
12. Estimates may vary: actual amount is 600.83 cm².
13. **(a)** the pentagonal pyramid
    (b) volume of cone 6194.17 cm², volume of pentagonal pyramid 7166.25 cm²

7.8 Surface Area of a Sphere

Practise, Apply, Solve

1. **(a)** 12 867.96 mm^2 **(b)** 66.48 cm^2
   (c) 1385.44 mm^2
2. **(a)** 1809.56 mm^2 **(b)** 153.94 cm^2
   (c) 804.25 cm^2 **(d)** 191.13 mm^2
3. **(a)** 509 295 818 km^2 **(b)** 6371 km
4. 29 cans of paint, $870
5. 168.39 cm^2 to 175.79 cm^2
6. 43 globes
7. 55.42 cm^2
8. 17.27 cm^2
9. **(a)** 5.05 cm **(b)** 2.82 mm
   (c) 5.00 m **(d)** 9.99 mm
10. radius $= \sqrt{\dfrac{\text{Surface Area}}{4\pi}}$
11. The cube with a side length of $2r$ has a larger surface area than a sphere with radius r.
12. The surface area of the sphere is two-thirds of the surface area of the cylinder that exactly contains it, and the volume of the sphere is $\frac{3}{2}$ that of the cylinder.

Chapter Review

1. 7.45 cm × 7.45 cm
2. 89 837 cm^2
3. **(a)** about 372 octagonal tiles and 93 square tiles
   (b) The total cost will be $341.31.
4. both height and radius must be 6.83 cm
5. 11.475 m^3
6. Planter 1: 24 360 cm^3, Planter 2: 143 260 cm^3, Planter 3: 193 220.51 cm^3
7. 3000 cm^3
8. **(a)** 347.49 m^3 **(b)** 237.50 cm^3
   (c) 218.65 mm^3
9. **(a)** 6.50 cm **(b)** 3.00 mm **(c)** 0.79 cm
10. **(a)** 33.51 m^3 **(b)** 14.14 m^3
    (c) 5 575 279.76 cm^3
11. The volume of the sphere increases by eight times.
12. **(a)** 1295.91 m^2 **(b)** 1033.10 L
13. 9.90 m^2
14. 24.79 m^2
15. 577.43 cm^2
16. 6433.98 cm^2.
17. the hollow sphere

Chapter Review Test

1. **(a)** 189 m^2 **(b)** 246.65 mm^2
   (c) 55.44 cm^2
2. **(a)** 668.66 cm^3 **(b)** 70 cm^3
3. **(a)** 327.04 mm^2 **(b)** 206.52 cm^3
4. **(a)** 2538.85 cm^3 or 2.538 85 L of helium
   (b) $65.47
5. surface area 9.68 m^2, volume 1.82 m^3
6. the cylindrical cup
7. 50 265.48 cm^3

8. 600 cm^2
9. 49 people

Chapter 8

Getting Ready

1. **(a)** 35.25 m **(b)** 17.1 m; 5.85 m; 5.85 m
2. **(a)** 8337.5 m^2 **(b)** 12 470.66 m^2
3. **(a)** 70.4 cm^2 **(b)** 642.1 m^2
   (c) 199.5 m^2 **(d)** 498.8 m^2
4. **(a)**

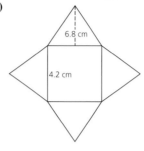

(b) $A_{\text{base}} = 17.64$ cm^2; $A_{\text{side}} = 14.28$ cm^2
   (c) 74.76 cm^2
5. 22.31 m
6. **(a)** $x = -15$ **(b)** $x = -4$ **(c)** $m = 4$
   (d) $r = 1$ **(e)** $y = 10$ **(f)** $x = -2$
   (g) $x = 10$ **(h)** $y = 5$ **(i)** $x = \dfrac{8}{9}$
7. **(a)** $V = 1646.04$ cm^3 **(b)** $A = 9.10$ mm^2
   (c) $h = 4.04$ m
8. **(a)** $r = 1.07$ m **(b)** $V = 39\ 064.21$ mm^3
   (c) $h = 0.014$ cm
9. **(a)** $r = 2.15$ cm **(b)** $V = 2084.17$ cm^3
   (c) $h = 0.026$ m
10. **(a)** $d = 25$ m, $V = 8181.23$ m^3
    (b) $r = 14.2$ mm, $V = 11\ 993.71$ mm^3
    (c) $r = 4.0$ cm, $d = 8.0$ cm
11. **(a)** $V = 211.34$ m^3; $SA = 219.92$ m^2
    (b) $V \doteq 12\ 802.56$ cm^3; $SA \doteq 3095.60$ cm^2
    (c) $V \doteq 301.59$ m^3; $SA \doteq 301.59$ m^2
    (d) $V \doteq 2.62$ m^3; $SA \doteq 9.19$ m^2

8.1 Investigating the Best Design: Cylinders

Practise, Apply, Solve

1. **(a)** 6 **(b)** 11 **(c)** 9 **(d)** 15
   (e) 2 **(f)** 3 **(g)** 5 **(h)** 6
2. **(a)** 3.46 **(b)** 8.25 **(c)** 12.45 **(d)** 32.06
   (e) 2.62 **(f)** 4.45 **(g)** 5.24 **(h)** 4.98
3. **(a)** $x = \pm5$ **(b)** $x = \pm4$
   (c) $x = \pm11$ **(d)** $x = \pm15$
   (e) $x \doteq \pm6.2$ **(f)** $x \doteq \pm9.8$ **(g)** $x \doteq \pm21.0$
   (h) $x \doteq \pm32.5$ **(i)** $x = \pm6$ **(j)** $x = \pm10$
   (k) $x = \pm2$ **(l)** $x \doteq \pm4.2$ **(m)** $x = \pm7$
   (n) $x = \pm6$ **(o)** $x = \pm3$ **(p)** $x \doteq \pm4.5$
4. **(a)** $x = 1$ **(b)** $x = 2$
   (c) $x = 4$ **(d)** $x = -3$

(e) $x \doteq 2.3$ (f) $x \doteq 3.7$
(g) $x \doteq 5.1$ (h) $x \doteq 6.0$
(i) $x = 5$ (j) $x = -2$
(k) $x = 4$ (l) $x = 10$
(m) $x = 3$ (n) $x = -1$
(o) $x \doteq 1.6$ (p) $x \doteq 2.7$

5. (a) $V \doteq 141.4 \text{ cm}^3$ (b) $V \doteq 1357.2 \text{ mm}^3$
(c) $V \doteq 226.2 \text{ m}^3$ (d) $V \doteq 39\ 141.1 \text{ cm}^3$
(e) $r \doteq 8.0$ cm (f) $r \doteq 12.0$ mm
(g) $h \doteq 5.0$ cm (h) $r \doteq 2.4$ mm
(i) $h \doteq 5.5$ cm (j) $r \doteq 18.0$ cm
(k) $r \doteq 2.5$ m

6. (a) $r \doteq 5.0$ cm; $h = 2r$
(b) $r \doteq 9.0$ cm; $h = 2r$
(c) $r \doteq 15.0$ cm; $h = 2r$
(d) $r \doteq 12.5$ cm; $h = 2r$

7. (a) $SA \doteq 471.2 \text{ cm}^2$ (b) $SA \doteq 1526.8 \text{ cm}^2$
(c) $SA \doteq 4241.2 \text{ cm}^2$ (d) $SA \doteq 2945.2 \text{ cm}^2$

8. (a) $r \doteq 5.4$ cm; $h = 2r$ (b) $SA \doteq 553.6 \text{ cm}^2$
(c) $15\ 611.52

9. (a) $r \doteq 4.3$ cm; $h = 2r$; $SA \doteq 348.7 \text{ cm}^2$
(b) 70¢

10. (a) 87.9 cm^2 (b) 471 mm^2
(c) 518.1 cm^2 (d) 272.1 m^2
(e) 5 cm (f) 10 mm (g) 12 cm (h) 4.8 mm

11. (a) $r = \pm\sqrt{\dfrac{A}{\pi}}$ (b) $r = \pm\sqrt{\dfrac{SA}{6\pi}}$

(c) $r = \sqrt[3]{\dfrac{3V}{4\pi}}$

12. (a) $r \doteq 10.0$ cm; $h = 2r$
(b) $r \doteq 5.0$ cm; $h = 2r$
(c) $r \doteq 11.5$ cm; $h = 2r$
(d) $r \doteq 7.0$ cm; $h = 2r$

13. (a) $V \doteq 6283.2 \text{ cm}^3$ (b) $V \doteq 784.8 \text{ cm}^3$
(c) $V \doteq 9548.7 \text{ cm}^3$ (d) $V \doteq 2153.5 \text{ cm}^3$

14. (a) $r \doteq 2$ cm; $h = 2r$ (b) 50.3 cm^3

15. (a) $r \doteq 0.9$ m; $h \doteq 1.8$ m
(b) $V \doteq 4.6 \text{ m}^3$

16. $r \doteq 4.5$ cm; $h = 2r$

19. 116 g

8.3 Investigating the Best Design: Rectangular Prisms

Practise, Apply, Solve

1. (a) 9 (b) 6 (c) 16.97 (d) 3.68
(e) 43.08 (f) 12.79 (g) 3.46 (h) 8.22

2. (a) $x = \pm10$ (b) $x = -4$
(c) $x = \pm9$ (d) $x = 2$
(e) $x = \pm1$ (f) $x = -2$
(g) $x = \pm3$ (h) $x = -3$
(i) $x = 5$ (j) $x = \pm4$
(k) $x = 3$ (l) $x = 2$

3. (a) 105 cm^3 (b) 21.8 cm^3 (c) 12 cm^3
(d) 3.4 cm (e) 216 mm^3 (f) 42.9 m
(g) 14 mm (h) 2.8 cm

4. (a) 5 m × 5 m × 5 m (b) 15 cm × 15 cm × 15 cm

(c) 2.8 cm × 2.8 cm × 2.8 cm
(d) 14.6 m × 14.6 m × 14.6 m

5. (a) 150 m^2 (b) 1350 cm^2
(c) 47.04 cm^2 (d) 1278.96 m^2

6. (a) 30.65 cm × 30.65 cm × 30.65 cm
(b) 23

7. (a) 1.5 cm × 1.5 cm × 1.5 cm
(b) 216 cm^3
(c) 6 cm × 6 cm × 6 cm

8. (a) 94 cm^2 (b) 102 cm^2
(c) 6 m (d) 4 m
(e) 54 cm^2 (f) 50.46 m^2
(g) 15 cm (h) 6.4 mm

9. (a) 5 m × 5 m × 5 m
(b) 12 cm × 12 cm × 12 cm
(c) 9.5 cm × 9.5 cm × 9.5 cm
(d) 28.5 m × 28.5 m × 28.5 m

10. (a) 125 m^3 (b) 1728 cm^3
(c) 857.375 cm^3 (d) $23\ 149.125 \text{ m}^3$

11. (a) 0.96 m by 0.96 m by 0.96 m
(b) 0.88 m^3

12. (a) 24.3 cm^3 (b) 729 cm^3
(c) 9 × 9 × 9 cm

13. (a) 27 cm × 36 cm × 11.3 cm
(b) 18 cm × 27 cm × 22.6 cm
(c) two layers of two rows
(d) no, because the height is not divisible by the diameter

14. the cylinder

15. (a) rectangular prism: $l = 10$ cm, $SA = 600 \text{ cm}^2$; cylinder: $r \doteq 5.4$ cm, $h \doteq 10.9$ cm, $SA \doteq 553.7 \text{ cm}^2$; sphere: $r \doteq 6.2$ cm, $SA \doteq 483.1 \text{ cm}^2$
(b) the sphere; yes

16. (a) rectangular prism: $l = 12.9$ cm, $V = 2151.7 \text{ cm}^2$; cylinder: $r \doteq 7.28$ cm, $h \doteq 14.6$ cm, $V = 2424.2 \text{ cm}^2$; sphere: $r \doteq 8.92$ cm, $V = 2972.9 \text{ cm}^2$
(b) the sphere; yes

17. A cube with a side length of about 21.123 cm uses the least cardboard. The box would have to be bigger to fit all 12, for example a 30 cm × 20 cm × 20 cm box.

18. the sphere

19. $r \doteq 7.816$ cm, $h \doteq 15.632$ cm.

20. (a) 351 mm^3 (b) 386 mm^3

Chapter Review

1. (a) $V \doteq 1225.925 \text{ cm}^3$ (b) $r \doteq 7.998$ cm
(c) $r \doteq 2.999$ mm (d) $h \doteq 15.492$ cm
(e) $SA \doteq 3298.672 \text{ cm}^2$
(f) $SA \doteq 1773.555 \text{ mm}^2$
(g) $h \doteq 7.993$ cm (h) $r \doteq 44.183$ mm

2. (a) $r \doteq 4.499$ cm, $h \doteq 8.998$ cm
(b) $r \doteq 17.997$ cm, $h \doteq 35.994$ cm
(c) $r \doteq 6.999$ cm, $h \doteq 13.998$ cm
(d) $r \doteq 2.100$ cm, $h \doteq 4.199$ cm

3. (a) $SA \doteq 381.534 \text{ cm}^2$

(b) $SA \doteq 6105.221$ cm^2
(c) $SA \doteq 923.364$ cm^2
(d) $SA \doteq 83.127$ cm^2
4. (a) $r \doteq 5.998$ cm, $h \doteq 11.997$ cm
(b) $r \doteq 1.118$ m, $h \doteq 2.236$ m
(c) $r \doteq 15.996$ cm, $h \doteq 31.992$ cm
(d) $r \doteq 19.995$ cm, $h \doteq 39.990$ cm
5. (a) $V \doteq 1355.811$ cm^3
(b) $V \doteq 8.780$ m^3
(c) $V \doteq 25\ 716.63$ cm^3
(d) $V \doteq 50\ 227.793$ cm^3
6. (a) $r \doteq 82.5$ cm, $h \doteq 165$ cm
(b) $V \doteq 3\ 528\ 106.725$ cm^3
7. $r \doteq 6.20$ cm, $h \doteq 12.41$ cm
8. (a) $V \doteq 79.0$ cm^3 (b) $V \doteq 79.0$ cm^3
(c) $w \doteq 6.2$ cm   (d) $V \doteq 216$ mm^3
(e) $l \doteq 15.5$ m   (f) $SA \doteq 376$ cm^2
(g) $l \doteq 8$ m   (h) $SA \doteq 1093.5$ cm^2
9. (a) $l \doteq 9$ m   (b) $l \doteq 21.5$ cm
(c) $l \doteq 0.85$ m   (d) $l \doteq 8.2$ m
10. (a) $SA \doteq 486$ m^2 (b) $SA \doteq 2773.5$ cm^2
(c) $SA \doteq 4.335$ m^2 (d) $SA \doteq 403.44$ m^2
11. (a) $l \doteq 15$ m   (b) $l \doteq 8.501$ cm
(c) $l \doteq 38$ cm   (d) $l \doteq 55$ m
12. (a) $V \doteq 3375$ m^3 (b) $V \doteq 614.342$ cm^3
(c) $V \doteq 54\ 872$ cm^3 (d) $V \doteq 166\ 375$ m^3
13. (a) 1 cm $\times$ 1 cm $\times$ 24 cm,
1 cm $\times$ 2 cm $\times$ 12 cm,
1 cm $\times$ 3 cm $\times$ 8 cm,
1 cm $\times$ 4 cm $\times$ 6 cm,
2 cm $\times$ 2 cm $\times$ 6 cm,
2 cm $\times$ 3 cm $\times$ 4 cm
(b) 2 cm $\times$ 3 cm $\times$ 4 cm
14. (a) a cube with side length 69.282 cm
(b) a cube with side length 75.895 cm

Chapter Review Test

1. $r \doteq 23.996$ cm, $h \doteq 47.992$ cm,
$SA \doteq 10\ 853.725$ cm^2
2. $l = 32$ cm, $SA = 6144$ cm^2
3. $r \doteq 29.992$ cm, $h \doteq 59.985$ cm,
$V \doteq 169\ 513.15$ cm^3
4. $l = 45$ cm, $V = 91\ 125$ cm^3
5. a cubical box with a side length of about 21.544 cm
6. a sphere with a radius of 9.42 cm
7. (a) $r \doteq 32.574$ cm, $h \doteq 65.147$ cm
(b) $r \doteq 35.682$ cm, $h \doteq 71.365$ cm
The cylinder has no top

Cumulative Review Test 3

1. (a) AB is not parallel to CD because the sum of the interior angles is 190°. If they were parallel, the sum would be 180°.
(b) $\angle BAC = 95°$
(c) $\angle CBA = 60°$
(d) 18 sides, 2880°
2. $\angle BCE = 75°$, since $\angle AED = 75°$, and DE is parallel to BC, making $\angle AED$ and $\angle BCE$ corresponding angles.
3. (a) $\angle BCD = 74°$, since $\angle BAD = \angle BCD$ (opposite angles of a rhombus are equal), and diagonal AC bisects each of these angles. Since $\angle EAD = 37°$, $\angle BAD = 74°$ and so $\angle BCD = 74°$.
(b) 25 cm^2
(c) 20 cm
4. The balance point would be at the centroid of the triangle, where the three medians intersect.
5. 12 000 cm^2
6. about 70.15 cm^3
7. (a) 4.2 cm × 4.2 cm × 12.6 cm
(b) 246.96 cm^2
(c) about 193.96 cm^2
(d) cylindrical package
8. (a) about 444.29 m^2
(b) about 1047.20 m^3
(c) about 55.85 trailer loads
9. about 628.32 m^2
10. (a) about 485.97 cm^3
(b) radius $\doteq 4.26$ cm, height $\doteq 8.52$ cm

acute triangle: a triangle in which no interior angle is greater than or equal to 90°.

algebraic expression: an acceptable combination of at least one variable and possibly numbers and operation symbols. For example, x, $2x - \dfrac{3}{x}$, and $12r^2 + 7s$ are all algebraic expressions.

algebraic modelling: representing a number pattern with an algebraic expression, or representing a relationship with an equation or a formula.

algorithm: a specific set of instructions for finding the solution to a problem.

altitude: the line segment representing the height of a polygon, drawn from a vertex of the polygon perpendicular to the opposite side.

analytic geometry: the branch of mathematics that uses the xy-plane to determine equations that represent lines and curves.

angle bisector: a line separating an angle into two equal parts.

astronomical unit (AU): the mean distance from the Earth to the Sun; about 149 000 km.

application: a practical situation outside mathematics to which mathematical concepts and skills can be applied to solve problems.

binomial: an algebraic expression that is the sum of two terms. For example, $4x - 7y$ and $5x^2 + 3$ are binomials.

census: the surveying of an entire population.

centroid of a triangle: the point where the three medians of a triangle intersect. Also is the centre of area.

chord: the line segment connecting two points on a curve.

circumcentre of a triangle: the centre of the circle passing through every vertex of a triangle.

coefficient: the number or constant by which a variable is multiplied. For example, in the term $3z$, the coefficient is 3; in the term by, b is the coefficient.

congruence: the property shared by geometric figures that are identical in shape and size.

constant rate of change: the relationship exhibited by two variables where the ratio of the change in one variable to the change in the other variable over any interval is constant.

coordinate plane: a grid on which coordinates can be plotted.

coordinates: an ordered pair of numbers that shows the position of a point on a grid.

curve of best fit: the curve that is drawn on a scatter plot to show the approximate relation between two variables.

dependent variable: in a relationship between two variables, the variable that depends on the other.

diagonal: a line segment joining two vertices of a polygon that are not next to each other (the two vertices are not joined by one side of the polygon).

difference table: the table formed when a third column, consisting of the differences of successive values of the dependent variable (y) of a relationship, is joined to an existing table of values of a relationship in which the values of the independent variable (x) increase by 1.

difference of squares: a technique of factoring applied to the difference of two perfect squares, of the form $a^2 - b^2 = (a + b)(a - b)$.

direct variation: the relationship exhibited by two variables where one variable is a constant multiple of the other.

dynamic geometry software (DGS): computer programs with a wide array of features that allow the user to construct, manipulate, and measure geometric figures.

evaluate: to determine a particular value for an expression.

exponent: the use of a superscript in mathematics to denote repeated multiplication. For example, 4^3 means $4 \times 4 \times 4$ and the exponent is 3.

exponential notation: scientific notation that is used by calculators to display numbers that are too small or too large to fit in the calculator screen. For example, the number 243 980 000 000 may appear as "2.4398 11" on the calculator screen. This indicates that the number displayed is equivalent to 2.4398×10^{11}.

extrapolate: to estimate a value that is beyond the range of given data by following a pattern.

factor: the method of expressing a number or algebraic expression as the product of two or more numbers and/or algebraic expressions. The numbers and/or algebraic expressions in such a product are also called factors.

finite differences: in a table of values where the x-coordinates are evenly spaced, the first differences are the differences between consecutive y-coordinates. The second differences are the differences between consecutive first differences, and so on. For a linear function, the first differences are constant, while for a quadratic function, they are not. The second differences are constant for a quadratic function.

first-degree equation: an equation in which the exponent of the variable is 1. For example, $2(6x - 3) - 5 = -8 + 3x + 1$.

first-degree inequation: an inequality in which the exponent of the variable is 1. For example, $3 - 2x \le 7x - 15$.

first-degree polynomial: a polynomial in which the exponent of the variable is 1. For example, $8x - 17$.

generalize: to create a general rule to represent a pattern or relationship between variables.

graphing calculator: the many features of this small device allow the user to create a graph from an equation, construct a scatter plot from a table of values, determine the equation of a curve of best fit for a scatter plot, and perform statistical calculations, among other tasks. Many graphing calculators can also be used in conjunction with scientific probes to directly collect data from physical measurements (for example, position, temperature, and force).

graphing software: computer programs that perform many of the functions that a graphing calculator is capable of.

guess-and-check: a problem solving strategy using a sequence of refined estimates. Each estimate is checked against the original problem and used to formulate a better estimate.

improper fraction: a fraction where the numerator is greater than or equal to the fraction.

independent variable: in a relationship between two variables, the variable that does not depend on the other.

infer from data: a method of reasoning that leads to a conclusion, based on a relationship between variables in a set of data.

integer: a positive or negative whole number (e.g., …−2, −1, 0, 1, 2, …).

intercept: the distance from the origin of the xy-plane to a point at which the graph meets either the x-axis or y-axis (for example, the x-intercept or y-intercept).

interpolate: to estimate a value that is between two other elements of given data.

linear relation: the relationship exhibited by two variables that appears as a straight line when graphed on a coordinate system.

linear system: two equations that represent straight lines.

line of best fit: the straight line that best describes the relationship between two variables in a scatter plot of the given data.

mathematical model: the use of a mathematical explanation to describe a real situation. The model may involve elements such as diagrams, graphs, physical models, computer models, equations, or formulas.

mathematical modelling: the process of explaining a real situation with mathematical descriptions. See also mathematical model.

mean: the sum of several numbers divided by how many numbers there are.

measure of central tendency: a value that can represent a set of data. Three commonly used measures of central tendency are the mean, the median, and the mode.

median: geometry: a line that joins a vertex of a triangle to the midpoint of the opposite side. Statistics: The middle number of a set of numbers arranged in order. If there are an even number of numbers in the set, the median is the mean of the two middle numbers.

method of elimination: a method used to solve linear systems by matching coefficients of one variable by multiplication, and then adding or subtracting the equations to eliminate that variable.

method of substitution: a method used to solve linear systems by rearranging one equation so that it can be substituted into the other equation.

mixed number: a number that has a whole part and a fraction part; for example $1\frac{3}{7}$.

mode: the number that occurs most often.

monomial: an algebraic expression made up of one term (for example, $6x^2$ and $-13y$ are monomials).

multiple trials: the repetition of an experiment several times to increase the accuracy of the results. The results of each individual trial are combined by a method such as averaging, so that any random occurrences that affect an individual trial have less impact on the accuracy of the results.

natural number: one of the counting numbers 1, 2, 3, …

nonlinear relation: the relationship exhibited by two variables that does not fit a straight line when graphed on a coordinate system.

nonreal root of an equation: a solution to an equation that is not a real number (for example, $\sqrt{-36}$).

optimal value: a variable's maximum or minimum value.

origin: the point at which the horizontal and vertical axes meet.

partial variation: the relationship exhibited by two variables where one variable is a constant multiple of the other, plus another constant.

period: the block of repeating digits in a repeating decimal number.

piecewise linear function: a function made up of parts of two or more linear functions with different slopes.

polygon: a closed plane figure formed by three or more line segments. Examples include triangles, quadrilaterals, hexagons, and decagons.

polynomial expression: an algebraic expression of the form $a + bx + cx^2 + …$, where a, b, c, and so on, are real numbers or constants.

population: the total number of individuals or subjects involved in a survey or sample.

primary trigonometric ratios: the three basic ratios of trigonometry (the sine, cosine, and tangent ratios).

prism: a three-dimensional solid with two parallel, congruent polygonal bases. The shape of the base of the prism determines the name of the prism, (for example, pentagonal prism, octagonal prism).

proportional reasoning: problem solving methods involving the examination of equal ratios.

Pythagorean theorem: for a right triangle, the square of the length of the hypotenuse (the longest side) is equal to the sum of the squares of the lengths of the other two sides.

quadrant: any one of four parts of the Cartesian plane.

quadratic function: a function with a quadratic equation based on the independent variable. For example, $y = x^2 - 3x + 9$.

quadrilateral: a four-sided polygon.

quotient: the result of dividing one number by another. For example, if 5 is divided by 2, the quotient is 2.5.

randomization: the process of selecting a sample in such a way that each member of the population has the same chance of being selected.

rate triangle: a triangle that can be drawn on a graph to show the steepness of a line.

ratio: a number or quantity compared with another, and expressed with the symbol ":".

rational number: a number of the form $\frac{a}{b}$, where a and b are integers and $b \neq 0$.

realistic situation: a description of an event or events encountered in everyday life, or an experiment imitating such an event.

real root of an equation: a solution to an equation that is a real number. Real numbers include all rational numbers as well as irrational numbers such as $\sqrt{2}$ or π.

region on the *xy*-plane: an area either fully or partly bounded by curves and/or lines on the *xy*-plane.

regression: a method used to determine the equation of a curve that corresponds to the distribution of points on a scatter plot.

relation: a property shared by variables that can be expressed as a table of values, a graph, or an equation.

relationship: in mathematics, how variables are related to one another, a relation. A relationship can be linear or nonlinear, as well as strong or weak.

representivity: the principle of selecting a sample in such a way that the properties of the sample accurately reflect the properties of the population.

right triangle: a triangle in which one of the interior angles measures 90°.

sample: a small group selected from a population to give information about the population as a whole.

sampling technique: a method of collecting data from a sample.

scatter plot: a graphical method of showing the relationship between two variables by plotting points on a coordinate grid. The coordinates of each point represent a pair of values of the two variables.

scientific probe: a device used in conjunction with a graphing calculator or a computer to directly collect data from physical measurements (for example, position, temperature, and force).

second-degree polynomial: a polynomial containing only terms with variables having whole number exponents, where at least one of the variables has an exponent of 2, and the exponents of the other variables are less than 2. For example, $-3x^2 - 2x + 5$ and $6y^2$ are second-degree polynomials.

similar triangles: triangles that have equal corresponding interior angles and proportional corresponding sides.

simulation: a method of studying an application of probability by conducting an experiment to estimate the likelihood of each outcome of the application.

slope: a measure of the steepness of a line, expressed as the rise (vertical distance) divided by the run (horizontal distance) between any two points on the line.

solution: the set of values that result in a true statement when replacing the unknowns in an equation.

spreadsheet: paper ruled in rows and columns with headings, labels, and numerical data. Computer software is used to create spreadsheets, which allow the user to enter formulas for repeated calculations.

square root: the number, which when multiplied by itself gives a required value.

substitution: the process of replacing part of an algebraic expression with another algebraic expression or value.

system of equations: a set of two or more equations in two or more variables.

table of values: a table used to record the values of two variables in a relation.

trend: the general direction in which something tends to move; for instance, a group of data points on a scatter plot might have the trend of going upward to the right.

variable: a symbol representing some quantity that can take on any one of a set of values. For example, x and y are variables in the algebraic expression $5x^2 - 12y + 67$.

vertex: a point of intersection of two sides of a polygon or the faces of a solid.

vertical stretch factor: a coefficient in an equation that determines the degree to which the corresponding graph is vertically stretched.

whole number: a positive integer (e.g., 0, 1, 2, 3, …). A natural number or zero (0).

***xy*-plane:** a coordinate system based on the intersection of perpendicular lines called axes. The *x*-axis is the horizontal axis, while the *y*-axis is the vertical axis. The origin is the point of intersection of the two axes.

zeros of a function: the *x*-intercepts of the graph of the function. The function takes the value of zero for these *x*-values.

Index

MATHEMATICS 9 PHOTO CREDITS

Chapter 1 Opener p. 39: Dick Hemingway; p. 40: inset New Balance Shoes, left PhotoDisc; p. 43: Dick Hemingway; p. 47: PhotoDisc; p. 48: Galerie Illusoria; p. 49: Corbis; p. 52: NASA; p. 54: Dave Starrett/ Courtesy of Chum Television; p. 55: Alexander Meyboom; p. 59: left PhotoDisc, right John Denniston/Vancouver Province; p. 61: Canapress; p. 65: PhotoDisc; p. 66: Dave Starrett; p. 71: left PhotoDisc, right CORBIS/Leonard de Selva; p. 72: Dick Hemingway; p. 77 left PhotoDisc, right CORBIS/Grant Smith; p. 79 Dave Starrett; p. 83: both PhotoDisc; p. 84: The photo used on page 84 is provided by and used with permission of Texas Instruments Incorporated.

Chapter 2 Opener p. 101: First Light; p. 102: left PhotoDisc, right Dave Starrett; p. 109: left PhotoDisc; right CORBIS/Jacqui Hurst; p. 110: Dick Hemingway; p. 112: IBM; p. 113: Dave Starrett; p. 117: PhotoDisc; p. 118: Dave Starrett; p. 119: Dave Starrett; p. 123: CORBIS/Leonard de Selva; p. 129: PhotoDisc; p. 131: Dick Hemingway; p. 135: PhotoDisc; p. 136: Dick Hemingway; p. 141: Wendy Murphy; p. 153: Reuters/Kimberly White/Archive Photos; p. 155 PhotoDisc; p. 159: Dick Hemingway

Chapter 3 Opener p. 179: Dick Hemingway; p. 180: Ontario Hydro Corporate Archives; p. 185: CORBIS/Bettman; p. 189: David Young-Wolfe/Photo Edit; p. 195: Bob Templeton; p. 196: NASA; p. 197: PhotoDisc; p. 198: CORBIS/Chris Simpson; Cordaiy Photo Library Ltd; p. 201: Comstock; p. 203: Ontario Hydro Corporate Archives; p. 213: Ontario Hydro Corporate Archives; p. 214: PhotoDisc; p. 219: Ontario Hydro Corporate Archives; p. 220: Ontario Hydro Corporate Archives; p. 226: right Wally Eberhart/Visuals Unlimited, bottom A.J Copley/Visuals Unlimited; p. 227: PhotoDisc; p. 231: Ontario Hydro Corporate Archives

Chapter 4 Opener p. 251: NASA; p. 252: Frank Whitney/Image Bank; p. 254:Comstock; p. 255: CORBIS; p. 258: Al Harvey/The Slide Farm; p. 259: Frank Whitney/Image Bank; p. 266: Frank Whitney/Image Bank; p. 268: CORBIS/Jonathan Blair; p. 273: Frank Whitney/Image Bank

Chapter 5 Opener p. 279:PhotoDisc; p. 280: PhotoDisc; p. 282: Comstock; p. 287:PhotoDisc; p. 290: PhotoDisc; p. 298: centre left PhotoDisc; bottom Archive Photos; p. 307 centre left: PhotoDisc; bottom: Archive Photos; p. 310: Mark E. Gibson/Visuals Unlimited; P. 311: Courtesy of the Department of Mathematics, University of Toronto; p. 315: PhotoDisc; p. 327: PhotoDisc

Chapter 6 Opener p. 353: Dick Hemingway; p. 354: Al Harvey/The Slide Farm; p. 356: Courtesy RH Imports, Inc.; p. 360: Al Harvey/The Slide Farm; p. 367: Al Harvey/The Slide Farm; p. 372: Al Harvey/The Slide Farm; p. 379: Al Harvey/The Slide Farm; p. 387: Al Harvey/The Slide Farm

Chapter 7 Opener p. 399: Victor Last/Geographical Visual Aids; p. 400: Photodisc; p. 409: Archive Photos; p. 410: R. Williamson, Bes/Visuals Unlimited; p. 415: centre left: PhotoDisc, bottom right: Canapress; p. 417: centre left: PhotoDisc, bottom right CORBIS/BETTMAN; p. 418: CORBIS/The Purcell Team; p. 424: left Jonathan Nourok/Photo Edit, right Mark E. Gibson/Visuals Unlimited; p. 425: Dave Starrett; p. 429: Scala/Art Resource, NY; p. 430: Dick Hemingway; p. 431: Dick Hemingway;p. 435: center left PhotoDisc, bottom right Jody Dole/Image Bank; p. 436: Bob Templeton; p. 437: Dave Starrett; p. 441: CORBIS: Charles & Josette Lenars; p. 442: center left PhotoDisc, bottom right: CORBIS/Gianni Dagli Orti; p. 443: top right Science VU/Visuals Unlimited, bottom Dave Starrett; p. 444: University of Toronto, Mathematics Department; p. 446: Mary Evans Picture Library

Chapter 8 Opener p. 457: Canapress, inset: Dick Hemingway; p. 458: PhotoDisc; p. 466: PhotoDisc; p. 467: Dave Starrett; p. 469: CORBIS/BETTMAN; p. 472: PhotoDisc; p. 473: both Dick Hemingway; p. 474: PhotoDisc

TEXT PERMISSIONS
p. 52: From Flare Magazine, December 1995 issue; p. 54: Ratings sheet courtesy of Nielsen Media Research; p. 84-85: Material extracted from CBL SYSTEM EXPERIMENT WORKBOOK © 1997 Experiment P2: Rebound Height of a Bouncing Ball. With permission of the publisher Copyright 1997, Texas Instruments Incorporated; p. 148: Statistics Canada, Income Distribution by Size in Canada, Catalogue No. 13-207; p. 162: Material extracted from CBL SYSTEM EXPERIMENT WORKBOOK © 1997 Experiment M1:Take A Hike. With permission of the published Copyright 1997, Texas Instruments Incororated p. 232-233: Material extracted from CBL SYSTEM EXPERIMENT WORKBOOK © 1997 Experiment M2: What Comes Up Must Come Down. With permission of the published Copyright 1997, Texas Instruments Incororated; p. 233-234: Material extracted from CBL SYSTEM EXPERIMENT WORKBOOK © 1997 Experiment M4: Name That Tune. With permission of the published Copyright 1997, Texas Instruments Incororated; p. 234-235 : Material extracted from CBL SYSTEM EXPERIMENT WORKBOOK © 1997 Experiment P3: Newton's Law of Cooling. With permission of the published Copyright 1997, Texas Instruments Incororated